Houghton Mifflin Mathematics 11

Jeri Lunney
Robert G. Dearborn
Les Dukowski
R. Geoffrey Roulet
Edward Barbeau Jr.

Houghton Mifflin Canada Limited
150 Steelcase Road West • Markham, Ontario • L3R 1B2

Houghton Mifflin Mathematics 11

Authors

Jeri Lunney, Vice Principal, St. Paul's High School, C.R.C.S.S.B., Nepean, Ontario
Robert G. Dearborn, Mathematics Dept. Head, Queen Elizabeth C.H.S., Edmonton, Alberta
Les Dukowski, Vice Principal, H.D. Stafford Jr. Secondary School, Langley, B.C.
R. Geoffrey Roulet, Special Assignment Teacher, Mathematics/Computers, Timmins (Ontario) Board of Education

Consultants

John Del Grande, Education Consultant, Houghton Mifflin Canada
Charles C. Edmunds, Mathematics Department, Mount Saint Vincent University
Linda L.B. Wheadon, Mathematics Teacher, Horton District H.S., Wolfville, Nova Scotia
Anne C. Vickers, Mathematics Consultant, New Brunswick

Canadian Cataloguing in Publication Data

Main entry under title:
Houghton Mifflin mathematics 11

For use in grade 11.
Includes index.

ISBN 0-395-42687-1

1. Mathematics—1961- I. Lunney, Jeri

QA39.2

Editorial Adviser

Edward Barbeau Jr.

Editors

Sindy Vertlieb
Claire Robitaille

Assembly and Technical Art

Dave Hunter

Cover Art

"Triad" by Ted Bieler
© Ted Bieler/ Marathon Realty Company Limited
Design by Dragon's Eye

Printed in Canada 12345/92108987

CONTENTS

1 Basic Skills

2 Polynomials and Rational Expressions

3 Radicals and Non-Linear Equations

4 Coordinate Geometry and Straight Line Graphs

5 The Parabolic Curve

6 Solving Systems of Equations

10 Mathematics of Finance

1 Basic Skills

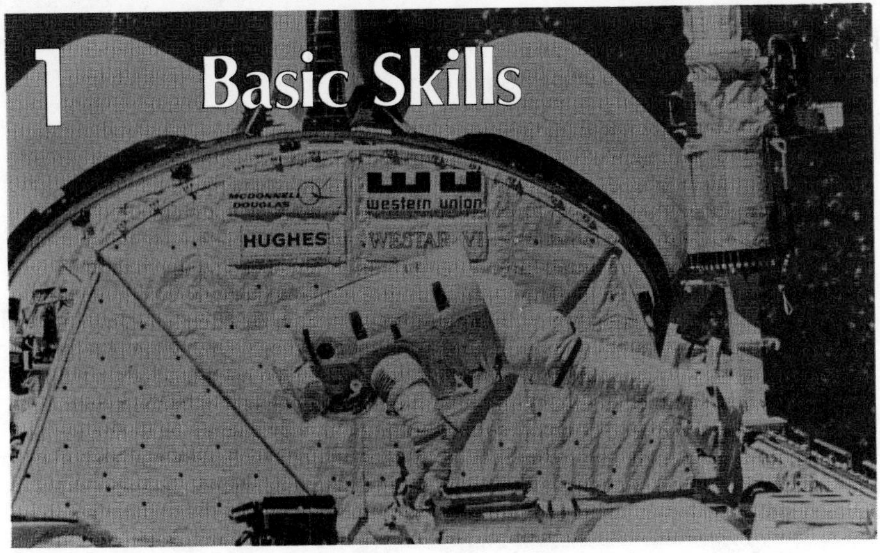

The Canadarm was designed, developed, and built by Canadian industrial firms under the direction of the National Research Council of Canada.

1-1 Substituting into Formulas

To gain a circular orbit around Earth, a shuttle must achieve a certain speed v, in metres per second, given by the formula below.

$$v = \sqrt{\frac{GM}{R}}$$

R is the radius of the orbit from Earth's centre, in metres;
M is the mass of Earth (5.9×10^{24} kg);
G is Newton's gravitational constant (6.67×10^{-11} N·m^2/kg^2)

To apply a formula, substitute known values for the variables and evaluate the resulting expression, following the correct order of operations, summarized below.

Working from left to right:

1. Evaluate within grouping symbols.
2. Evaluate powers and roots.
3. Multiply and divide.
4. Add and subtract.

Brackets and fraction bars are grouping symbols.

In this text, numerical solutions will be rounded to two decimal places, where necessary.

Space exploration is just one of the many areas of interest where formulas are applied to solve for unknown values. The following application takes place in a more familiar setting: when an object is swung in a vertical circle from a cord, the tension in the cord at the top and bottom of a swing can be found by the following formulas.

$$T_{\text{Top}} = m\left(\frac{v^2}{r} - g\right) \qquad T_{\text{Bottom}} = m\left(\frac{v^2}{r} + g\right)$$

m is the mass of the object in kilograms; r is the radius of the circle in metres; v is the speed of the object in metres per second; g is acceleration due to gravity on Earth's surface, 9.8 m/s^2. The tension, T, is then given in newtons (N).

EXAMPLE 1: Find the tension in the cord at the bottom of a swing when a mass of 500 g is swung from a cord 80 cm long at a speed of 4 m/s.

$$T_{\text{Bottom}} = m\left(\frac{v^2}{r} + g\right)$$

$$= 0.5\left(\frac{4^2}{0.8} + 9.8\right) \qquad 500\text{ g} = 0.5\text{ kg}, \; 80\text{ cm} = 0.8\text{ m}$$

$$= 0.5(20 + 9.8)$$

$$= 14.9$$

The tension at the bottom of the swing is 14.9 N.

Like formulas, algebraic expressions are evaluated by substituting given values for the variables and then evaluating the resulting expression.

EXAMPLE 2: Evaluate the expression for $a = 6$, $b = 8$, and $c = 5$.

$$\frac{5a - 3b}{2c} - \sqrt{2b} = \frac{5(6) - 3(8)}{2(5)} - \sqrt{2(8)}$$

$$= \frac{6}{10} - 4$$

$$= -3.4$$

EXERCISE 1-1

A **1.** Evaluate each of the following expressions.

a. $7^2 - 3 + 8$ **b.** $2 \times 8 - 5 + 12 \div 2^2$ **c.** $2.4 \div 0.75 - (2.5)^2$

d. $\frac{3}{5} - \frac{1}{10} \div \frac{1}{2}$ **e.** $\frac{2}{3} \times \frac{1}{2} - \frac{3}{4} \times \frac{1}{3}$ **f.** $\left(1\frac{1}{2}\right)^2 \times 2.4 - 3.5 \times 1\frac{1}{5}$

g. $\dfrac{3[-5 + 4(2 - 1)]}{7 - 2^2}$ **h.** $\dfrac{4[5 \times 6 \div 3]}{(3 \times 6 \div 9)^3}$ **i.** $\dfrac{3.2 \times 1.5 - 0.6}{4.5 \div (3 \times 2.5)}$

2. Rewrite, inserting brackets to make a true statement.

a. $4 - 6 \div 2 \times 3 + 8 = 11$ **b.** $3 \times 5 + 4 - 8 \times 3 = 9$

c. $7 - 8 \div 2 + 3 \times 6 \div 4 - 1 = 12$ **d.** $-3 \times 7 + 3 \times 5 \div 3 - 8 = -10$

B **3.** Evaluate the following expressions for the given values of the variables.

a. $3x + y$; $x = 7$, $y = 5$ **b.** $3(a + 5)$; $a = -2$

c. $2a - 6b + 7$; $a = 5$, $b = -2$ **d.** $3x^2 - 2xy + y^2$; $x = 4$, $y = 1$

e. $\dfrac{3x - 1}{x + 3}$; $x = 7$ **f.** $3m^2 + 5m - 2$; $m = -2$

g. $\dfrac{2x^2 - 3x + 5}{(x + 1)^2}$; $x = 4$ **h.** $\dfrac{2ab - 3b^2 + 5}{3a(b + 2)}$; $a = 4$, $b = -1$

i. $\dfrac{m + n}{m - n}$; $m = 0.6$, $n = 1.2$ **j.** $\dfrac{x(y - z)}{y^2}$; $x = \frac{1}{3}$, $y = \frac{1}{2}$, $z = \frac{1}{4}$

4. a. The area of a triangle with base b and height h is $A = \frac{1}{2}bh$. Find the area of a triangle with base 5 m and height 3 m.
   b. The area of a trapezoid with the lengths of the parallel sides given by a and b, and with height h, is $A = \frac{1}{2}(a + b)h$. Find the area of a trapezoid with height 0.8 m and with parallel sides 3.2 m and 4.6 m long.
   c. The surface area of a cylinder with height h and radius of the base r is $A = 2\pi r(r + h)$. Find the surface area of a cylinder with height 1.2 cm and radius of the base 3 mm. Use $\pi = 3.14$.
   d. The surface area of a cone with radius of the base r and slant height s is $A = 2\pi rs + \pi r^2$. Find the surface area of a cone with $r = 150$ cm and $s = 2$ m.

5. A formula is given for each item described. Evaluate each formula using the given value of the variables.
   a. Force of a moving body: $F = ma$; $m = 3.5$, $a = 0.8$
   b. Distance fallen by an object dropped from rest: $d = \frac{1}{2}gt^2$; $g = 9.8$, $t = 3.5$
   c. Kinetic energy: $KE = \frac{1}{2}mv^2$; $m = 10$, $v = 1.2$
   d. Distance between two points on a grid: $d = \sqrt{(x_1 - x_2)^2 + (y_1 - y_2)^2}$; $(x_1, y_1) = (7, 5)$, $(x_2, y_2) = (3, -1)$
   e. Resistance in a parallel circuit: $R = \frac{R_1R_2}{R_1 + R_2}$; $R_1 = 3500$, $R_2 = 1500$

C 6. To answer the following, refer to the formulas for the tension in a cord when an object is swung in a vertical circle.
   a. What is the tension in a 1.5 m cord at the top and bottom of a swing if the object, with a mass of 2.5 kg, is being swung at a speed of rotation of 5 m/s?
   b. The minimum speed required to keep a mass swinging in a vertical circle is such that the tension at the top of the swing is zero. What is the minimum speed needed to keep a mass swinging at the end of a 1 m cord?
   c. As the cord becomes shorter, how does it affect the speed needed to maintain a circular path?
   d. A cord will break at a tension of 100 N. How fast can you swing an object with a mass of 1 kg before a 1 m cord will break?
   e. How fast can you swing a 1 kg mass on a 1.5 m cord? a 0.5 m cord? (Assume that the cord can handle a tension of up to 100 N.)

7. a. One newton (N) is the force required to accelerate a mass of 1 kg at a rate of 1 m/s². A car of mass 1200 kg is accelerated smoothly at a rate of 8 m/s². What is the net force accelerating the car?
   b. The same car in part **f** can decelerate from 60 km/h to zero in three seconds. What is the average net braking force?

1-2 Evaluating Powers

Many formulas, like the formulas for finding the tension in a cord when swinging an object, involve **powers**.

$T = m\left(\frac{v^2}{r} \pm g\right)$ v^2 is a **power**: v is its **base**; 2 is the **exponent**.

Exponents of zero and integer exponents less than zero can be assigned meanings by observing the pattern illustrated in the list below.

Any power with an exponent of 0 and a non-zero base is defined to be 1.

$$b^0 = 1, b \neq 0$$

A power with a negative exponent is defined to be the reciprocal of the corresponding power with positive exponent.

$$b^{-x} = \frac{1}{b^x}, b \neq 0$$

exponents decreasing by 1

$3^5 = 243$
$3^4 = 81$
$3^3 = 27$
$3^2 = 9$
$3^1 = 3$
$3^0 = 1$
$3^{-1} = \frac{1}{3^1}$ or $\frac{1}{3}$
$3^{-2} = \frac{1}{3^2}$ or $\frac{1}{9}$

reduced by a factor of 3

When an exponent appears outside of a pair of parentheses, the exponent applies to the entire expression within the parentheses.

EXAMPLE 1: Evaluate each expression below.

a. $\left(\frac{2}{3}\right)^{-3} = \left(\frac{3}{2}\right)^3$
$= \frac{3^3}{2^3}$
$= \frac{27}{8}$

b. $(-3)^0 - 3^{-2} = 1 - \frac{1}{3^2}$
$= 1 - \frac{1}{9}$
$= \frac{8}{9}$

Operations with powers can be simplified by applying the following laws of exponents.

Product rule: $(b^x)(b^y) = b^{x+y}$
To multiply powers *of the same base*, add the exponents.

Quotient Rule: $b^x \div b^y = b^{x-y}$
To divide powers *of the same base*, subtract exponents.

Power rule: $(b^x)^y = b^{xy}$
To take the power of a power, multiply the exponents.

EXAMPLE 2: Simplify each expression below.

a. $(5x^2y)(-3x^3y^2) = (5)(-3)(x^{2+3})(y^{1+2})$
$= -15x^5y^3$

b. $(-2x^3y)^3 = (-2)^3(x^{3\times 3})(y^3)$
$= -8x^9y^3$

c. $\dfrac{18x^5y^2}{3x^7y} = \dfrac{6y}{x^2}$

d. $\dfrac{1}{a^2a^{-5}} = \dfrac{1}{a^{-3}}$

$= \dfrac{1}{\frac{1}{a^3}}$

$= a^3$

The exponent laws can also simplify computations with numbers written in scientific notation.

EXAMPLE 3: As described at the beginning of lesson 1-1, a shuttle can gain a circular orbit by achieving a certain speed v, in metres per second, as given by the formula below.

$$v = \sqrt{\frac{GM}{R}}$$

R metres is the radius of the orbit from Earth's centre;
M is the mass of Earth, 5.9×10^{24} kg;
G is Newton's gravitational constant, 6.67×10^{-11} N·m²/kg²

What speed is required for the shuttle to achieve an orbit 250 km from Earth's surface, given that Earth's radius is 6378 km?

Apply the formula.

$$v = \sqrt{\frac{GM}{R}} = \sqrt{\frac{(6.67 \times 10^{-11})(5.9 \times 10^{24})}{(6378 + 250) \times 10^3}}$$

$$= \sqrt{\frac{(6.67 \times 10^{-11})(5.9 \times 10^{24})}{6628 \times 10^3}}$$

$$= \sqrt{\frac{(6.67 \times 10^{-11})(5.9 \times 10^{24})}{6.628 \times 10^6}}$$

$$= \sqrt{\frac{6.67 \times 5.9}{6.628} \times 10^{-11+24-6}}$$

$$\doteq \sqrt{5.937 \times 10^7}$$

$$= \sqrt{59.37 \times 10^6}$$

$$\doteq 7.71 \times 10^3 \text{ m/s}$$ in scientific notation

To gain an orbit 250 km from Earth's surface, the shuttle must achieve a speed of about 7.71×10^3 m/s or, in decimal notation, 7710 m/s.

EXERCISE 1-2

A 1. Simplify each expression.

a. x^8x^2 **b.** $x^8 \div x^2$ **c.** $(x^8)^2$ **d.** $(8x)^2$

e. x^5x^3 **f.** $3^2 \times 3^3$ **g.** $3^0 \times 3^2$ **h.** $(ab)^3$

i. $(-3m^2)^2$ **j.** $(-3m)^4$ **k.** $(r^5)^3$ **l.** $a^7 \div a^3$

m. $5^3 \div 5^4$ **n.** $3m^3 \times 2m^2$ **o.** $(-y^3)^2$ **p.** $(-5m)^3(2m)^2$

2. Rewrite using only positive exponents.

a. $5xy^{-2}$　b. r^{-3}　c. $3rs^{-3}$

d. $\frac{1}{x^{-2}}$　e. $\frac{1}{m^2n^{-3}}$　f. $\left(\frac{x^2}{x^5}\right)^{-1}$

3. Rewrite using no fractions.

a. $\frac{1}{a^5}$　b. $\frac{17}{x}$　c. $\frac{3x}{y}$

d. $\frac{1}{3^2y^5}$　e. $\frac{4z}{x^3y^2}$　f. $\frac{x^{-5}}{y^{-2}}$

B 4. Evaluate each of the following.

a. 2^{-3}　b. 5^{-2}　c. 8^0　d. $\left(\frac{2}{3}\right)^{-2}$

e. $3^0 + 3^{-2}$　f. $2^{-2} + 3^{-1}$　g. $5^{-2} + 2^{-1}$　h. $\left(\frac{-3}{5}\right)^{-1}$

i. $(3 \times 2^{-2})^{-3}$　j. $(-5 \times 3^{-1})^{-1}$　k. $(10^1 + 10^{-1})^{-2}$　l. $(1.2)^{-2}$

5. Write each number in scientific notation.

a. 2700　b. 85 000 000　c. 0.003 95　d. 0.000 058

e. 38×10^4　f. 0.03×10^3　g. 520×10^{-7}　h. 0.0092×10^{-5}

6. Write each number in decimal notation.

a. 2.5×10^3　b. 1.6×10^{-8}　c. 3.7×10^{-2}　d. 4.6×10^1

e. 7.02×10^5　f. 0.085×10^4　g. 0.029×10^5　h. 0.055×10^{-4}

7. Evaluate each expression, giving your answer in scientific notation.

a. $(7.5 \times 10^6)(2.2 \times 10^3)$　b. $(4.8 \times 10^5) \div (3.2 \times 10^{-3})$

c. $(5.5 \times 10^{-6}) \div (8 \times 10^{-3})$　d. $\frac{(4.5 \times 10^{-3})(4.0 \times 10^7)}{1.5 \times 10^8}$

e. $\frac{(3.6 \times 10^{-4})(2.5 \times 10^{-3})}{(8 \times 10^{-5})(1.5 \times 10^4)}$　f. $\frac{(6.4 \times 10^{12})(2.5 \times 10^{-7})}{(8 \times 10^4)(5 \times 10^{11})}$

g. $\frac{600 \times 0.0025}{0.008 \times 0.75}$　h. $\frac{0.000\,024 \times 720}{4800 \times 150}$　i. $\frac{700 \times (0.006)^2}{0.035 \times 3}$

8. Simplify the following expressions, giving your answer using positive exponents only.

a. $(4xy^2)^3(xy)^2$　b. $(3x^3y^2)^3(2y^5)^2$　c. $(a^5b^{-3})^2$

d. $(2m^3y)^2(3m^{-2}y^4)^3$　e. $(-5a^3b^{-2})^{-2}$　f. $(15x^3y^4)(6x^5y^2)^{-1}$

g. $\frac{(-2x^2yz^4)^3}{-2xy}$　h. $\frac{a^5b^{-3}}{a^{-2}b^{-4}}$　i. $\frac{(x^3y^4)^2}{(x^{-2}y^3z^{-1})^3}$

j. $\frac{1}{(3x)^0} + \frac{2}{(3y)^0}$　k. $\frac{(4mn)^3(2m^2n)}{20mn^{-5}}$　l. $\left(\frac{8x}{12x^2y^{-2}}\right)^{-3}$

m. $\frac{1}{2x^0} + \frac{1}{3y^0}$　n. $\left(\frac{3ab}{-5}\right)^{-2}$　o. $\left(\frac{3x^5}{y^2}\right)^{-2}\left(\frac{5x^3}{3y}\right)^3$

p. $\frac{5}{(3x)^0} - \frac{3}{4y^0}$　q. $\frac{1}{x^{-2}} + \frac{1}{y^{-3}}$　r. $\frac{10a^{-3}}{b^2} \times \frac{-4a}{b^{-3}} \times \left(\frac{a^3}{b^2}\right)^{-3}$

9. Find the missing value to make each statement true.

a. $x^3 = 8$
b. $(-5)^x = -125$
c. $(0.4)^x = 0.16$
d. $a^5 = 32$
e. $m^{-2} = \frac{1}{9}$
f. $\left(\frac{2}{5}\right)^x = 0.16$
g. $\left(\frac{2}{3}\right)^x = 2\frac{1}{4}$
h. $4^x = \frac{1}{64}$
i. $x^{-3} = 27$
j. $(-5)^y = 1$
k. $n^{-2} = 1\frac{7}{9}$
l. $0.2^x = 25$

C 10. On its second flight, the space shuttle *Columbia* travelled approximately 1 500 000 km in orbit at a speed of about 28 000 km/h. About how long was the shuttle in orbit?

11. Earth's orbit is roughly circular, with a radius of 1.5×10^8 km. What is the orbital velocity of Earth if the length of the year is 365.25 days?

12. The radius of Earth is 6.378×10^3 km. Using the fact that one complete rotation takes 24 h, find the speed of a point on the surface of Earth due to daily rotation? Answer in metres per second.

13. Einstein's famous equation, $E = mc^2$, provides the formula to find the energy equivalent of a given object with mass m kilograms, where E is measured in joules and c is the speed of light, 3.0×10^8 m/s. If a single grape with a mass of 10 g were converted entirely to energy, how many joules of energy would be given off?

14. Not all exponents are integers. Use the clues below to determine a reasonable meaning for $x^{\frac{1}{2}}$ and $x^{\frac{1}{3}}$.

a. $x^{\frac{1}{2}} \times x^{\frac{1}{2}} = x^1 = x$ or $(x^{\frac{1}{2}})^2 = x$
$\therefore x^{\frac{1}{2}} = ■$

b. $x^{\frac{1}{3}} \times x^{\frac{1}{3}} \times x^{\frac{1}{3}} = x^1 = x$ or $(x^{\frac{1}{3}})^3 = x$
$\therefore x^{\frac{1}{3}} = ■$

15. The number of bacteria cells in a culture doubles each day. If the number of cells is 350×2^n where n is the number of days since the culture started, find the number of cells in the culture after one week has elapsed.

16. The amount of memory capacity that a computer has is expressed in bytes. A kilobyte is 2^{10} bytes or approximately 1000 bytes. Find the exact number of bytes in a kilobyte. A megabyte is 2^{20} bytes or approximately one million bytes. Find the exact number of bytes in a megabyte.

17. The area of a circular pizza is $\frac{\pi d^2}{4}$, where d is the diameter of the pizza. At Alfredo's, a 20 cm pizza costs \$5.75. How much would you expect to pay for a 30 cm pizza?

1-3 Solving Linear Equations

Tickets for the final game at Eastwood High were \$3 in advance and \$4 at the door. There were 420 tickets sold altogether, with total receipts of \$1410. If n represents the number of advance tickets sold, then an equation to represent the total receipts is $3n + 4(420 - n) = 1410$.

This equation contains one variable only, and that variable has exponent 1; the equation is a **linear equation** in one unknown. Finding the solution or **root** of the equation would give the number of advance tickets sold. Solve the equation by transforming it into simpler, equivalent equations until the variable has been isolated.

EXAMPLE 1: Solve and check the given equation.

$$\begin{aligned} 3n + 4(420 - n) &= 1410 \\ 3n + 1680 - 4n &= 1410 \\ -n + 1680 &= 1410 \\ -n &= -270 \\ n &= 270 \end{aligned}$$

There were 270 advance tickets sold.

Check: $\text{L.S.} = 3n + 4(420 - n)$
$= 3(270) + 4(420 - 270)$
$= 810 + 4(150)$
$= 1410$
$\text{R.S.} = 1410$ ✓

Since L.S. = R.S., $n = 270$ is correct.

The same process can be applied to isolate a variable in a formula.

EXAMPLE 2: Given the formula for the surface area A of a cone, isolate s.

$$A = \pi r^2 + \pi rs \longrightarrow \pi rs = A - \pi r^2$$
$$s = \frac{A - \pi r^2}{\pi r}$$

Equations can be used to solve word problems, following a five-step plan.

EXAMPLE 3: In his second year on the basketball team, Jonas scored 118 points. This was 7 points more than triple the number he scored the first year. How many points did he score the first year?

Let p be the number of points scored the first year. — **1.** Select a variable.

Then: $3p + 7 = 118$ — **2.** Write an equation.

$$\begin{aligned} 3p &= 111 \\ p &= 37 \end{aligned}$$

3. Solve the equation.

Jonas scored 37 points the first year. — **4.** Write a conclusion.

Triple 37 is 111; 7 more than that is 118. ✓ — **5.** Check.

EXERCISE 1-3

A **1.** Solve the following equations.

a. $2x + 5 = 11$ **b.** $17 = 5m - 3$ **c.** $3x + 7 = x - 3$

d. $3y - 8 = 12 - y$ **e.** $6 - 2m = -2 - 3m$ **f.** $4x - 2 = -8 + x$

g. $\frac{1}{3}x + 5 = 7$ **h.** $-5 = -\frac{3}{4}x + 1$ **i.** $2\frac{1}{2}m = 10$

2. Isolate the indicated variable in each of the following formulas.

a. $P = 4s$; s **b.** $T = f + 3n$; f **c.** $A = lw$; w

d. $C = 2\pi r$; r **e.** $A = 2\pi rh$; h **f.** $d = vt + x$; t

g. $L = d + km$; m **h.** $P = 2\pi r + 2l$; r **i.** $A = 4lw + l^2$; w

j. $A = 2\pi r^2 + \pi rh$; h **k.** $E = mgh + kx^2$; m **l.** $E = mgh + \frac{1}{2}mv^2$; h

B **3.** Solve and check.

a. $8x + 3 = 4(x - 1) + 11$ **b.** $3(2x + 1) - 2(x - 1) = 13$

c. $3(x + 5) - 4 = 2(4x + 8) - 3(x + 1)$ **d.** $5(3x + 2) - 5 = 7(x + 2) + 2$

e. $3(5 - x) - (2 + x) = 4 - x$ **f.** $x(x + 1) + 3(x - 4) = x(x - 2)$

g. $3x(x - 1) + 2x(x + 4) = 7 + x(5x + 4)$ **h.** $3x(4x + 3) - 3(x + 8) = 2x(6x - 5)$

4. Substitute the given values in the formulas below and then solve for the variable which remains.

a. $F = ma$; $F = 15$, $m = 3$ **b.** $P = \frac{kT}{v}$; $P = 18$, $k = 750$, $v = 250$

c. $E = \frac{1}{2}mv^2$; $E = 640$, $v = 16$ **d.** $E = mgh + \frac{1}{2}kx^2$; $E = 150$, $m = 8$, $g = 10$, $h = 1.5$, $x = 2$

5. The sides of a triangle have lengths that are three consecutive integers. The perimeter of the triangle is 45 cm. What are the lengths of the sides?

6. Lisa is now working at the bakery where she apprenticed. Her weekly salary of $342 is $15 more than double an apprentice's weekly income. How much does an apprentice make each week?

7. The annual average area from which timber is harvested in Canada is 800 000 ha. This is 67 000 ha less than triple the area destroyed by fire in 1978. What area of timber was destroyed by fire in 1978?

8. In an airtight stove, one cord of Douglas fir will provide 8 Gj (gigajoules) of heat. A cord of alder will provide 7 Gj. Tracey has 12 cords of wood in total and calculates that it will provide 91 Gj of heat, enough for two years of heating. How many cords of each type of wood does Tracey have?

C **9.** In the first election in Canada in 1867, there were 181 seats in the House of Commons. If the Liberals had managed to win 11 of the ridings taken by the Conservatives, they would have held a one-seat majority. How many seats did each party win in 1867?

1-4 Solving Equations Containing Fractions

On a satellite in space, electricity can be generated using solar panels and fuel cells. If the solar panels in a communications satellite were not functioning, the satellite could continue to communicate for 90 days using its fuel cells. If the satellite used only its data-gathering equipment, the fuel cells would be exhausted in 60 days.

How long would the fuel cells last if *both* communications equipment and data-gathering equipment were used?

Questions like this can be solved by applying equations containing fractions. Solving equations that contain fractions, decimals, or percents can be simplified by first mutliplying both sides of the equation by the lowest common denominator (LCD), to eliminate unwanted denominators.

EXAMPLE 1: Solve each equation.

a.

$$\frac{3}{4}x - \frac{2}{3} = \frac{1}{2}$$

$$12\left(\frac{3}{4}x - \frac{2}{3}\right) = 12\left(\frac{1}{2}\right)$$

Multiply both sides by 12, the LCD.

$$9x - 8 = 6$$

$$9x = 14$$

$$x = \frac{14}{9}$$

b.

$$\frac{x-6}{5} = x - 7.6$$

Multiply by 10.

$$10\left(\frac{x-6}{5}\right) = 10(x - 7.6)$$

$$2x - 12 = 10x - 76$$

$$-8x = -64$$

$$x = 8$$

EXAMPLE 2: How long would a fuel cell last if both communications and data-gathering equipment are employed?

Let t be the number of days in the life of a fuel cell. Then, in one day, the communications system would use up $\frac{1}{90}$ of the fuel; in t days, the fraction would be $t\left(\frac{1}{90}\right)$ or $\frac{t}{90}$.
Similarly, the data-gathering system would use $\frac{t}{60}$ of the fuel.

1. Select a variable.

The combined use in t days, then, is $\frac{t}{90} + \frac{t}{60} = 1$.

2. Write an equation.

3. Solve the equation.

$$180\left[\frac{t}{90} + \frac{t}{60}\right] = 180[1]$$

$$2t + 3t = 180$$

$$5t = 180$$

$$t = 36$$

The fuel cell would be exhausted in 36 days.

4. Write a conclusion.

In 36 days, the communications system would use $\frac{36}{90}$ of the fuel; the data-gathering system would use $\frac{36}{60}$.
Their total is 1. ✓

5. Check.

EXERCISE 1-4

A 1. What should be multiplied on both sides of the equation to remove denominators and decimal numbers?

a. $\frac{5}{6}x + \frac{1}{2} = \frac{3}{4}$ b. $0.3x - 2.58 = 1.7$ c. $\frac{3}{5} - \frac{3}{8}x = 1\frac{1}{4}$

d. $\frac{x}{4} + 0.35 = 2.5$ e. $0.65 - 3.8x = 0.02$ f. $\frac{4x}{9} + \frac{5}{8} = \frac{1}{6}$

g. $\frac{3x-5}{8} = \frac{2x+3}{3}$ h. $\frac{5x+7}{2} = -4$ i. $\frac{5(3-y)}{6} = \frac{3y-2}{5}$

B 2. Solve and check.

a. $\frac{x}{3} + \frac{3}{5} = \frac{1}{15}$ b. $\frac{x}{4} - \frac{1}{2} = \frac{1}{4}$ c. $\frac{x}{10} + \frac{x}{15} = \frac{9}{10}$

d. $\frac{2x}{7} - \frac{1}{2} = \frac{x}{3} - \frac{11}{14}$ e. $\frac{3}{4}(x-2) = \frac{2}{3}(x-1)$ f. $\frac{3x+1}{3} = \frac{x+1}{2}$

g. $\frac{x+2}{5} = x - 4$ h. $0.8(30 - x) = 0.2x - 1$ i. $\frac{5x+1}{8} = \frac{3x-5}{2}$

j. $0.6(5x+3) = \frac{10x+3}{3}$ k. $\frac{0.7x+1.5}{3} = \frac{1.2x-2}{4}$ l. $\frac{3x+1}{2} - \frac{x-2}{5} = \frac{4x+2}{3}$

3. Solve each equation in exercise 1.

4. A cold-water faucet can fill a washbasin in 2 min. The hot-water faucet will fill the basin in 3 min. How long will it take to fill the basin using both faucets?

5. Frances cycles to and from the beach in 5 h. Her cycling speed is 30 km/h going to the beach and 20 km/h on the return trip. How far is it to the beach?

6. An orbiting spacecraft has two maneuvering engines. If one engine is fired continuously, it will use up all the fuel in 12 h. If the other is fired continuously, it will use all the fuel in 15 h. How long will the fuel last if both engines are fired continuously?

7. The Student Society had a $5000 surplus at the end of the term. It was invested in two term deposits. One deposit yielded 10% and the other 15%. The total yield for the two was $600. How much was deposited at each rate?

8. The works department of a city owns two machines for placing cement curbs on new roadways. One machine will place 1 km of curb in 12 h; the other will place 1 km of curb in 8 h. How long will it take to place 5 km of curb if the machines work together?

C 9. A cooling system contains 10 L of 30% antifreeze solution. Some of the coolant is drained and replaced with pure (100%) solution to produce a 40% antifreeze solution. How much of the original coolant is drained and replaced?

1-5 Solving Inequalities

Like equations, inequalities can be solved by transforming successive inequalities to simpler, equivalent, inequalities. There is one important difference, however, between solving equations and solving inequalities, illustrated by the following examples.

Each inequality below is a true statement.	Multiply both sides by a negative number.	For the resulting inequality to be true, the inequality signs must be *reversed.*
$-15 < -2$	$(-1)(-15)\ ?\ (-1)(-2)$	$15 > 2$
$4.3 > -1.4$	$(-20)(4.3)\ ?\ (-20)(-1.4)$	$-86 < 28$
$-11 \leq 2.5$	$(-2)(-11)\ ?\ (-2)(2.5)$	$22 \geq -5$

> When both sides of an inequality are either multiplied or divided by a negative number, the direction of the inequality is reversed.

Unless otherwise stated, when solving inequalities, assume that the variable is an element of the set of real numbers. Solving an inequality usually results in a solution *set*, rather than a single root.

EXAMPLE 1: Solve each of the following. Illustrate each solution set on a number line. Check for one value from the solution set.

a.
$$5x + 1 < 11$$
$$5x < 10$$
$$x < 2$$

Check for $x = -3$:
L.S. $= 5x + 1$ R.S. $= 11$
$= 5(-3) + 1$
$= -14$
L.S. $<$ R.S. ✓

b.
$$-2x + 3 \leq 7$$
$$-2x \leq 4$$
$$x \geq -2$$

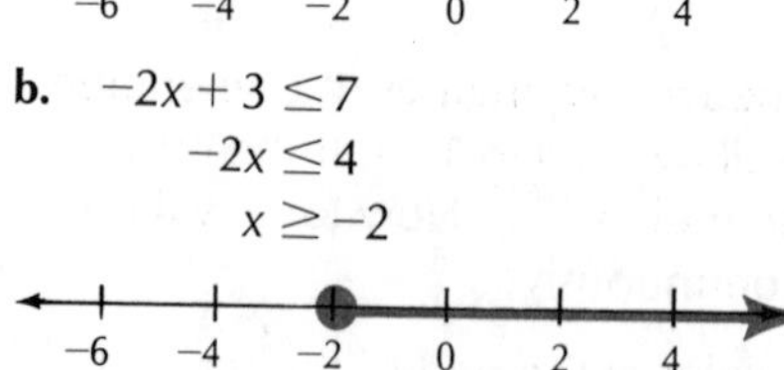

Check for $x = 5$:
L.S. $= -2x + 3$ R.S. $= 7$
$= -2(5) + 3$
$= -7$
L.S. $\leq$ R.S. ✓

Compound inequalities are two simple inequalities connected with the words "and" or "or". Compare the following examples of compound inequalities.

$n < 3$ and $n > -1$ For the statement to be true, both parts of the statement must be true.

$t \leq 3$ or $t > 5$ For the statement to be true, it is sufficient that either part of the statement is true.

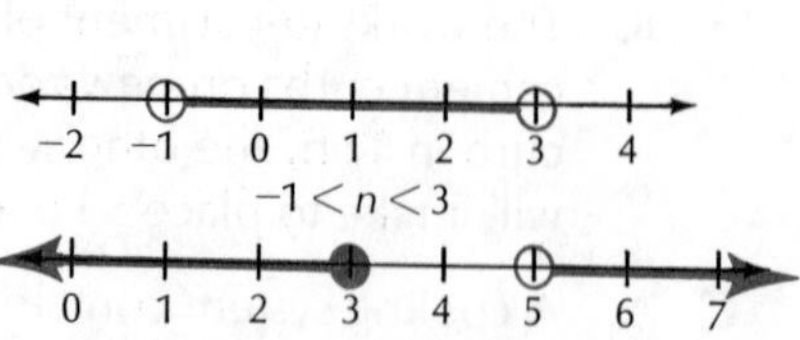

$x < 1$ and $x > 2$ It is impossible for both statements to be true. The solution set in this case is the empty set, ϕ.

EXAMPLE 2: Solve each combined inequality and graph the solution set.

a. $2x + 5 \geq 1$ and $3x - 2 < 10$ — Solve each part of the combined inequality.

$2x \geq -4$ and $3x < 12$

$x \geq -2$ and $x < 4$

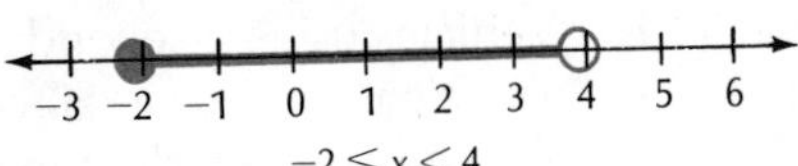

$-2 \leq x < 4$

b. $3 - y > 5$ or $2y + 1 \geq 7$

$-y > 2$ or $2y \geq 6$

$y < -2$ or $y \geq 3$

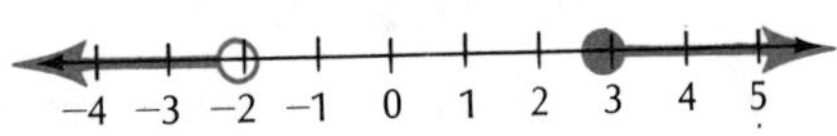

A mathematical application of compound inequalities is given by inequality statements that contain the *absolute value* of a variable expression. The absolute value of a number is its magnitude.

EXAMPLE 3: Graph the solution set of each of the following.

a. $|w| < 2$ Look for specific values of w that satisfy the inequality: 1, 1.5, 0, −1, −1.5; not −2; not −2.5.

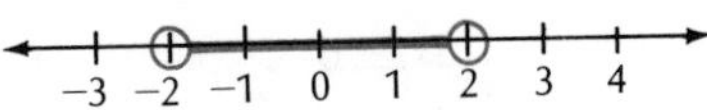

The number line illustrates $-2 < w < 2$.

$\therefore |w| < 2$ is equivalent to $w > -2$ and $w < 2$, or $-2 < w < 2$.

b. $|m| > 1$ Specific values of m that satisfy the inequality are: 1.5, 2, 5, 19; also −19 (since $|-19| = 19$), −5, −2, −1.5.

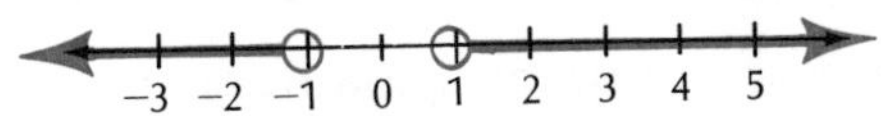

The number line illustrates $m < -1$ or $m > 1$.

$\therefore |m| > 1$ is equivalent to $m < -1$ or $m > 1$.

EXAMPLE 4: Solve $2|t - 5| > 6$, and graph the solution set.

First, simplify the inequality so that the absolute value is isolated.

$2|t - 5| > 6$

$|t - 5| > 3$

The form of $|t - 5| > 3$ is similar to that of $|m| > 1$ in Example 3.

For $|t - 5| > 3$ to be true, you need $(t - 5) < -3$ or $(t - 5) > 3$.

$t - 5 < -3$ or $t - 5 > 3$

$t < 2$ or $t > 8$

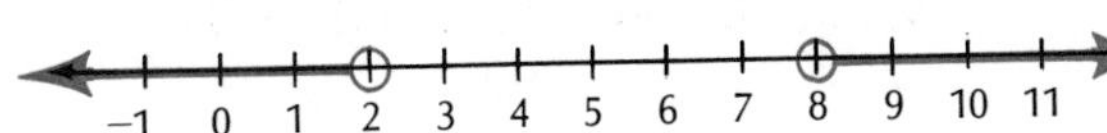

EXERCISE 1-5

A 1. For each of the following, define a variable and write an appropriate inequality or combined inequality.

- **a.** The legal voting age in Canada is 18.
- **b.** Vehicles using a secondary road should have a mass lower than 2.5 t.
- **c.** The clearance for a railroad underpass is 2.2 m.
- **d.** The youngest student in class 11B is 15 years old. The oldest was 18 years old last month.
- **e.** Speeds on the freeway must be no less than 40 km/h and no more than 100 km/h.

2. Graph each of the following inequalities.

a. $x > 3$ **b.** $x < -1$ **c.** $x \geq 5$ **d.** $x \geq -3$

3. State the inequalities shown by the following graphs.

a.
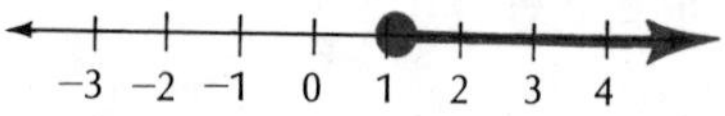

b.
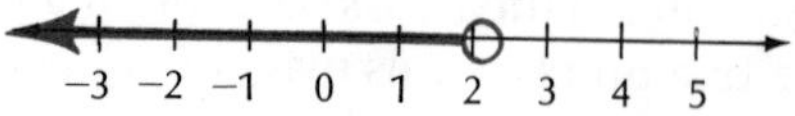

c.
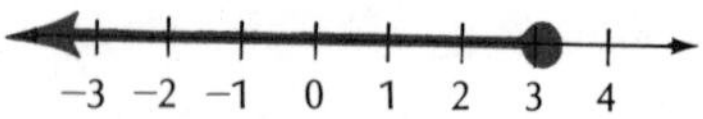

d.
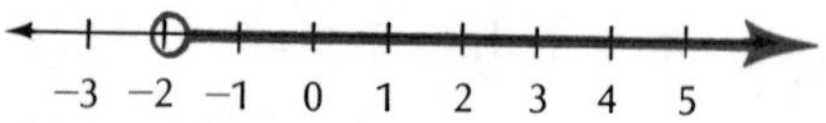

4. Solve the following inequalities. Check for two values from each solution set.

a. $x - 2 < 8$ **b.** $x + 5 \geq 3$ **c.** $3x \geq 6$ **d.** $-2x < 6$
e. $2x - 5 \geq 7$ **f.** $3x - 1 < 8$ **g.** $9 \leq 4x - 7$ **h.** $3 - 2x < 7$
i. $5 - x \geq 4$ **j.** $-3 \geq 9 - 4x$ **k.** $7x + 1 \geq 3x - 1$ **l.** $4x + 1 \geq 7 - 2x$

B 5. Graph the following compound inequalities.

a. $x < 5$ and $x \geq 1$ **b.** $x > 3$ or $x < -1$ **c.** $x < 0$ or $x \geq 3$
d. $x \leq -3$ and $x > -6$ **e.** $x \geq 5$ or $x < -2$ **f.** $-4 \leq x < 3$

6. State the compound inequalities shown by the following graphs.

a.
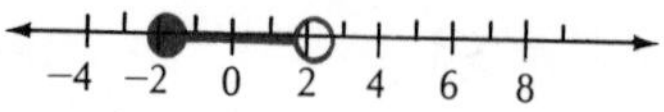

b.
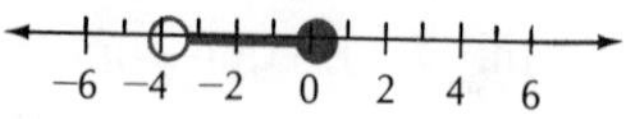

c.
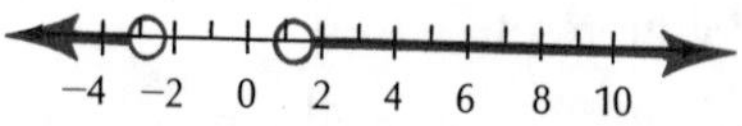

d.
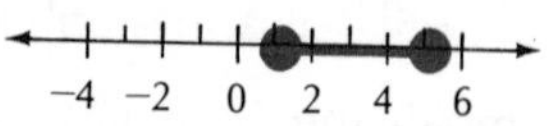

e.
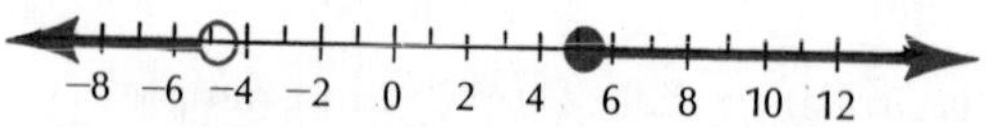

7. Solve each compound inequality and graph the solution set.

a. $5x - 2 < 8$ or $x + 3 > 9$ **b.** $2x + 1 \leq 5$ and $3x - 5 \geq -2$
c. $7x - 10 < 4$ or $7 - x \leq 2$ **d.** $2x - 1 > 5$ or $3 - x > 2$
e. $2x + 5 \leq 11$ and $5x + 10 > 0$ **f.** $4x + 3 < 7$ and $x + 3 > 6$
g. $4 \leq x + 3 < 5$ **h.** $3 < 2y + 5 < 9$
i. $-2 < 3y - 2 < 10$ **j.** $-4 \leq 2 - 3x \leq 8$

8. Solve and graph the following.

a.	$\|x-2\|<6$	b.	$\|x+3\|\geq 0$	c.	$\|4x+2\|\geq 6$
d.	$\|2x-1\|\leq 5$	e.	$5\|x\|-3\geq 7$	f.	$\|x+2\|+3<5$
g.	$\|2y+7\|-2\geq 1$	h.	$3-\|5-x\|\leq 7$	i.	$3\|x+3\|\geq 6$
j.	$6-5\|4-3x\|>-4$	k.	$2+\|3-5x\|>10$	l.	$4+\|8-2x\|\leq 20$

9. By the end of the month, John must have more than $350 in the bank. He already has $75. If he earns $5.00/h, what is the minimum number of hours he must work?

10. A sawmill has two headsaws for sawing logs into timbers. One saw can produce 30 m of timbers per minute, while the other saw can produce 20 m of timbers per minute. To fill an order, the mill must produce 2000 m of timbers. There are already 800 m of timbers in the yard. What is the least amount of time needed to produce the remainder?

11. To pass a motion at a meeting, one more than half the votes must be cast in favour of the motion. How many votes must be cast to pass a motion if a total of 275 votes are cast?

12. A store owner calculates that in order to make a profit on sales of china sets, the price of each set must be marked up at least 50% above the cost price with another three dollars added for handling. Find the selling price of a set with a cost price of $12.50.

13. Carla wants to maintain a scoring average of 15 points per game during her team's basketball season. In the first four games of the season, she scored 18, 16, 14, and 10 points. What is the minimum number of points she must score in the fifth game to maintain her average?

14. A salad recipe for six people calls for no less than 80 mL of salad oil. What is the minimum amount of oil needed to prepare enough salad for twenty?

15. A courier has a route of 180 km. She has driven the first 80 km at an average speed of 25 km/h. How fast must the last portion be driven if she must finish the route in less than 8 h?

C 16. The Triangle Inequality states that if a, b, and c are the lengths of the three sides of a triangle, then $a+b>c$.

a. Explain how you could use this inequality to decide whether or not three given lengths could form the sides of a triangle.

b. Can you find a similar inequality for quadrilaterals and show that it must be true?

Applying Ratio

Whales sometimes leap from the water in a maneuver referred to as a breach. A biologist studying this behaviour related the rate of breaching for certain species of whales to something referred to as the *rotundity index*. This index is the ratio of mass to cube of body length (m/L^3) when mass is measured in kilograms and length is measured in metres.

1. The following table contains a list of whale species, their masses, body lengths, and rate of breaching. Is the breaching rate related to rotundity in your opinion?

Whale Species	Length	Mass	Breaching Rate
Blue Whale	27 m	150 t	Almost never
Sperm Whale	18 m	70 t	Often
Minke Whale	10 m	10 t	Unusual
Finback Whale	25 m	80 t	Rare
Bryde's Whale	13 m	26 t	Occasional
Bowhead Whale	17 m	80 t	Occasional
Right Whale	15 m	55 t	Often
Sei Whale	18 m	25 t	Almost never
Humpback Whale	14 m	32 t	Very frequent

2. The Gray Whale has a rotundity index of 14.3. If the length of a Gray Whale is 12 m, what is its mass?

3. What would be the expected length of a large Humpback Whale with a mass of 33 t?

4. Calculate your rotundity index using your mass in kilograms and height in metres. How does it compare with your classmates? What does the rotundity index measure?

5. The table gives *Desirable Masses* for males of varying heights. Compute m/h, m/h^2, and m/h^3 for each height. Which index is most constant?

Height	Mass
130 cm	28 kg
150 cm	44 kg
170 cm	64 kg

6. Use your index to determine the desirable mass of a man 180 cm tall and 190 cm tall. The desirable masses for these two heights given in a standard table are 72 kg and 84 kg. Explain any discrepancies between these masses and the ones you obtain.

7. Assume that the human body is roughly cylindrical in shape and has a density of approximately 0.9 g/cm^3. Measure your height and estimate the average diameter of your body. Use the formulas for the volume and surface area of a cylinder ($V = \pi r^2 h$ and $A = 2\pi r(r + h)$) to estimate your mass and surface area. How does the calculated mass compare with your actual mass?

Review

1. Evaluate the following for the given values of the variables.

   a. $2x + 3y;\ x = 7, y = -2$ b. $\frac{4rs - 3r}{2s};\ r = 4, s = 3$

   c. $\frac{p+q}{p-q};\ p = 1.8, q = 0.2$ d. $3x - y + 2z;\ x = \frac{1}{2}, y = \frac{1}{3}, z = \frac{1}{5}$

   e. $(x - y)^2;\ x = \frac{3}{5}, y = 0.25$ f. $5x^2 - 3xy + 2y^2;\ x = 2, y = -3$

2. Evaluate the following.

   a. $\frac{3^4}{3^{-3}}$ b. $-\frac{8^3}{8^5}$ c. $\frac{\left(-\frac{4}{5}\right)^{-2}}{5^{-3}}$

   d. $0.3^{-2}(0.5)^2(1.6)^2$ e. 2×2^5 f. $\left(\frac{4}{5}\right)^8\left(\frac{5}{4}\right)^6$

3. Simplify the following expressions. Use positive exponents only in your final answer.

   a. $(-3m^2)^3$ b. $\frac{4n^2p^3}{3np^5}$ c. $(-3x^3y^{-2})^{-3}$

   d. $\frac{(2ab)^2(3a^2b)}{6a^2b^{-3}}$ e. $\left(\frac{2xy}{-3}\right)^{-3}$ f. $\frac{b^{-2}}{a^0}$

4. Graph each inequality on a number line.

   a. $x > 3$ b. $-3 \leq x \leq 0$ c. $x \leq 3$ and $x > -1$

   d. $x < 3$ or $x > 5$ e. $x > 2$ or $x > 5$ f. $x > 2$ and $x > 5$

5. Solve each inequality and graph the solution set.

   a. $5x - 1 > 4$ b. $-1 < 2x - 5 \leq 7$

   c. $8x + 1 > 17$ or $3x - 2 \geq 10$ d. $2|x + 1| - 1 > 3$

   e. $-2 < 3 - x \leq 4$ f. $|4 - x| > 4$

6. Rockdale High School sold 430 tickets to the dance. Some of the tickets were sold in advance at \$3.50 and the rest were sold at the door for \$4.00. The total receipts were \$1615.00. How many of each ticket were sold?

7. Two companies bid on a tunnelling job for the railway. One company uses a boring machine and promises completion in 80 days. The other company uses blast and dig techniques and can finish in 100 days. The railway hires them both starting at opposite ends of the tunnel. How long will it take to finish the tunnel?

8. It takes no more than 45 s for a pastry chef to decorate a small cake. It takes 5 min to prepare the icing. What is the maximum time it will take to decorate twelve cakes?

1-6 Applying Ratios

Orbiting satellites can provide information about atmospheric pollution by using detectors to measure the thermal radiation emitted from Earth's surface. By comparing readings from different detectors, scientists can study the movement of pollution. If one detector gives a reading of 28 while another gives a reading of 16, the **ratio** of the readings is 28:16, which can be reduced to lowest terms. A ratio in lowest terms contains no fractions or decimals, and the terms have no common factors.

EXAMPLES:

a. $28:16 = 7:4$ — Divide by 4, the greatest common factor (GCF) of 28 and 16.

b. $\frac{2}{3} : \frac{1}{6} = 4:1$ — Multiply by 6, the least common mutliple (LCM) of 3 and 6.

c. $4.9:3.75 = 490:375$ — Multiply by 100.
$= 98:75$ — Divide by 5.

An equality between ratios is a **proportion**. Apply the following law to solve proportions.

> **Law of Proportions** If $a:b = x:y$, that is, if $\frac{a}{b} = \frac{x}{y}$, then $ay = bx$.
>
> The product of the inner terms equals the product of the outer terms.

EXAMPLE 1: The ratio of length to width of a poster is $8:5$. If the poster is enlarged to a billboard 3.5 m wide, how tall will it be?

Let the poster be l metres tall. Write a proportion and solve it.

$$8:5 = l:3.5$$
$$5l = 8(3.5)$$
$$l = 5.6$$

The billboard will be 5.6 m tall.

Some ratios contain more than two terms.

EXAMPLE 2: Find the missing values in the proportion $9:a:7 = 6:10:b$.

To find a: $9:a = 6:10$, $6a = 90$, $a = 15$

To find b: $9:7 = 6:b$, $9b = 42$, $b = 4.67$

EXAMPLE 3: There are 27 debaters in the Viking Cup. The ratio of male students to female students is $4:5$. How many of each are there?

Let $4x$ be the number of males.
Let $5x$ be the number of females. $4x + 5x = 27$
Solve the equation. $9x = 27$
There are 12 males and 15 females. $x = 3$

EXERCISE 1-6

A **1.** Rewrite each ratio in lowest terms.

a. $8:24$ **b.** $27:18$ **c.** $28:35$ **d.** $12:16:36$

e. $15:24:54$ **f.** $0.8:0.6$ **g.** $3.6:2.4$ **h.** $5\frac{1}{2}:3.3$

2. Find the missing terms.

a. $x:8=7:4$ **b.** $5:y=15:12$ **c.** $12:18=15:m$

d. $7:5=21:b$ **e.** $3:r=5:9$ **f.** $t:11=5:4$

g. $k:7:l=25:35:15$ **h.** $4:a:9=6:10:b$ **i.** $8:15:9=r:t:6$

j. $2.8:3\frac{1}{2}:a=b:0.5:\frac{3}{8}$ **k.** $2\frac{2}{3}:m:n=4:0.8:2.4$ **l.** $7.2:g:h=0.9:1\frac{3}{5}:\frac{1}{3}$

B **3.** Solve for x.

a. $x:x+2=6:10$ **b.** $x:5=x+4:15$ **c.** $x+2:x-2=21:15$

d. $12:x+5=16:2x$ **e.** $x-3:12=2x+1:36$ **f.** $2x-5:7=x+2:14$

4. The ratio of the masses of hydrogen to oxygen in a water molecule is $2:16$.

a. If 9 g of water are converted to hydrogen and oxygen gas by electrolysis, what is the total mass of each gas produced?

b. Liquid oxygen and liquid hydrogen are used for propellant in rocket motors, where they burn to produce water. If the total mass of propellant consumed is 900 000 kg, how much is hydrogen and how much is oxygen?

5. A photograph negative is 12 mm longer than it is wide. An enlargement is made which is 10 cm by 15 cm. What are the length and width of the negative?

C **6.** The chain wheel sprockets on a 10-speed bicycle have 52 and 42 teeth. The drive gears have 28, 24, 20, 17, and 15 teeth. In what combination of gears will one revolution of the pedals most closely give two revolutions of the rear wheel?

Historical Note

The Music of the Spheres

Pythagoras and his followers, the **Pythagoreans**, were the first to study the relation between music and mathematics. They noted that a stretched string of a given length produces a musical note. Dividing the string into equal parts produces notes harmonious with that one. If the string is divided into two equal parts, the new note is an octave above the original. String lengths in the ratio $3:2$ produce notes that are a fifth apart, and those in the ratio $4:3$ produce notes that are a fourth apart.

The Pythagoreans believed so strongly in the connection between number and nature that they developed a theory relating the motion of the planets, which were assumed to move on crystalline spheres, to musical intervals. Hence the movement of the heavens, according to Pythagoras and his followers, must produce heavenly music, the "music of the spheres".

1-7 Drawing to Scale

In order for maps, drawings, and blueprints to be meaningful, they must be drawn to scale. **Scale** is often represented as a ratio, $d:l$, where d corresponds to the diagram measurement and l corresponds to the life-size measurement.

The **scale factor** k of a diagram is the decimal value of $\frac{d}{l}$, and, since $k = \frac{d}{l}$, it is also true that $d = kl$.

EXAMPLE 1: A drafting student is making a blueprint with a scale of 1 : 20.

a. Find the scale factor and apply it to calculate the blueprint measurement that the student should use to represent a door opening 76 cm wide.

$k = \frac{1}{20}$
$= 0.05$

$d = kl$ Substitute for k and l.
$d = (0.05)(76)$
$= 3.8$ 3.8 cm = 38 mm

The student should represent the door opening as 38 mm.

b. The student has used a width of 60 mm to represent a staircase that is actually 1.2 m wide. Is the measurement on the drawing correct? Check whether 60 (mm) : 1.2 (m) = 1 : 20.

60 (mm) : 1.2 (m) = 60 (mm) : 1200 (mm)
= 1 : 20 ✓

The measurement on the drawing is correct.

EXAMPLE 2: An anatomical drawing has been drawn to a scale of 15 : 2. What is the drawing measurement of a muscle ligament that is 3 mm long?

$k = \frac{15}{2}$
$= 7.5$

A scale factor greater than 1 indicates a magnification.

$d = kl$
$= 7.5(3)$
$= 22.5$

In the drawing, the ligament is 22.5 mm.

EXERCISE 1-7

A

1. Determine the scale factor for each scale ratio.

a. 1 : 50 **b.** 1 : 80 **c.** 30 : 1 **d.** 15 : 5
e. 4 : 50 **f.** 1 : 10 000 **g.** 1 : 1 000 000 **h.** 12 : 26

2. Write each scale factor as a ratio in lowest terms.

a. 0.01 **b.** 0.005 **c.** 2.5 **d.** 18 **e.** 1.25
f. 0.000 01 **g.** $0.\overline{3}$ **h.** $0.0\overline{3}$ **i.** 0.0125 **j.** 7.5

B 3. When Angie learned that her department's offices would be relocated within her building, she made a scale diagram of the new area so that she could decide, *before* the move, where each piece of furniture would go. She selected a scale of 1 : 40. Copy and complete the table, which summarizes some of her calculations.

	Item	Life-Size Dimensions	Scale Dimensions
a.	Common Work Area	5 m by 3.2 m	
b.	Computer Area	1.6 m by 2.2 m	
c.	Manager's Office	3.5 m by 4 m	
d.	Angie's Desk	1.7 m by 0.8 m	
e.	Filing Cabinet	45 cm by 62 cm	

4. Angie's representation of a closet in the new office area, with life-size dimensions 1 m by 65 cm, is 25 mm by 16 mm. Were Angie's calculations correct, given that the scale is 1 : 40? If not, find the correct scale dimensions.

5. Using a scale of 1 : 25, make a scale diagram of one of the classrooms in your school. Include doorways, windows, and electrical outlets.

6. Steve's blueprint of an apartment unit represents a life-size dimension of 2.8 m as 56 mm. Find the scale ratio and the scale factor that Steve used.

7. Copy and complete the following table.

	Drawing Measurement	Life-Size Measurement	Scale	Scale Factor
a.	2.5 cm	50 m	■	■
b.	7.5 cm	150 km	■	■
c.	■	5 m	3 : 500	■
d.	3 m	0.6 mm	■	■
e.	7 mm	■	■	25
f.	■	15 cm	■	3.6
g.	3.6 cm	■	■	0.0002
h.	■	23 km	1 : 100 000	■

8. Team A of the Fairbridge Locals Car Rally are following a map with a scale of 1 : 10 000. The plotted course is made up of straight-line distances, with map lengths of 7.5 cm, 1.2 cm, 18.1 cm, 5.3 cm, and 4.3 cm. What is the total distance Team A travels?

C 9. City planners are making a scale model of a proposed city block. The model represents a block 500 m by 400 m, and will be made in an area 10 m by 10 m.

a. What is an appropriate scale?

b. The five largest buildings will have actual dimensions as given in the table. Copy and complete the table.

Length	Width	Height	Scale Length	Scale Width	Scale Height
100 m	70 m	150 m			
45 m	60 m	200 m			
60 m	90 m	230 m			
80 m	80 m	240 m			
50 m	50 m	50 m			

1-8 Applying Rate

Pam directs traffic for a highway construction crew. Her pay for a 30 h week was \$373.50. Her *hourly* pay provides an example of rate.

dollars → $\frac{373.50}{30} = 12.45$ ← hours

Pam's regular rate of pay is \$12.45/h.

By expressing rates with a denominator of 1, comparisons of rates are simplified.

EXAMPLE 1: There are two tubes of toothpaste for sale, one at 79¢ for 75 mL and one at \$1.29 for 125 mL. Which is the better buy?

cents → $\frac{79}{75} = 1.05$ (¢/mL) ← millilitres $\qquad \frac{129}{125} = 1.03$ (¢/mL)

The larger tube is the better buy.

A familiar example of rate is given by speed, which is distance travelled over a period of time.

$$\text{Speed} = \frac{\text{Distance}}{\text{Time}}$$

Diagrams or tables can often help in solving speed problems.

EXAMPLE 2: A small plane sets out due east, 30 min before another plane. The second plane, also moving due east, travels 80 km/h faster. It overtakes the first plane in 1.5 h. Find the speed of each plane.

Let r be the speed of the first plane in kilometres per hour. Notice that the first plane travelled for 2 h before being overtaken by the second plane.

	Speed	Time	Distance ($d = rt$)
First Plane	r	2	$2r$
Second Plane	$r + 80$	1.5	$1.5(r + 80)$

Because the planes travel the same distance as one plane overtakes the other, the two expressions for distance *must* be equal.

$$2r = 1.5(r + 80)$$
$$2r = 1.5r + 120$$
$$0.5r = 120$$
$$r = 240$$

The first plane travels at 240 km/h; the second, 80 km/h faster, travels at 320 km/h.

EXERCISE 1-8

A 1. Write a rate as indicated by each example.

a. 120 km are travelled in 3 h
b. 7200 m travelled in 18 s
c. 28¢ for 350 mL
d. 2500 revolutions in 4 min

2. Which is the better buy?

a. 250 mL for 78¢ or 340 mL for $1.00
b. $1.53 for 300 g or $2.60 for 0.5 kg
c. $15.50 for 2.5 m or $27.50 for 4 m
d. 98¢ for 175 mL or $4.20 for 720 mL
e. 7.5 kg for $97.10 or 12 kg for $150
f. 38 cm for $1.50 or 27 cm for $1.00

3. Kathy earns $6.55/h working part-time at a greenhouse. How much would she make during a week when she worked 16 h?

4. Ron completed the 28.6 km of a cross-country course in 3 h. Find his average rate of speed.

5. Chris bought 3.5 m of corduroy at $7.59/m and 2.8 m of lining at $2.99/m. Find the total cost of the two lengths of fabric.

B 6. A car starts out at 9:00 on the highway. At 11:00, another car, travelling 20 km/h faster, sets out in the same direction, overtaking the first car at 19:00. How far from the starting point are the two cars when they meet?

7. Two planes take off at the same time, travelling in opposite directions. One travels 300 km/h, the other at 450 km/h. When will they be 2000 km apart?

8. By increasing his cycling speed by 5 km/h, Bill could cover the same distance in 4 h which now takes him 5 h. What is his average speed now?

9. It takes Suzanne 3 h to hike in to Garibaldi Lake, but only 2 h to hike out. Her average speed out is 1.5 km/h greater than her average speed going in. How far is it to Garibaldi Lake?

10. A grocer mixed two different types of coffee to produce 50 kg of a blend, using 15 kg of coffee which usually sells for $7.90/kg and 35 kg which usually sells at $8.60/kg. What should the blend sell for?

C 11. Fifty kilograms of coffee which sells for $6.92/kg is blended from two types of bean. One type sells for $6.50/kg and the other for $7.25/kg. How much of each type was used?

12. Bob reinvests his savings in a term deposit, increasing the rate of return on his savings by 2%. This increases the simple interest he earns by $15 per year. How much money does he have in the bank?

13. Sixteen thousand dollars is split between two investments. One provides an annual rate of return of 12%, the other a return of 15%. If the earnings of the investments total $2100.00, how much is invested at each rate?

Review

1. The length of string needed to tie a boxed parcel can be approximated by the expression $2(l + w + 2h) + 30$, where l is the parcel's length, w is its width, and h is its height. About how much string would you need to tie a parcel 28 cm long, 17 cm wide, and 8 cm high?

2. The area of a flat ring can be calculated by the formula $\pi(R^2 - r^2)$, where R is the radius of the outer circle of the ring and r is the radius of the inner circle. Calculate the area of the ring illustrated at the right.

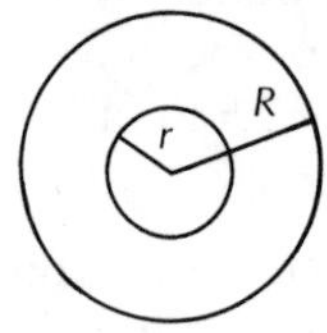

$R = 3.5$ cm

$r = 1.2$ cm

3. Rewrite the following without using fractions.
   a. $\frac{1}{x^5}$ b. $\frac{3x}{x^2y^3}$ c. $\frac{a^{-3}}{b^{-2}}$

4. Solve and check.
   a. $2\frac{1}{2}y = 10$ b. $\frac{3}{4}x - 1 = 5$
   c. $\frac{9}{2}x + 3 = x + 10$ d. $\frac{3x}{2} + 3 = 9$
   e. $2(\frac{1}{3}a + 1) = \frac{4}{3}a - 4$ f. $5(\frac{1}{2}t - 1) = 2t - 1$
   g. $3(2x + 1) - 2(x - 1) = 13$ h. $5(3v + 2) - 10 = 7(v + 2) + 2$

5. Illustrate the following on a number line.
   a. $|k| < 7$ b. $|t| \geq 4$
   c. $-5 < x < 4.5$ d. $|3b| < 9$

6. It takes a clerk no less than 2.5 min to print each page of a financial statement using a desk-top computer. It also takes 15 min to set up the files and another 1.5 min to sign off. What is the maximum number of pages that the clerk can print in an hour?

7. Find the value of each variable.
   a. $x : 15 = 12 : 60$ b. $14 : 21 = 6 : x$
   c. $7 : 9 = 9 : x$ d. $12 : 10 : 9 = x : y : 6$
   e. $3.5 : a : \frac{3}{4} = b : 2.5 : 6$ f. $x : 2x + 1 = 9 : 21$
   g. $(x - 1) : 12 = (x + 2) : 18$ h. $6 : (3x - 1) = 9 : (4x + 2)$

8. Determine the scale factor for each of the following scales.
   a. $1 : 200$ b. $40 : 1$ c. $1 : 100\,000$ d. $25 : 6$

9. Write each of the following as a rate.
   a. 500 km travelled in 8 h b. 3600 revolutions in 12 min
   c. \$1.80 for 0.25 kg d. 750 m in 40 s

10. Which is the better buy?
   a. $7.50 for 3.5 kg or 23 cents for 100 g
   b. 4 m for 68 cents or 1.5 m for 25 cents
   c. 3 items for the price of 1 or 66% off.
   d. 50 mL in the travel size for $1.29 or the family size of 250 mL for $5.20

11. An interior designer uses diagrams at a standard scale of 1 : 50. If the length of one wall in a room is represented on the designer's scale diagram as 2.8 cm long, will a sofa 2 m long fit along that wall. If so, how much space could be left on either side?

12. A scale diagram in a biology text shows a blood cell 15 cm long. If the actual length of the cell is 0.3 mm, then what is the scale of the drawing?

13. Methane contains carbon molecules and hydrogen molecules in the ratio 3 : 1, by mass. What is the total mass of hydrogen in 15 g of methane?

14. A recipe for eight requires 350 mL of flour and 150 mL of milk. What are the proportions of flour and milk in the same recipe, increased to serve twenty? What are the quantities of each?

15. The speed limit over a stretch of highway was raised by 20 km/h following construction that upgraded the highway surface. After the increase in speed limit, drivers travelling at an average speed equal to the speed limit could save 1 h in a trip that had previously taken 4 h. What is the new speed limit?

16. When Kim and Sandy were jogging along the beach, Kim stopped for 40 s to get some sand out of her shoe, then ran to catch up to Sandy in 1 min. If Kim ran at a rate 1.5 m/s faster than Sandy was jogging, then how fast was Sandy jogging?

17. The perimeter of a triangle is 30 cm. One side is 3 cm longer than the shortest side and the other side is 3 cm less than double the length of the shortest side. What are the lengths of the three sides?

18. In the plans for a landscape site, a planter is shown with a length of 3.2 cm. The actual length of the planter will be 8 m.
   a. What is the scale that was used in the plans?
   b. What is the scale factor?
   c. What measure should be used on the plans to represent a sidewalk that will be 15 m long?

EXTRA

All Aboard!

Two trains pass each other on parallel tracks. One train is 150 m long; the other is 50 m long. Travelling in opposite directions, they pass in 5 s. Travelling in the same direction, the faster train passes the slower in 20 s. How fast is each train going?

Test Unit 1

1. Evaluate the following expressions for the given values of the variables.

   a. $x(2 - y);\ x = -3,\ y = -1$ b. $2x^2 - 3xy + y^2;\ x = -2,\ y = 3$

   c. $\frac{a(a - b)}{a + b};\ a = \frac{1}{2},\ b = 1.1$

2. The surface area of a cone can be calculated by evaluating the expression $2\pi rs + \pi r^2$, where r is the radius of the circular base of the cone and s is the height along the curved surface, or the slant height. Calculate the surface area of a cone for which $r = 1.5$ cm and $s = 2.4$ cm.
   Use $\pi = 3.14$ and answer correct to two decimal places.

3. Simplify the following, writing your final answer without fractions.

   a. $(-3x^2)^3$ b. $5^{-2} + 10^{-1}$ c. $\frac{(6m^2n)(15m^2n^3)}{3mn^3}$

4. Solve and check.

   a. $\frac{1}{3}x + 5 = 7$ b. $8y + 3 = 4(y - 1) + 11$

   c. $3(m + 5) - 4 = 2(4m + 8) - 3(m + 1)$ d. $4(b + 3) - 2b = 5(7 - b)$

   e. $x - 2(3 + x) = 4(x + 1) - 2$ f. $3(5 - t) - (2 + t) = 4 - t$

   g. $\frac{a}{7} - \frac{1}{2} = \frac{a}{4}$ h. $\frac{3}{4} - \frac{d}{2} + \frac{1}{12} = 0$

   i. $v - \frac{3v}{4} = 2$ j. $k - \frac{3k}{5} + \frac{k}{2} = -\frac{1}{10}$

5. Solve each inequality and graph its solution set.

   a. $x + 3 \leq 5$ b. $3 - x > 4x - 2$

   c. $-4 \leq 2x - 2 < 6$ d. $3|2x - 3| - 1 \leq 8$

6. An investment firm guarantees its clients an annual return on investments of at least 11% and it also wants to make 1% on the money it handles. The firm has two investment opportunities, a very safe one which returns 8.5% per annum and another, riskier venture which will return 16.5%. If the firm has $1000 to invest, what is the most that can be invested in the safer venture and still have the firm meet its financial goals?

7. The members of a construction crew work at a regular rate of $17.20/h. When the crew works more than 35 h during a week, the crew members are paid at an overtime rate of "time and a half". For work completed during statutory holidays, they are paid double time.

   a. Find the amount earned by one member of the crew when they worked 48 h during the course of the week.

   b. Find the amount earned by one member of the crew for a week that went into a holiday weekend when the crew worked 60 h, 8 of which were on the holiday.

2 Polynomials and Rational Expressions

Geoff earns \$4.95/h plus tips waiting table part-time. When he works h hours and earns t dollars in tips, his earnings are $4.95h + t$. The expression $4.95h + t$ is an example of a **polynomial**.

2-1 Adding and Subtracting Polynomials

A single-term expression, like $4.95h$, is a **monomial**. It is the product of a *constant* (the number 4.95) and variables with whole-number exponents. An expression consisting of sums of monomials is a **polynomial**.

Polynomial	**Not Polynomial**	
$3x^7$	$\frac{1}{x^2}$	Since $\frac{1}{x^2} = x^{-2}$, and -2 is not a whole number.
$3x^3 - 4x^2 + 2x - 7$	$x^{\frac{2}{3}}$	Since the exponent $\frac{2}{3}$ is not a whole number.
$5y^2 + 4xy$	2^x	
$ab^2c - 4a + 3b - 5c^4$	$3x^2 + x^{\frac{1}{2}} + x^{-3}$	

The **degree** of a monomial is the sum of the exponents of its variables. The **degree of a polynomial** is the greatest degree of any term it contains.

$3x^2$ is a monomial of degree 2;
4 can be thought of as a monomial of degree 0, since $4 = 4x^0$.

Binomials contain two terms: $2x^4 + 3y^3$ is a binomial of degree 4.

Trinomials contain three terms: $2x^3 - 3x + 5$ is a trinomial of degree 3.

The expression $2x^2y^3 - 3xy + 5x^4 - 2xy^2$ is a polynomial of degree 5.

Add or subtract polynomials by collecting like terms.

EXAMPLE 1: Simplify each given expression.

a. $(2x^2 - 5x + 3) + (3x^2 - 4) - (2x - 5)$
$= 2x^2 - 5x + 3 + 3x^2 - 4 - 2x + 5$
$= 5x^2 - 7x + 4$

The minus sign applies to each term within the parentheses.

b. $(3x^4 - 2x^3y + 5x^2y^2 - 3xy^3 + 4y^4) - (2x^4 + 5x^2y^2 + 3xy^3)$
$= 3x^4 - 2x^3y + 5x^2y^2 - 3xy^3 + 4y^4 - 2x^4 - 5x^2y^2 - 3xy^3$
$= x^4 - 2x^3y - 6xy^3 + 4y^4$

Evaluate expressions by first simplifying the expression and then substituting for given values of the variables.

EXAMPLE 2: Evaluate the given expression for $a = 5$ and $b = -4$.

$$\begin{aligned}(2a - 3b) - (3a - b) + (4a + b) &= 2a - 3b - 3a + b + 4a + b \\ &= 3a - b \\ &= 3(5) - (-4) \\ &= 19\end{aligned}$$

EXERCISE 2-1

A **1.** Define and give an example of each of the following. Use the glossary at the back of this text to check your answers.

a. algebraic expression **b.** term **c.** coefficient
d. degree of a term **e.** polynomial **f.** constant

2. Which of the following expressions are polynomials? For those expressions that are polynomials, give the degree.

a. $\frac{3}{4}x + 5$ **b.** $5 - 2y^{-2}$ **c.** $2x^2y - 3x^2 + 7$
d. $\pi(R^2 - r^2)$ **e.** 2^{3x+1} **f.** $2x - 3x^{\frac{1}{2}} + 5$
g. $5 - 3a^3 + 4a^2$ **h.** $5c^2d^3$ **i.** $4 - 3x^2 + 8x^3 - 5x$

3. Identify the monomials, binomials, and trinomials in exercise 2.

B **4.** Simplify.

a. $(2x^2 - 3x + 1) + (4x - 3)$
b. $(2y - 3) - (3y + 1) + (2y + 4)$
c. $(3x^3 - 10x^2 + 4x - 3) - (8x^2 + 4x - 2x^3 + 1)$
d. $(2z^2 - 3) - (5z + 1) - (4z^3 + 6)$
e. $(3m^2 - 2m + 4) - (2m - 3m^2 + 1) + (2m - 6m^2 - 3)$

5. Simplify.

a. $(2x^2 - 3xy + 3y^2) - (x^2 - 5xy + y^2)$

b. $(3a^3 - 4a^2b + 2ab^2 + 3b^3) + (4a^3 + 4a^2b + 2ab^2 - 5b^3)$

c. $(2c^4d - 3c^2d^2 + 3cd^3 + 5cd) - (2c^2d^2 + 4c^3d + 3cd)$

6. Simplify each expression and evaluate for $x = -2$ and $y = 3$.

a. $(x^2 - 2x + 3) - (3x + 1)$

b. $(3x^2 - 5x + 4) - (2x^2 - x - 1)$

c. $(3x - 2y) - (2x + y)$

d. $(2x - 5y) + (4x - 3y) - (x - y)$

e. $(3x^2 - 2xy + y^2) + (x^2 + 5xy - 3y^2)$

f. $(2x^2 - 3xy - 4y^2) - (3x^2 - 5xy - 6y^2)$

7. Find the perimeter of each figure in terms of x.

a.

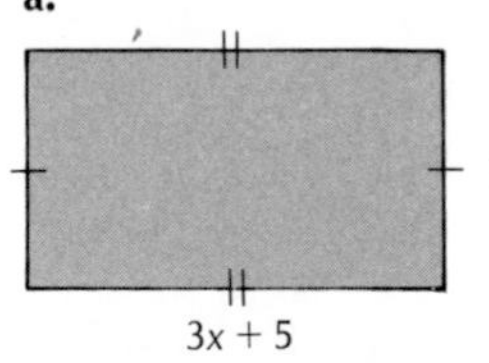

b.

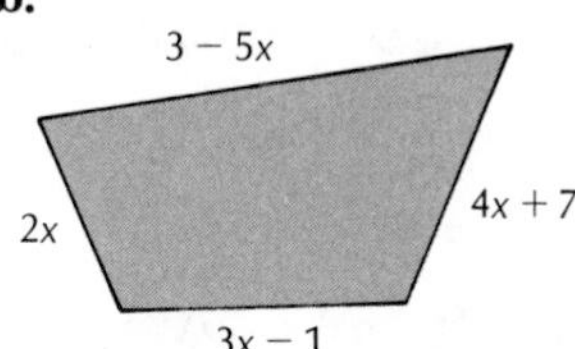

c.

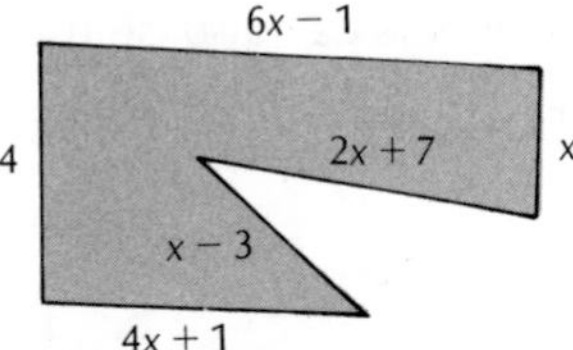

C 8. a. For the figure at the right, find the perimeter in terms of x.

b. What is the numerical value of the perimeter?

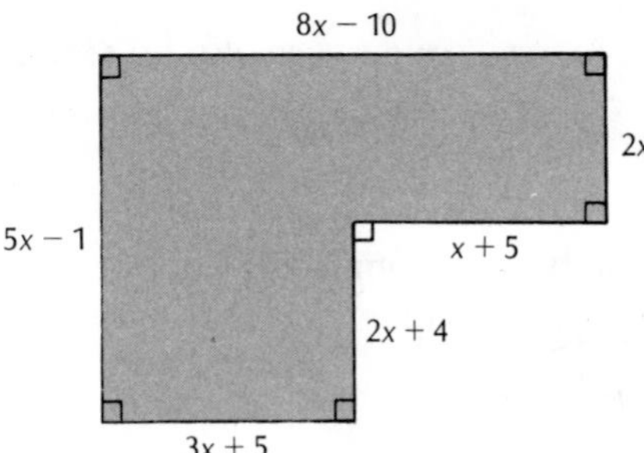

9. Find values of a and b for which each equation is true.

a. $(ax^2 + 2xy) - (3x^2 - bxy) = 2x^2 - xy$

b. $(5x^2 - ay^2) + (6x^2 + 2y^2) - (2bx^2 + 4y^2) = (-4bx^2 + 3y^2) - (x^2 - ay^2)$

EXTRA

Making Ends Meet

The formula below can be used to predict the cost \$C of an item in n years, if it costs \$c today, assuming an annual inflation rate of 8%.

$$C = c(1.08)^n$$

1. If a pair of designer jeans presently costs \$45, what would you pay for the same jeans in 50 years?

2. If a labourer now earns \$8.95/h, what wage would likely be in effect for a labourer in 50 years?

2-2 Multiplying Polynomials

Jan bought 4 lunches at the corner diner, each consisting of a drink worth \$0.75 and a salad worth \$3.50. Jan figured out the cost by noticing that 4 drinks would cost \$3.00, 4 salads would cost \$14, and \$3 + \$14 = \$17. Jan has applied a general property of real numbers, the **Distributive Property**:

$$a(b + c) = ab + ac$$

$4(0.75 + 3.50) = 4(0.75) + 4(3.50)$

and $$(a + b)c = ac + bc.$$

Since variables represent real numbers, the Distributive Property for real numbers can also be used to multiply a polynomial by a monomial.

EXAMPLE 1: Expand each given expression.

a. $2x(x + 3) = 2x^2 + 6x$

b. $3x^3(2x^2 - 5x + 7) = 6x^5 - 15x^4 + 21x^3$

The Distributive Property can also be applied to multiply two binomials.

$$\begin{aligned}(a + b)(c + d) &= a(c + d) + b(c + d)\\ &= ac + ad + bc + bd\end{aligned}$$

The first step can be omitted by noting that each term in the first polynomial is multiplied by each term in the second polynomial.

$$(a + b)(c + d) = ac + ad + bc + bd$$

EXAMPLE 2: Expand and simplify each expression.

a. $$\begin{aligned}(2x + 3)(3x - 1) &= 6x^2 - 2x + 9x - 3\\ &= 6x^2 + 7x - 3\end{aligned}$$

b. $$\begin{aligned}(3x - 5)^2 &= (3x - 5)(3x - 5)\\ &= 9x^2 - 15x - 15x + 25\\ &= 9x^2 - 30x + 25\end{aligned}$$

c. $$\begin{aligned}(2x - 5)(x^2 - 2x + 3) &= 2x^3 - 4x^2 + 6x - 5x^2 + 10x - 15\\ &= 2x^3 - 9x^2 + 16x - 15\end{aligned}$$

d. $$\begin{aligned}3x(2x - 5)(3x + 4) &= 3x(6x^2 + 8x - 15x - 20)\\ &= 3x(6x^2 - 7x - 20)\\ &= 18x^3 - 21x^2 - 60x\end{aligned}$$

Save the multiplication by the monomial for the final step.

e. $$\begin{aligned}2(3x + 5)(2x - 4) - 3x(x + 1)^2 &= 2(3x + 5)(2x - 4) - 3x(x + 1)(x + 1)\\ &= 2(6x^2 - 12x + 10x - 20) - 3x(x^2 + x + x + 1)\\ &= 2(6x^2 - 2x - 20) - 3x(x^2 + 2x + 1)\\ &= 12x^2 - 4x - 40 - 3x^3 - 6x^2 - 3x\\ &= -3x^3 + 6x^2 - 7x - 40\end{aligned}$$

EXERCISE 2-2

A **1.** Expand and simplify.

a. $3(x^2 - 5x + 4)$ **b.** $2x(3x^2 - 5)$ **c.** $(x + 3)(2x - 5)$
d. $(3x - 2)^2$ **e.** $(2x + 5)^2$ **f.** $(x - 3)(x^2 - 4x + 3)$

2. Without necessarily expanding first, state the degree of each product and determine whether it will be a monomial, binomial, or trinomial.

a. $5x(2x - 3x^3)$ **b.** $(2a - 3)(3a + 1)$ **c.** $(3b - 5)(3b + 5)$
d. $(2y^2 - 3)(3y^2 + 1)$ **e.** $2x - 3(x + 4)$ **f.** $(3x^2 - 1)^2$

B **3.** Expand and simplify.

a. $(2t + 7)(3t - 4)$ **b.** $(2x - 3)(3x^2 - 7x + 6)$ **c.** $(4w + 3)^2$
d. $2x(3x - 1)^2$ **e.** $(4 - 3a)(4 + 3a)$ **f.** $3x^2(2x + 7)(x - 1)$

4. Expand and simplify.

a. $(x + y)^2$ **b.** $(x + y)^3$ **c.** $(x + y)^4$ **d.** $(x + y)^5$ **e.** $(x + y)^6$

5. Expand and simplify.

a. $(2x + 1)(3x - 4) - (x + 3)^2$ **b.** $3(x + 1)(x + 5) + 2(x + 3)(3x - 1)$
c. $2x - 3(x + 5) - (3x + 1)^2$ **d.** $3x(2x + 5)(x - 1) - 2x(3x - 4)(x + 1)$

6. Find the area of each figure in terms of x.

a.

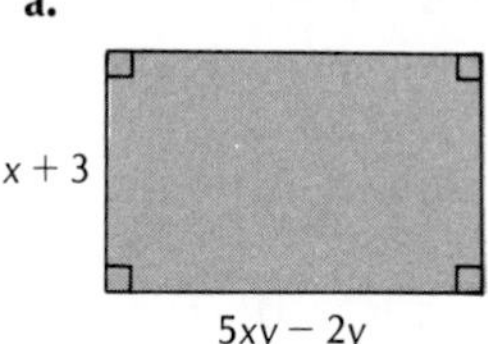

b.

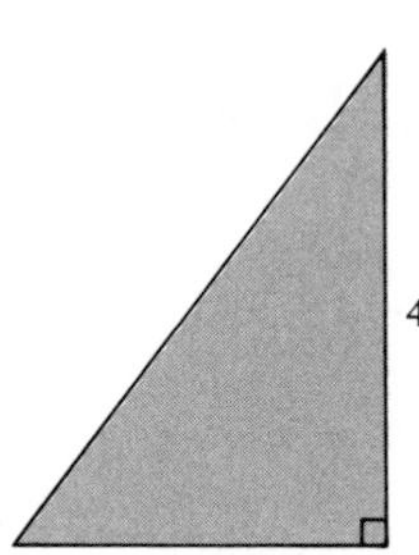

c.

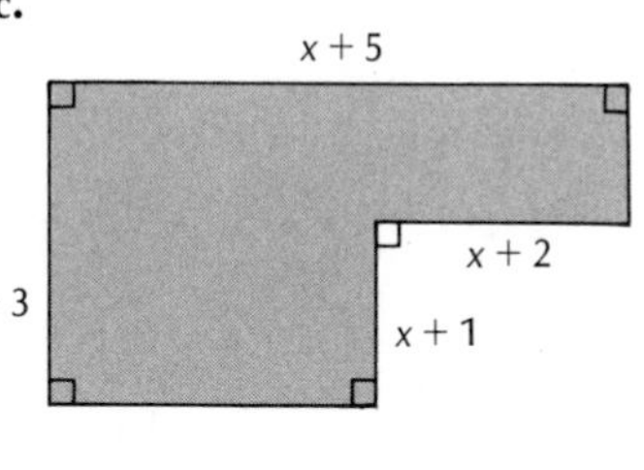

7. Expand and simplify.

a. $(2a - 3b)(3a + b)$ **b.** $(3p - 2q)^2$ **c.** $3(5x + 2y)(3x - 2y)$
d. $(4x - 7y)(4x + 7y)$ **e.** $2m(3m - 4n)(m + 2n)$ **f.** $3x^2y^3(2x - 3y)^2$
g. $(2a + b)(3a - 4b) - (2a + 5b)^2$ **h.** $3(5p - t)(2p + t) - 2(3p - 5t)(p + t)$
i. $(3c - 5d)^2 - (3c + 5d)^2$ **j.** $2x(3x - y)(x + y) - 3y(2x - y)(x - y)$

8. Evaluate for $x = -3$ and $y = 2$.

a. $3(2x - 5) - 2(x + 3)$ **b.** $3(4x - y) - (x - 5y) - 2(y - x)$
c. $(x - 3y)(x + 3y) - (x + 2y)(x - 2y)$ **d.** $x(x - y) - y(y - x) - (x - y)(x + y)$

C **9.** Expand and simplify.

a. $2x^2y^3(3x^2 - y)(2x + y^2)$ **b.** $2c^2d(3c - 5d)(2d + 3c)$
c. $(2a^2 - 3b)(3a^2 - 5ab + 2b^2)$ **d.** $(4x + 3y)(x - 2y)^2$
e. $(3x - 2y)(2x - y)(2x + y)$ **f.** $(x - 3y)(2x + 3y)(x - y)$
g. $(3p - q)^3$ **h.** $(3x^2 - 2y^3)^2 + 2x^2(x^2 + 6y^3)$

2-3 Finding Common Factors

Many polynomials are made up of terms that have factors in common. While there may be many **common factors** among the terms, there is only one **greatest common monomial factor (GCF)**.

Polynomial	Common Factors	GCF
$4x^3 + 12x^2$	$1, 4, x, 4x, x^2, 4x^2$	$4x^2$
$2ab^2 - 2a^2b - 8ab$	$1, 2, a, b, 2a, 2b, 2ab$	$2ab$
$5x^2 + 6y^2 - 12$	1	1

The GCF is the common factor with the greatest degree and the greatest numerical coefficient. A polynomial with common factors other than 1 can be **factored** by writing it as a product, as illustrated in example 1. Identifying the GCF as a first step will speed your work.

EXAMPLE 1:

a. Factor $3x^2y + 9y$.

The GCF is $3y$.

$3x^2y + 9y = 3y(x^2 + 3)$

Check by expanding.
$3y(x^2 + 3) = 3x^2y + 9y$ ✓

b. Factor $15a^2bc + 20ab^2c - 25ac^2 - 5ac$.

The GCF is $5ac$.

$15a^2bc + 20ab^2c - 25ac^2 - 5ac = 5ac(3ab + 4b^2 - 5c - 1)$

c. Factor $7mn^2 + 12p - 3$.

Since the GCF is 1, the expression is left as is.

Expanding an expression sometimes reveals a common factor.

EXAMPLE 2: Expand and factor.

a.
$$\begin{aligned} 12x^3y + 3x(x^2y^2 - 4y) &= 12x^3y + 3x^3y^2 - 12xy \\ &= 3xy(4x^2 + x^2y - 4) \end{aligned}$$

b.
$$\begin{aligned} 2x(x - 3y)(2x + y) - 2x(xy + y^2) &= 2x(2x^2 - 5xy - 3y^2) - 2x(xy + y^2) \\ &= 4x^3 - 10x^2y - 6xy^2 - 2x^2y - 2xy^2 \\ &= 4x^3 - 12x^2y - 8xy^2 \\ &= 4x(x^2 - 3xy - 2y^2) \end{aligned}$$

EXERCISE 2-3

A **1.** Find all common factors of the terms in each polynomial.

a. $7x^2 + 28xy$ **b.** $-9bc - 3ac$

c. $2pq + 3p^2 + 8pqr^2$ **d.** $4xy^2z^3 + 8y^2z^2 - 12y^2z$

e. $5m^2n - 11m^2 + 2n$ **f.** $-12k^3l^3 - 36k^3l^2 + 4k^2l^3$

2. Find the GCF of each set of monomials.

a. $9x^3y^2, 3x^2$ **b.** $-10ts, 100ts^2$

c. $5a^5b^4c, 11bc^3d, 10c^2$ **d.** $12a^3b^4, 96c, 4ab^2$

e. $52m^3n^2, 3pn, 13p^2$ **f.** $-35x^4y^2z^2, -5x^3y^2, -50x^2y^3z^2$

B **3.** Find the GCF of each polynomial in exercise 1.

4. Find the GCF of each polynomial.

a. $2m^3n^2 + 18m^2n^3$ **b.** $-5x^5y^3z^2 - 30x^4y^2z^2$

c. $xy^3 - y^3z - 10z^2$ **d.** $15a^4b^2 + 5a^3b^4 - 35b^3c^2$

e. $21t^3s^2 + 6t^2s^3 + 15t^2s^2$ **f.** $-9p^4q^2r^5 - 27p^4q^2r - 3p^3q^2r^2$

5. Write each polynomial in factored form.

a. $2x^3yz + 6x^2y^2$ **b.** $5m^4n^2 - 10m^3n^3$

c. $7a^2bc^2 - 5b^2c$ **d.** $15x^5y^2z^2 + 3x^4yz^2 - 21x^2z$

e. $-2x^3y^3 - 4x^2y^2 + 6x^2y$ **f.** $11s^4t^5 + 30t^3 - 5s$

g. $-x^6y^4z^3 - x^5y^4z^2 - x^4y^4z$ **h.** $7p^5q^3r^2 + 28p^2q^2r - 14pq^3r^2 + 21pqr^2$

6. Factor each polynomial.

a. $15m^4n^2 - 3m^2n + 9n^2$ **b.** $6a^3b^2 + 21a^3b^2 - 18a^3bc$

c. $-8w^2z^4 - 8x^2y$ **d.** $3c^2d^3 - 5c^3d + 7c^2d^2 - 9cd^2$

e. $a^2bc + ab^2c - abc^2$ **f.** $\frac{1}{2}x^2y^2 - \frac{3}{4}xy^3z + \frac{1}{2}xy^4$

C **7.** Expand and factor each expression.

a. $xy(3x + 2y) + 4xy^2$ **b.** $2a^2(2ab - a^2) - 2a^2$

c. $16cd^2 + 4d(3cd + c^2)$ **d.** $xyz(xy - y^2z) + yz^2$

e. $3mn^2(2m - 3n) - 6m^2n$ **f.** $5b^2c + 3b(b^2c^2 - 2c)$

8. Expand and factor each expression. Simplify where appropriate.

a. $2x(xy + 3) + 6y(x + 2x^2)$ **b.** $xy(2xz + 2y) - 2x^2y(z + 3)$

c. $4a(b + 2)(b - 1) + 2ab^2$ **d.** $3(ab - 4a^2) + 2(b + 3a)(a + 1)$

e. $-2xy(2x^2 + 4x) + 16xy(x + 1)^2$ **f.** $-3m(-m^2n + 3)(m - 2) - 3n^2(mn - 7m^2)$

2-4 Dividing Polynomials

A polynomial can be divided by a monomial by dividing each term of the polynomial by the monomial.

$$\begin{aligned}(4x^4 - 8x^3 + 2x^2) \div 2x &= \frac{4x^4 - 8x^3 + 2x^2}{2x} \\ &= \frac{4x^4}{2x} - \frac{8x^3}{2x} + \frac{2x^2}{2x} \\ &= 2x^3 - 4x^2 + x\end{aligned}$$

Use the laws of exponents to simplify.

$$\begin{aligned}(6x^3 + 5x^2y) \div 3x &= \frac{6x^3 + 5x^2y}{3x} \\ &= \frac{6x^3}{3x} + \frac{5x^2y}{3x} \\ &= 2x^2 + \tfrac{5}{3}xy\end{aligned}$$

Since division by zero is undefined, it is necessary to restrict x in each expression above so that the divisor is not zero. That is, restrict x so that $x \neq 0$.

Division of a polynomial by a binomial can be modelled after long division in arithmetic.

EXAMPLE 1:

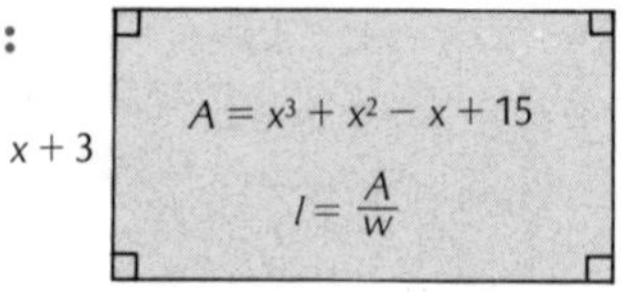

Find an expression for the length of the rectangle.

$$l = \frac{x^3 + x^2 - x + 15}{x + 3}$$

$$\begin{array}{r|l} & x^2 - 2x + 5 \\ \hline x + 3 & x^3 + x^2 - x + 15 \\ & \underline{x^3 + 3x^2} \\ & -2x^2 - x \\ & \underline{-2x^2 - 6x} \\ & 5x + 15 \\ & \underline{5x + 15} \\ & 0 \end{array}$$

Check by multiplying $x^2 - 2x + 5$ by $x + 3$.

Therefore, the length can be represented by $x^2 - 2x + 5$.

Since $x + 3$ divides the polynomial evenly, it is a **factor** of the polynomial.

Some divisions will yield a non-zero remainder.

EXAMPLE 2: Simplify $(15 - 13x + x^3) \div (x - 3)$, given that $(x - 3) \neq 0$.

$$\begin{array}{r|l} & x^2 + 3x - 4 \\ \hline x - 3 & x^3 + 0x^2 - 13x + 15 \\ & \underline{x^3 - 3x^2} \\ & 3x^2 - 13x \\ & \underline{3x^2 - 9x} \\ & -4x + 15 \\ & \underline{-4x + 12} \\ & 3 \end{array}$$

Like the number, 509, which has a zero digit as a placeholder, insert $0x^2$ as a placeholder in the polynomial $15 - 13x + x^3$. Write the polynomial in descending powers of x.

$$\therefore (15 - 13x + x^3) \div (x - 3) = x^2 + 3x - 4 + \frac{3}{x - 3}, \text{ where } x - 3 \neq 0 \text{ or } x \neq 3$$

EXERCISE 2-4

A 1. Rewrite as a product of positive prime factors.

a. $12b$ **b.** $18a^2$ **c.** $20b^2c$ **d.** $16xy^3$ **e.** $24x^3y^2$ **f.** $30fg^2$

2. Divide as indicated.

a. $9x^5 - 3x^3 - 6x^2$ by $3x^2$
b. $12x^4 - 8x^3 + 16x$ by $4x$
c. $25y^8 - 20y^4 + 15y^2$ by $-5y$
d. $6x^2y^4 - 3xy^3 + 9x^2y^2$ by $3xy^2$

3. Find an expression for the missing dimension of each rectangular tile.

a.

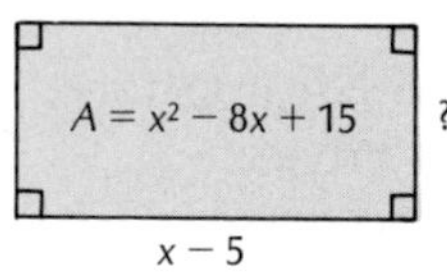

b.

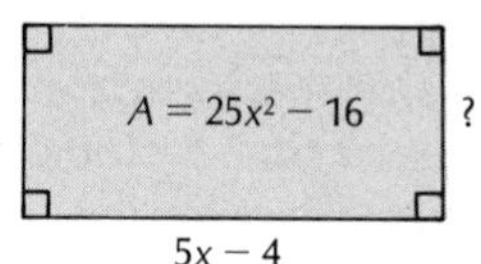

c.

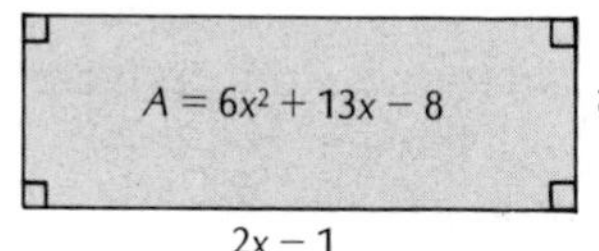

4. Divide as indicated.

a. $(x^3 - 10x^2 + 26x - 5) \div (x - 5)$
b. $(a^3 + 7a^2 + 10a - 6) \div (a + 3)$
c. $(6y^3 + y^2 - 4y + 1) \div (3y - 1)$
d. $(6x^4 + 3x^3 - 8x^2 - 2x + 1) \div (2x + 1)$
e. $(3 - 11c + 4c^3) \div (2c - 3)$
f. $(8n^3 - 27) \div (2n - 3)$

5. Divide.

a. $(t^4 + 3t^3 - 7t^2 - 9t + 12) \div (t^2 - 3)$
b. $(3x^4 - x^3 + 16x^2 - 5x + 5) \div (x^2 + 5)$
c. $(x^6 + 3x^2 - 5x^4 + 9) \div (x^2 - 3)$
d. $(27p^6 - 64) \div (3p^2 - 4)$
e. $(x^3 - 9x^2 + 24x + 4) \div (x - 4)$
f. $(x^3 + 5x^2 - 8) \div (x + 3)$
g. $(4k^3 - 7k - 1) \div (2k - 1)$
h. $(13z^2 - 5z^4 + 2z^6 - 19) \div (2z^2 - 3)$

C 6. Divide.

a. $(x^4 - x^3 - 6x^2 - x + 3) \div (x^2 + x - 1)$
b. $(2m^4 + 3m^3 + 3m^2 + 5m + 3) \div (2m^2 - m + 3)$
c. $(s^3 + s^2t - 5st^2 + 3t^3) \div (s - t)$
d. $(2x^3 - 5x^2y + xy^2 + 2y^3) \div (2x + y)$
e. $(x^6 - 4x^4y + 4x^2y^2 - y^3) \div (x^2 - y)$
f. $(k^9 + 2k^6l^2 - 4k^3l^4 + l^6) \div (k^3 - l^2)$

7. **a.** Notice that, in exercises 3 and 4, all the remainders were zero; that is, the divisor was a factor of the polynomial. Examine the constant terms in both the divisor and the original polynomial to find a pattern in the questions.

b. Use the pattern to predict possible factors for the following. Use long division to check which of your predictions are indeed factors.

i. $x^3 + 4x^2 - 4x - 16$ **ii.** $x^3 - x^2 - 14x + 24$

8. A triangle has an area that can be expressed by $6x^4 + 9x^3 - 30x^2 - 45x$. Find the height of the triangle if the base can be represented by $2x + 3$.

2-5 Factoring Trinomials

Earlier in this chapter, we have shown how to multiply polynomials to give more complex polynomials. But sometimes we want to go the other way. For example, in solving equations or inequalities, writing a polynomial as a product of polynomials of smaller degree often leads to a straightforward solution.

You can rewrite $2a^2 + 4a + 6ab$ as $2a(a + 2 + 3b)$; expanding $2a(a + 2 + 3b)$ gives $2a^2 + 4a + 6ab$. ✓

One process can serve as a check for the other.

Often, we want to factor trinomials of the form $x^2 + bx + c$ into linear factors with integer coefficients. This is done by trial. By looking for a pattern in products like $(x + 3)(x + 2)$ or $(x + 3)(x - 2)$, we can see how to proceed.

Find the coefficient of the middle term by adding the second terms of each of the original binomials.

$$(x + 3)(x + 2) = x^2 + 5x + 6 \qquad 3 \times 2 = 6$$

$$(x + 3)(x - 2) = x^2 + x - 6 \qquad 3 + 2 = 5$$

$$(x + m)(x + n) = x^2 + mx + nx + mn \qquad 3 - 2 = 1$$
$$= x^2 + (m + n)x + mn$$

When factoring trinomials, we are usually looking for factors with integer coefficients.

To factor a trinomial of the form $x^2 + bx + c$, look for two factors of c that have a sum of b. A table is a useful way of organizing your trials.

EXAMPLE 1: **a.** Factor $x^2 + 16x + 28$.

Factor Pairs of 28	1 28	−1 −28	7 4	2 14
Sum	29	−29	11	16

$\therefore x^2 + 16x + 28 = (x + 14)(x + 2)$

Check by expanding.

b. Factor $x^2 - 7xy - 144y^2$.

Factor Pairs of −144	1 −144	−1 144	−2 72	2 −72	9 −16
Sum	−143	143	70	−70	−7

These sums are much too high.

$\therefore x^2 - 7xy - 144y^2 = (x - 16y)(x + 9y)$

Always check for a common factor first. You will find that you don't always need to use a table to find the correct pair of binomial factors.

EXAMPLE 2: Factor $2a^3 - 16a^2 + 30a$.

$$2a^3 - 16a^2 + 30a = 2a(a^2 - 8a + 15)$$
$$= 2a(a - 3)(a - 5)$$

−3 and −5 are factors of 15. Their sum is −8.

In factoring trinomials of the form $ax^2 + bx + c$, where x^2 has a coefficient other than 1, there are more possibilities to consider. You still want to examine possible pairs of binomial factors, trying them out to determine which will yield the correct middle term.

EXAMPLE 3: Factor $2x^2 + 5x + 3$.

The answer must be of the form $(2x \blacksquare)(x \blacksquare)$.

Because 3 is positive, the signs of the two numbers are the same. Because 5 is positive, the two numbers must be positive. Thus the form becomes $(2x + \blacksquare)(x + \blacksquare)$.

Try possible factor pairs of 3 until a product yields the desired middle term, $5x$.

$(2x + 1)(x + 3) = 2x^2 + 7x + 3$ — $7x$ is not the correct middle term.
$(2x + 3)(x + 1) = 2x^2 + 5x + 3$ ✓

$\therefore 2x^2 + 5x + 3 = (2x + 3)(x + 1)$

EXAMPLE 4: Factor $3x^2 + 17x - 6$.

The answer must be of the form $(3x \blacksquare)(x \blacksquare)$.

Because −6 is negative, the signs of the two numbers are different. Thus the form is either $(3x + \blacksquare)(x - \blacksquare)$ or $(3x - \blacksquare)(x + \blacksquare)$.

Try possible factor pairs of 6 until you find the correct answer.

* $(3x + 3)(x - 2) = 3x^2 - 3x - 6$	* $(3x - 3)(x + 2) = 3x^2 + 3x - 6$
$(3x + 2)(x - 3) = 3x^2 - 7x - 6$	$(3x - 2)(x + 3) = 3x^2 + 7x - 6$
* $(3x + 6)(x - 1) = 3x^2 + 3x - 6$	* $(3x - 6)(x + 1) = 3x^2 - 3x - 6$
$(3x + 1)(x - 6) = 3x^2 - 17x - 6$	$(3x - 1)(x + 6) = 3x^2 + 17x - 6$ ✓

$\therefore 3x^2 + 17x - 6 = (3x - 1)(x + 6)$

Example 4 illustrates that you really need to check only the *middle* term in each trial. Once you've identified the binomial factors, the first and last terms will always be correct. You could also save time by noticing that, since the trinomial has no common factor, you need not check the items marked *, as each of them has a common factor of 3.

EXAMPLE 5: Factor $4x^2 - 5x - 9$.

The answer must be in one of two forms: $(2x + \blacksquare)(2x - \blacksquare)$ or $(4x\ \blacksquare)(x\ \blacksquare)$. Try possible factor pairs of 9 in $(2x + \blacksquare)(2x - \blacksquare)$ and check the product.

Factor Pairs Product	$9, -1$ $(2x + 9)(2x - 1)$	$1, -9$ $(2x + 1)(2x - 9)$	$3, -3$ $(2x + 3)(2x - 3)$
Middle Term	$16x$	$-16x$	0

None of these pairs work, so try $(4x\ \blacksquare)(x\ \blacksquare)$.

Factor Pairs Product	$9, -1$ $(4x + 9)(x - 1)$	$-9, 1$ $(4x - 9)(x + 1)$
Middle Term	$5x$	$-5x$

$\therefore 4x^2 - 5x - 9 = (4x - 9)(x + 1)$

EXERCISE 2-5

A **1.** Copy and complete.

a. $x^2 + 2x + 1 = (x + 1)(x + \blacksquare)$
b. $2y^2 + 7y - 15 = (2y - \blacksquare)(y + 5)$
c. $a^2 - 3a - 4 = (a + 1)(a - \blacksquare)$
d. $9p^2 - 16 = (3p - 4)(3p + \blacksquare)$
e. $m^2 - 6m + 8 = (m - \blacksquare)(m - 2)$
f. $4h^2 - 13h + 9 = (4h - 9)(h - \blacksquare)$

2. Copy and complete the given table, then write the trinomial as a product of binomials.

a. $x^2 - 3x + 2$

Factor Pairs of 2	
Sum	

b. $b^2 - 2b - 8$

Factor Pairs of -8	
Sum	

c. $d^2 - 9d + 8$

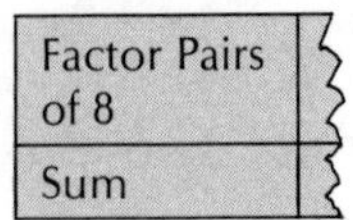

Factor Pairs of 8	
Sum	

d. $w^2 + 4w - 12$

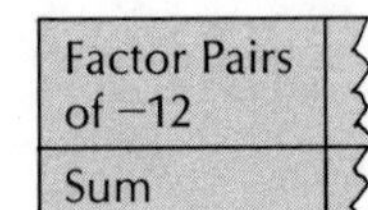

Factor Pairs of -12	
Sum	

3. Factor and check by expanding.

a. $x^2 + 11x + 18$
b. $y^2 + 8y + 7$
c. $x^2 + 3x - 18$
d. $z^2 + 5z - 6$
e. $c^2 + 4c - 12$
f. $a^2 + 12a + 20$
g. $g^2 - 11g + 24$
h. $b^2 - 10b + 9$
i. $p^2 - 12p - 28$
j. $a^2 - 7a + 12$
k. $x^2 + 7x - 8$
l. $d^2 - 13d + 12$
m. $m^2 - 9m + 20$
n. $w^2 - 12w + 32$
o. $x^2 - 5x + 6$

4. Find the common factor and rewrite as a product of polynomials.

a. $2t^2 - 20t + 18$ b. $5x^3 - 20x^2 + 15x$ c. $3x^2 + 6x - 72$
d. $3a^3 - 6a^2 - 24a$ e. $x^2y - 13xy - 48y$ f. $-5x^2 - 25x - 30$
g. $2m^3n - 14m^2n + 24mn$ h. $a^3b^3 - a^2b^2 - 6ab$ i. $x^3y^3 - 2x^2y^2 - 8xy$

5. Without expanding, give the middle term of each binomial product.

a. $(x + 6)(x - 9)$ b. $(y + 4)(y + 6)$ c. $(xy - 3)(xy + 7)$
d. $(xy - 5)(xy - 4)$ e. $(a - 3b)(a + 8b)$ f. $(3a - b)(3a + b)$
g. $(2k - 5)(k + 5)$ h. $(3f - 4g)(3f - 4g)$ i. $(4x - y)(3x - y)$

B 6. Factor.

a. $x^2 - 10x - 39$ b. $x^2 + 13x - 48$ c. $36 - 13x + x^2$
d. $z^2 - 23z + 42$ e. $30 + 17y + y^2$ f. $10 + 3a - a^2$
g. $12a^2 - 7ab + b^2$ h. $c^2 + 15cd + 50d^2$ i. $24b^2 - 10b + 1$

7. Factor.

a. $2x^3 + 22x^2 - 120x$ b. $x^4 - 12x^3 + 27x^2$ c. $36x^3y^3 + 18x^2y^2 + 2xy$
d. $3x^2y^2 - 30xy^2 - 72y^2$ e. $2x^3y + 34x^2y + 84xy$ f. $-2a - 24a^2 - 64a^3$
g. $x^2y^2 + 3xy^3 - 40y^4$ h. $5x^3y + 25x^2y^2 - 30xy^3$ i. $20xy - 14x^2y^2 + 2x^3y^3$

8. Factor.

a. $2x^2 - 17x + 8$ b. $6c^2 + 11c - 35$ c. $4x^3y^3 + 2x^2y^2 - 6xy$
d. $15x^2 - 56x + 48$ e. $27z^2 + 36z - 96$ f. $-4a^4 + 17a^3b - 4a^2b^2$
g. $105x^3y - 110x^2y - 120xy$ h. $20x^3 - 14x^2 - 12x$ i. $18x^3y^2 + 30x^2y + 8x$

9. Find each missing dimension.

a.
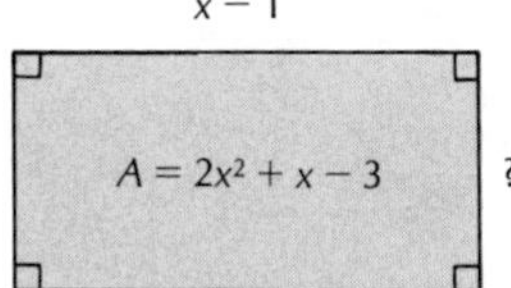

b.
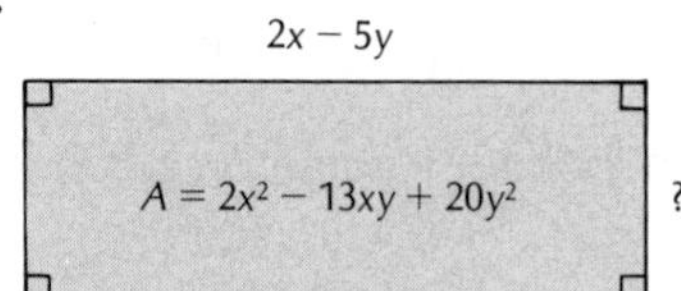

c.
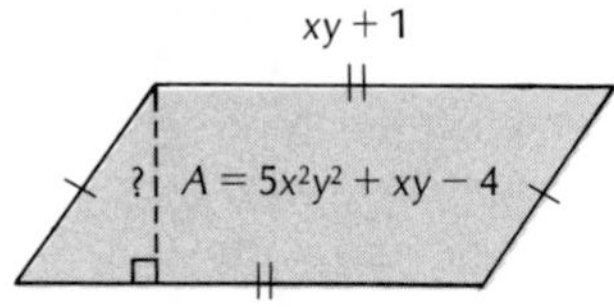

d.
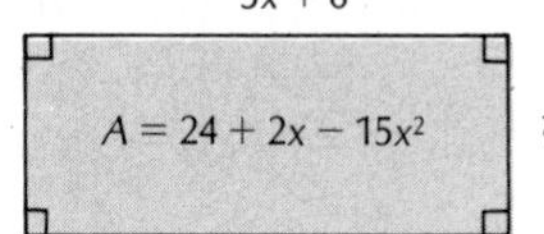

C 10. The following are in the form of a trinomial and can be factored in the same fashion. Factor fully.

a. $(x - y)^2 - 7(x - y) + 12$ b. $(2x - 3y)^2 + 8(2x - 3y) - 48$
c. $(y^2 - y) - 18(y^2 - y) + 72$ d. $(z - 4)^2 + 8(z - 4) + 7$
e. $(x - 5)^2 + 3(x - 5) - 10$ f. $(2a - 3)^2 + 2(2a - 3) - 35$

11. In each of the following, expand and collect like terms, then factor the result.

a. $(x - 2)(2x + 3) - (x + 8)(x + 2) + 50$
b. $(2x + 3)^2 - 3(x - 1)^2 + 4x - 54$
c. $(3x - 1)(2x + 1) - 2(2x + 3)(x - 1) + 12(x - 1) + 1$

2-6 Difference of Squares and Trinomial Squares

Looking for patterns in typical examples often leads to generalizations that can simplify your work. In this lesson, two such general results will be established, both of which are related to the concept of perfect squares.

Multiplying two binomials often results in a trinomial, but this is not *always* the case.

same terms

$$(2x + 3)(2x - 3) = 4x^2 - 6x + 6x - 9$$
$$= 4x^2 - 9$$

opposite terms

same terms

$$(3x - 5)(3x + 5) = 9x^2 + 15x - 15x - 25$$
$$= 9x^2 - 25$$

opposite terms

> The product of the sum and difference of two terms is the difference of the squares of the two terms.
>
> $$a^2 - b^2 = (a + b)(a - b)$$

EXAMPLE 1: Factor the given difference of squares.

a. $9x^2 - 4 = (3x)^2 - (2)^2$
$= (3x - 2)(3x + 2)$

b. $36x^2y^2 - 49 = (6xy)^2 - (7)^2$
$= (6xy + 7)(6xy - 7)$

You may need to look for a common factor before a difference of squares is apparent.

EXAMPLE 2: Factor $81x^5y - 16xy$.

$81x^5y - 16xy = xy(81x^4 - 16)$
$= xy(9x^2 - 4)(9x^2 + 4)$ Another difference of squares results.
$= xy(3x - 2)(3x + 2)(9x^2 + 4)$ A *sum* of squares cannot be factored.

You can also factor $a^2 - b^2$ where a, or b, or both, are not necessarily monomials.

EXAMPLE 3: Factor the given expression.

a. $(2x - y)^2 - 25 = [(2x - y) - 5][(2x - y) + 5]$
$= (2x - y - 5)(2x - y + 5)$

b. $25 - (2p - 7)^2 = [5 + (2p - 7)][5 - (2p - 7)]$
$= (-2 + 2p)(12 - 2p)$ Identify
$= 2(p - 1)(-2)(p - 6)$ common
$= -4(p - 6)(p - 1)$ factors.

A pattern can also be found in the trinomial resulting from squaring a binomial.

$$\begin{aligned}(2x-3)^2 &= (2x-3)(2x-3)\\ &= 4x^2-6x-6x+9\\ &= 4x^2-12x+9\end{aligned}$$

$$\begin{aligned}(5x+4)^2 &= (5x+4)(5x+4)\\ &= 25x^2+20x+20x+16\\ &= 25x^2+40x+16\end{aligned}$$

The first and last terms of each **trinomial square** are perfect squares. Notice also that the sign of the second term in the binomial is identical to the sign of the middle term in the trinomial. Apply these observations to factor trinomial squares like the following:

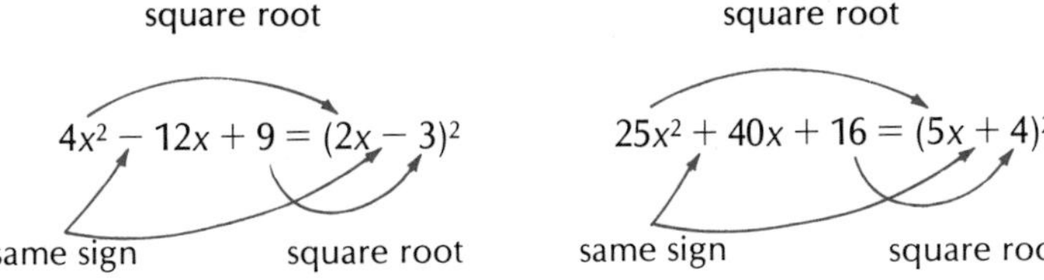

EXAMPLE 4: Factor $36a^2 - 96ab + 64b^2$.

$$\begin{aligned}36a^2 - 96ab + 64b^2 &= 4(9a^2 - 24ab + 16b^2)\\ &= 4(3a - 4b)^2\end{aligned}$$

Not all trinomials that have perfect squares for the first and third terms are trinomial squares.

EXAMPLE 5: Factor $4x^2 - 13x + 9$.

$4x^2 - 13x + 9 = (4x - 9)(x - 1)$

$4x^2 - 13x + 9 \neq (2x - 3)^2$
If you square $(2x - 3)$, the middle term is $-12x$.

Some of the questions in the exercise set will be like example 5: check your answers by expanding to ensure that the middle term is correct.

EXERCISE 2-6

A **1.** Identify those monomials that can be rewritten as perfect squares and rewrite as $(\blacksquare)^2$.

a. $25x^2$ **b.** $9a^6$ **c.** $4x^2y$ **d.** $49x^{10}y^{12}$ **e.** $64(xy^2)^2$
f. $36c^2d^4$ **g.** $25m^6n^8$ **h.** $16x^4y^{10}$ **i.** $6x^2y^4$ **j.** $16x^6y^{10}$

2. Factor and check by expanding.

a. $9x^2 - 49$ **b.** $64a^2b^2 - 1$ **c.** $4c^8 - 25d^6$ **d.** $81x^4 - 1$ **e.** $0.01x^2 - 0.25$
f. $64x^4 - 16$ **g.** $\frac{25m^2}{16} - \frac{1}{4}$ **h.** $\frac{n^2}{4} - \frac{1}{9}$ **i.** $\frac{4}{x^2} - 1$ **j.** $\frac{x^4}{y^2} - \frac{y^2}{x^4}$

3. Factor and check.

a. $49c^2 - 28c + 4$ b. $25x^2 + 30x + 9$ c. $9x^2 - 30xy + 25y^2$
d. $4z^2 - 4z + 1$ e. $36x^2y^2 + 60xy + 25$ f. $16 - 24xy + 9x^2y^2$

B 4. Factor.

a. $50p^2 - 32$ b. $16q^4 - 36q^2$ c. $32x^4 - 72x^2$
d. $5k^3 - 80kl^2$ e. $27x^3y - 75xy^3$ f. $36x^4y^2 - 16x^2$

5. Factor.

a. $(x - y)^2 - 49$ b. $(2x - 3y)^2 - 25$ c. $(x - 3)^2 - 25$
d. $4(h - 3g)^2 - 9$ e. $49 - 25(2x + y)^2$ f. $(3x + 5)^2 - 9x^2$
g. $(2r - 5)^2 - 36$ h. $(2t - 5)^2 - 49$ i. $36 - (x + 4)^2$
j. $144 - (x^2 - y)^2$ k. $(w^2 - 1)^2 - 9$ l. $49x^2 - (2x + 5)^2$

6. Factor.

a. $(2x - 3)^2 - (3y + 2)^2$ b. $(3x + 5)^2 - (2y - 1)^2$ c. $(5x + 1)^2 - (3x + 7)^2$
d. $(3x - 8)^2 - (3y - 5)^2$ e. $(4x - 7)^2 - (3x + 1)^2$ f. $(5x^2 + 1)^2 - (x^2 + 5)^2$
g. $(5x - 2)^2 - (3x - 8)^2$ h. $(4x + 3)^2 - (x + 12)^2$ i. $(x^2 - x)^2 - (x - 4)^2$

7. Factor.

a. $147a^2 - 210a + 75$ b. $405x^3 - 180x^2 + 20x$ c. $32x^3y^3 + 112x^2y^2 + 98xy$
d. $50f^4 + 40f^3g + 8f^2g^2$ e. $12x^5y^2 - 36x^3y^3 + 27xy^4$ f. $36y^4 + 148y^3 + 16y^2$
g. $48x^3 - 72x^2 + 27x$ h. $8m^6 - 72m^3n + 162n^2$ i. $64x^4y^2 - 288x^2y^2 + 324y^2$

8. Find the missing dimensions.

a. $A = 25x^2 - 20x + 16$?

b.

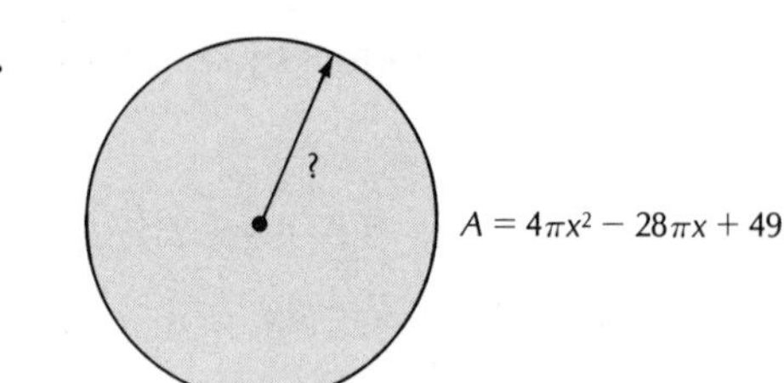

c.

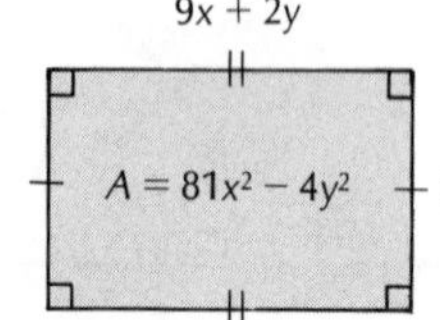

d.

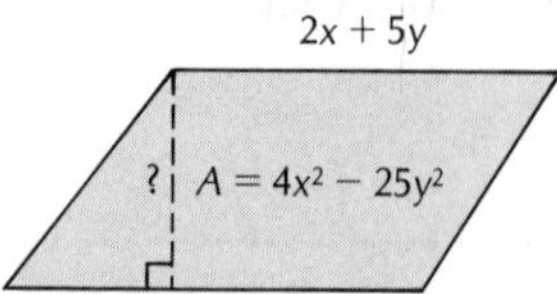

9. Familiarity with the square of a binomial can help you to evaluate perfect squares of whole numbers mentally. The following example illustrates how.

$$\begin{aligned} 32^2 &= (30 + 2)(30 + 2) \\ &= 900 + 60 + 60 + 4 \\ &= 1024 \end{aligned}$$

Now try the following without the aid of pencil, paper, or calculator.

a. 21^2 b. 42^2 c. 31^2 d. 29^2 e. 18^2

10. Since $(x + y)(x - y) = x^2 - y^2$ it follows that

$$\begin{aligned}[x + y + z][x + y - z] &= [(x + y) + z][(x + y) - z] \\ &= (x + y)^2 - z^2 \\ &= x^2 + 2xy + y^2 - z^2\end{aligned}$$

Use the above approach to simplify the following.

a. $(2x - 3y - 5)(2x - 3y + 5)$ **b.** $(3x - 2y + 5)(3x + 2y + 5)$
c. $(8 + x - y)(8 - x + y)$ **d.** $(2x - y + z - 4)(2x - y - z + 4)$

11. Factor.

a. $16x^4 - 40x^2 + 9$ **b.** $81x^4y^4 - 18x^2y^2 + 1$
c. $(x^2 + 12)^2 - 49x^2$ **d.** $(4x^2 + 9)^2 - 144x^2$
e. $(x^2 - 3x - 1)^2 - (x^2 - 5x + 7)^2$ **f.** $(x^2 + 5x + 1)^2 - (x^2 + 3x + 5)^2$
g. $(9x^2 + 3x)^2 - (3x + 1)^2$ **h.** $(x^2 - 7xy)^2 - (3xy - 21y^2)^2$
i. $(4x + 1)^2 - (16x^2 + 4x)^2$ **j.** $81x^2 - (9x^2 + 2)^2$

C 12. Factor.

a. $16x^4 - 72x^2 + 81$ **b.** $243x^9 - 54x^5 + 3x$
c. $\frac{25x^2}{2} - 13x + \frac{1}{2}$ **d.** $(x - 1)^2 + 6y(x - 1) + 9y^2$
e. $(2x - 1)^2 - 10(2x - 1) + 25$ **f.** $(y^2 - y)^2 - 64$
g. $(y^2 - 4y)^2 - (3y - 12)^2$ **h.** $(6y^2 - 5y)^2 - (3y - 28)^2$

13. A rectangular box with a square base has a volume that can be represented by $27x^2 - 90x + 75$. If the box is 3 units high, find the perimeter of its base.

14. A circle has an area that can be represented by $25\pi x^2 + 40\pi x + 16\pi$. Find the circumference of the circle.

15. A rectangular box is x centimetres high with its length exceeding its height by 5 cm. If the volume of the box can be represented by $2x^3 + 7x^2 - 15x$ cubic centimetres, find the width of the box.

EXTRA

An Algebraic Puzzle

The following algebraic development leads to the contradictory conclusion that $2 = 1$. Which line of the development contains an error?

1.	Let $x = y$	
2.	Then: $x^2 = xy$	Multiply by x.
3.	$x^2 - y^2 = xy - y^2$	Subtract y^2.
4.	$(x - y)(x + y) = y(x - y)$	Factor both sides.
5.	$x + y = y$	Divide both sides by $(x - y)$.
6.	$y + y = y$	From line 1, you may replace x with y.
7.	$2y = y$	Collect like terms.
8.	$\therefore 2 = 1$	Divide both sides by y.

2-7 Sum and Difference of Cubes

Find an expression for the area of a rectangle with the given dimensions.

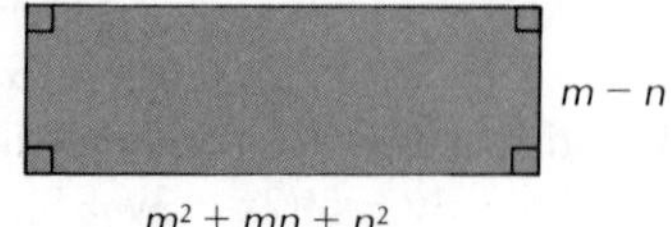

$$(m - n)(m^2 + mn + n^2) = m^3 - m^2n + mn^2 + m^2n - mn^2 - n^3$$
$$= m^3 - n^3$$

This result suggests a formula for factoring the **difference of cubes.**

$$m^3 - n^3 = (m - n)(m^2 + mn + n^2)$$

There is also a formula for the **sum of cubes.**

$$m^3 + n^3 = (m + n)(m^2 - mn + n^2)$$

EXAMPLE: Factor the given polynomial.

a. $x^3 + 27 = x^3 + 3^3$
$= (x + 3)(x^2 - 3x + 9)$

b. $8a^3 + 27b^3 = (2a)^3 + (3b)^3$
$= (2a + 3b)(4a^2 - 6ab + 9b^2)$

c. $x^6 - 64 = (x^2)^3 - 4^3$
$= (x^2 - 4)(x^4 - 4x^2 + 16)$
$= (x - 2)(x + 2)(x^4 + 4x^2 + 16)$

EXERCISE 2-7

A **1.** Complete.

a. $a^3 - 27 = (\blacksquare)(a^2 + 3a + 9)$ **b.** $x^3 - 64 = (\blacksquare)(x^2 + 4x + 16)$

c. $y^3 + 1 = (y + 1)(\blacksquare)$ **d.** $8m^3 - 27 = (2m - 3)(\blacksquare)$

e. $64x^3 + 1 = (4x + 1)(\blacksquare)$ **f.** $8t^3 + 27s^3 = (2t + 3s)(\blacksquare)$

g. $64 + a^6 = (4 + a^2)(\blacksquare)$ **h.** $64x^3 - y^6 = (4x - y^2)(\blacksquare)$

B **2.** Factor.

a. $125x^3 - 1$ **b.** $y^3 - 8$ **c.** $1 - 27a^3$

d. $8b^6 + 27$ **e.** $x^6y^6 - 64$ **f.** $125 - 8d^3$

g. $a^6 + b^6$ **h.** $64m^3n^3 - 27$ **i.** $8x^6y^6 + 125$

3. Factor, simplifying where appropriate.

a. $24x^6 + 81$ **b.** $81y - 3y^4$ **c.** $(2a - 1)^3 - 27$

d. $(5b - 2c)^3 + 216$ **e.** $81t^2 - 3t^5$ **f.** $(2w - 3)^3 + (w + 3)^3$

g. $(3z - 5)^3 - (z - 1)^3$ **h.** $(3x + y)^3 - (3x - y)^3$ **i.** $(3a - 2b)^3 + (4a^2 - b)^3$

Using the Computer

The following program will factor trinomials of the form $ax^2 + bx + c$ when there are linear factors with integer coefficients.

```
10 DIM FA(50,2), FC(50,2), AN(50,4)
20 FLAG =.5
30 CLS:LOCATE 6,24:PRINT"2"
40 PRINT"For the quadratic    AX  +BX + C  ,"
50 PRINT
60 INPUT"Input the values for A,B,C";A,B,C
70 PRINT
80 IF A=0 AND B=0 AND C=0 THEN 190
90 FOR I=-ABS(A) TO ABS(A)
100 IF I<>0 THEN IF A/I=INT(A/I) THEN FA(CA,1)=I:FA(CA,2)=A/I:CA=CA+1
110 NEXT I
120 FOR I=-ABS(C) TO ABS(C)
130 IF I<> 0 THEN IF C/I=INT(C/I) THEN FC(CC,1)=I:FC(CC,2)=C/I:CC=CC+1
140 NEXT I
150 FOR I=0 TO CA:FOR J=0 TO CC
160 IF FA(I,1)*FC(J,1)+FA(I,2)*FC(J,2)<>B THEN 180
170 CN=CN+1:AN(CN,1)=FA(I,1):AN(CN,2)=FC(J,2):AN(CN,3)=FA(I,2):AN(CN,4)=FC(J,1)
180 NEXT J:NEXT I
190 IF CN=0 THEN PRINT"There are no integer factors.":END
200 FOR I=1 TO CN:FOR J=I TO CN
210 IF AN(I,1)=AN(J,3) AND AN(I,1)<>AN(I,3) THEN AN(J,1)=FLAG
220 NEXT J:NEXT I
230 FOR I=1 TO CN
240 IF AN(I,1)=FLAG THEN 280
250 PRINT"("AN(I,1)"X ";:IF AN(I,2)>=0 THEN PRINT"+";
260 PRINT AN(I,2)")("AN(I,3)"X ";:IF AN(I,4)>=0 THEN PRINT"+";
270 PRINT AN(I,4)")   is an answer."
280 NEXT I
```

Note that there can be more than one form in which factors can be expressed. For example:

$$2x^2 - 7x + 3 = (2x - 1)(x - 3) \\ = (1 - 2x)(3 - x)$$

$$2x^2 - 5x - 3 = (2x + 1)(x - 3) \\ = -(2x + 1)(3 - x)$$

Test the program on the following examples:

1. $x^2 + 3x + 2 = (x + 1)(x + 2)$
2. $x^2 + x - 2 = (x - 1)(x + 2)$
3. $x^2 - x - 2 = (x + 1)(x - 2)$
4. $x^2 - 3x + 2 = (x - 1)(x - 2)$
5. $x^2 + 3x = x(x + 3)$ $c = 0$
6. $x^2 + 2$ $b = 0$ and there are no factors with integer coefficients.
7. $x^2 - 4 = (x - 2)(x + 2)$
8. $3x + 2$ $a = 0$

Use the program to factor question 6 of Exercise 2-5 and question 7 of Exercise 2-6.

2-8 Factoring by Grouping

This lesson will extend your factoring skills, providing you with a method for factoring polynomials with more than three terms.

In the expression $14xy + 15 - 10x - 21y$, there is no common factor for all four terms.

However, $14xy + 15 - 10x - 21y$ can be rewritten by grouping *pairs* of terms that *do* have a common factor. Factoring each pair reveals $(7y - 5)$ as a common binomial factor.

$$\begin{aligned} 14xy + 15 - 10x - 21y &= 14xy - 10x - 21y + 15 \\ &= 2x(7y - 5) - 3(7y - 5) \\ &= (7y - 5)(2x - 3) \end{aligned}$$

Check by expanding.

The expression has been factored by **grouping to obtain a common factor.**

EXAMPLE 1: Factor the given polynomial by grouping to obtain a common factor.

a. $$\begin{aligned} 6xy + 18x - 21y - 63 &= 2x(3y + 9) - 7(3y + 9) \\ &= (3y + 9)(2x - 7) \\ &= 3(y + 3)(2x - 7) \end{aligned}$$

b. $$\begin{aligned} (2a - 5)^2 - 6a + 15 &= (2a - 5)^2 - 3(2a - 5) \\ &= (2a - 5)(2a - 5 - 3) \\ &= (2a - 5)(2a - 8) \\ &= 2(2a - 5)(a - 4) \end{aligned}$$

Grouping may not yield a common binomial factor, as is the case with the expression $4x^2 - 28xy - 36 + 49y^2$. Notice, however, that the expression contains three perfect squares. The xy term suggests that it be grouped with the x^2 and y^2 terms.

Group three terms that may form a trinomial square. Factoring the trinomial results in a difference of squares, which can be factored.

$$\begin{aligned} &4x^2 - 28xy + 49y^2 - 36 \\ &= (2x - 7y)^2 - 36 \\ &= (2x - 7y - 6)(2x - 7y + 6) \end{aligned}$$

The expression has been factored by **grouping to obtain a difference of squares.** When applying this method, the term which is *not* a perfect square provides a hint as to which terms should be grouped to result in a trinomial square.

EXAMPLE 2: Factor the given polynomial.

a. $$\begin{aligned} 25x^2 + y^2 - 4z^2 + 10xy &= (25x^2 + 10xy + y^2) - 4z^2 \\ &= (5x + y)^2 - 4z^2 \\ &= (5x + y - 2z)(5x + y + 2z) \end{aligned}$$

b. $$\begin{aligned} 80a + 16b^2 - 64a^2 - 25 &= 16b^2 - (64a^2 - 80a + 25) \\ &= 16b^2 - (8a - 5)^2 \\ &= [4b - (8a - 5)][4b + (8a - 5)] \\ &= [4b - 8a + 5][4b + 8a - 5] \end{aligned}$$

EXERCISE 2-8

A **1.** Factor.

a. $3a(2a - 5) - 5(2a - 5)$
b. $3y(3y + 4) + 4(3y + 4)$
c. $4x^2(3x - 1) - 9(3x - 1)$
d. $4m(3n - 7) - 8(3n - 7)$
e. $(2s - 5)^2 - t(2s - 5)$
f. $(3w - 7)^2 - 2(3w - 7)$

B **2.** Factor.

a. $(2x - y)^2 - 9$
b. $(2a - 5)^2 - 49$
c. $(3c + 5)^2 - 25c^2d^2$
d. $(7x^2 - 1)^2 - 9x^4$
e. $(ab - 3)^2 - a^2b^2$
f. $(m^2 - 6)^2 - m^2$

3. Factor by grouping to obtain a common factor.

a. $2x^2 - 10x - 3x + 15$
b. $15x^2 + 3x - 5xy - y$
c. $8s^2t + 9 + 4s^2 + 18t$
d. $3a(b + 4) - 4c - cb$
e. $10xy - 8y - 5x + 4$
f. $x^2y^2 - xy + x^3 - y^3$

4. Factor by grouping to obtain a difference of squares.

a. $4x^2 - 12x + 9 - y^2$
b. $25x^2 + y^2 - 49 - 10xy$
c. $25 - 9y^2 + 6y - 1$
d. $20x + 49y^2 - 4x^2 - 25$
e. $25x^2 + 30xz + 9z^2 - 64y^2$
f. $28x - 4x^2 + 16z^2 - 49$

5. Factor.

a. $12y(x - 2) + 16x - 32$
b. $x^3 + 4x - x^2 - 4$
c. $x^2y - 12 + 3x^2 - 4y$
d. $3x^2y + 21x^2 - 15xy - 105x$
e. $8x^3 - 20x^2 - 50x + 125$
f. $(x - 3y)^2 - 3(x - 3y)$
g. $(x^2 - 7)^2 - 2(x^2 - 7)$
h. $(x^2 - 1)^2 - 8x + 8$

6. Factor.

a. $4x^4 + 12x^2 + 9 - 16y^2$
b. $16x^4 + 1 - 25y^2 - 8x^2$
c. $16 - y^4 - 2y^3 - y^2$
d. $8p^2 - 24p + 18 - 98q^2$
e. $3ab^2 + 30a^2 - 3a - 75a^3$
f. $16x^4y^4 + 81 - 25x^2 - 72x^2y^2$

C **7.** Factor.

a. $(x^2 - 8x)^2 - 144$
b. $f^4 - 2f^3 + f^2 - 16f^6$
c. $9y^2 - x^4y^4 + 2x^3y^2 - x^2$
d. $4z^2 - 4z - 20 - z^2w + zw + 5w$
e. $x^2y - xy - 20y - 5x^2 + 5x + 100$
f. $2x^4 - 5x^3 - 2x + 5$
g. $9a^2 - 30ab + 25b^2 - 4c^2 - 4c - 1$
h. $m^2 + 9n^2 - 4p^2q^2 - 6mn + 12pq - 9$

8. If irrational square roots are allowed as possible factors of a number, then $x^2 - 7$ can be written as $x^2 - \sqrt{7}^2$, which can then be factored as a difference of squares: $(x - \sqrt{7})(x + \sqrt{7})$. Factor the following as a difference of squares over the set of real numbers.

a. $x^2 - 5$
b. $4x^2 - 3y$
c. $6x - 49$
d. $5x - 2$

2-9 Factoring Incomplete Squares

A familiarity with factoring trinomial squares can be applied as a strategy for factoring other polynomials. To find the missing term of a trinomial square like $x^2 + \blacksquare + 9$, follow these steps.

1. Take the square roots of the first and last terms. $\quad x^2 + \blacksquare + 9 = (x \blacksquare 3)^2$
2. Since the sign of the middle term is unknown, there are two possible solutions. $\quad (x + 3)^2$ and $(x - 3)^2$
3. Expand each possibility to find the middle term. $\quad (x + 3)^2 = x^2 + 6x + 9$, $\quad (x - 3)^2 = x^2 - 6x + 9$

Therefore, the middle term of $x^2 + \blacksquare + 9$ is $\pm 6x$.

EXAMPLE 1: Complete $9x^2 + \blacksquare + 25$ to make it a trinomial square.

$9x^2 + \blacksquare + 25 = (3x \blacksquare 5)^2$

The possibilities are $(3x + 5)^2$ and $(3x - 5)^2$.

$(3x + 5)^2 = 9x^2 + 30x + 25$
$(3x - 5)^2 = 9x^2 - 30x + 25$

The completed trinomial square is $9x^2 \pm 30x + 25$.

Now consider the expression $x^4 - 22x^2 + 9$. The expression is not a trinomial square but it can be rewritten to reveal a trinomial square by first putting the middle term aside.

Find a middle term to complete the square. Try $-6x^2$.

Factor the trinomial and collect like terms to reveal a difference of squares.

$$\begin{aligned} x^4 - 22x^2 + 9 &= (x^4 + \blacksquare + 9) - 22x^2 \\ &= (x^4 - 6x^2 + 9) - 22x^2 + 6x^2 \\ &= (x^2 - 3)^2 - 16x^2 \\ &= (x^2 - 3 - 4x)(x^2 - 3 + 4x) \end{aligned}$$

If $-6x^2$ hadn't led to a possible factorization, you could still try $+6x^2$.

EXAMPLE 2: Factor $x^4 - 39x^2 + 25$.

$$\begin{aligned} x^4 - 39x^2 + 25 &= (x^4 + \blacksquare + 25) - 39x^2 \\ &= (x^4 - 10x^2 + 25) - 39x^2 + 10x^2 \\ &= (x^2 - 5)^2 - 29x^2 \end{aligned}$$

Try a middle term of $-10x^2$. This is not a difference of squares.

$$\begin{aligned} x^4 - 39x^2 + 25 &= (x^4 + \blacksquare + 25) - 39x^2 \\ &= (x^4 + 10x^2 + 25) - 39x^2 - 10x^2 \\ &= (x^2 + 5)^2 - 49x^2 \\ &= (x^2 + 5 - 7x)(x^2 + 5 + 7x) \end{aligned}$$

Try again, using $+10x^2$.

This *does* result in a difference of squares.

With practice, you will know which sign to select for the middle term. In some questions, you will find that either sign will work.

EXAMPLE 3: Factor $x^4 - 13x^2y^2 + 36y^4$.

$$\begin{aligned} x^4 - 13x^2y^2 + 36y^4 &= (x^4 + \blacksquare + 36y^4) - 13x^2y^2 \\ &= (x^4 - 12x^2y^2 + 36y^4) - 13x^2y^2 + 12x^2y^2 \\ &= (x^2 - 6y^2)^2 - x^2y^2 \\ &= (x^2 - 6y^2 - xy)(x^2 - 6y^2 + xy) \\ &= (x^2 - xy - 6y^2)(x^2 + xy - 6y^2) \\ &= (x - 3y)(x + 2y)(x + 3y)(x - 2y) \end{aligned}$$

On your own, try example 3 again, this time inserting $+12x^2y^2$ for the middle term. Notice that this question could also be done using the factoring skills established in lesson 2-5.

$$\begin{aligned} x^4 - 13x^2y^2 + 36y^4 &= (x^2 - 9y^2)(x^2 - 4y^2) \\ &= (x - 3y)(x + 3y)(x - 2y)(x + 2y) \end{aligned}$$

EXERCISE 2-9

A 1. Find the missing middle term of each expression to make it a trinomial square.

- **a.** $x^2 + \blacksquare + 81$
- **b.** $y^4 + \blacksquare + 49$
- **c.** $36a^4 + \blacksquare + 49b^2$
- **d.** $16d^6 + \blacksquare + 121c^8$
- **e.** $9m^4 + \blacksquare + 144n^6$
- **f.** $4x^4y^2 + \blacksquare + 16z^2$

2. Factor.

- **a.** $(x^2 + 3)^2 - 4x^2$
- **b.** $(a^2 + b^2)^2 - 9a^2b^2$
- **c.** $(m^2n^2 - 3)^2 - 25m^2n^2$
- **d.** $(x^2 - 3y^2)^2 - 49x^2y^2$
- **e.** $(3c^2 - 2d^2)^2 - 36c^2d^2$
- **f.** $(4p^2 + 2q^2)^2 - 144p^2q^2$

3. Factor.

- **a.** $x^4 - 39x^2 + 49$
- **b.** $y^4 + 12y^2 + 64$
- **c.** $g^4 - 32g^2 + 4$
- **d.** $z^4 - 22z^2 + 81$
- **e.** $a^4b^4 - 19a^2b^2 + 9$
- **f.** $j^4k^4 + 10j^2k^2 + 49$

B 4. Factor.

- **a.** $4x^4 - 28x^2 + 9$
- **b.** $9x^4 + 29x^2 + 25$
- **c.** $x^4 + 4$
- **d.** $64x^4 + 1$
- **e.** $16x^4 - 65x^2 + 4$
- **f.** $25x^4 - 55x^2y^2 + 9y^4$
- **g.** $4x^4 - 21x^2y^4 + 49y^8$
- **h.** $64x^4 - 32x^2y^2 + y^4$
- **i.** $36c^4 - 85c^2d^2 + 9d^4$
- **j.** $16x^4 - 72x^2y^2 + 81y^4$
- **k.** $25x^4 + 21x^2 + 9$
- **l.** $x^4 - 29x^2 + 100$

C 5. Find the last term of each trinomial square.

- **a.** $x^2 + 16x + ?$
- **b.** $25x^2 - 40x + ?$
- **c.** $49x^2 - 28xy^4 + ?$
- **d.** $64x^4 + 80x^2y^3 + ?$
- **e.** $25x^2 - 60xy^4 + ?$
- **f.** $\frac{x^2}{16} + 4xy + ?$

6. Factor each trinomial square.

- **a.** $x^8 - 27x^4 + 1$
- **b.** $9x^8 + 5x^4 - 25$
- **c.** $16x^8 - 12x^4y^2 + y^4$

Factoring Problems

1. Show how an $a \times a$ square with a $b \times b$ square removed from one corner can be cut into two pieces and rearranged to form an $(a+b) \times (a-b)$ rectangle. ($a > b$, of course.)

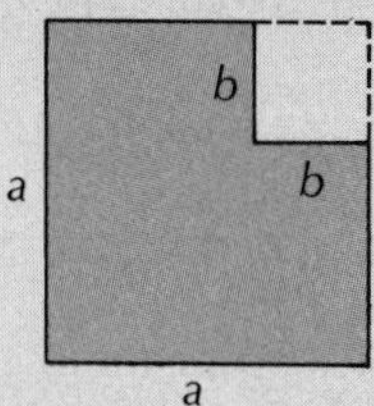

2. List the set of integers that cannot be written as the difference of two square integers. Describe the set in words.

3. Show that for any choice of integers m and n, $(m^2 - n^2, 2mn, m^2 + n^2)$ is a pythagorean triple.

4. **a.** By factoring as a difference of squares, verify that:

$$\left(\frac{x+y}{2}\right)^2 - \left(\frac{x-y}{2}\right)^2 = xy.$$

b. Use (a) to establish the arithmetic mean-geometric mean inequality:

$$\sqrt{xy} \leq \frac{x+y}{2} \qquad \text{whenever } x, y \geq 0.$$

c. Two positive integers have a sum of 56. What is the largest possible product they could have?

5. By factoring as a difference of squares, show that:

a.
$$\begin{aligned} 27^2 - 3^2 &= 28^2 - 8^2 \\ &= 29^2 - 11^2 \\ &= 1 \times 2 \times 3 \times 4 \times 5 \times 6 \end{aligned}$$

b.
$$\begin{aligned} 71^2 - 1^2 &= 72^2 - 12^2 \\ &= 73^2 - 17^2 \\ &= 1 \times 2 \times 3 \times 4 \times 5 \times 6 \times 7 \end{aligned}$$

6. Show that:

$$\begin{aligned} &100^2 - 99^2 + 98^2 - 97^2 + 96^2 - 95^2 + \cdots + 2^2 - 1^2 \\ &\quad = 100 + 99 + 98 + 97 + 96 + 95 + \cdots + 2 + 1 \end{aligned}$$

7. Show that the product of four consecutive integers is always one less than a perfect square.

Review

1. Which of the following are polynomials? Give the degree of each expression that is a polynomial.

   a. $(2x^3 - 3x)(4 - x^2)$ b. $\sqrt{(x^3 - 5)}$

   c. $\dfrac{x^2 - 5x + 1}{3x}$ d. $\sqrt{3}x^2 - \frac{3}{4}x + \pi$

2. Simplify.

   a. $3(2t - 5) - 4(3 - t)$ b. $2x^2(x - 3)(2x + 5)$

   c. $3m(5 - 7m)^2$ d. $(2v - 3)(3v + 1) - (v + 2)^2$

   e. $(3x - 2)(5x^2 - x + 1)$ f. $(8y - 1)(3 - 4y) - (2 - 3y)(3y - 2)$

3. Find the GCF and factor.

   a. $7x^2 - 28x^3$ b. $15x^3y^3 - 25xy^2z$

   c. $-4x^4y^2z - 8y^3z^2 - 12xy^2z^2$ d. $x^5y^4z^3 + 7x^3y^3z^3 - 28y^2z^3$

4. Divide as indicated.

   a. $(6x^4 - 3x^3 + 9x^2) \div 3x$ b. $(16x^5y^3 - 8xy^4 + 12x^2y^2) \div (4xy^2)$

   c. $(2x^4 + x^3 - x - 2) \div (x + 1)$ d. $(x^4 - 3x^3 - 2x^2 - 4x + 15) \div (x - 3)$

   e. $(3x^3 - 11x + 2) \div (x + 2)$ f. $(6x^4 - 17x^3 + 17x^2 - 7x + 1) \div (3x - 1)$

5. Rewrite as a product of positive factors in as many ways as possible.

   a. $36a$ b. $48x^2$ c. $60mn$ d. $50w^2y$ e. $14x^3y^2$

6. Factor.

   a. $x^2 - 11x + 18$ b. $6b^2 + 7b - 24$ c. $x^4 - 37x^2 + 36$

   d. $75r^2 - 48$ e. $49t^2 - 42t + 9$ f. $x^4 - 13x^2 + 36$

   g. $(w - 3)^2 - 25$ h. $5n(2n - 3) - 10(2n - 3)$ i. $2x^2 - 2xy - 3x + 3y$

   j. $(2x - 5)^2 - 4(2x - 5)$ k. $49 - (2x - 5)^2$ l. $9x^2 - 49y^2 + 25 - 30x$

7. Factor.

   a. $27 - x^3$ b. $8x^3 + 1$ c. $27a^3 + 8b^3$

   d. $125x^6 - 64y^3$ e. $(2x - 3)^3 + (x - 2)^3$ f. $81x^3 - 192y^9$

8. Factor.

   a. $4 - 25x^2$ b. $51x^2 - 14x - 1$ c. $4x^2 - 101x + 25$

   d. $15x^2 + 55x + 40$ e. $3x(x - 5) - 6(x - 5)$ f. $48x^3 - 12x$

   g. $10xy - 6y - 21 + 35x$ h. $4(x - 9)^2 - 25$ i. $25x^2 + 9y^2 - 16 - 30xy$

   j. $9x^2 - (5x + 1)^2$ k. $72x^3 - 105x^2 + 12x$ l. $12x^2 - 44x - 45$

   m. $(3x - 5)^2 - 4(3x - 5)$ n. $x^4 - 26x^2 + 25$ o. $(x^2 - 8)^2 - 4x^2$

   p. $y^3 - 8 - 4y + 2y^2$ q. $81x^4 - 4y^2$ r. $x^2y^2 - y^2 - x^2 + 1$

2-10 Simplifying Rational Expressions

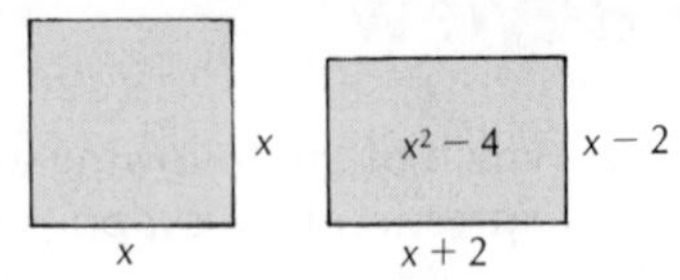

The area of the square is x^2 m². If we reduce its area by 4 m² and one dimension by 2 m, what is the other dimension?

The answer, $\frac{x^2 - 4}{x - 2}$, is an example of a **rational expression**, formed by one polynomial being divided by another. Since division by 0 is undefined, it is necessary that the denominator never equal 0.

Therefore: $x - 2 \neq 0$

$$x \neq 2$$

In the problem, $x = 2$ would not be a sensible dimension, since reducing x by 2 leaves a rectangle of side 0 m. Impossible!

EXAMPLE 1: For each expression, state any necessary restrictions on the variable.

a. $\frac{5}{x - 4}$ Restrict x so that $x - 4 \neq 0$. That is, $x \neq 4$.

b. $\frac{3x + 1}{2x + 1}$ The denominator cannot be 0.

$$\therefore 2x + 1 \neq 0$$
$$2x \neq -1$$
$$x \neq -\frac{1}{2}$$

c. $\frac{2x + 1}{3x^2 - 12x} = \frac{2x + 1}{3x(x - 4)}$ $3x \neq 0$ *and* $x - 4 \neq 0$ $\therefore x \neq 0$ *and* $x \neq 4$

Some rational expressions can be simplified by dividing common factors from the numerator and denominator.

EXAMPLE 2: Simplify each expression and state any necessary restrictions on x.

a. $$\frac{x^2 - x - 12}{x^2 - 9} = \frac{(x - 4)(x + 3)}{(x - 3)(x + 3)} = \frac{x - 4}{x - 3}$$ Note that $x \neq \pm 3$.

b. $$\frac{6x^2 + 9x}{4x^3 - 14x^2 - 30x} = \frac{3x(2x + 3)}{2x(x - 5)(2x + 3)} = \frac{3}{2x - 10}$$ Note that $x \neq 0, 5, -\frac{3}{2}$.

c. $$\frac{2x^2 - 15x + 27}{9 - x^2} = \frac{(x - 3)(2x - 9)}{(3 - x)(3 + x)} = \frac{9 - 2x}{3 + x}$$ $x \neq \pm 3$

Note that $\frac{x - 3}{3 - x} = -1$.

EXERCISE 2-10

A **1.** State any necessary restrictions on the variables.

a. $\frac{5}{2x+7}$ b. $\frac{3x}{x^2-12x+20}$ c. $\frac{6}{15x^2-25x}$

d. $\frac{3x-1}{25x^3-49x}$ e. $\frac{4x+1}{36x^2-60x+25}$ f. $\frac{2x-3}{x^2-4xy-21y^2}$

2. Simplify and state any necessary restrictions on the variables.

a. $\frac{2t-6}{t^2+2t-15}$ b. $\frac{x^2-25}{x^2+3x-10}$ c. $\frac{y^2-8y+16}{2y^2-7y-4}$

d. $\frac{2x^2y-6xy}{6x^2y+18xy}$ e. $\frac{x^2-25}{15+2x-x^2}$ f. $\frac{10x-15}{3-2x}$

B **3.** Simplify.

a. $\frac{4b^2-37b+9}{b^2-81}$ b. $\frac{12m^2-20m+3}{4m^2-12m+9}$ c. $\frac{3v^3-24v^2+45v}{2v^3-5v^2-25v}$

d. $\frac{60-8x-4x^2}{24+16x-8x^2}$ e. $\frac{3x^2+2xy-5y^2}{6x^2+7xy-5y^2}$ f. $\frac{9x^2-27xy+14y^2}{14y^2-15xy-9x^2}$

g. $\frac{(x-3)^2-25}{x^2-6x-16}$ h. $\frac{(x-3)^2-6x+18}{15-2x-x^2}$ i. $\frac{36-(x-5)^2}{x^2+7x+6}$

4. Simplify and state any necessary restrictions.

a. $\frac{3y^2+y-4}{3xy-12+4x-9y}$ b. $\frac{y^3+y^2-y-1}{y^2+2y+1}$

c. $\frac{(2x-7)^2-49}{4x^3-24x^2-28x}$ d. $\frac{xy-9+3x-3y}{x^2y-27+3x^2-9y}$

e. $\frac{x^2+15y-3xy-5x}{2x^2-3y-6xy+x}$ f. $\frac{x^3-4y^3-4xy^2+x^2y}{x^3-x^2y-2xy^2}$

C **5.** Simplify.

a. $\frac{4y^2+10x-1-25x^2}{6xy^2+15x^2y-3xy}$ b. $\frac{12x^4-60x^2+75}{12x^4-34x^2+10}$

c. $\frac{(x^2+5)^2+3x^3+15x}{x^4+10x^3+25}$ d. $\frac{(2x-3)^2-9(2x-3)+20}{4x^2+2x-56}$

e. $\frac{48x^2-37x-36}{36x^2-90x+56}$ f. $\frac{x^2y^2-4y^2-9x^2+36}{2x^2y-4xy-6x^2+12x}$

Using the Calculator

In Your Best Interests

One of the largest Canadian lottery wins was for 13.8 million dollars. If you could invest this money at an annual interest rate of 9%, what would be the simple interest earned over the given time period?

1. one year **2.** one day **3.** one minute **4.** a 40 min Mathematics period

2-11 Multiplying and Dividing Rational Expressions

To multiply and divide rational expressions, first factor numerators and denominators, then look for common factors.

EXAMPLE 1: Multiply or divide as indicated and state any restrictions on the variable.

a. $$\frac{x^2-9}{x^2+8x+15} \times \frac{x^2-2x-35}{x^2-9x+14} = \frac{(x-3)\cancel{(x+3)}}{\cancel{(x+3)}\cancel{(x+5)}} \times \frac{\cancel{(x+5)}\cancel{(x-7)}}{\cancel{(x-7)}(x-2)}$$
$$= \frac{x-3}{x-2}$$

The restrictions on the variables are $x \neq -3, x \neq -5, x \neq 7, x \neq 2$.

b. $$\frac{x^2+5x+6}{x^2-3x-10} \div \frac{x+3}{x+5} = \frac{(x+2)(x+3)}{(x-5)(x+2)} \div \frac{(x+3)}{(x+5)}$$
$$= \frac{\cancel{(x+2)}\cancel{(x+3)}}{(x-5)\cancel{(x+2)}} \times \frac{(x+5)}{\cancel{(x+3)}}$$
$$= \frac{x+5}{x-5}$$

The restrictions are $x \neq -2, x \neq 5, x \neq -5, x \neq -3$.

Some questions will combine both multiplication and division.

EXAMPLE 2: Simplify.

$$\frac{a^2-6a+9}{a^2+a-20} \times \frac{a^2+7a+10}{a^2-a-6} \div \frac{a^2-9}{a^2-4a}$$

$$= \frac{\cancel{(a-3)}\cancel{(a-3)}}{\cancel{(a+5)}\cancel{(a-4)}} \times \frac{\cancel{(a+5)}\cancel{(a+2)}}{\cancel{(a-3)}\cancel{(a+2)}} \times \frac{a\cancel{(a-4)}}{\cancel{(a-3)}(a+3)}$$

$$= \frac{a}{a+3}$$

Note that $a \neq -5, -3, -2, 0, 3, 4$.

EXERCISE 2-11

A **1.** State any necessary restrictions on the variable.

a. $\frac{2x-3}{x+5} \times \frac{x-2}{x+3}$

b. $\frac{3y-1}{y-4} \div \frac{2y+3}{y+1}$

c. $\frac{3a-1}{2a(a+4)} \times \frac{5a+1}{a-4}$

d. $\frac{4k}{2k+3} \div \frac{2k(k+5)}{k-1}$

2. Simplify.

a. $\frac{6xy}{2x^2 - 6x} \times \frac{x^2 - 6x + 9}{3xy + 12y}$

b. $\frac{m^2 - 5m + 6}{m^2 + 2m - 8} \times \frac{m^2 + 6m + 8}{m^2 + 5m + 6}$

c. $\frac{4a^2 - 12a + 9}{2a^2 + a - 6} \div \frac{2a^2 - a - 3}{a^2 - 4a - 5}$

d. $\frac{9x^2 - 16}{6x^2 + 11x + 4} \div \frac{9x^2 - 24x + 16}{6x^2 - 11x + 4}$

e. $\frac{5r - 15}{r^2 + 5r} \times \frac{r^3 - 5r^2}{10r - 30}$

f. $\frac{c^2 + 2c - 3}{c^2 - 8c + 12} \times \frac{c^2 + 10c + 24}{c^2 + 3c - 4} \div \frac{c^2 + 4c + 3}{c^2 - 3c + 2}$

B 3. Simplify.

a. $\frac{25b^2 - 16}{2b^2 - 7b + 3} \times \frac{6 + b - b^2}{5b^2 + 14b + 8}$

b. $\frac{x^2 - 10x - 24}{2x^2 - 24x} \div \frac{x^2 - 6x - 16}{x^2 - 4x - 32}$

c. $\frac{48x^2 - 16x - 15}{144x^2 - 25} \div \frac{32x^2 - 20x - 3}{8x^2 - 31x - 4}$

d. $\frac{x^2 - 12x + 20}{x^2 - 6x + 8} \times \frac{x^2 - x - 12}{x^2 - 7x - 30}$

e. $\frac{x^2y^2 + 6xy + 9}{3x^2y^3 + 9xy^2} \times \frac{4x^3y^3 + 13x^2y^2 + 9xy}{x^2y^2 + 4xy + 3}$

f. $\frac{x^2 + 7x + 12}{9 - x^2} \div \frac{x^2 + 5x + 4}{x^2 - 7x + 12}$

g. $\frac{4a^4 - 13a^2 + 9}{2a^2 - a - 3} \div \left[\frac{16a^2 + 22a - 3}{24ab - 3b} \times \frac{8a^2 - 17a + 9}{16a^2 - 18a}\right]$

h. $\frac{6t^2 + 29t - 5}{36t^2 - 12t + 1} \times \frac{6t^2 - 19t + 3}{15 - 2t - t^2} \div \frac{12t^2 - 13t - 14}{12t^2 - 29t + 14}$

i. $\frac{9x^2 - 13x + 4}{4x^2 - 28x + 49} \div \frac{18x^2 - 17x + 4}{16x^2 - 54x - 7} \times \frac{7 - 16x + 4x^2}{8x^2 - 7x - 1}$

4. In the expression $\frac{3x^4 + 14x^2 - 5}{x^4 + 9x^2 + 20}$, x can be any real number. That is, there are *no* restrictions on x. Why is this so?

C 5. Simplify.

a. $\frac{x^2 - 6y + 3x - 2xy}{x^2 - 9y + 3xy - 3x} \div \frac{x^2 - 7xy + 10y^2}{x^2 - 2xy - 15y^2}$

b. $\frac{(2m - 9)^2 - 25}{2m^2 + 5m - 18} \times \frac{m^3 - 10 + 5m - 2m^2}{(m - 2)^2 - 5(m - 2)} \div \frac{4m^3 + 20m}{2m^2 + 11m + 9}$

c. $\frac{(2x - 3)^2 - 49y^2}{10x^2 + 27x - 9} \times \frac{x^2 - 5x - 24}{(2x - 3)^2 - 14xy + 21y} \div \frac{2x^2 - 19x + 24}{20x^2 - 36x + 9}$

d. $\frac{15 - 11c + 2c^2}{9 - c^2} \div \left[\frac{2c^2 + 9c - 35}{3c^2 - 21c} \times \frac{2c^3 + 2c^2 + 6c}{(c + 3)^2 + c^2(c + 3)}\right]$

6. Simplify. State any restrictions on x.

a. $\frac{x^2 - a^2}{x - b} \div \frac{x + a}{x^2 - b^2}$

b. $\frac{a^2x^2 + 3abx + 2b^2}{a^2x^2 + 4abx + 4b^2} \times \frac{a^2x^2 - 4b^2}{a^2x^2 + 2abx + b^2}$

2-12 Adding and Subtracting Rational Expressions

Adding and subtracting rational expressions can be modelled after adding and subtracting fractions. In algebra, as in arithmetic, it is necessary to have a common denominator. Look for the *lowest* common denominator (LCD) to simplify your work.

EXAMPLE 1: Add or subtract as indicated.

a. $$\frac{2x}{5}+\frac{5x}{6}-\frac{7}{10}=\frac{6(2x)+5(5x)-3(7)}{30}$$
$$=\frac{12x+25x-21}{30}$$
$$=\frac{37x-21}{30}$$

b. $$\frac{x-2}{3}+\frac{5x-1}{6}-\frac{x-4}{9}=\frac{6(x-2)+3(5x-1)-2(x-4)}{18}$$
$$=\frac{6x-12+15x-3-2x+8}{18}$$
$$=\frac{19x-7}{18}$$

Each part in example 1 contained numerical denominators only. Denominators may also have algebraic factors.

EXAMPLE 2: Find the LCD for the expression $\frac{1}{3xy^3}-\frac{2}{2x^2y}+\frac{4}{5x^3y^2}$.

The LCD is $(3)(2)(5)(x^3)(y^3)$, or $30x^3y^3$.

EXAMPLE 3: Add or subtract as indicated.

a. $$\frac{3y}{2x}+\frac{5x}{3y}-\frac{5}{xy}=\frac{(3y)(3y)+(2x)(5x)-6(5)}{6xy}$$
$$=\frac{9y^2+10x^2-30}{6xy}$$

Note that $x \neq 0$, $y \neq 0$.

b. $$\frac{2}{5x^3y}-\frac{3}{4xy^2}+\frac{1}{10x^2y^4}=\frac{4y^3(2)-5x^2y^2(3)+2x(1)}{20x^3y^4}$$
$$=\frac{8y^3-15x^2y^2+2x}{20x^3y^4}$$

Note that $x \neq 0$, $y \neq 0$.

If binomial denominators are treated as single factors, then the method used in examples 1 and 2 will still apply.

EXAMPLE 4: Add or subtract.

a. $$\frac{3}{x-5} - \frac{4}{x+3} = \frac{3(x+3) - 4(x-5)}{(x-5)(x+3)}$$
$$= \frac{3x + 9 - 4x + 20}{x^2 - 2x - 15}$$
$$= \frac{-x + 29}{x^2 - 2x - 15}$$

Note $x \neq -3, 5$.

b. $$\frac{x+1}{x-4} - \frac{3x+5}{x+5} = \frac{(x+5)(x+1) - (x-4)(3x+5)}{(x-4)(x+5)}$$
$$= \frac{(x^2 + 6x + 5) - (3x^2 - 7x - 20)}{x^2 + x - 20}$$
$$= \frac{-2x^2 + 13x + 25}{x^2 + x - 20}$$

Note $x \neq 4, -5$.

c. $$\frac{x-2}{x+5} - \frac{x+1}{x-5} + \frac{x}{x^2 - 25} = \frac{x-2}{x+5} - \frac{x+1}{x-5} + \frac{x}{(x+5)(x-5)}$$
$$= \frac{(x-5)(x-2) - (x+5)(x+1) + (1)(x)}{(x-5)(x+5)}$$
$$= \frac{(x^2 - 7x + 10) - (x^2 + 6x + 5) + x}{x^2 - 25}$$
$$= \frac{-12x + 5}{x^2 - 25}$$

Note $x \neq 5, -5$.

Often, in arithmetic problems like the one at the right, you can save yourself extra work by simplifying the fractions before adding or subtracting. The same concept applies in adding and subtracting rational expressions.

$$\frac{5}{15} - \frac{12}{24} = \frac{1}{3} - \frac{1}{2}$$
$$= \frac{2-3}{6}$$
$$= -\frac{1}{6}$$

EXAMPLE 5: Add or subtract.

$$\frac{5x}{x^2 - 3x} - \frac{x^2 + 2x - 3}{x^2 + 3x - 4} = \frac{5x}{x(x-3)} - \frac{(x+3)(x-1)}{(x-1)(x+4)}$$
$$= \frac{5}{x-3} - \frac{x+3}{x+4}$$
$$= \frac{5(x+4) - (x-3)(x+3)}{(x-3)(x+4)}$$
$$= \frac{-x^2 + 5x + 29}{x^2 + x - 12}$$

Note $x \neq 0, 3, 1, -4$.

EXERCISE 2-12

A **1.** Add or subtract.

a. $\frac{2x}{3} - \frac{5x}{8} + \frac{5}{6}$ **b.** $\frac{4p}{5} - \frac{3p}{4} + \frac{3}{10}$

c. $\frac{h-3}{6} + \frac{2h+4}{3} - \frac{3h+1}{4}$ **d.** $\frac{4x-1}{9} + \frac{2x+1}{3} - \frac{3x-1}{6}$

e. $\frac{3b-1}{15} + \frac{4b-1}{12} - \frac{2b+3}{10} - \frac{b-1}{4} + \frac{b+3}{5}$ **f.** $\frac{2a+6}{4} - \frac{2a-2}{6} + \frac{2a-3}{5}$

2. Find the LCD.

a. $\frac{3}{5a^4b^2} - \frac{2}{10a^3b^3}$ **b.** $\frac{3}{8xy^4} - \frac{5}{12x^3y} + \frac{7}{3x^2y^2}$

c. $\frac{3}{2c-10} + \frac{5}{3c+15}$ **d.** $\frac{5}{m^2+2m-3} - \frac{3}{m^2+4m+3}$

3. Add or subtract.

a. $\frac{5}{3x} - \frac{5}{6y}$ **b.** $\frac{3}{a} - \frac{4}{b} + \frac{5}{c}$ **c.** $\frac{3}{10x^2y} - \frac{7}{15xy^2} + \frac{5}{6x^3y^3}$

d. $\frac{3}{7e^4f} + \frac{5}{14e^3f^2} - \frac{7}{4e^4f^3}$ **e.** $\frac{s+t}{2s} - \frac{s-t}{5t}$ **f.** $\frac{x-3}{4x} - \frac{x+7}{8x}$

4. Add or subtract.

a. $\frac{3}{x-4} - \frac{2}{x+5}$ **b.** $\frac{2b}{b+3} - \frac{3b}{b+2}$ **c.** $\frac{4}{x-5} - \frac{2}{5-x}$

d. $\frac{7}{y-3} + \frac{4}{3-y}$ **e.** $\frac{5}{x+3} - \frac{4}{x-3}$ **f.** $\frac{3d}{d-5} + \frac{2}{d+5}$

g. $\frac{m}{m-4} + \frac{4}{4-m}$ **h.** $\frac{3}{2x} - \frac{5}{2x+1}$ **i.** $\frac{3x}{5x+1} + \frac{2}{5x}$

j. $\frac{2}{3x-1} - \frac{4}{7x}$ **k.** $\frac{6}{3k+15} - \frac{8}{2k-10}$ **l.** $\frac{4}{6z} + \frac{10}{10z-25}$

B **5.** Add or subtract.

a. $\frac{3x-4}{x+3} - \frac{2x+1}{x-5}$ **b.** $\frac{5x-4}{3x-1} + \frac{2x+3}{4x+1}$ **c.** $\frac{6x-5}{3x+1} - \frac{4x+5}{2x-1}$

d. $\frac{6x+3}{4x-3} + \frac{2x+6}{3-4x}$ **e.** $\frac{2x+1}{2x-1} + \frac{2x+1}{1-2x}$ **f.** $\frac{3x}{3x-1} + \frac{1}{1-3x}$

6. Add or subtract.

a. $\frac{3x}{4x-5} - \frac{2}{4x+5} + \frac{5}{16x^2-25}$ **b.** $\frac{5}{2p-3} - \frac{2p}{2p+3} + \frac{4}{9-4p^2}$

c. $\frac{y}{3y-5} - \frac{1}{3y+5} + \frac{10}{25-9y^2}$ **d.** $\frac{2x}{3x-1} - \frac{2}{2x+5} - \frac{3}{6x^2+13x-5}$

e. $\frac{3x}{2x-5} - \frac{1}{x+1} - \frac{x}{2x^2-3x-5}$ **f.** $\frac{5}{4a+1} - \frac{6a}{a-3} + \frac{25a^2}{4a^2-11a-3}$

7. Simplify and state any restrictions on the variables.

a. $\frac{5b + 15}{b^2 + 5b + 6} - \frac{4b + 4}{b^2 - 3b + 2}$ **b.** $\frac{2x^2 + 6x}{2x^3 + 4x^2 - 6x} + \frac{3x^2 + 15x}{3x^3 + 18x^2 + 15x}$

c. $\frac{z^2 - 9}{z^2 - z - 12} - \frac{z^2 + 2z - 8}{z^2 + z - 6}$ **d.** $\frac{4x^2 - 9}{6x^2 - 13x + 6} - \frac{5 + 24x - 5x^2}{15x^2 - 7x - 2}$

e. $\frac{25x^2 - 20x + 4}{15x^2 - 11x + 2} - \frac{3x^2 + 17x + 10}{5 - 14x - 3x^2}$ **f.** $\frac{2g^2 - 10g}{25 - g^2} - \frac{2g^2 - g - 3}{9 - 12g + 4g^2}$

8. Simplify and state any restrictions on the variables.

a. $\frac{x^2 - xy - 2y^2}{x^2 + 3xy + 2y^2} - \frac{x^2 + xy - 2y^2}{x^2 - 3xy + 2y^2}$ **b.** $\frac{x^2 - 9y^2}{x^2 - 6xy + 9y^2} + \frac{3x^2 + 2xy - y^2}{3x^2 + 5xy - 2y^2}$

C **9.** Add or subtract.

a. $\frac{5}{c^2 - 3c + 2} + \frac{2}{c^2 - 5c + 6} - \frac{3}{c^2 - 4c + 3}$

b. $\frac{4}{d^2 - 9d + 18} - \frac{3}{d^2 + 2d - 15} - \frac{1}{d^2 - d - 30}$

c. $\frac{1}{x + 2} - \frac{1}{(x + 2)(x + 3)} + \frac{4}{(x + 2)(x + 3)(x + 4)}$

d. $\frac{n}{n^2 + 3n + 2} - \frac{2}{n^2 + 5n + 6} + \frac{4}{n^2 + 4n + 3}$

e. $\frac{xy - 6 + 3x - 2y}{x^2y^2 - 9x^2 - 4y^2 + 36} + \frac{xy + 3x}{xy - 6 + 2y - 3x} - \frac{xy + 5y}{xy - 15 - 3x + 5y}$

10. Find values of a and b that make the following equations true.

a. $\frac{a}{x + 1} + \frac{b}{x - 1} = \frac{3x + 1}{x^2 - 1}$ **b.** $\frac{a}{2y - 1} - \frac{b}{y + 2} = \frac{4y + 3}{2y^2 + 3y - 2}$

EXTRA

Odd Predictions

Inductive reasoning involves looking for a pattern in a series of observations, then making a prediction based on the pattern. Describe the pattern in the following series of calculations.

$1 = 1$ The first odd integer.
$1 + 3 = 4$ The sum of the first 2 odd integers.
$1 + 3 + 5 = 9$ The sum of the first 3 odd integers.
$1 + 3 + 5 + 7 = 16$ The sum of the first 4 odd integers.

Use the pattern to predict the sum of the first 53 odd integers; the first 67 odd integers.

2-13 Solving Equations Involving Rational Expressions

In Unit 1, equations containing fractions were solved by multiplying both sides of the equation by the lowest common denominator. If some denominators contain variables—that is, if the equation contains rational expressions—handle the question in the same way.

$$\frac{x+2}{5} - \frac{x-3}{4} = 1$$
$$20\left(\frac{x+2}{5} - \frac{x-3}{4}\right) = (1)\ 20$$
$$4(x+2) - 5(x-3) = 20$$
$$4x + 8 - 5x + 15 = 20$$
$$-x + 23 = 20$$
$$-x = -3$$
$$x = 3$$

EXAMPLE 1: Solve the given equation and check the solution.

$$\frac{3}{x+1} - 2 = \frac{5}{x+1}$$

Note that $x \neq -1$.

$$\frac{5}{x+1} - \frac{3}{x+1} = -2$$
$$\frac{2}{x+1} = -2$$
$$(x+1)\left[\frac{2}{x+1}\right] = -2(x+1)$$
$$2 = -2x - 2$$
$$x = -2$$

Check:

$$\text{L.S.} = \frac{3}{x+1} - 2 = \frac{3}{-1} - 2 = -3 - 2 = -5$$

$$\text{R.S.} = \frac{5}{x+1} = \frac{5}{-1} = -5 = \text{L.S.} \checkmark$$

Restricting the variable to avoid division by zero may lead to an interesting situation, as described in example 2.

EXAMPLE 2: Solve. $\frac{2}{x-2} - 1 = \frac{x}{x-2}$

Note that $x \neq 2$.

$$\frac{2}{x-2} - \frac{x}{x-2} = 1$$
$$\frac{2-x}{x-2} = 1$$
$$(x-2)\left[\frac{2-x}{x-2}\right] = x - 2$$
$$2 - x = x - 2$$
$$2x = 4$$
$$x = 2$$

The only value that might work in this question is $x = 2$ but, for the equation to be defined, $x \neq 2$. There is, then, no *real* solution to this equation.
The solution set is the empty set { } or ϕ (phi).

EXERCISE 2-13

A **1.** Solve.

a. $\frac{x}{6} - \frac{1}{4} = \frac{x}{12} + \frac{1}{6}$

b. $\frac{5y}{18} + \frac{5}{9} = \frac{1}{18} + \frac{y}{9}$

c. $\frac{d+3}{6} = \frac{1}{2} + \frac{d}{3}$

d. $\frac{2z}{5} - \frac{z}{3} = \frac{5}{6}$

e. $\frac{x+2}{5} - \frac{x-3}{2} = \frac{x-5}{10}$

f. $\frac{2m+3}{8} - \frac{3m+1}{4} = \frac{5}{6} - \frac{5m-1}{3}$

2. Solve.

a. $\frac{5}{b} - \frac{1}{3} = \frac{3}{b}$

b. $\frac{5}{3x} + 1 = \frac{23}{3x}$

c. $\frac{3}{2k} - 1 = 3 - \frac{5}{2k}$

d. $\frac{3}{2y} - 1 = \frac{5}{y} + 2$

e. $\frac{3}{x} + 5 = \frac{3}{x} - 4$

f. $\frac{3}{p} - \frac{1}{4} = \frac{5}{2p} + \frac{1}{3}$

g. $\frac{3}{5w} - \frac{1}{3} = \frac{7}{15w} - 1$

h. $\frac{3}{4x} - \frac{5}{6} = \frac{1}{3x} - \frac{5}{12}$

i. $\frac{3}{x} - 1 = 1 - \frac{3}{x}$

B **3.** Solve.

a. $\frac{5}{x+2} - 1 = \frac{-1}{x+2}$

b. $\frac{1}{5-z} + 1 = \frac{9}{5-z}$

c. $\frac{3}{t-3} - 3 = \frac{t}{t-3}$

d. $\frac{4}{x+1} - 2 = \frac{x}{x+1}$

e. $\frac{9}{s+1} + \frac{s}{s+1} = 5 + \frac{4}{s+1}$

f. $\frac{3}{h+4} - \frac{h}{h+4} = \frac{7}{h+4} - 2$

g. $\frac{2x}{x-3} - \frac{3}{x-3} = 1 + \frac{5}{x-3}$

h. $\frac{3r}{r-6} - 5 = \frac{5r}{r-6} + 1$

4. Solve.

a. $\frac{3w}{w-2} - \frac{2}{3} = \frac{5}{w-2} + 1$

b. $\frac{2f}{2f-5} - 3 = \frac{5}{2f-5}$

c. $\frac{2}{x-4} + \frac{2}{3} = \frac{x}{x-4} + \frac{1}{2}$

d. $\frac{1}{x+4} - 1 = \frac{x}{x+4} - \frac{3}{4}$

e. $\frac{y}{y+3} - \frac{2}{3} + \frac{3}{y+3} = 0$

f. $\frac{9}{2x+3} - \frac{2}{15} = \frac{x}{2x+3} + \frac{1}{2x+3}$

g. $\frac{m}{2m-1} - \frac{3}{2m-1} = \frac{1}{2}$

h. $\frac{3x}{2x+1} - \frac{2}{2x+1} - \frac{3}{4} = 0$

C **5.** Solve.

a. $\frac{x}{x+5} - \frac{3}{x-2} = 1$

b. $\frac{x}{x-4} - 1 = \frac{2}{3x+1}$

c. $\frac{x}{x-4} - \frac{1}{x-4} = 4$

d. $\frac{3}{2x-5} + \frac{2x}{2x+5} = 1$

2-14 Complex Fractions

Between any two rational numbers, no matter how close together they are, there is another rational number. This is a remarkable property of the number system that is easy to prove. We just have to remember that the average of two numbers always lies between them.

EXAMPLE 1: Find a rational number between $\frac{1}{7}$ and $\frac{1}{8}$.

Find the average $\dfrac{\frac{1}{7}+\frac{1}{8}}{2} = \dfrac{\left(\frac{1}{7}+\frac{1}{8}\right)}{\left(\frac{2}{1}\right)} \times \dfrac{56}{56}$ Multiply numerator and denominator by the L.C.D.

$$= \frac{8+7}{112}$$

$$= \frac{15}{112}$$

Use your calculator to check that $\frac{1}{8} < \frac{15}{112} < \frac{1}{7}$

Mathematicians say that the rational numbers are **dense**.

The same approach can be used to simplify complex rational expressions.

EXAMPLE 2: Simplify the following

a. $$\frac{\frac{x}{y}-\frac{y}{x}}{\frac{1}{y}-\frac{1}{x}} = \frac{\left(\frac{x}{y}-\frac{y}{x}\right)}{\left(\frac{1}{y}-\frac{1}{x}\right)} \times \frac{xy}{xy}$$

$$= \frac{x^2-y^2}{x-y}$$

$$= \frac{\cancel{(x-y)}(x+y)}{\cancel{(x-y)}}$$

$$= x+y$$

b. $$\frac{x+3+\frac{x-x^2}{x-4}}{x+\frac{4x}{x-4}} = \frac{\left(\frac{x+3}{1}+\frac{x-x^2}{x-4}\right)}{\left(\frac{x}{1}+\frac{4x}{x-4}\right)} \times \frac{x-4}{x-4}$$

$$= \frac{x^2-x-12+x-x^2}{x^2-4x+4x} = \frac{-12}{x^2}$$

c. $$\frac{\frac{3}{x}+\frac{5}{x+1}}{1-\frac{x}{x+1}} = \frac{\left(\frac{3}{x}+\frac{5}{x+1}\right)}{\left(1-\frac{x}{x+1}\right)} \times \frac{x(x+1)}{x(x+1)}$$

$$= \frac{3x+3+5x}{x^2+x-x^2} = \frac{8x+3}{x}$$

EXERCISE 2-14

A 1. Find the average of each of the following pairs of rational numbers.

a. $\frac{1}{6}$ and $\frac{1}{8}$ **b.** $\frac{2}{3}$ and $\frac{1}{2}$ **c.** $\frac{3}{5}$ and $-\frac{1}{3}$ **d.** $-\frac{2}{5}$ and $-\frac{5}{6}$

2. Simplify.

a. $\dfrac{3-\frac{3}{4}}{3+\frac{2}{3}}$ **b.** $\dfrac{\frac{5}{6}-1}{\frac{2}{3}-2}$ **c.** $\dfrac{2-\frac{3}{5}}{\frac{3}{10}-1}$ **d.** $\dfrac{\frac{3}{4}-\frac{1}{3}}{\frac{2}{3}+\frac{5}{6}}$

3. Simplify.

a. $\dfrac{\frac{2x}{3}-\frac{x}{2}}{\frac{5x}{6}+\frac{x}{3}}$ **b.** $\dfrac{\frac{5a}{2}-a}{\frac{3a}{5}+a}$ **c.** $\dfrac{\frac{x-3}{2}+\frac{x+1}{6}}{\frac{x+1}{4}+\frac{x-3}{3}}$ **d.** $\dfrac{\frac{4x-3}{10}-\frac{2x+5}{6}}{\frac{3x+1}{5}-\frac{2x-1}{3}}$

B 4. Simplify.

a. $\dfrac{\frac{3}{2x}-\frac{1}{3x}}{1+\frac{5}{6x}}$ **b.** $\dfrac{\frac{4}{x}-\frac{1}{3x}}{\frac{3}{5x}-\frac{1}{15x}}$ **c.** $\dfrac{\frac{3}{y}+\frac{1}{x}}{\frac{x}{y}+\frac{y}{x}}$ **d.** $\dfrac{\frac{2x}{5y}-\frac{3x}{4y}}{\frac{x}{2y}+\frac{x}{10y}}$

e. $\dfrac{3-\frac{3x}{x+2}}{3+\frac{3x}{x+2}}$ **f.** $\dfrac{\frac{3x}{2x+1}-1}{\frac{3}{2x+1}+1}$ **g.** $\dfrac{\frac{3x}{x-1}+1}{\frac{3x}{x-1}-1}$ **h.** $\dfrac{\frac{12x^2}{3x-1}-4x}{\frac{x}{3x-1}+x}$

5. Simplify the following.

a. $\dfrac{\frac{3}{x}-\frac{4}{x+1}}{\frac{5}{x+1}-\frac{2}{x}}$ **b.** $\dfrac{\frac{3x}{x+2}-\frac{2}{x}}{\frac{2x}{x+2}+\frac{3}{x}}$ **c.** $\dfrac{\frac{2}{2x-3}-\frac{4}{3x}}{\frac{3}{2x-3}-\frac{2}{3x}}$ **d.** $\dfrac{\frac{4}{3x+1}-\frac{5}{3x}}{\frac{5}{3x+1}+\frac{4}{3x}}$

e. $\dfrac{\frac{3y}{12y+1}-\frac{y}{4}}{\frac{4y}{12y+1}-\frac{y}{4}}$ **f.** $\dfrac{\frac{x}{3x+1}-\frac{5}{10x}}{\frac{1}{3x+1}+\frac{3}{2x}}$ **g.** $\dfrac{\frac{2x}{2x-5}-\frac{3}{6x}}{\frac{3x}{2x-5}+\frac{4}{8x}}$ **h.** $\dfrac{\frac{3}{4x+1}-\frac{8}{6x}}{\frac{2}{4x+1}+\frac{6}{9x}}$

6. Simplify the following.

a. $\dfrac{\frac{3x}{x^2-4}-\frac{3}{x+2}}{\frac{5}{x^2-4}+\frac{3}{x-2}}$ **b.** $\dfrac{\frac{2x}{4x^2-9}-\frac{x}{2x-3}}{\frac{3}{4x^2-9}+\frac{1}{2x+3}}$ **c.** $\dfrac{\frac{3x}{x^2+x-12}-\frac{4x}{x-3}}{\frac{2}{x^2+x-12}+\frac{3}{x+4}}$

2-15 Solving Quadratic Equations

A small neighbourhood park is to have an area of 1400 m^2. The length of the park is to be 5 m more than the width.

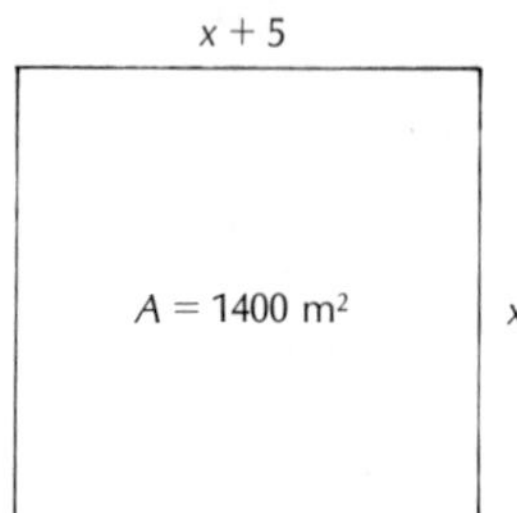

If the width is represented by x, then the length can be represented by $x + 5$.

Since $A = 1400$, then $x(x + 5) = 1400$, or $x^2 + 5x = 1400$.

This equation differs from those you have solved so far, in that it contains a term with degree 2. A second-degree equation such as this is called a **quadratic equation**. You can solve quadratic equations by first observing the following fact:

> Given that $ab = 0$, it follows that $a = 0$, or $b = 0$, or both.
> Similarly, if $(a + m)(b + n) = 0$, then $(a + m) = 0$ or $(b + n) = 0$, or both.

EXAMPLE 1: Solve $x^2 - x - 12 = 0$.

$x^2 - x - 12 = 0$

$(x - 4)(x + 3) = 0$ — Factoring the left side gives a product equal to zero. At least one factor must be zero.

$\therefore\ x - 4 = 0$ or $x + 3 = 0$.

That is, $x = 4$ or $x = -3$. — On your own, check whether $4^2 - 4 - 12 = 0$.

EXAMPLE 2: Solve $x^2 + 5x = 1400$ to find the dimensions of the park described above.

$x^2 + 5x = 1400$ — The right side must be zero in order to apply the property.

$x^2 + 5x - 1400 = 0$

$(x + 40)(x - 35) = 0$

$\therefore\ x + 40 = 0$ or $x - 35 = 0$

That is, $x = -40$ or $x = 35$

Since the length must be positive, $x = 35$.
Then $x + 5 = 40$.

The dimensions of the park will be 35 m by 40 m.

A quadratic equation generally has two solutions.

EXAMPLE 3: **a.** Solve $4x^2 - 25 = 0$.

$4x^2 - 25 = 0$

$(2x - 5)(2x + 5) = 0$

$\therefore\ 2x - 5 = 0$ or $2x + 5 = 0$

$2x = 5$ $\qquad$ $2x = -5$

$x = \frac{5}{2}$ $\qquad$ $x = -\frac{5}{2}$

b. Solve $9x^2 - 24x + 16 = 0$.

$$9x^2 - 24x + 16 = 0$$
$$(3x - 4)(3x - 4) = 0$$

$$\therefore 3x - 4 = 0 \quad \text{or} \quad 3x - 4 = 0$$
$$3x = 4 \qquad\qquad 3x = 4$$
$$x = \frac{4}{3} \qquad\qquad x = \frac{4}{3}$$

The equation in part **b** has two equal solutions, sometimes called a **double root**. Always give both solutions when solving quadratic equations.

A useful method of solving quadratic equations is called **completing the square**. For a quadratic equation in the form:

$$ax^2 + bx = c$$

we try to find a perfect square n such that

$$ax^2 + bx + n$$

is a perfect square.

Solve: $x^2 - 6x - 16 = 0$

Write: $x^2 - 6x = 16$

Add 9 to both sides of the equation:

$$x^2 - 6x + 9 = 16 + 9$$
$$\therefore (x - 3)^2 = 25$$
$$x - 3 = \pm 5$$

If $x - 3 = +5$, then $x = 8$.
If $x - 3 = -5$, then $x = -2$.

EXERCISE 2-15

A **1.** Solve for x.

a. $(x - 3)(x + 5) = 0$ **b.** $(2x + 3)(3x - 1) = 0$ **c.** $x(x + 5) - 3(x + 5) = 0$

d. $x(x + 3) = 0$ **e.** $3x(x - 3) = 0$ **f.** $-2x(x - 2) = 0$

g. $(3 - x)(5 + x) = 0$ **h.** $(5 - 2x)(3 + 5x) = 0$ **i.** $(5x + 3)(5 - 3x) = 0$

2. Solve.

a. $x^2 - 8x + 12 = 0$ **b.** $x^2 - 49 = 0$ **c.** $12x^2 - 27 = 0$

d. $x^2 + 18x + 81 = 0$ **e.** $x^2 + 11x = 42$ **f.** $x^2 - 7x = 8$

g. $25x^2 - 64 = 0$ **h.** $x^2 - 7x = 30$ **i.** $24 - 2x - x^2 = 0$

3. Solve.

a. $xy - 5y + 3x - 15 = 0$ **b.** $2x^2 - x = 3$ **c.** $ab + 6a - 3b - 18 = 0$

d. $3x^2 + 14x = -15$ **e.** $xy + 6 - 2y - 3x = 0$ **f.** $4x^2 + 37x + 9 = 0$

g. $6xy - 3 + 2x - 9y = 0$ **h.** $5x^2 - 8x + 3 = 0$ **i.** $15x^2 = 3x$

B **4.** Solve.

a. $6m^2 - 25m + 4 = 0$ **b.** $2t^2 - 17t + 8 = 0$ **c.** $10m^2 + 19m = 15$

d. $48y^2 - 75 = 0$ **e.** $4z^2 + z = 60$ **f.** $25 - 30a + 9a^2 = 0$

g. $36x^2 - 24x + 3 = 0$ **h.** $5g^2 - 7g = 0$ **i.** $2x(x - 4) = 3(x - 4)$

5. Solve.

a. $(x - 7)^2 - 16 = 0$ **b.** $(2x - 7)^2 - 25 = 0$ **c.** $9 - (2x - 3)^2 = 0$

d. $36 - (w - 3)^2 = 0$ **e.** $(5t - 2)^2 - (2t + 1)^2 = 0$ **f.** $x^4 - 29x^2 + 100 = 0$

g. $d^3 + 2d^2 - 15d = 0$ **h.** $18x^3 - 50x = 0$ **i.** $15xy + 3x = 25y + 5$

j. $2x^3 - 3x^2 - 2x + 3 = 0$ **k.** $b^2 - 64 - 12b + 36 = 0$ **l.** $69xy - 45x^2y - 12y = 0$

6. Solve.

a. $a + \frac{1}{a + 1} = \frac{3}{a + 1}$ **b.** $b - \frac{1}{b + 2} = \frac{7}{b + 2}$ **c.** $\frac{2x}{2x + 1} - 4 = 2x$

d. $\frac{x}{x + 1} - x = 4$ **e.** $y + \frac{y}{y + 1} + \frac{1}{y + 1} = 0$ **f.** $\frac{1}{3k - 1} + 4 = \frac{6}{3k + 2}$

g. $w - \frac{12}{w + 2} = \frac{6w}{w + 2}$ **h.** $4 - \frac{6}{k + 2} + \frac{1}{k - 1} = 0$ **i.** $\frac{x}{2} + \frac{x}{x + 2} + \frac{2}{x + 2} =$

7. A rectangular lot is 10 m longer than it is wide. If the total area is 600 m^2, find the dimensions of the lot.

8. One leg of a right-angled triangle is 7 cm shorter than the other. If the hypotenuse measures 17 cm, find the lengths of the two legs.

9. A rectangular box is 7 cm deep and has a length that is 1 cm more than its width. If its volume is 210 cm^3, find the dimensions of the box.

10. The length of a rectangular field is 10 m longer than twice its width. Its total area is 2100 m^2. A river runs along the length of the field, so that only three sides need to be fenced. How much fencing is needed?

C **11.** Solve for all real values of the variable.

a. $x^2y^2 + 4 - 4x^2 - y^2 = 0$ **b.** $x^4 - 13x^2 = -36$ **c.** $x^4 - 21x^2 = 100$

d. $4x^4 - 25x^2 + 36 = 0$ **e.** $4x^4 - 25x^3 + 25x^2 = 0$ **f.** $(x^2 - 4)^2 - 5(x^2 - 4) = 0$

12. Solve the following by "completing the square".

a. $x^2 - 8x + 15 = 0$ **b.** $x^2 + 6x - 72 = 0$ **c.** $x^2 + 10x + 9 = 0$

d. $x^2 - 4x = 32$ **e.** $x^2 + 2x = 99$ **f.** $x^2 + 12x = 0$

g. $4x^2 + 4x = 3$ **h.** $9x^2 - 12x = 5$ **i.** $x^2 + 2x = 3$

Historical Note

Primes and Squares

Pierre Fermat (1601-1665) was a French mathematician who did much of the early work in number theory. Fermat proved that any prime number that can be written in the form $4x + 1$, $x \in \mathbf{Z}$ can be written as the sum of two squares. For example $4(13) + 1 = 53 = 49 + 4$. Find other primes less than 50 that can be written as the sum of two squares.

Historical Note

Blaise Pascal

Blaise Pascal, born in France in 1623, was a mathematical prodigy. By the age of 16, he had written a complete manuscript on quadratic relations; by 19, he had invented and built a calculating machine, the forerunner of the pre-electronic cash register. Perhaps one of Pascal's most interesting areas of mathematical study was probability and its application to games of chance.

Pascal developed a triangular array of numbers, often called **Pascal's Triangle**, that has applications in both probability and the algebra of polynomials.

Pascal's Triangle is constructed by placing a 1 in the top row, which is considered to be row 0, and two 1's in the next row. Subsequent rows are found by placing a 1 at the beginning and end of the row, and filling in blank spots by adding the numbers above and to either side of the blank.

Row Number		Totals
$n = 0$	1	1
$n = 1$	1 1	2
$n = 2$	1 2 1	4
$n = 3$	1 3 3 1	8
$n = 4$	1 4 6 4 1	16
$n = 5$	1 5 10 10 5 1	32
$n = 6$	1 6 15 20 15 6 1	64

Suppose a coin is tossed 4 times. What is the probability that it will land heads all 4 times? 3 times? twice? once? not at all? The answers are found in row four of Pascal's Triangle, which indicates a total of 16 possible outcomes. Reading the numbers from left to right.

$P(4 \text{ heads}) = \frac{1}{16}$; $P(3 \text{ heads}) = \frac{4}{16}$; $P(2 \text{ heads}) = \frac{6}{16}$; $P(1 \text{ head}) = \frac{4}{16}$; $P(0 \text{ heads}) = \frac{1}{16}$

Pascal's Triangle can be used for *any* question of repeated trials where the probability of each individual outcome is $\frac{1}{2}$.

Another application of Pascal's Triangle is in the expansion of binomials.

$$(a + b)^0 = 1$$
$$(a + b)^1 = 1a + 1b$$
$$(a + b)^2 = 1a^2 + 2ab + 1b^2$$
$$(a + b)^3 = 1a^3 + 3a^2b + 3ab^2 + 1b^3$$

The coefficients of the terms, when arranged in descending powers of a, correspond to the numbers in successive rows of Pascal's Triangle.

Extend Pascal's Triangle to expand the following.

1. $(a + b)^5$ **2.** $(a + b)^6$

Review

1. Simplify.

   a. $2x + 3(5x - 1)$
   b. $3(4x - 5)^2$
   c. $3x^2y^3(2xy + 4x^2y - 3xy^3)$
   d. $(5x - 3)(2x + 7)$
   e. $3(2x - 1)^2 + 2(x - 5)(x + 7)$
   f. $(6x^2y^4 - 9xy^3 + 12x^2y^2) \div (3xy)$
   g. $(2x^4 - 5x^3 - 5x^2 + 3x + 9) \div (x - 3)$
   h. $(6x^3 - 26x + 4) \div (2x - 4)$

2. Find the perimeter or area as indicated.

   a.

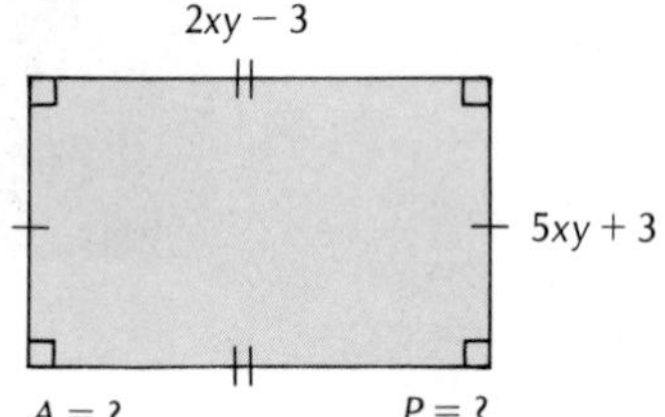

   b.

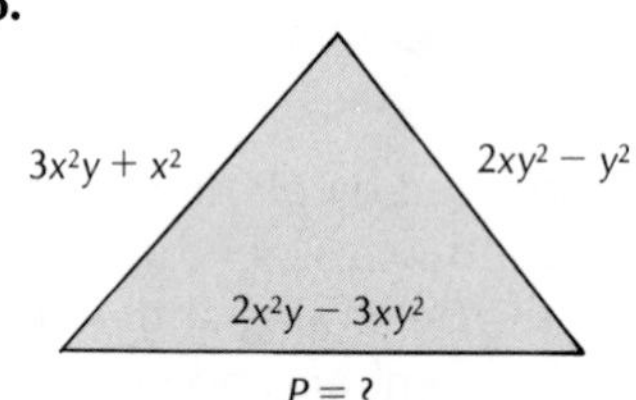

   c.

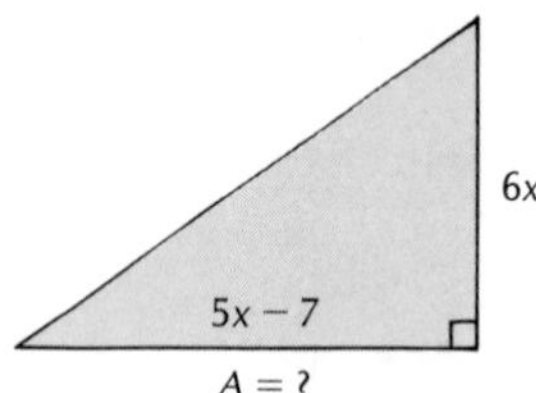

   d.

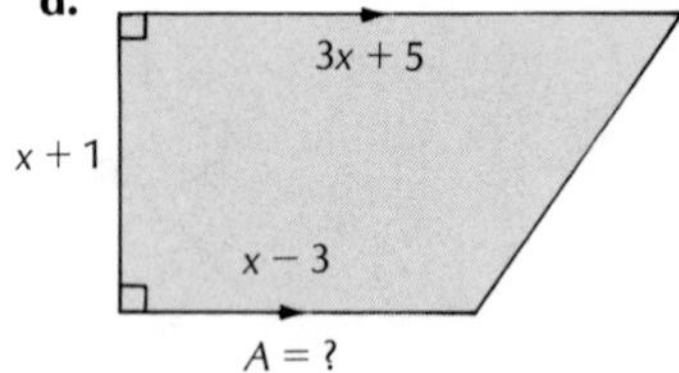

3. Factor fully.

   a. $20a^2 - 45$
   b. $25x^2 - 49y^2 + 28y - 4$
   c. $25x^2 - 26x + 1$
   d. $30b^2 + 71b - 24$
   e. $9w^4 - 42w^2 + 49$
   f. $(3x - 1)^2 - 15x + 5$
   g. $3x^2y - 5 - y + 15x^2$
   h. $36m^2 - 60m + 25$
   i. $(4k - 1)^2 - (2k + 5)^2$
   j. $6x^2 - 3xy - 30y^2$
   k. $4x^2y^2 + 7xy - 2$
   l. $2s^2 + 14s^2t - 36s^2t^2$

4. Factor.

   a. $4x^3 + 32y^3$
   b. $64k^6 - 8$
   c. $(2m - 2)^3 - (3 + m)^3$
   d. $27d^3 + 125c^3b^6$

5. Simplify. State all necessary restrictions on the variables.

   a. $\dfrac{2x^2 + 6x}{x^2 + 9x + 18}$
   b. $\dfrac{16 - 6x - x^2}{12 - 4x - x^2}$
   c. $\dfrac{x^2 - 5x - 24}{x^2 - 3x - 18} \times \dfrac{x^2 - 10x + 24}{x^2 - 16}$
   d. $\dfrac{x^2 + 12x - 28}{x^2 - 12x + 20} \div \dfrac{x^2 + 9x + 8}{x^2 - 9x - 10}$
   e. $\dfrac{2x^2 - 10x}{x^2 - 2x - 15} \times \dfrac{xy - 3x + 3y - 9}{4y^2 - 12y}$
   f. $\dfrac{2x^2 - 5x - 3}{2x^2 + 19x + 17} \div \dfrac{9 - x^2}{15 - x - 2x^2}$

6. Simplify.

a. $\frac{5x-3}{12} - \frac{x+5}{8} - \frac{2x-1}{6}$

b. $\frac{3}{y+5} - \frac{5}{y+1}$

c. $\frac{5}{2z^3w^2} - \frac{3}{5z^2w^3} + \frac{7}{10z^3w^3}$

d. $\frac{2}{x-4} - \frac{3}{x+5} + \frac{1}{x^2+x-20}$

e. $\frac{4}{3x+1} + \frac{5}{1-3x} + \frac{2}{9x^2-1}$

f. $\frac{h-5}{h+5} - \frac{h+5}{h-5}$

g. $\frac{3r^2}{r^2-5r} - \frac{r^2-2r-8}{r^2-r-12}$

h. $\frac{x+3}{x-3} - \frac{x-3}{x+3} + \frac{36}{x^2-9}$

7. Find each missing dimension.

a.

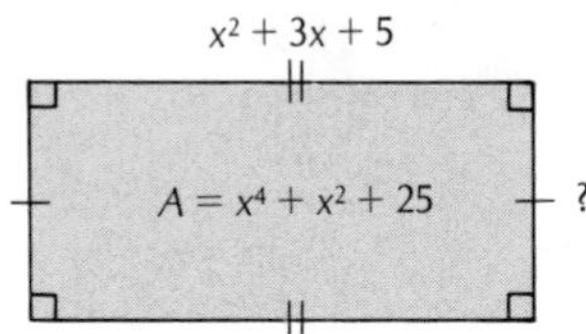

b.

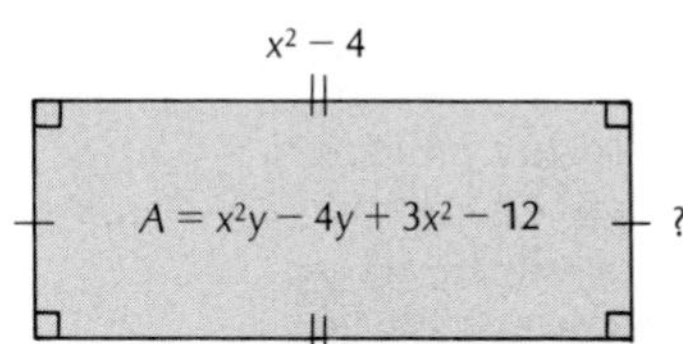

c.

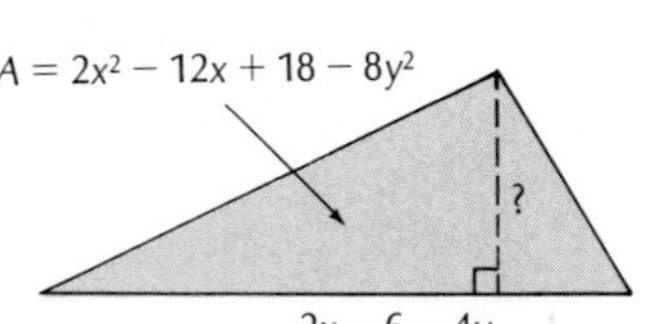

d.

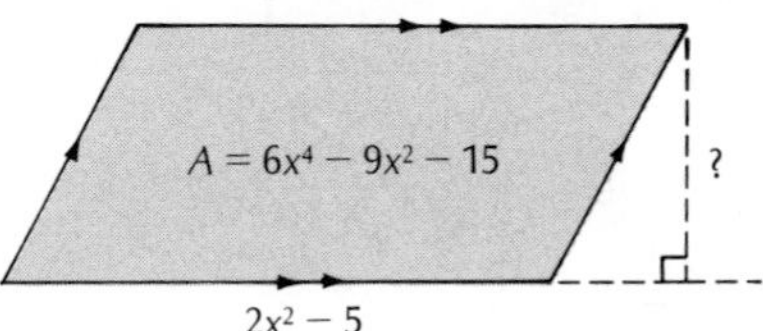

8. Solve.

a. $\frac{3x}{2} - \frac{1}{3} = \frac{5x}{6} + 1$

b. $\frac{3}{4x} - \frac{1}{2} = \frac{5}{8x} + 1$

c. $\frac{7}{x+3} - 4 = \frac{3}{x+3}$

d. $\frac{3x}{x-2} - 2 = \frac{6}{x-2}$

e. $\frac{5x}{x+3} - 2 = \frac{2x}{x+3}$

f. $\frac{x}{x-3} - \frac{1}{x+2} = 1$

9. Simplify.

a. $\dfrac{\frac{3}{2} - \frac{5}{9}}{\frac{5}{6} + \frac{2}{3}}$

b. $\dfrac{\frac{2x+3}{3} - \frac{5x-1}{9}}{\frac{x-1}{6} + \frac{3x+1}{2}}$

c. $\dfrac{\frac{5x}{5x-1} - \frac{1}{5x-1}}{\frac{5x}{5x-1} - 1}$

10. Solve.

a. $2g(g-3) = 0$

b. $(3x-5)(x+2) = 0$

c. $12y + 9y^2 = 0$

d. $b^2 - 9b + 8 = 0$

e. $36x - 25x^3 = 0$

f. $(k-8)^2 - 25 = 0$

g. $(x-3)^2 - 6x + 18 = 0$

h. $(4x-1)^2 = (x+3)^2$

i. $d^4 - 17d^2 + 16 = 0$

11. A rectangular backyard pool is 2 m longer than twice its width. If the surface area is 60 m², find the dimensions of the pool.

12. A right-angled triangle with hypotenuse 25 cm has one leg 10 cm longer than twice the other. Find the dimensions of the triangle.

13. A square garden has an area 25 m² greater than a rectangular garden. The second garden is 1 m longer and 3 m narrower than the square garden. Find the dimensions of each garden.

Test

Unit 2

1. Simplify.
   a. $2t(t - 3) - 3(2t + 1)$
   b. $3x - 4(2x + 5)$
   c. $2a^2b(3ab^2 + 2ab - 1)$
   d. $5mn(3mn - 1)$
   e. $(10x^4y^2 - 35x^3y^3 + 15x^2y^4) \div (5x^2y^2)$
   f. $(2w^4 - 11w^3 + 5w^2 + 3w - 15) \div (w - 5)$
   g. $(12x^4 - 2x^3 - 17x^2 + x + 2) \div (3x + 1)$
   h. $3(2x - 5y)(2x + y) - 2(x - 3y)^2$

2. Factor fully.
   a. $x^2 - 14x + 24$
   b. $6q^2 + 13q - 15$
   c. $36x^2y^2 - 16x^2$
   d. $25x^2y^2 - 40xy + 16$
   e. $25 - (2s - 9)^2$
   f. $9v^4 - 58v^2 + 49$
   g. $20x^2y + 15xy^2 - 12x - 9y$
   h. $49x^2 - 49 - 42xy + 9y^2$

3. Find the quantity indicated.

a.

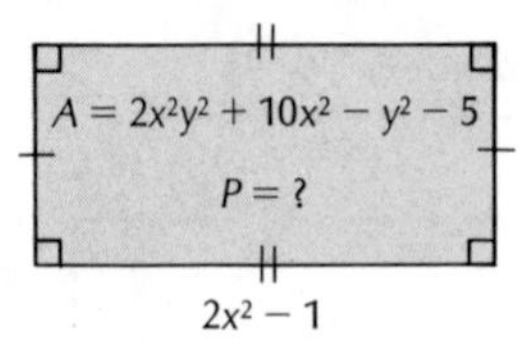

b.

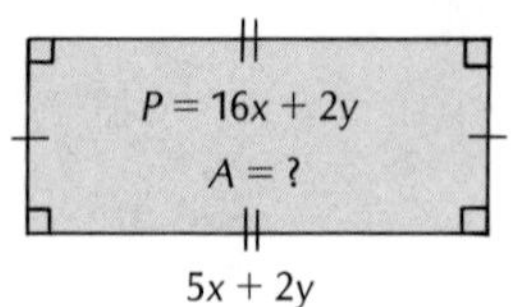

c.

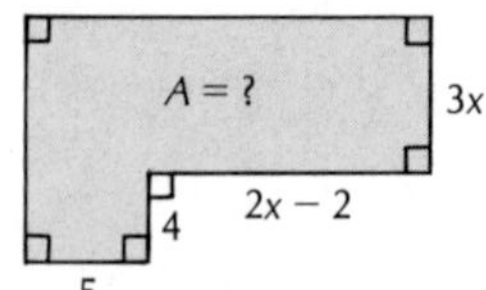

4. Simplify.
   a. $\dfrac{x^2 + x - 12}{x^2 - 8x + 15}$
   b. $\dfrac{6x^2 - 10x}{25 - 9x^2}$
   c. $\dfrac{2x^2 + 3x - 20}{x^2 - 3x - 28} \times \dfrac{x^2 - 49}{6x - 15}$
   d. $\dfrac{4x^2 - 25x + 6}{x^2 - 7x + 6} \div \dfrac{4x^2 - 47x - 12}{x^2 - 13x + 12}$
   e. $\dfrac{2x - 3}{5} - \dfrac{x + 1}{3} + \dfrac{4}{15}$
   f. $\dfrac{2x}{3x - 5} - \dfrac{1}{3x - 5}$
   g. $\dfrac{x^2 + 2x - 15}{x^2 + 3x - 18} - \dfrac{x^2 - 16}{x^2 - x - 20}$
   h. $\dfrac{5}{x + 3} - \dfrac{3}{x - 3} + \dfrac{1}{9 - x^2}$
   i. $\dfrac{\dfrac{9x}{y} - \dfrac{y}{x}}{\dfrac{3}{y} - \dfrac{1}{x}}$
   j. $\dfrac{\dfrac{2y}{x + 1} - \dfrac{3y}{2x}}{\dfrac{5y}{x + 1} + \dfrac{y}{2x}}$

5. Solve for x.
   a. $5x^2(x - 3) = 0$
   b. $(2x - 3)(2x + 5) = 0$
   c. $6x^2 - 5x = 1$
   d. $(3x - 1)^2 - 25 = 0$
   e. $12xy - 15y + 4x - 5 = 0$
   f. $36x^4 - 25x^2 + 4 = 0$
   g. $6x^3 - 27x^2 - 15x = 0$
   h. $4(2x - 3)^2 - 25 = 0$

6. In a right-angled triangle, the hypotenuse is 3 units longer than twice the length of the shortest side. The longer leg of the triangle is 3 units less than three times the length of the shortest side. Find the lengths of the sides.

7. A house has a foundation with length 6 m less than twice its width. If the total floor area is 216 m², find the dimensions of the foundation.

Cumulative Review

1. Evaluate for the given values of the variables.
   a. xyz; $x = 1, y = 2, z = 3$
   b. $s + 5r$; $s = 3, r = 2$
   c. $x^2 + 2xy + y^2$; $x = -3, y = 1$
   d. $(w + z)(w - z)$; $w = 2, z = 1$

2. Simplify.
   a. $\frac{a^3b}{a^2b^4}$
   b. $(x^2y)\frac{y^2}{x}$
   c. $(a)(a)(a)(a)(a)$
   d. $\frac{y}{y^8}$

3. Solve.
   a. $x - 3 = 5x + 9$
   b. $3(x - 5) + 5 = 5$
   c. $3y + 10 = 4(2y + 3) + 23$
   d. $9w - 3(w + 4) = w + 3$
   e. $\frac{q - 3 + 4(q + 1)}{q + 4} = 2$
   f. $a + \frac{4}{3} - \frac{2a}{3} = 0$

4. Define a variable and write an inequality or combined inequality to represent each of the following.
   a. A computer holds programs no larger than 600 K.
   b. The lowest mark in a class is 42%. The highest is 97%.
   c. Jo reads no faster than 400 words per minute.
   d. A river flows no slower than 5 km/h, and no faster than 15 km/h.
   e. A fire burns between 200°C and 500°C.
   f. The ruler cannot accurately measure lengths longer than 30 cm or smaller than 1 cm.

5. Suzy has made a scale diagram of her room that is 14.5 times smaller than real life.
   a. To what scale did Suzy draw her diagram?
   b. Given that her room is 3 m by 4 m, write an inequality to express the size of the paper she needed to draw the diagram.

6. A baker hires part-time help, increasing cake production by 2 per hour. The bakery can now produce 10 cakes in the time it previously took to make 6 cakes. How fast are cakes produced now?

7. Solve each inequality and graph the solution set on a number line.
   a. $|3x - 4| \leq 5$
   b. $5x + 4 > 3x + 7$
   c. $6x + 3 \geq 12$ or $2x - 1 < 1$
   d. $9|2x + \frac{2}{3}| \geq 9$

8. A brokerage firm charges a fixed commission on stock transactions. To keep up with inflation, it raised its commission by 1%. Before raising the commission, the firm made \$1500 on an average day. Now it makes \$2500 each day. What is the value of the stock transactions that pass through the office on a typical day?

9. Town Council plans to tear down an entire city block. One demolition company promises to complete the job in 60 days, and another promises completion within 40 days. If the city engages both companies, how long does the job take?

3 Radicals and Non-Linear Equations

3-1 Evaluating Powers with Fractional Exponents

Under ideal conditions, a population will double at fixed time intervals. For humans, this time interval might be 20 years. For some bacteria, it is one day: if there were 1 bacteria on day 0, then there would be 2 on the next day, 4 on the following day, 8 on the day after, and so on.

The graph illustrates the population growth, which can also be represented by the equation below.

$P = 2^n$ P is population size; n is number of days.

The number of bacteria after $4\frac{1}{2}$ days can be estimated from the graph to be about 23. In other words, when $n = 4.5$, 2^n or $2^{4.5}$ is about 23.

Fractional exponents *do* have a meaning. Powers with fractional exponents can be evaluated on a calculator with a power key. For instance, the keypresses shown could be used to evaluate $2^{4.5}$.

[2] [y^x] [4] [·] [5] [=]

Fractional exponents are defined so that the laws of exponents will still apply.

Since: $x^a \times x^b = x^{a+b}$

Then: $x^{\frac{1}{2}} \times x^{\frac{1}{2}} = x^{\frac{1}{2}+\frac{1}{2}}$
$= x^1$
$= x$

Since: $\sqrt{x}\,\sqrt{x} = \sqrt{x^2}$
$= x^1$

Therefore: $x^{\frac{1}{2}} = \sqrt{x}$

$\sqrt{x}$ is called a **radical**; x is the **radicand.**

Similarly, $x^{\frac{1}{3}} = \sqrt[3]{x}$, $x^{\frac{1}{4}} = \sqrt[4]{x}$, and so on.

> In general, if n is a positive integer and $x > 0$, then $x^{\frac{1}{n}} = \sqrt[n]{x}$.

The value of x *must* be restricted to positive values, since $x < 0$ could result in a contradiction. For instance, $(-5)^{\frac{1}{2}}$ has no meaning as $\sqrt{-5}$, since there is no real square root of -5.

EXAMPLE 1: Rewrite as radicals.

a. $10^{\frac{5}{3}} = (10^5)^{\frac{1}{3}}$
$= \sqrt[3]{10^5}$

b. $3^{2.5} = 3^{\frac{5}{2}}$
$= (3^5)^{\frac{1}{2}}$
$= \sqrt{3^5}$

c. $k^{\frac{1}{3}}m^{\frac{2}{5}} = \sqrt[3]{k}\,\sqrt[5]{m^2}$

EXAMPLE 2: Rewrite as powers.

a. $\sqrt[3]{5^2} = (5^2)^{\frac{1}{3}}$
$= 5^{\frac{2}{3}}$

b. $\sqrt{7^3} = (7^3)^{\frac{1}{2}}$
$= 7^{\frac{3}{2}}$

c. $\sqrt{xy^2} = (xy^2)^{\frac{1}{2}}$
$= x^{\frac{1}{2}}y$

The definition of fractional exponents can be applied to evaluate or simplify expressions.

EXAMPLE 3: Evaluate as far as possible.

a. $8^{\frac{2}{3}} = (\sqrt[3]{8})^2$
$= (2)^2$
$= 4$

b. $9^{-\frac{5}{2}} = (\sqrt{9})^{-5}$
$= 3^{-5}$
$= \frac{1}{3^5}$
$= \frac{1}{243}$

c. $5^{1.5} = 5^{\frac{3}{2}}$
$= 5^1 \times 5^{\frac{1}{2}}$
$= 5\sqrt{5}$

If you evaluate $5\sqrt{5}$ as a decimal number, you get an approximate value only for $\sqrt{5}$, as its decimal equivalent has a decimal expansion that never terminates and is non-repeating. Therefore, the only *precise* way of representing $\sqrt{5}$ is to leave it as a radical.

EXERCISE 3-1

A **1.** Apply the exponent laws to simplify.

a. $3x^5 2x^3$ **b.** $(a^2b)^3$ **c.** $(5xy^2)(-2x^2y^2)$ **d.** $(z^3)^{-2}$

e. $(c^2d^{-3})^{-2}$ **f.** $(4mn^2)(3m^2n)$ **g.** $\dfrac{8x^3y^2}{2xy}$ **h.** $\dfrac{(g^3)^{-3}}{h^2}$

2. Evaluate.

a. $\sqrt{49}$ **b.** $\sqrt{256}$ **c.** $\sqrt{8}$ **d.** $\sqrt{50}$

e. $\sqrt{125}$ **f.** $\sqrt{175}$ **g.** $\sqrt{169}$ **h.** $\sqrt{363}$

3. Rewrite as a radical and evaluate.

a. $9^{\frac{1}{2}}$ **b.** $125^{\frac{1}{3}}$ **c.** $0.25^{\frac{1}{2}}$ **d.** $\left(\frac{4}{9}\right)^{\frac{1}{2}}$

e. $(0.125)^{\frac{1}{3}}$ **f.** $25^{-\frac{1}{2}}$ **g.** $\left(\frac{1}{49}\right)^{-\frac{1}{2}}$ **h.** $\left(\frac{8}{27}\right)^{-\frac{1}{3}}$

B **4.** Evaluate.

a. $16^{\frac{3}{2}}$ **b.** $125^{\frac{2}{3}}$ **c.** $16^{\frac{3}{4}}$ **d.** $4^{1.5}$

e. $81^{\frac{3}{4}}$ **f.** $8^{\frac{2}{3}}$ **g.** $0.01^{\frac{3}{2}}$ **h.** $-0.008^{\frac{4}{3}}$

5. Write each as a power.

a. $\sqrt{x^3}$ **b.** $\sqrt[3]{y^5}$ **c.** $\sqrt[4]{z^3}$ **d.** $\sqrt[3]{m^6}$

e. $(\sqrt{a})^4$ **f.** $\sqrt[4]{x^2}$ **g.** $\sqrt[6]{y^8}$ **h.** $\sqrt[5]{m^3}$

6. Write each as a radical.

a. $7^{\frac{2}{3}}$ **b.** $5^{\frac{5}{2}}$ **c.** $8^{\frac{3}{4}}$ **d.** $a^{\frac{4}{5}}$

e. $x^{\frac{4}{3}}$ **f.** $x^{0.5}$ **g.** $3^{1.5}$ **h.** $6^{0.75}$

7. Evaluate each expression by first rewriting as powers.

a. $\sqrt{27}\sqrt{3}$ **b.** $\sqrt{9}\sqrt{9}$ **c.** $\sqrt{4}\sqrt{32}$ **d.** $\sqrt{3}\sqrt{81}$

e. $\sqrt{8} \div \sqrt{4}$ **f.** $\sqrt{9} \div \sqrt{3}$ **g.** $\sqrt{32} \div \sqrt{4}$ **h.** $\sqrt{25} \div \sqrt{5}$

8. The definition of fractional exponents can be applied to prove the following properties of square roots, covered in earlier grades.

The Product Property: For $a \geq 0$ and $b \geq 0$, $\sqrt{ab} = \sqrt{a}\sqrt{b}$

The Quotient Property: For $a \geq 0$ and $b \geq 0$, $\sqrt{a \div b} = \sqrt{a} \div \sqrt{b}$

a. Prove each property by starting with the left side of the equation and showing that you can justify a series of steps to reach the right side. Then show that you can start with the right side and reach the left side.

b. State a pair of similar properties for cube roots and prove them.

9. Apply the product or quotient property to rewrite as whole numbers.

a. $\sqrt{5} \times \sqrt{20}$ **b.** $\dfrac{\sqrt{28}}{\sqrt{7}}$ **c.** $\sqrt{7} \times \sqrt{63}$ **d.** $\sqrt{6} \times \sqrt{24}$

e. $\dfrac{\sqrt{135}}{\sqrt{15}}$ **f.** $\dfrac{\sqrt{726}}{\sqrt{6}}$ **g.** $\sqrt{22} \times \sqrt{88}$ **h.** $\dfrac{\sqrt{500}}{\sqrt{20}}$

10. Find the exact value of each.

a. $\left(\frac{9}{16}\right)^{\frac{1}{2}}$ b. $\left(\frac{24}{45}\right)^{-\frac{1}{2}}$ c. $\left(\frac{16}{625}\right)^{\frac{1}{4}}$ d. $\left(\frac{64}{125}\right)^{-\frac{4}{3}}$

e. $\left(\frac{81}{625}\right)^{\frac{1}{4}}$ f. $(0.04)^{-\frac{5}{2}}$ g. $(6.25)^{-\frac{3}{2}}$ h. $(0.125)^{\frac{2}{3}}$

C 11. Simplify, leaving answers in exponential form if necessary.

a. $4^{2.9} \times 4^{0.3} \div 4^{1.7}$ b. $7^{0.8} \div 7^{1.2} \times 7^{0.9}$ c. $4^{\frac{2}{3}} \times 2^{\frac{1}{2}} \div 8^{\frac{1}{3}}$

d. $\sqrt[4]{8}\sqrt[3]{2}$ e. $\sqrt[3]{16} \times \sqrt{8} \div \sqrt{2}$ f. $(9^{\frac{3}{2}} + 8^{\frac{2}{3}})^{\frac{1}{2}}$

g. $(5x)^{\frac{1}{3}}(2x)^{\frac{1}{2}}$ h. $(5x^3)^{\frac{1}{2}} \times 3x$ i. $\sqrt{\sqrt[3]{a^5}}$

Biography

Marie Curie (1867-1934)

Marie Curie's early life in Poland did not foretell the remarkable contribution she would make to the world of science. Unable to afford a post-secondary education, she began work as a governess, when she became an avid reader of science. At the age of 24, Marie left Poland for France to study physics at the Sorbonne. Her success at this institution, where she ranked first, marked the initial step in her brilliant career.

In Paris, Marie met and married Pierre Curie, a renowned French chemist. Together, their scientific work dramatically advanced the fields of physics and chemistry. Marie Curie's experiments using the electrometer, invented by her husband Pierre and his brother, enabled her to measure the rays emitted by uranium as it underwent radioactive decay. Marie herself coined the word "radioactive".

The uranium-rich ore that was necessary for the Curies' experiments was donated by the Vienna Academy of Sciences; however, the Curies had to use their life savings to pay the costs of bringing the ore to France. The purification of 1 t of ore over a four-year period yielded 1 g of radium.

The Curies' tremendous devotion to their work was recognized throughout the world in 1903, when they and Henri Becqueral were awarded the Nobel prize in physics for their discovery of radioactivity. The Curies neither patented their discoveries nor sought any royalties, deliberately denouncing a fortune as they found sufficient reward in furthering science to the benefit of humanity.

Pierre Curie's death in 1906 did not halt Marie's involvement in the scientific world. She was the first woman to teach at the Sorbonne, and was awarded the Nobel prize for chemistry in 1911. After World War I, she accepted positions at the Radium Institute and the Académie de Médecine.

In 1934, Marie Curie died of leukemia, a result of prolonged exposure to high levels of radiation.

3-2 Rational and Irrational Numbers

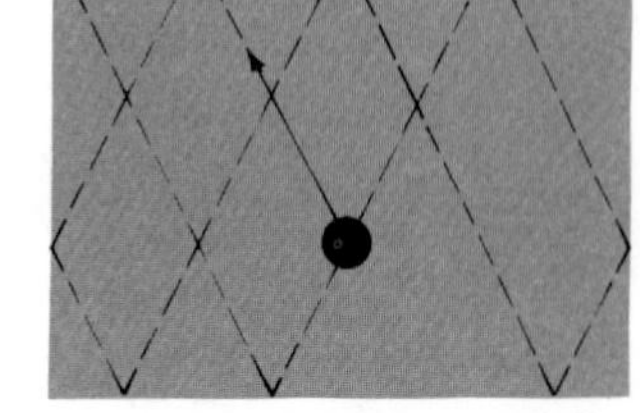

On any conventional billiard table, if a ball could be hit and allowed to roll and bounce off the cushions indefinitely, it would eventually retrace its path or go into a corner. This property results from the fact that the side lengths of a conventional billiard table are in a ratio that can be expressed as a quotient of integers.

A number that can be expressed as a quotient of integers is a **rational number**. The set of rational numbers is represented by ***Q***,

and $\boldsymbol{Q} = \{\frac{a}{b}, \text{ where } a, b \in \boldsymbol{Z}, b \neq 0\}$.   ***Z*** is the set of integers.

If a rational number is expressed as a decimal, its decimal expansion is **periodic**. That is, the digits in the decimal expansion eventually repeat.

$\frac{3}{8} = 0.375$ $\frac{17}{36} = 0.47\overline{2}$ $\frac{81}{44} = 1.84\overline{09}$ In 0.375, a zero repeats.

Converting a terminating decimal to a quotient of integers is a straightforward task. For 0.25, write $\frac{25}{100} = \frac{1}{4}$. For 0.132, write $\frac{132}{1000} = \frac{33}{250}$.

To convert a repeating, non-terminating decimal like $0.\overline{32}$ to a quotient of integers, follow the steps below.

1. Let x be the given number.
2. Multiply by an appropriate power of ten to bring one period of digits left of the decimal point.
3. Subtract left sides and right sides of each equation.
4. Solve for x.

$x = 0.\overline{32}$

$$\begin{aligned} 100x &= 32.\overline{32} \\ x &= 0.\overline{32} \\ \hline 99x &= 32 \\ x &= \frac{32}{99} \\ \therefore 0.\overline{32} &= \frac{32}{99} \end{aligned}$$

Numbers that do not have periodic decimal expansions cannot be expressed as quotients of integers and are called **irrational numbers**. The following numbers are irrational.

0.12345678910111213...   0.12112111211112... $\pi = 3.14159265...$

The first two decimal expansions have a pattern, but the pattern is not periodic.

The set of irrational numbers is represented by $\overline{\boldsymbol{Q}}$. $\overline{\boldsymbol{Q}}$ is an infinite set containing, for instance, many square roots. In fact, if a number n is not a perfect square, then $\sqrt{n} \in \overline{\boldsymbol{Q}}$.

$\sqrt{2}$ is irrational. $\sqrt{16}$ is rational because $\sqrt{16} = 4$, which can be written as $\frac{4}{1}$.

$\sqrt{10}$ is irrational. $\sqrt{2.25}$ is rational because $\sqrt{2.25} = 1.5$, which can be written as $\frac{15}{10}$.

The set of **real numbers**, represented by ***R***, is the set containing all the rational and irrational numbers.

EXERCISE 3-2

A **1.** True or false?

a. No number is both rational and irrational.
b. $\sqrt{7}$ is irrational.
c. 0 is a rational number.
d. $\sqrt{25}$ is irrational.
e. Every rational number is a real number.
f. There is one real number that is neither rational nor irrational.
g. The product of two rational numbers is rational.
h. The product of two irrational numbers is irrational.
i. Every rational number has a reciprocal.
j. Every real number is a rational number.
k. The sum of two real numbers is rational.

2. Express each as a periodic decimal. Use a calculator if necessary.

a. $\frac{5}{6}$ **b.** $\frac{2}{9}$ **c.** $\frac{4}{11}$ **d.** $\frac{23}{15}$
e. $\frac{17}{8}$ **f.** $\frac{3}{7}$ **g.** $-\frac{8}{21}$ **h.** $-\frac{41}{25}$

B **3.** Identify those that you know are rational numbers.

a. $\frac{3}{7}$ **b.** $\sqrt{9}$ **c.** $\sqrt{15}$ **d.** $\dfrac{1}{\sqrt{2}}$
e. $0.\overline{35}$ **f.** 4.31415161... **g.** $4.72\overline{19}$ **h.** $\sqrt{12}\sqrt{3}$
i. $\sqrt{5}\sqrt{10}$ **j.** $\dfrac{\sqrt{8}}{\sqrt{2}}$ **k.** $\dfrac{\sqrt{8}}{\sqrt{10}}$ **l.** $\sqrt{7}\sqrt{28}$

4. Express each as a quotient of integers.

a. 0.6 **b.** 0.28 **c.** 0.0625 **d.** $0.\overline{7}$
e. $0.\overline{2}$ **f.** $0.3\overline{5}$ **g.** $0.\overline{21}$ **h.** $0.\overline{122}$
i. $-0.\overline{316}$ **j.** $0.2\overline{19}$ **k.** $2.\overline{45}$ **l.** $35.\overline{26}$
m. $0.5\overline{2}$ **n.** $0.2\overline{17}$ **o.** $-3.1419\overline{2}$ **p.** $-5.\overline{782}$

C **5.** Between any two real numbers, you can find both a rational and an irrational number. Verify this for each pair of real numbers.

a. 1, 2 **b.** $\frac{1}{4}, \frac{1}{2}$ **c.** $\sqrt{3}, \sqrt{5}$ **d.** 0.38, 0.5121314...
e. $\frac{7}{11}, \frac{7}{9}$ **f.** $\sqrt{8}, \sqrt{9}$ **g.** $4.35, \sqrt{20}$ **h.** $0.2\overline{75}$, 0.3
i. $\sqrt{1.44}$, 1.5 **j.** $\sqrt{1000}, \sqrt{1001}$ **k.** $-1, \sqrt{2}$ **l.** $\pi, \sqrt{10}$

EXTRA

One Decimal Surprise

Decimals with repeating, non-terminating patterns can lead to surprising results. The sequence 0.9, 0.99, 0.999, 0.9999, . . . , gets closer and closer to 1. Use the algebraic method on page 76 to show that the decimal $0.\overline{9}$ is actually *equal* to 1.

3-3 Simplifying Radical Expressions

At the time of its construction, the Annacis Island Bridge in British Columbia was the longest cable-stayed bridge ever built. If one end of a cable is anchored on the main tower 40 m above the bridge's deck, and the other end is anchored 80 m along the deck from the foot of the tower, the length of cable needed can be found by the Pythagorean Theorem. Let the length be *l* metres.

$$80^2 + 40^2 = l^2$$
$$l^2 = 6400 + 1600$$
$$l^2 = 8000$$
$$\therefore l = \sqrt{8000}$$

Applying the Pythagorean Theorem often results in answers that are in radical form. These **radical expressions** correspond to *real* distances used in architecture, surveying, and other fields. Because they can be more awkward to work with than integers, methods have been established to simplify radical expressions.

A radical like $\sqrt{8000}$ is considered to be in simplest form when there are no perfect-square factors in the radicand.

EXAMPLE 1: Simplify each radical.

a. $\sqrt{8000} = \sqrt{1600 \times 5}$
$= \sqrt{1600}\sqrt{5}$
$= 40\sqrt{5}$

b. $\sqrt{98} = \sqrt{2 \times 49}$
$= \sqrt{2}\sqrt{49}$
$= 7\sqrt{2}$

c. $\sqrt{8x^2y^5} = \sqrt{(4x^2y^4)(2y)}$
$= \sqrt{4x^2y^4}\sqrt{2y}$
$= 2xy^2\sqrt{2y}$

Since principal square roots are positive, restrict x to be positive.

The method used in example 1 can be *reversed* to write an expression as an entire radical.

EXAMPLE 2: Rewrite as entire radicals.

a. $3\sqrt{5} = \sqrt{9}\sqrt{5}$
$= \sqrt{45}$

b. $x\sqrt{y} = \sqrt{x^2}\sqrt{y}$
$= \sqrt{x^2y}$

c. $2m\sqrt{5n^2} = \sqrt{4m^2}\sqrt{5n^2}$
$= \sqrt{20m^2n^2}$

Cube roots can be simplified by extracting perfect-cube factors.

EXAMPLE 3: Simplify each radical.

a. $\sqrt[3]{32} = \sqrt[3]{8 \times 4}$
$= \sqrt[3]{8}\sqrt[3]{4}$
$= 2\sqrt[3]{4}$

b. $\sqrt[3]{625} = \sqrt[3]{125 \times 5}$
$= \sqrt[3]{125}\sqrt[3]{5}$
$= 5\sqrt[3]{5}$

c. $\sqrt[3]{16m^5n} = \sqrt[3]{8m^3 \times 2m^2n}$
$= \sqrt[3]{8m^3}\sqrt[3]{2m^2n}$
$= 2m\sqrt[3]{2m^2n}$

Radicals *of the same degree* can be multiplied or divided by multiplying or dividing their radicands, as specified by the product and quotient properties of roots.

EXAMPLE 4: Simplify. Use factoring to find repeated factors that may simplify your work.

a. $$\begin{aligned}\sqrt{6}\sqrt{15} &= \sqrt{2}\sqrt{3}\sqrt{3}\sqrt{5}\\ &= \sqrt{2}\sqrt{9}\sqrt{5}\\ &= 3\sqrt{2}\sqrt{5}\\ &= 3\sqrt{10}\end{aligned}$$

b. $$\begin{aligned}\frac{\sqrt{42}}{\sqrt{15}} \times \frac{\sqrt{35}}{\sqrt{28}} &= \frac{\cancel{\sqrt{14}}\cancel{\sqrt{3}}}{\cancel{\sqrt{5}}\cancel{\sqrt{3}}} \times \frac{\cancel{\sqrt{5}}\sqrt{7}}{\cancel{\sqrt{14}}\sqrt{2}}\\ &= \frac{\sqrt{7}}{\sqrt{2}}\end{aligned}$$

Since it is easier to divide by integers than by irrational numbers, quotients with radicals in the denominator are simplified by rewriting to eliminate the radical from the denominator. Multiplying both numerator and denominator by the same number leaves the value of the quotient unchanged.

$$\begin{aligned}\frac{\sqrt{7}}{\sqrt{2}} &= \frac{\sqrt{7}}{\sqrt{2}} \times \frac{\sqrt{2}}{\sqrt{2}}\\ &= \frac{\sqrt{14}}{2}\end{aligned}$$

Use the fact that multiplying $\sqrt{2}$ by itself results in an integer.

Rewriting an expression so that the denominator does not contain irrational numbers is described as **rationalizing the denominator**.

EXAMPLE 5: Rationalize each denominator.

a. $$\begin{aligned}\frac{2\sqrt{3}}{\sqrt{5}} &= \frac{2\sqrt{3}}{\sqrt{5}} \times \frac{\sqrt{5}}{\sqrt{5}}\\ &= \frac{2\sqrt{15}}{5}\end{aligned}$$

b. $$\begin{aligned}\frac{\sqrt{6x}}{2\sqrt{3y}} &= \frac{\sqrt{6x}}{2\sqrt{3y}} \times \frac{\sqrt{3y}}{\sqrt{3y}}\\ &= \frac{3\sqrt{2xy}}{6y}\\ &= \frac{\sqrt{2xy}}{2y}\end{aligned}$$

Like radicals, which have the same radicand and the same degree, can be added or subtracted.

EXAMPLE 6: Simplify.

a. $$\begin{aligned}7\sqrt{5} + 2\sqrt{5} - 6\sqrt{5} &= (7 + 2 - 6)\sqrt{5}\\ &= 3\sqrt{5}\end{aligned}$$

b. $$\begin{aligned}4\sqrt{8} + 2\sqrt{18} - \sqrt{3} &= 4\sqrt{4}\sqrt{2} + 2\sqrt{9}\sqrt{2} - \sqrt{3}\\ &= 8\sqrt{2} + 6\sqrt{2} - \sqrt{3}\\ &= 14\sqrt{2} - \sqrt{3}\end{aligned}$$

Adding and subtracting like radicals will not always result in single-term radical expressions. In part (b) of example 6, for instance, the operations result in a two-term radical expression.

EXERCISE 3-3

A **1.** Simplify by removing perfect-square factors from the radicand.

a. $\sqrt{28}$ **b.** $\sqrt{56}$ **c.** $\sqrt{32}$ **d.** $\sqrt{128}$

e. $\sqrt{250}$ **f.** $\sqrt{147}$ **g.** $\sqrt{150}$ **h.** $\sqrt{567}$

2. Simplify by removing perfect-cube factors from the radicand.

a. $\sqrt[3]{54}$ **b.** $\sqrt[3]{200}$ **c.** $\sqrt[3]{64}$ **d.** $\sqrt[3]{128}$

e. $\sqrt[3]{24}$ **f.** $\sqrt[3]{250}$ **g.** $\sqrt[3]{0.125}$ **h.** $\sqrt[3]{0.002}$

3. Rewrite as an entire radical.

a. $2\sqrt{5}$ **b.** $7\sqrt{3}$ **c.** $5\sqrt{6}$ **d.** $2\sqrt{7}$

e. $0.5\sqrt{6}$ **f.** $10\sqrt{5}$ **g.** $8\sqrt{5}$ **h.** $5\sqrt{8}$

4. Rewrite as an entire radical.

a. $3\sqrt[3]{5}$ **b.** $2\sqrt[3]{6}$ **c.** $-5\sqrt[3]{3}$ **d.** $2\sqrt[3]{3}$

e. $7\sqrt[3]{2}$ **f.** $-5\sqrt[3]{4}$ **g.** $4\sqrt[3]{6}$ **h.** $-4\sqrt[3]{3}$

5. Apply the Pythagorean Theorem to find each missing dimension. Express each answer in simplest radical form.

a.

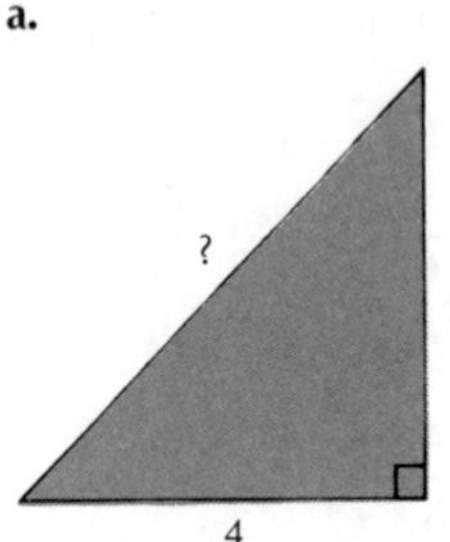

b.

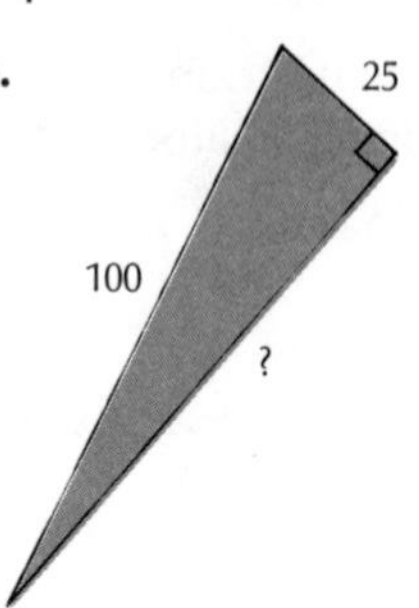

c.

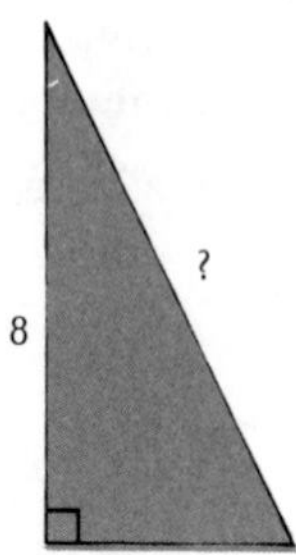

d.

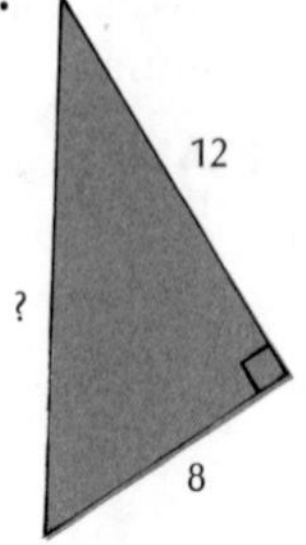

B **6.** Simplify by rationalizing the denominator.

a. $\frac{1}{\sqrt{5}}$ **b.** $\frac{1}{\sqrt{7}}$ **c.** $\frac{3}{\sqrt{2}}$ **d.** $\frac{5}{\sqrt{6}}$

e. $\frac{1}{\sqrt{8}}$ **f.** $\frac{2}{\sqrt{6}}$ **g.** $\frac{1}{\sqrt{98}}$ **h.** $\frac{5}{\sqrt{250}}$

i. $\frac{6}{\sqrt{10}}$ **j.** $\frac{\sqrt{3}}{\sqrt{7}}$ **k.** $\frac{\sqrt{5}}{\sqrt{2}}$ **l.** $\frac{\sqrt{3}}{\sqrt{6}}$

7. Simplify by adding and subtracting as indicated.

a. $5\sqrt{3} + \sqrt{3}$

b. $6\sqrt{7} - 3\sqrt{7}$

c. $6\sqrt{2} + 3\sqrt{5} - \sqrt{2} + \sqrt{5}$

d. $4\sqrt{10} - 3\sqrt{6} + \sqrt{10} - \sqrt{6}$

e. $\sqrt{8} - \sqrt{18} + \sqrt{50}$

f. $\sqrt{75} + \sqrt{48} - \sqrt{12}$

g. $3\sqrt{27} + \sqrt{128} - \sqrt{75} - \sqrt{8}$

h. $\sqrt{84} + 3\sqrt{243} - \sqrt{3}$

i. $\sqrt{90} - \sqrt{160} + \sqrt{24}$

j. $3\sqrt{7} - \sqrt{20} + \sqrt{175} + 2\sqrt{125}$

8. Rewrite as entire radicals.

a. $x\sqrt{2}$ **b.** $4m\sqrt{3m}$ **c.** $3a^2\sqrt{5a}$ **d.** $xy^{-2}\sqrt{2x}$
e. $2mn\sqrt{3m^3}$ **f.** $7a\sqrt{bc^2}$ **g.** $5x^2y^{-1}\sqrt{3yz}$ **h.** $2ab^2c\sqrt{5abc^{-3}}$

9. Rewrite as entire radicals.

a. $m\sqrt{3m}$ **b.** $-2x\sqrt{3xy^2}$ **c.** $2x\sqrt[3]{5x}$ **d.** $a^{-1}\sqrt[3]{b^2c}$
e. $-2ab\sqrt[3]{b}$ **f.** $3n\sqrt[3]{-2m^2n^2}$ **g.** $-x^{-2}y\sqrt[3]{xy^2z}$ **h.** $5ac^{-2}\sqrt[3]{2ab^2c}$

10. Simplify each variable expression, given that all variables are positive.

a. $\sqrt{28x^3y^2}$ **b.** $\sqrt{8x^6y^3}$ **c.** $\sqrt{81x^{10}y^3}$ **d.** $\sqrt{72m^6y^2}$
e. $\sqrt{a^{-3}b^6y^4}$ **f.** $\sqrt{63m^3n^{-5}}$ **g.** $\sqrt{27x^{-2}y^{-4}}$ **h.** $\sqrt{75m^7n^{-6}p^{-5}}$

11. Simplify each variable expression.

a. $\sqrt[3]{27x^5y^3}$ **b.** $\sqrt[3]{16x^4y^4}$ **c.** $\sqrt[3]{-24ab^7}$ **d.** $\sqrt[3]{m^3n^{-8}}$
e. $\sqrt[3]{-54x^{-4}y^3}$ **f.** $\sqrt[3]{250a^4b^3c^6}$ **g.** $\sqrt[3]{40m^{-4}n^{-5}p^2}$ **h.** $\sqrt[3]{-xy^{-5}z^{-4}}$

12. Multiply and simplify.

a. $\sqrt{6}\sqrt{10}$ **b.** $\sqrt{5}\sqrt{15}$ **c.** $\sqrt{3x}\sqrt{6xy}$ **d.** $\sqrt{21a}\sqrt{14ab^2}$
e. $\frac{\sqrt{24}}{\sqrt{3}} \times \frac{\sqrt{6}}{\sqrt{2}}$ **f.** $\frac{\sqrt{32}}{\sqrt{15}} \times \frac{\sqrt{35}}{\sqrt{8}}$ **g.** $\frac{\sqrt{2m}}{\sqrt{6n}} \times \frac{\sqrt{3n}}{\sqrt{2m}}$ **h.** $\frac{\sqrt{3x}}{\sqrt{8y^3}} \times \frac{\sqrt{y}}{\sqrt{3x^2}}$

13. Simplify.

a. $\sqrt[3]{12}\sqrt[3]{4}$ **b.** $\sqrt[3]{20}\sqrt[3]{10}$ **c.** $\sqrt[3]{6a^2b}\sqrt[3]{4ab}$
d. $\frac{\sqrt[3]{30}}{\sqrt[3]{5}} \times \frac{\sqrt[3]{20}}{\sqrt[3]{3}}$ **e.** $\frac{\sqrt[3]{4}}{\sqrt[3]{18}} \times \frac{\sqrt[3]{10}}{\sqrt[3]{75}}$ **f.** $\frac{\sqrt[3]{3x^2}}{\sqrt[3]{y}} \times \frac{\sqrt[3]{x^2y^2}}{\sqrt[3]{xy}}$

14. Simplify.

a. $\sqrt{2} + \frac{1}{\sqrt{2}}$ **b.** $\sqrt{5} + \frac{2}{\sqrt{5}}$ **c.** $\sqrt{10} + \frac{\sqrt{2}}{\sqrt{5}}$ **d.** $\sqrt{8} - \frac{3}{\sqrt{2}}$

15. A bridge cable is anchored with one end 25 m above the bridge deck and the other end 45 m along the deck. What is the length of the cable? Express the answer as a simplified radical.

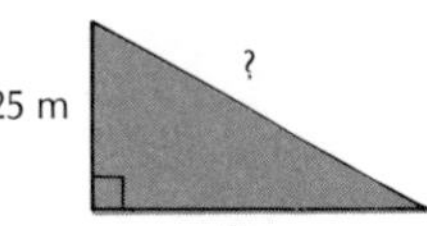

16. A rectangular skating area is 60 m by 30 m. Express the diagonal distance as a simple radical.

C **17.** A lab technician uses a microscope to view a blood sample on a slide marked off in 1 mm squares. Six blood cells line up along the diagonal of one of the squares. What is the approximate diameter of each cell?

18. Could $\sqrt{a^2 + b^2}$ ever equal $\sqrt{a + b}$? Explain.

19. Express as a single radical, and simplify, if possible.
For example: $\sqrt[3]{x^2}\sqrt{x} = \sqrt[6]{x^4}\sqrt[6]{x^3}$

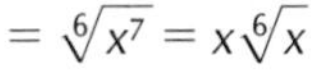

$= \sqrt[6]{x^7} = x\sqrt[6]{x}$

a. $\sqrt[3]{m^2} \times \sqrt{m}$ **b.** $\sqrt[3]{x} \times \sqrt[5]{x^3}$ **c.** $\sqrt[3]{a^2} \times \sqrt[4]{a^3}$ **d.** $\sqrt{b} \times \sqrt[4]{b}$

3-4 Simplifying Two-Term Radical Expressions

Radical expressions that contain unlike radicals can be multiplied by an integer, or by another radical, by applying the Distributive Property.

EXAMPLE 1: Multiply.

a. $5(2\sqrt{3} - 7) = 5(2\sqrt{3}) - 5(7)$
$= 10\sqrt{3} - 35$

b. $\sqrt{2}(\sqrt{6} - 3\sqrt{2}) = \sqrt{12} - 3\sqrt{4}$
$= 2\sqrt{3} - 6$

Extending this concept, products of radical sums can also be found by applying the Distributive Property. The process is similar to multiplying two binomials.

EXAMPLE 2: Multiply and simplify.

a. $(2\sqrt{3} - 1)(2 + \sqrt{3})$
$= 4\sqrt{3} + 2\sqrt{3}\sqrt{3} - 2 - \sqrt{3}$
$= 4\sqrt{3} + 6 - 2 - \sqrt{3}$
$= 3\sqrt{3} + 4$

b. $(5 - \sqrt{3})(5 + \sqrt{3})$
$= 25 + 5\sqrt{3} - 5\sqrt{3} - \sqrt{3}\sqrt{3}$
$= 25 - 3$
$= 22$

The second part of example 2 recalls the difference of squares: $(a + b)(a - b) = a^2 - b^2$. It illustrates that a product of two-term radical expressions can result in a rational number. This observation can be applied to rationalize two-term denominators.

EXAMPLE 3: Rationalize the denominator in the expression $\dfrac{1 + 3\sqrt{5}}{1 - \sqrt{5}}$.

Multiplying $1 - \sqrt{5}$ by $1 + \sqrt{5}$ would yield an integer answer. The expressions $(1 - \sqrt{5})$ and $(1 + \sqrt{5})$ are called **conjugates**.

$(1 - \sqrt{5})(1 + \sqrt{5})$
$= 1 - \sqrt{5^2}$
$= -4$

Rationalize the denominator in the given expression by multiplying numerator and denominator by the conjugate of $1 - \sqrt{5}$.

$$\frac{1 + 3\sqrt{5}}{1 - \sqrt{5}} = \frac{1 + 3\sqrt{5}}{1 - \sqrt{5}} \times \frac{1 + \sqrt{5}}{1 + \sqrt{5}}$$
$$= \frac{(1 + 3\sqrt{5})(1 + \sqrt{5})}{-4}$$
$$= \frac{1 + 4\sqrt{5} + 15}{-4}$$
$$= \frac{16 + 4\sqrt{5}}{-4}$$
$$= -4 - \sqrt{5}$$

EXERCISE 3-4

A **1.** Multiply.

a. $\sqrt{18}\sqrt{5}$ **b.** $3\sqrt{7}\sqrt{14}$ **c.** $\sqrt{3}\sqrt{27}$

d. $\sqrt{7}\sqrt{56}$ **e.** $\sqrt{3}(\sqrt{27}-1)$ **f.** $\sqrt{7}(\sqrt{7}-5\sqrt{56})$

g. $5\sqrt{2}(\sqrt{3}-1)$ **h.** $2\sqrt{3}(3\sqrt{3}+\sqrt{6})$

B **2.** Multiply and simplify.

a. $(3+\sqrt{5})(1-\sqrt{5})$ **b.** $(\sqrt{7}+3)(2-\sqrt{7})$ **c.** $(4-\sqrt{2})(3-\sqrt{2})$

d. $(2\sqrt{5}+6)(\sqrt{5}-2)$ **e.** $(3\sqrt{10}+6)(2-\sqrt{10})$ **f.** $(5\sqrt{6}+3\sqrt{5})(-\sqrt{6}+3\sqrt{5})$

g. $(3\sqrt{11}+\sqrt{6})(\sqrt{11}-5\sqrt{6})$ **h.** $(\sqrt{7}-2\sqrt{2})^2$ **i.** $(3\sqrt{3}+\sqrt{5})^2$

3. State the conjugate of each.

a. $(1-\sqrt{2})$ **b.** $(3+\sqrt{5})$ **c.** $(2-\sqrt{3})$ **d.** $(4+2\sqrt{3})$

e. $(\sqrt{5}+2\sqrt{3})$ **f.** $(3\sqrt{10}-5)$ **g.** $(4\sqrt{7}-3\sqrt{3})$ **h.** $(2\sqrt{5}+\sqrt{13})$

4. For each expression in exercise 3, find the product of the expression and its conjugate.

5. Simplify by rationalizing the denominator.

a. $\frac{6}{1+\sqrt{5}}$ **b.** $\frac{9}{5-\sqrt{7}}$ **c.** $\frac{-12}{\sqrt{7}+2}$ **d.** $\frac{3-\sqrt{2}}{1+\sqrt{2}}$

e. $\frac{2\sqrt{3}}{4-\sqrt{3}}$ **f.** $\frac{5\sqrt{2}}{\sqrt{2}+\sqrt{3}}$ **g.** $\frac{5+\sqrt{3}}{\sqrt{3}-1}$ **h.** $\frac{1-\sqrt{10}}{3+\sqrt{10}}$

i. $\frac{4\sqrt{6}+3}{2\sqrt{6}+1}$ **j.** $\frac{1+\sqrt{3}}{3+\sqrt{2}}$ **k.** $\frac{2\sqrt{5}-\sqrt{3}}{3\sqrt{5}-\sqrt{3}}$ **l.** $\frac{\sqrt{6}-\sqrt{10}}{3\sqrt{10}+\sqrt{6}}$

6. Write an equivalent expression with no radicals in the denominator.

a. $\frac{1}{\sqrt{x+1}+\sqrt{2}}$ **b.** $\frac{2}{\sqrt{x+3}+\sqrt{3}}$ **c.** $\frac{x}{\sqrt{x+4}+\sqrt{x}}$

d. $\frac{y}{\sqrt{3}-\sqrt{y+30}}$ **e.** $\frac{2}{\sqrt{x+y}-\sqrt{y}}$ **f.** $\frac{5}{\sqrt{a}-\sqrt{a+b}}$

C **7.** How many times longer than the length of each leg is the hypotenuse of an isosceles right triangle?

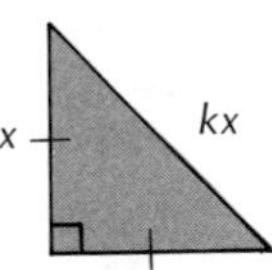

8. Some quadratic expressions cannot be factored if only rational numbers are used in the factors. If irrational numbers are allowed, however, then the expressions can be factored. Factor each expression.

a. x^2-2 **b.** x^2-1000 **c.** $x^2+2\sqrt{5}x+5$

d. $y^2-2\sqrt{3}y+3$ **e.** $a^2+4\sqrt{2}a+8$ **f.** $x^2+5\sqrt{7}x+42$

g. $x^2-\sqrt{6}x-12$ **h.** $m^2-3\sqrt{5}m+10$

Historical Note

Keeping Time

In the fifteenth century, Europeans began sailing out of sight of land with some confidence, using navigation methods that are still in use today. Some of their navigation *instruments*, however, were crude and unreliable.

Clocks, for instance, can be used to calculate longitude: two clocks are carried on board, one set to Greenwich time (0° longitude), the other according to high noon. A difference of 1 h ($\frac{1}{24}$ of a day) indicates a difference in longitude of 15° ($\frac{1}{24}$ of 360°).

The clocks of the fifteenth and sixteenth centuries were not accurate, either losing or gaining about fifteen minutes a day. This discrepancy could add up to an error of eight hours over the course of a one-month trip, resulting in a navigation error of up to 120° longitude! Developing an accurate and portable clock, therefore, was critical to safe and predictable ocean travel.

One who contributed to the development of such a clock was Galileo Galilei. At the age of 19, Galileo watched a cathedral chandelier as it swung in the wind. A strong wind caused the chandelier to swing in large arcs; when the wind lessened, the chandelier swung in smaller arcs. Yet, as Galileo observed, and later verified by experimentation, the length of time taken for one full swing appeared to remain constant.

In other words, the time taken for one full swing of a pendulum, its **period**, does *not* depend on the width of the swing. The following equation gives the period of a pendulum with length l metres, where acceleration due to gravity is g metres per second per second.

$$T = 2\pi\sqrt{\frac{l}{g}}$$

At sea level at the equator, $g = 9.8$ m/s^2.

Eventually, Galilieo's discovery did lead to the use of pendulums in clocks, resulting in more reliable timepieces. By the end of the seventeenth century, the typical time error had been reduced from fifteen minutes per day to only ten seconds.

---

1. Using $g = 9.8$ and $\pi = 3.1416$, calculate the length of a pendulum that has a period of exactly one second.
2. On the moon, the acceleration due to gravity is 1.6 m/s^2. What length of pendulum would have a period of one second?
3. On Venus, a pendulum 1.0 m long has a period of 2.153 s. What is the acceleration due to gravity on Venus?

Review

1. Evaluate.

   a. $64^{\frac{2}{3}}$ b. $(0.0016)^{\frac{3}{4}}$ c. $9^{\frac{5}{2}}$ d. $(0.25)^{-\frac{3}{2}}$

2. Write as a radical.

   a. $5^{\frac{2}{3}}$ b. $9^{\frac{3}{4}}$ c. $7^{1.5}$ d. $8^{0.75}$

3. Evaluate, leaving each answer in exponential form.

   a. $3^{1.6} \div 3^{0.8} \times 3^{2.4}$ b. $9^{\frac{2}{3}} \times 3^{\frac{1}{3}} \div 27^{\frac{1}{3}}$

   c. $(1000^{\frac{2}{3}} - 512^{\frac{2}{3}})^{\frac{1}{3}}$ d. $(25^{\frac{3}{5}} - 125^{\frac{2}{3}})^{\frac{1}{4}}$

4. Express as a periodic decimal.

   a. $\frac{7}{8}$ b. $\frac{26}{18}$ c. $\frac{8}{11}$ d. $\frac{17}{12}$

5. Express as a quotient of integers.

   a. 0.08 b. 0.0625 c. $0.\overline{15}$ d. $0.3\overline{25}$

6. Find both an irrational and a rational number between the numbers $3.\overline{14}$ and π.

7. Rewrite as an entire radical.

   a. $4\sqrt{3}$ b. $5\sqrt{6}$ c. $2\sqrt{3}$ d. $-3\sqrt[3]{5}$

8. Simplify.

   a. $\sqrt{72}$ b. $\sqrt[3]{125}$ c. $\sqrt{50x^3y^2}$ d. $\sqrt{x^{-5}y^3z^4}$

   e. $\sqrt{x^2 + 2x + 1}$ f. $\sqrt[3]{18}\sqrt[3]{15}$ g. $\sqrt{6xy^3}\sqrt{8x^2y}$ h. $\sqrt[3]{40a^{-5}b^4}$

9. Add and subtract as indicated.

   a. $7\sqrt{6} - 3\sqrt{6}$ b. $\sqrt{48} - 2\sqrt{12} + \sqrt{75}$

   c. $\sqrt[3]{16} + \sqrt[3]{40} - 5\sqrt[3]{2} + \sqrt[3]{135}$ d. $5\sqrt{3} - \sqrt{\frac{1}{3}}$

10. Multiply.

    a. $2\sqrt{3}(3\sqrt{3} - \sqrt{2})$ b. $5\sqrt{7}(2\sqrt{7} + 3\sqrt{3})$ c. $(4 + \sqrt{2})(3 - \sqrt{2})$

    d. $(2\sqrt{3} + 4)(2 + 3\sqrt{3})$ e. $(\sqrt{3} + 2\sqrt{3})(2\sqrt{3} - \sqrt{5})$ f. $(\sqrt{2} + 3\sqrt{18})^2$

    g. $(2\sqrt{3} + 3\sqrt{5})(2\sqrt{3} - 3\sqrt{5})$ h. $(\sqrt{7} - 2\sqrt{3})(2\sqrt{3} + \sqrt{7})$

11. Find the product of each expression with its conjugate.

    a. $(3 - \sqrt{7})$ b. $5 + 3\sqrt{8}$ c. $\sqrt{2} - 1$ d. $2\sqrt{3} - \sqrt{5}$

12. Rationalize each denominator and simplify.

    a. $\frac{3}{\sqrt{6}}$ b. $\frac{\sqrt{6}}{\sqrt{8}}$ c. $\frac{3}{1 - \sqrt{2}}$ d. $\frac{4}{6 + \sqrt{8}}$

    e. $\frac{\sqrt{24} - \sqrt{6}}{\sqrt{2}}$ f. $\frac{3 + \sqrt{5}}{4 - \sqrt{5}}$ g. $\frac{\sqrt{7} + 3\sqrt{2}}{\sqrt{2} - \frac{1}{\sqrt{2}}}$ h. $\sqrt{2} - \frac{1}{\sqrt{2}}$

3-5 Solving Radical Equations

In Unit 1, *linear* equations in one unknown were solved by transforming them into simpler, equivalent equations until the variable was isolated. A **radical equation** is one, like $\sqrt{x} + 1 = 2$, in which a variable appears as part of a radicand.

Solving a radical equation is not unlike solving a linear equation, with one additional consideration. $\quad \sqrt{x} + 1 = 2$

Start by isolating the radical. $\quad \sqrt{x} = 1$

Square both sides to remove the radical. $\quad (\sqrt{x})^2 = 1^2$

Solve for the variable. $\quad x = 1$

The special consideration stems from the fact that squaring both sides of an equation is *not* a reversible step. An **extraneous root** might be introduced when squaring both sides of an equation. Therefore, always verify all solutions by checking whether the left and right sides are equal.

If: $x = -3$
then: $x^2 = 9$
But, if: $x^2 = 9$
then: $x = +3$ *or* -3

EXAMPLE 1: Solve $x + \sqrt{x + 3} = 3$.

$$
\begin{aligned}
x + \sqrt{x+3} &= 3 \\
\sqrt{x+3} &= -x + 3 \\
(\sqrt{x+3})^2 &= (-x+3)^2 \\
x + 3 &= x^2 - 6x + 9 \\
x^2 - 7x + 6 &= 0 \\
(x-1)(x-6) &= 0 \\
\therefore x = 1 &\text{ or } x = 6
\end{aligned}
$$

Check for $x = 1$:
$$
\begin{aligned}
\text{L.S.} &= x + \sqrt{x+3} \\
&= 1 + \sqrt{4} \\
&= 3 \\
&= \text{R.S.} \quad \checkmark
\end{aligned}
$$

Check for $x = 6$:
$$
\begin{aligned}
\text{L.S.} &= x + \sqrt{x+3} \\
&= 6 + \sqrt{9} \\
&= 9 \\
&\neq \text{R.S.}
\end{aligned}
$$

6 is an extraneous root.

The solution is $x = 1$.

A radical equation may not necessarily contain a *square* root.

EXAMPLE 2: Solve $\sqrt[3]{x-2} + 5 = 7$.

$$
\begin{aligned}
\sqrt[3]{x-2} + 5 &= 7 \\
\sqrt[3]{x-2} &= 2 \\
(\sqrt[3]{x-2})^3 &= (2)^3 \\
x - 2 &= 8 \\
x &= 10
\end{aligned}
$$

Check:
$$
\begin{aligned}
\text{L.S.} &= \sqrt[3]{x-2} + 5 \\
&= \sqrt[3]{10-2} + 5 \\
&= \sqrt[3]{8} + 5 \\
&= 2 + 5 \\
&= 7 \\
&= \text{R.S.} \quad \checkmark
\end{aligned}
$$

The solution is $x = 10$.

EXERCISE 3-5

A 1. Solve by inspection. If there are no real solutions, then state that fact.

a. $\sqrt{m} = 8$ b. $\sqrt{y} = 3$ c. $3\sqrt{a} = 15$ d. $\sqrt{b} - 4 = 0$

e. $\sqrt{t} + 3 = 0$ f. $\sqrt{x} + 7 = 0$ g. $\sqrt{\frac{a}{2}} = 3$ h. $\sqrt{3y} = 3$

i. $\sqrt{\frac{z}{2}} = 5$ j. $2\sqrt{x} = 10$ k. $5 + \sqrt{y} = 3$ l. $3\sqrt{x} - 15 = 0$

m. $5 + 2\sqrt{b} = 3$ n. $2\sqrt{x} + 5 = 0$ o. $\frac{\sqrt{x} - 3}{2} = 1$ p. $\sqrt{n^2 + 11} = 6$

2. Solve each radical equation. Verify all solutions.

a. $\sqrt{a + 1} = 3$ b. $\sqrt{3k + 1} = 4$ c. $\sqrt{2x - 7} = -2$

d. $\sqrt{6x + 3} = 3$ e. $\sqrt{5x + 4} - 3 = -4$ f. $\sqrt{2t + 2} - 1 = 1$

B 3. Solve each radical equation.

a. $x + \sqrt{x} = 6$ b. $x - \sqrt{x} = 20$ c. $\sqrt{3z + 6} - z = -4$

d. $\sqrt{m^2 - 9} = 3$ e. $x - 2\sqrt{x - 5} = 5$ f. $\sqrt{y^2 - 2y + 1} = 3$

g. $\sqrt{2x^2 - 4x} = 4$ h. $\sqrt{n^2 + 4} - 1 = 0$ i. $a + \sqrt{a + 9} = 2a - 3$

4. Solve each radical equation.

a. $\sqrt[3]{x} + 3 = 5$ b. $\sqrt[3]{x - 2} = -1$ c. $\sqrt[3]{2p + 3} = -3$

d. $\sqrt[3]{5 - 3y} = 2$ e. $\sqrt[3]{2t - 4} + 3 = 1$ f. $\sqrt[3]{3y - 2} - 3 = 1$

g. $\sqrt[3]{n^2 - 1} - 1 = 2$ h. $\sqrt[3]{\frac{b}{2} + 3} - 5 = -2$ i. $\sqrt[3]{-x + 5} + 3 = 5$

5. The perimeter of a right-angled triangle is 12 m. One leg of the triangle is 1 m longer than the other. What are the dimensions of the triangle?

EXTRA

Continued Radicals

Continued radicals are expressions of the form $\sqrt{n + \sqrt{n + \sqrt{n + \sqrt{n + \ldots}}}}$.
Sometimes, these radicals are actually equal to a *rational* number. To find the value of such a radical notice that, if $n = 2$ and x is equal to the entire expression, then:

$$x = \sqrt{2 + \underbrace{\sqrt{2 + \sqrt{2 + \sqrt{2 + \ldots}}}}}$$

This is also equal to x.

Therefore, this equation is equivalent to the equation $x = \sqrt{2 + x}$, which is readily solved. Use this concept to find the value of each expression.

1. $\sqrt{2 + \sqrt{2 + \sqrt{2 + \ldots}}}$ 2. $\sqrt{6 + \sqrt{6 + \sqrt{6 + \ldots}}}$

3-6 Solving Equations with Two Radicals

Radical equations with more than one radical term can also be solved by isolating radicals and raising both sides of the equation to an appropriate power.

EXAMPLE 1: Solve $\sqrt{x} + \sqrt{x+21} = 7$.

$$\sqrt{x+21} = 7 - \sqrt{x}$$ Isolate one radical.

$$(\sqrt{x+21})^2 = (7 - \sqrt{x})^2$$ Square both sides.

$$x + 21 = 49 - 14\sqrt{x} + x$$

$$14\sqrt{x} = 28$$ Isolate the other radical.

$$\sqrt{x} = 2$$

$$(\sqrt{x})^2 = (2)^2$$ Square both sides.

$$x = 4$$

Check: $\text{L.S.} = \sqrt{x} + \sqrt{x+21}$
$= \sqrt{4} + \sqrt{4+21}$
$= \sqrt{4} + \sqrt{25}$
$= 2 + 5$
$= 7$
$= \text{R.S.}$ ✓

Verify the root by checking whether the left side equals the right side.

The solution to the given equation is $x = 4$.

Your work is simplified if you leave the simpler radical for last.

EXAMPLE 2: Solve $\sqrt{3x+1} - \sqrt{x-1} = 2$.

$$\sqrt{3x+1} = \sqrt{x-1} + 2$$

$$(\sqrt{3x+1})^2 = (\sqrt{x-1} + 2)^2$$

$$3x + 1 = x - 1 + 4\sqrt{x-1} + 4$$

$$2x - 2 = 4\sqrt{x-1}$$

$$(2x-2)^2 = (4\sqrt{x-1})^2$$

$$4x^2 - 8x + 4 = 16(x-1)$$

$$4x^2 - 8x + 4 = 16x - 16$$

$$4x^2 - 24x + 20 = 0$$

$$4(x-1)(x-5) = 0$$

$$\therefore x = 1 \text{ or } x = 5$$

Verify both roots.
Check for $x = 1$:
$\text{L.S.} = \sqrt{3x+1} - \sqrt{x-1}$
$= \sqrt{3(1)+1} - \sqrt{1-1}$
$= \sqrt{4} - \sqrt{0}$
$= 2$
$= \text{R.S.}$ ✓

Check for $x = 5$.
$\text{L.S.} = \sqrt{3x+1} - \sqrt{x-1}$
$= \sqrt{3(5)+1} - \sqrt{5-1}$
$= \sqrt{16} - \sqrt{4}$
$= 4 - 2$
$= 2$
$= \text{R.S.}$ ✓

The solutions to the equation are $x = 1$ and $x = 5$.

EXERCISE 3-6

A 1. Solve each radical equation. Verify all roots.

a. $\sqrt{x} + \sqrt{x-5} = 5$

b. $\sqrt{2x-7} - \sqrt{x} = 1$

c. $\sqrt{y-9} = \sqrt{y} - 1$

d. $\sqrt{3b} - \sqrt{b-3} = 3$

e. $\sqrt{x+5} = \sqrt{x} + \sqrt{5}$

f. $\sqrt{z+5} = \sqrt{z} - \sqrt{5}$

g. $\sqrt{m-5} = \sqrt{m} - \sqrt{5}$

h. $\sqrt{x-5} = \sqrt{x} + \sqrt{5}$

i. $\sqrt{3x+1} - \sqrt{2x} = 1$

j. $\sqrt{3a+1} - \sqrt{5a} = -1$

B 2. Solve each radical equation.

a. $\dfrac{1}{\sqrt{x-2}} = \dfrac{2}{\sqrt{x+2}}$

b. $\dfrac{1}{\sqrt{y+5}} = \dfrac{\sqrt{y+5}}{2y-1}$

c. $\sqrt{z+1} = \dfrac{6}{\sqrt{z-4}}$

d. $\sqrt{x-1} = \dfrac{x+1}{\sqrt{x+4}}$

e. $\dfrac{1}{\sqrt{3x}} = \dfrac{\sqrt{x+1}}{2x}$

f. $\dfrac{3}{\sqrt{2t+5}} = \dfrac{2\sqrt{t-1}}{t}$

3. Solve.

a. $\sqrt{a+4} + \sqrt{a-4} = 4$

b. $\sqrt{x+3} + \sqrt{x-3} = 3$

c. $\sqrt{4x+5} - \sqrt{2x} = \sqrt{5}$

d. $\sqrt{x+3} - \sqrt{x-2} = 1$

e. $\sqrt{k^2-9} - \sqrt{k^2+11} = -1$

f. $\sqrt{x^2+3x-1} + \sqrt{x^2-x-1} = 2$

g. $\sqrt{x^2+2x+1} - \sqrt{x^2-x+4} = 1$

h. $\sqrt{3m+2} - \sqrt{m+2} = \sqrt{8}$

i. $\sqrt{b^2+3b+2} - \sqrt{b^2+1} = \sqrt{2}$

j. $\sqrt{x^2-1} - \sqrt{x^2-2x-3} = \sqrt{2}$

k. $\sqrt{x} + \sqrt{x-5} = \dfrac{10}{\sqrt{x}}$

l. $\dfrac{3\sqrt{x}}{\sqrt{x-3}} + 2 = 5$

m. $\sqrt{y-1} + \dfrac{2}{\sqrt{y-1}} = \sqrt{y+4}$

n. $\sqrt{x+4} - \dfrac{12}{\sqrt{x-3}} = 0$

o. $\dfrac{1}{\sqrt{x-5}} + \dfrac{1}{\sqrt{x}} = \dfrac{5}{3\sqrt{x-5}}$

p. $\dfrac{1}{\sqrt{g-6}} + \dfrac{1}{\sqrt{g+6}} = \dfrac{3}{\sqrt{g+6}}$

4. Isolate the indicated variable.

a. $V = \sqrt{\dfrac{GM}{R}}$; R

b. $T = 2\pi\sqrt{\dfrac{l}{g}}$; l

c. $\dfrac{1}{f} = \sqrt{d^2 + l^2}$; d

d. $\dfrac{1}{\sqrt{z}} = \dfrac{1}{r} + \dfrac{1}{x}$; z

C 5. A hydro pole is supported by 18 m of guy wire in two pieces. One piece is attached 3 m up the pole and the other is attached 12 m up the pole. The longer piece is secured 1 m further away from the base of the pole than the shorter. How far from the pole is each piece secured?

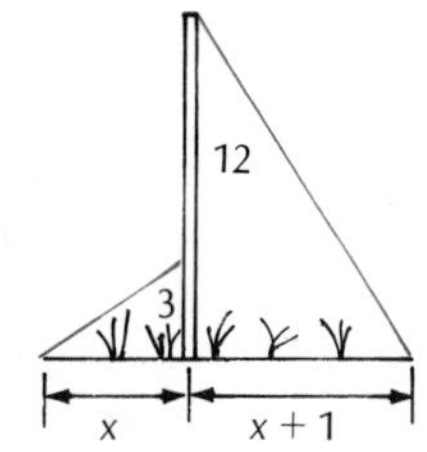

3-7 Solving Exponential Equations

Many natural systems, like population growth, can be described by equations of the form $y = ab^x$, where a variable appears in an exponent. These **exponential equations** can be solved by noting that, if $b^m = b^n$, then it must be true that $m = n$.

EXAMPLE 1: Solve and check.

a.
$$3^x = 81$$
$$3^x = 3^4$$
$$\therefore x = 4$$

Rewrite 81 as a power with base 3: $3 \times 3 \times 3 \times 3$, or 3^4.

Check: L.S. $= 3^x$ $= 3^4$ $= 81$ R.S. $= 81$ $=$ L.S. ✓

b.
$$2^{2x+1} = 128$$
$$2^{2x+1} = 2^7$$
$$\therefore 2x + 1 = 7$$
$$x = 3$$

Rewrite 128 as 2^7.

Check: L.S. $= 2^{2x+1}$ $= 2^{2(3)+1}$ $= 2^7$ $= 128$ R.S. $= 2^7$ $= 128$ $=$ L.S. ✓

Positive or negative exponents may arise in practical applications involving exponential change.

EXAMPLE 2: The amount of sunlight reaching below the surface of the ocean decreases exponentially with the depth of the water. For each increase in depth of 1.5 m, the light intensity is decreased by one half. If I represents the percentage of light and d represents the depth in metres, then an equation relating I and d is $I = 100\% \left(\frac{1}{2}\right)^{\frac{d}{1.5}}$

a. What percentage of light reaches 6 m below the surface?

$$\begin{aligned} I &= 100\% \left(\tfrac{1}{2}\right)^{\frac{d}{1.5}} \\ &= 100\% \left(\tfrac{1}{2}\right)^{\frac{6}{1.5}} \\ &= 100\% \left(\tfrac{1}{2}\right)^{4} \\ &= 100\% \left(\tfrac{1}{16}\right) \\ &= 6.25\% \end{aligned}$$

At the surface, when $d = 0$, $I = 100\%$.

b. A certain underwater plant needs at least 25% sunlight. What is the maximum depth at which that plant could survive?

$$\begin{aligned} I &= 100\%\left(\tfrac{1}{2}\right)^{\frac{d}{1.5}} \\ 25\% &= 100\%\left(\tfrac{1}{2}\right)^{\frac{d}{1.5}} \\ \tfrac{1}{4} &= \left(\tfrac{1}{2}\right)^{\frac{d}{1.5}} \\ \therefore \frac{d}{1.5} &= 2 \\ d &= 3 \end{aligned}$$

EXERCISE 3-7

A 1. For each pair of numbers (n, b), rewrite n as a power with base b.

a. $(81, 3)$ **b.** $(125, 5)$ **c.** $(100, 10)$
d. $(\frac{1}{16}, 2)$ **e.** $(9, \frac{1}{3})$ **f.** $(0.001, 10)$

2. Solve each exponential equation.

a. $2^x = 64$ **b.** $3^y = 243$ **c.** $5^b = 25$
d. $x^3 = 125$ **e.** $y^4 = 10\,000$ **f.** $3^z = 2187$
g. $4^y = 256$ **h.** $10^a = 1000$ **i.** $7^x = 343$

B 3. Solve and check.

a. $3^x = \frac{1}{27}$ **b.** $5^y = 0.2$ **c.** $2^m = 0.0625$
d. $2^x = \frac{1}{8}$ **e.** $10^y = 0.0001$ **f.** $3^a = 0.\overline{1}$
g. $4^r = \frac{1}{64}$ **h.** $2^t = \frac{1}{32}$ **i.** $5^x = \frac{1}{625}$

4. Solve for x.

a. $3^{x+1} = 27$ **b.** $2^{x-2} = 64$ **c.** $2^{3x} = 512$
d. $5^{x+2} = 5$ **e.** $7^{3x+1} = \frac{1}{49}$ **f.** $2^{4x+1} = 0.125$
g. $2^{\frac{x}{5}} = \frac{1}{16}$ **h.** $10^{\frac{24}{x}} = 0.0001$ **i.** $4^{\frac{x}{3}+2} = 4$

5. Solve.

a. $15(3)^a = 135$ **b.** $3.5(2)^x = 28$ **c.** $1500(2)^y = 375$
d. $0.65(10)^x = 6500$ **e.** $4800(10)^m = 4.8$ **f.** $2.4(2)^{x+2} = 0.15$
g. $5(2)^{\frac{x}{7}} = 0.625$ **h.** $7.5(5)^z = 1.2 \times 10^{-2}$ **i.** $18(5)^{\frac{9}{h}} = 0.72$

C 6. Solve.

a. $6(4)^x = 12$ **b.** $15(9)^x = 45$ **c.** $7(8)^x = 3.5$
d. $5(8)^x = 20$ **e.** $54(9)^x = 2$ **f.** $10(8)^x = 40$

7. The air pressure exerted on an object depends on the object's height above Earth. An equation relating air pressure in kilopascals (kPa), P, and height in metres, h, is: $P = 100\left(\frac{1}{2}\right)^{\frac{h}{5000}}$.

a. Apply the equation to verify that the air pressure at sea level is 100 kPa and that, at 5000 m, air pressure is approximately 50 kPa.
b. What air pressure is exerted on an object at a height of 15 000 m?

8. The Richter Scale provides a measure of the amount of energy released by an earthquake. Each increase of one in the Richter number indicates an increase by a factor of 30 in the energy released:
Energy $= 63000(10)^{1.5R}$ J (joules), where R is the Richter number.

a. An earthquake in Alaska in 1964 had a Richter number of 8.6 and released 5.0×10^{17} J of energy. In 1976, an earthquake in China measured 7.6 on the Richter scale. How much energy was released by that earthquake?
b. The 1897 earthquake in Assam, India measured 8.7 on the Richter Scale. In the same year, an earthquake in San Francisco registered 8.25. Find the energy of each of these earthquakes.

Application

Growth and Decay

In an ideal system, one where factors such as food supply, disease, and so on, can be controlled, population undergoes exponential growth. For example, some bacteria double their amount every 16 h. The following equation gives the population size P after t hours have elapsed, where P_0 is the original population.

$$P = P_0 2^{\frac{t}{16}}$$

If originally there were 250 bacteria on a Petri dish, the equation could be applied to find the length of time that must elapse before there will be 4000.

Substitute $P_0 = 250$ and $P = 4000$ into the equation and solve for t.

$$\begin{aligned} 4000 &= 250(2^{\frac{t}{16}}) \\ 2^{\frac{t}{16}} &= \frac{4000}{250} \\ 2^{\frac{t}{16}} &= 16 \qquad 16 = 2^4 \\ 2^{\frac{t}{16}} &= 2^4 \\ \frac{t}{16} &= 4 \\ t &= 64 \end{aligned}$$

Therefore, there will be 4000 bacteria when 64 h have elapsed.

Some systems undergo *decay* at an exponential rate. Many radioactive substances, for instance, decay in such a way that the amount present is halved after a certain time period, which is called the **half-life** of that particular substance.

The following equation gives the amount A of radioactive material that is left after t days have elapsed, where A_0 is the original amount and h is the half-life of the substance.

$$A = A_0\left(\frac{1}{2}\right)^{\frac{t}{h}}$$

Given that 8 mg of radon gas decayed at such a rate that only 0.25 mg was left after 19 days, the equation can be applied to find the half-life of radon gas. Substitute $A_0 = 8$, $A = 0.25$, and $t = 19$ into the equation and solve for h.

$$\begin{aligned} 0.25 &= 8\left(\frac{1}{2}\right)^{\frac{19}{h}} \\ \left(\frac{1}{2}\right)^{\frac{19}{h}} &= \frac{0.25}{8} \\ \left(\frac{1}{2}\right)^{\frac{19}{h}} &= 0.03125 \\ \left(\frac{1}{2}\right)^{\frac{19}{h}} &= \frac{1}{32} \qquad \frac{1}{32} = \left(\frac{1}{2}\right)^5 \\ \left(\frac{1}{2}\right)^{\frac{19}{h}} &= \left(\frac{1}{2}\right)^5 \\ \frac{19}{h} &= 5 \\ h &= 3.8 \end{aligned}$$

Therefore, the half-life of radon gas is 3.8 days. This value for h could now be applied to predict the amount left after a given time period, for instance.

1. Under certain conditions, you could expect a rabbit population to double at approximately regular intervals. Suppose that one hundred rabbits were brought to a small island where there had been no rabbit population previously. Two years later, there are 6400 rabbits on the island.

   a. About how long does it take the rabbit population to double?
   b. What will be the population in an additional year?
   c. How long would it be from the original introduction of rabbits before there were one million rabbits on the island?
   d. Can the population keep doubling forever? Discuss various reasons for your answer.

2. Cobalt 60 (written Co_{60}) is a radioactive substance, used widely in medicine and industry when powerful x-rays are required. Co_{60} has a half-life of 5.3 years.

   a. How much of a 100 mg sample of Co_{60} is left after 21.2 years?
   b. Will there be more or less than 50 mg left after 10 years?
   c. How long will it take before there is less than 1 mg left?

3. All living things contain a constant proportion of carbon 14 (C_{14}), which undergoes exponential decay after death with a half-life of 5750 years. Because of this comparatively long half-life, archaeological finds of bones, fossils, and other organic matter can be dated by measuring the amount of C_{14} left.

   a. An archaeologist tests some organic matter from an ancient campsite and finds there is between 10% and 15% of the original amount of C_{14} left in the sample. About how old is the sample?
   b. An ancient grave is presumed to be about 12 000 years old. About what percentage of C_{14} should be present in any organic material taken from the site?

4. The table at right gives Canada's population each decade from 1851-1981. Use the table to answer the following.

   a. Starting from the year 1851, about how long did it take for the population to double? Starting from each year given, 1861 through to 1941, about how long did it take?
   b. Use your calculator to find the ratios of populations between each 10 year interval (for instance, the ratio of the 1851 population to the 1861 population, the 1861 population to the 1871 population, and so on). Use those ratios to predict Canada's population in 1991, 2001, 2011, and 2021.

Year	Population (in millions)
1851	2.4
1861	3.2
1871	3.7
1881	4.3
1891	4.8
1901	5.4
1911	7.2
1921	8.8
1931	10.4
1941	11.5
1951	14.0
1961	18.2
1971	21.6
1981	24.3

Review

1. Evaluate.

a. $81^{\frac{3}{4}}$ **b.** $9^{1.5}$ **c.** $4^{-2.5}$ **d.** $\left(\frac{16}{25}\right)^{-\frac{3}{2}}$

2. Write as a radical.

a. $7^{\frac{3}{4}}$ **b.** $12^{\frac{2}{3}}$ **c.** $5^{0.8}$ **d.** $11^{1.5}$

3. Evaluate.

a. $\sqrt[3]{9}\sqrt[6]{27}$ **b.** $\sqrt{3}\sqrt[4]{9}$ **c.** $\sqrt{27} \div \sqrt[3]{9}$ **d.** $\sqrt[4]{10} \div \sqrt{5}$

4. Evaluate and leave each answer in exponential form.

a. $4^{2.5} \div 4^{0.75} \times 4^{0.6}$ **b.** $8^{\frac{2}{3}} \times 2^{\frac{1}{3}} \div 4^{\frac{3}{2}}$

5. Write as a power.

a. $\sqrt[3]{x^2}$ **b.** $\sqrt[4]{a^3}$ **c.** $\sqrt[5]{m^6}$ **d.** $\sqrt[4]{z^8}$

6. Write as a quotient of integers.

a. 0.68 **b.** -0.0125 **c.** $0.\overline{36}$ **d.** $1.3\overline{2}$

7. Rewrite as entire radicals.

a. $3\sqrt{5}$ **b.** $-2\sqrt[3]{3}$ **c.** $x\sqrt{3xy}$ **d.** $-2ab^2\sqrt[3]{ab}$

8. Simplify.

a. $\sqrt{45}$ **b.** $\sqrt[3]{16}$ **c.** $\sqrt{20x^3y^{-4}}$ **d.** $\sqrt[3]{72x^4y}$

9. Multiply and divide.

a. $\sqrt{8}\sqrt{12}$ **b.** $\sqrt[3]{15}\sqrt[3]{75}$ **c.** $\frac{\sqrt{x}}{\sqrt{2}}$ **d.** $\frac{\sqrt[3]{48}}{\sqrt[3]{3}}$

e. $\frac{\sqrt{30}}{\sqrt{7}} \times \frac{\sqrt{14}}{\sqrt{3}}$ **f.** $\frac{\sqrt[3]{10}}{\sqrt[3]{3}} \times \frac{\sqrt[3]{75}}{\sqrt[3]{2}}$ **g.** $\frac{\sqrt{4a}}{\sqrt{18b}} \times \frac{\sqrt{b^3}}{\sqrt{2a}}$ **h.** $\frac{\sqrt[3]{3m^2}}{\sqrt[3]{4n}} \times \frac{\sqrt[3]{12n}}{\sqrt[3]{m}}$

10. Add and subtract, as indicated.

a. $3\sqrt{5} - 7\sqrt{5}$ **b.** $\sqrt{12} - \sqrt{75} + 2\sqrt{27}$

c. $\sqrt{45} + \sqrt{8} - \sqrt{20} + \sqrt{32}$ **d.** $3\sqrt[3]{16} + \sqrt[3]{250} - \sqrt[3]{54}$

11. Multiply.

a. $\sqrt{5}(2\sqrt{2} - \sqrt{5})$ **b.** $3\sqrt{2}(2 + 3\sqrt{8})$ **c.** $(3 + \sqrt{3})(2 - \sqrt{3})$

d. $(3\sqrt{5} + 1)(\sqrt{5} - \sqrt{2})$ **e.** $(\sqrt{6} + 2\sqrt{3})^2$ **f.** $(\sqrt{6} - 2\sqrt{3})(\sqrt{2} + 3\sqrt{3})$

12. Find the product of each expression with its conjugate.

a. $1 - \sqrt{2}$ **b.** $3 + 2\sqrt{5}$ **c.** $\sqrt{7} - \sqrt{2}$ **d.** $2\sqrt{6} - \sqrt{5}$

13. Rationalize each denominator and simplify.

a. $\frac{2}{\sqrt{5}}$ **b.** $\frac{\sqrt{10} - \sqrt{15}}{\sqrt{2}}$ **c.** $\frac{\sqrt{2} + 3\sqrt{5}}{2\sqrt{5} - \sqrt{2}}$ **d.** $\sqrt{6} - \frac{\sqrt{2}}{\sqrt{3}}$

14. Solve each radical equation.

a. $3\sqrt{x} = 15$
b. $2\sqrt{a} - 1 = 3$
c. $\sqrt{x - 3} = 4$
d. $\sqrt{y^2 + 3y - 4} = 0$
e. $x + \sqrt{2x + 2} = 2x - 3$
f. $\sqrt[3]{m - 2} - 3 = 5$

15. Solve each radical equation.

a. $\sqrt{x} + \sqrt{x + 7} = 7$
b. $\sqrt{3x - 2} - 1 = \sqrt{2x - 2}$
c. $\dfrac{1}{\sqrt{x}} + \dfrac{1}{\sqrt{3x + 4}} = \dfrac{3}{\sqrt{3x + 4}}$
d. $\sqrt{x^2 + x + 5} - \sqrt{x^2 - 2x + 1} = 2$
e. $\sqrt{x - 1} + \sqrt{3x + 1} = 6$
f. $\sqrt{x - 6} + \dfrac{4}{\sqrt{x - 6}} = \sqrt{x + 6}$

16. Isolate the indicated variable.

a. $v = \sqrt{\dfrac{2E}{m}}$; E
b. $a = \sqrt{\dfrac{12I}{m} - b^2}$; I

17. Solve each exponential equation.

a. $3^x = 243$
b. $b^3 = 216$
c. $10^a = 0.0001$
d. $6^y = 0.02\overline{7}$
e. $10^{b-1} = 1000$
f. $3^{3x} = 81$
g. $5^{2x+1} = 0.2$
h. $25(4^z) = 1600$
i. $18(3^{x+3}) = \frac{2}{3}$

18. Apply the Pythagorean Theorem to find each missing dimension. Express answers in simplest radical form.

a.

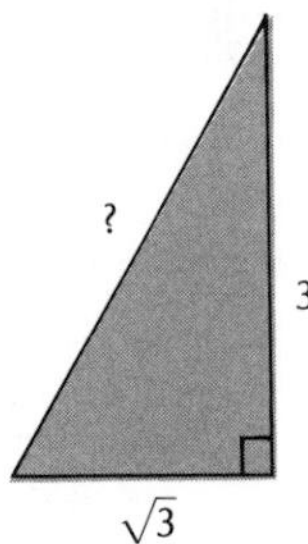

b.

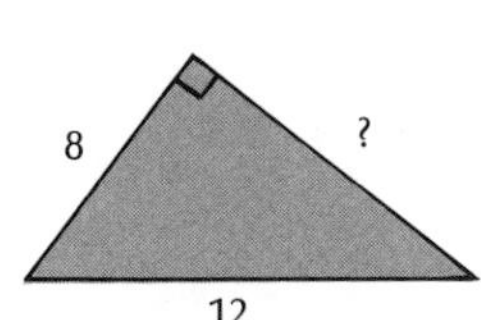

c.

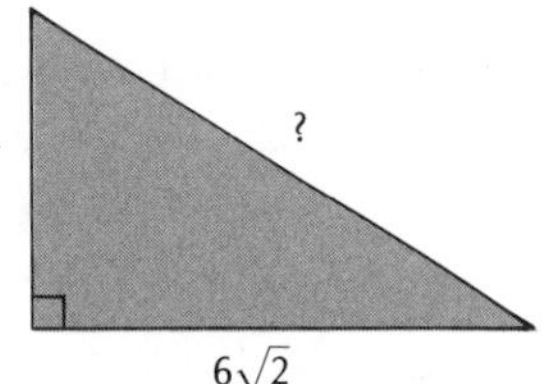

19. The decibel (dB) scale is used to measure loudness. Sound intensity, measured in watts per square metre (W/m²), increases by a factor of 10 for each 10 dB increase. The equation for converting decibel scale numbers to sound intensity (I) is: $I = (10^{\frac{x}{10} - 12})$ W/m².

a. Using a calculator as necessary, apply the formula to find each sound intensity.
   i. Street traffic: 70 dB
   ii. Interior of a discotheque: 110 dB
   iii. Pneumatic drill at 15 m: 85 dB

b. What would be the decibel rating for a rocket with a sound intensity of 1 000 000 W/m²?

Test

Unit 3

1. Evaluate.

   a. $81^{\frac{3}{4}}$ b. $64^{-\frac{2}{3}}$ c. $25^{1.5}$ d. $\left(\frac{8}{27}\right)^{-\frac{2}{3}}$

2. Evaluate and leave each expression in simplest radical form.

   a. $\sqrt{6}\sqrt{3}$ b. $\dfrac{\sqrt{8}}{\sqrt[4]{4}}$ c. $7^{3.5} \div 7^{4} \times 7$ d. $8^{\frac{2}{3}} \div 8^{\frac{1}{2}} \times 8^{\frac{1}{3}}$

3. Write each as a quotient of integers.

   a. 0.35 b. $0.\overline{72}$ c. $-3.\overline{7}$ d. $0.3\overline{24}$

4. Rewrite as entire radicals.

   a. $2\sqrt{11}$ b. $-3\sqrt[3]{5}$ c. $x^2y\sqrt{xy}$ d. $2xy^2\sqrt{3x^2y}$

5. Multiply and divide, as indicated. Leave answers in simplest radical form.

   a. $\sqrt{6}\sqrt{15}$ b. $\sqrt[3]{18}\sqrt[3]{20}$ c. $\dfrac{\sqrt{72}}{\sqrt{6}}$ d. $\dfrac{\sqrt[3]{108}}{\sqrt[3]{2}}$

   e. $\dfrac{\sqrt{280}}{\sqrt{6}} \times \dfrac{\sqrt{15}}{\sqrt{14}}$ f. $\dfrac{\sqrt[3]{12}}{\sqrt[3]{5}} \times \dfrac{\sqrt[3]{45}}{\sqrt[3]{2}}$ g. $\dfrac{\sqrt{x^4}}{\sqrt{y}} \times \dfrac{\sqrt{xy^2}}{\sqrt{x^2}}$ h. $\dfrac{\sqrt[3]{12b^2}}{\sqrt[3]{5b}} \times \dfrac{\sqrt[3]{20a}}{\sqrt[3]{3a}}$

6. Add and subtract as indicated.

   a. $8\sqrt{8} - 3\sqrt{2}$ b. $3\sqrt{12} + \sqrt{27} - \dfrac{2}{\sqrt{3}}$ c. $\sqrt[3]{16} - \sqrt{12} + \sqrt{50} + \sqrt[3]{2}$

7. Rationalize each denominator and simplify.

   a. $\dfrac{1}{\sqrt{7}}$ b. $\dfrac{1}{\sqrt{12}}$ c. $\dfrac{8}{\sqrt{10}}$ d. $\dfrac{1}{2 + \sqrt{3}}$

   e. $\dfrac{5}{4 - \sqrt{6}}$ f. $\sqrt{5} - \dfrac{3}{\sqrt{5}}$ g. $\dfrac{\sqrt{6}}{\sqrt{3} - \sqrt{6}}$ h. $\dfrac{\sqrt{5} + \sqrt{2}}{3\sqrt{5} - \sqrt{2}}$

8. Solve each radical equation.

   a. $\sqrt{3x + 1} = 5$ b. $\sqrt{100 - 2x} = 5\sqrt{2}$ c. $\sqrt{y^2 - 3y - 6} = 2$

   d. $m + \sqrt{2m + 1} = 2m - 1$ e. $\sqrt{3z + 4} - \sqrt{z + 2} = 2$ f. $\dfrac{1}{\sqrt{3a + 1}} = \dfrac{\sqrt{3a + 1} -}{a + 2}$

9. Solve each exponential equation.

   a. $3^x = 81$ b. $5^m = 0.04$ c. $2^{x + 1} = 32$

   d. $220(2)^b = 27.5$ e. $0.2(10)^{\frac{x}{3} + 1} = 2000$ f. $40(2)^{\frac{8}{h}} = 10$

10. An amount of money (A_0) invested at an interest rate of $14\frac{7}{8}\%$ per annum will increase according to the equation $A = A_0(2)^{\frac{n}{5}}$ where n is the number of years.

    a. What will be the net amount of investing \$1000 for 15 years?

    b. How long will it take \$1 to increase to \$100, to the nearest year? You may use a calculator to find the answer.

Cumulative Review

1. Simplify.
   a. $(x^2 + 2xy + x + 4) - 5x$
   b. $6x + 5x^2 + (3y - 4)$
   c. $3t^2 + 4t + 5 - (6t + 2t^2)$
   d. $(5x^4 + 6x^3 + 7x^2) - (4x^2 - 3)$

2. Multiply.
   a. $(x + 3)(5x^3 + x + 1)$
   b. $(x^2 + x + 1)(x^3 + x^2 + 2)$
   c. $(x + 7)(x^2 + 6x + 9)$
   d. $x(x^2 + 1)(x^3 + 1)$
   e. $(5x + 7)(x^3 - 3)$
   f. $(x + 1)(x^2 + 2)(x^3 + 3)$

3. Divide.
   a. $(x^3 + 6x^2 + 6x + 2) \div (x + 2)$
   b. $(x^2 + 1) \div x$
   c. $(x^3 + x + 2) \div (x + 1)$
   d. $(x^5 - 1) \div (x - 1)$

4. Solve.
   a. $x + 5 + 4(x - 2) = 15 - x$
   b. $3x(2x + 2) - x(5x - 2) = x^2 + 64$
   c. $(x^3 + x^2 + 4) \div (x + 2) = x^2$
   d. $x^2 + x - 132 = 0$
   e. $48x^2 + 22x - 15 = 0$
   f. $\dfrac{x + 5}{2x + 1} = x - 3$

5. Factor fully.
   a. $x^3 + x^2y + x^2 + xy - 6x - 6y$
   b. $x^3 - 2x^2 - x - 6$
   c. $12x^2 + 24x + 16$
   d. $x^3 + x^2 + x + 1$

6. Multiply or divide, as indicated.
   a. $\dfrac{2a^2 + a - 6}{4a^2 - 3a - 1} \times \dfrac{4a^3 - 3a^2 - 1}{2a^2 - a - 3}$
   b. $\dfrac{a^2 + a - 2}{a^3 + a^2} \div \dfrac{a - 2}{a^4 - a^3 - 2a^2}$

7. A bus starts from an intersection with an acceleration of 2 m/s². Its distance from the intersection, *d* metres, at time *t* seconds, is given by the equation $d = t^2$. A man 12 m behind the bus as it starts immediately begins to sprint at a constant speed of 7 m/s. His distance in metres from the intersection is given by the equation $d = 7t - 12$.
   a. Does the man catch the bus? If so, when?
   b. How far does he have to run before catching up with it?

8. Jane and Rita shared a rental car to drive from Quebec to Los Angeles, a distance of about 4000 km. Jane drove at an average speed of 80 km/h and Rita drove at an average speed of 110 km/h. Each drove for an equal length of time on the trip. How far did Jane drive?

9. A herd of 50 caribou migrates from its summer to its winter grazing grounds, a distance of 500 km. Each caribou will graze 0.1 hectares of land per day for every 10 km the herd travels in a day. Also, 5 caribou will fall to the wolves midway through the journey. The herd covers the distance in 20 days.
   a. What is the average speed of the herd? Answer in kilometres per day.
   b. How many hectares of land does the herd graze?

4 Coordinate Geometry and Straight Line Graphs

4-1 The Cartesian Coordinate Plane

Student Council hired a band for \$250 for the annual fund-raising dance and sold tickets at \$5 each. An equation to represent the amount raised, y dollars, given that x tickets are sold, is: $y = 5x - 250$.

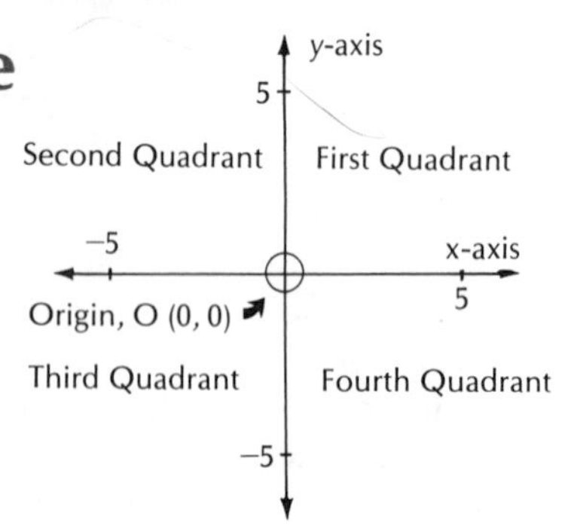

Graphing an equation on the **Cartesian coordinate plane** is a useful method for illustrating the relationship between two variables. On the grid at the right, some basic terminology of graphing is reviewed.

EXAMPLE 1: Graph the equation $y = 5x - 250$, for $x \geq 0$, $x \in \boldsymbol{R}$, by first making a table of values.

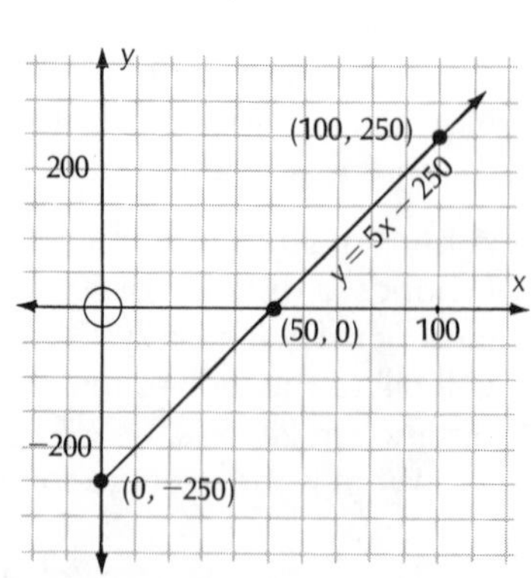

x	y
0	−250
50	0
100	250

Since the equation contains no variables of degree greater than 1, the equation is **linear** and its graph is a straight line. Two points are sufficient to determine the line. A third point provides a valuable check.

The line represented by $y = 5x - 250$ crosses the x-axis at $(50, 0)$. The **x-intercept** of the line is 50. The line crosses the y-axis at $(0, -250)$. The **y-intercept** is -250. In the context of the school dance, the x-intercept corresponds to the break-even point for holding the dance, since it indicates that $0 is raised when 50 tickets are sold. The y-intercept corresponds to Student Council's expenses for the dance, or the $250 spent to hire the band.

Linear equations can often be graphed by finding the intercepts.

EXAMPLE 2: Draw the graph of $4x - y = 8$ by finding the intercepts. Check by finding a third point.

To find the x-intercept, let $y = 0$.

$$4x - y = 8$$
$$4x - 0 = 8$$
$$x = 2$$

To find the y-intercept, let $x = 0$.

$$4x - y = 8$$
$$0 - y = 8$$
$$y = -8$$

The x-intercept is 2 and the y-intercept is -8, so two points on the graph are $(2, 0)$ and $(0, -8)$. To find a third point on the line, select a vlaue for x or y and solve for the remaining variable.

Let $x = 1$. Then: $4(1) - y = 8$

$$4 - y = 8$$
$$-y = 4$$
$$y = -4$$

A third point is $(1, -4)$.

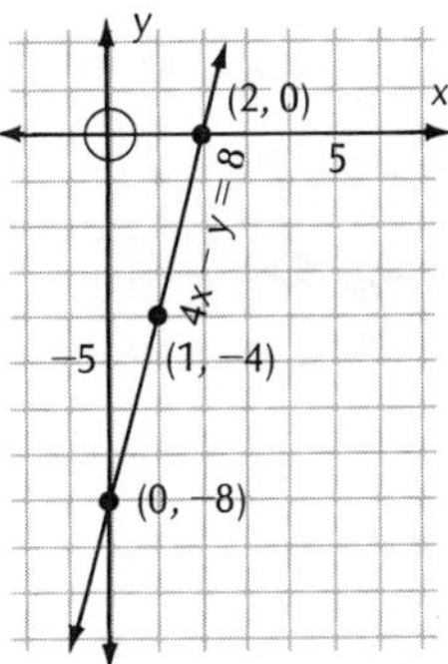

If a linear relation has only one intercept, then its graph is a horizontal or vertical line through that intercept.

EXAMPLE 3: Graph each equation for $x, y \in \mathbf{R}$.

a. $y + 2x = 0$

x	0	1	−1
y	0	−2	2

Rewrite as $y = -2x$.

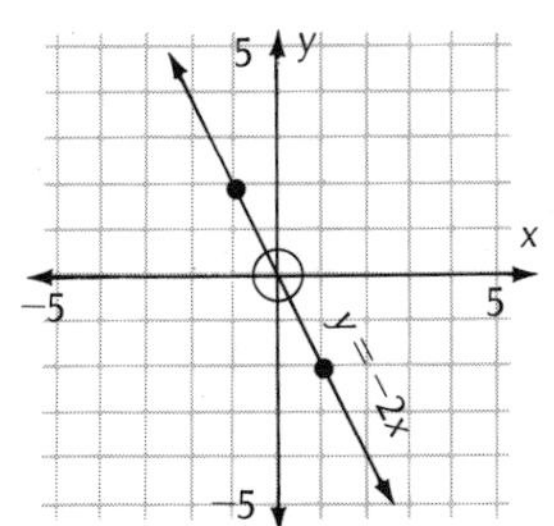

The intercepts yield one point only.

b. $y = 3$

x	0	1	−1
y	3	3	3

y always has a value of 3.

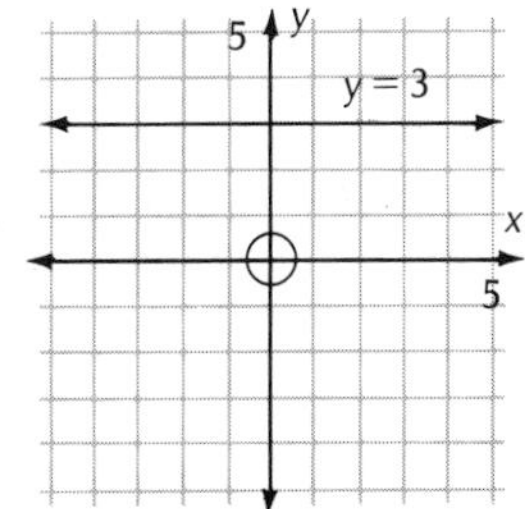

There is only one intercept.

c. $x = -2$

x	−2	−2	−2
y	0	1	−1

x always has a value of −2.

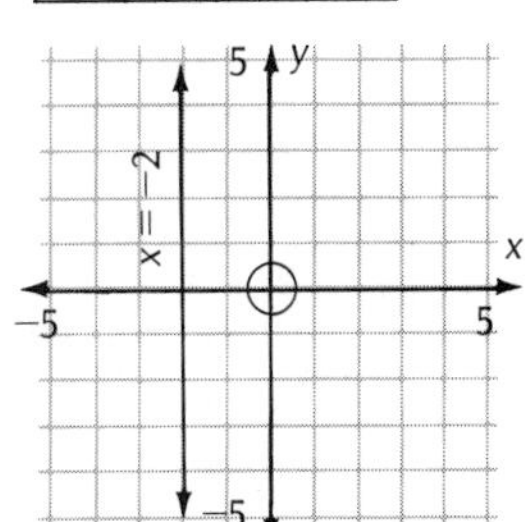

EXERCISE 4-1

A **1.** For the first graph at the right, name the points in the indicated quadrant.

- **a.** first quadrant
- **b.** second quadrant
- **c.** third quadrant
- **d.** fourth quadrant

2. For the first graph, name the points on the x-axis; on the y-axis.

3. For the first graph, name the point with the given coordinates.

- **a.** $(3, 5)$ **b.** $(0, -3)$
- **c.** $(-3, 0)$ **d.** $(-6, -6)$

4. State the x- and y-intercepts of each line in the second graph at the right.

5.
- **a.** For line b, state the value of x when $y = -1$.
- **b.** For line a, state the value of y when $x = 6$.
- **c.** For line c, find y when $x = 2$.
- **d.** For line a, find x when $y = 4$.

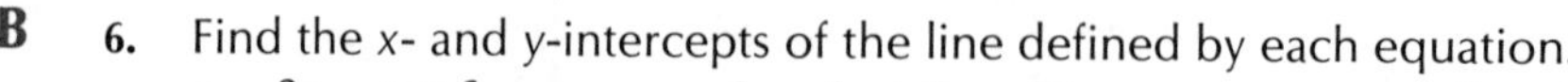

B **6.** Find the x- and y-intercepts of the line defined by each equation.

- **a.** $3x - y = 6$ **b.** $4x + 5y = 20$ **c.** $x - 7y = 14$
- **d.** $y = 2x + 4$ **e.** $x = -3y - 1$ **f.** $y = \frac{1}{2}x$

7. Graph each equation, using separate sets of axes.

- **a.** $3x + 5y = 15$ **b.** $y = -4x$ **c.** $x - 2y + 4 = 0$
- **d.** $5x + 6y + 30 = 0$ **e.** $y = \frac{1}{2}x - 2$ **f.** $y = -\frac{1}{3}x + 1$
- **g.** $x = \frac{1}{4}y$ **h.** $2x - 7y + 14 = 0$ **i.** $8x + 7y - 56 = 0$

8. Graph each equation, using the same set of axes.

- **a.** $x = 5$ **b.** $y = 2$ **c.** $x - 4 = 0$
- **d.** $y = -3$ **e.** $y + 2 = 0$ **f.** $x = 0$
- **g.** $y = 0$ **h.** $x = -1$ **i.** $2x + 3 = 0$

9. Graph each pair of equations on the same set of axes. State the point of intersection of each pair of lines.

- **a.** $2x - y = 6$ and $x + 2y = 8$ **b.** $x + y = 3$ and $x - y = 1$
- **c.** $y = 2 - x$ and $x = 6 - 2y$ **d.** $5x + y = 5$ and $x + 2y = -8$

10. Use the graph from example 1 of this lesson to answer the following:

- **a.** How much money is raised if 100 tickets are sold?
- **b.** How many tickets must they sell in order to raise $300?

C **11.** A routine surgical procedure in a veterinary hospital costs \$50 plus \$10 per day for boarding.

a. Write an equation to represent the cost.
b. Graph the equation.
c. What restrictions, if any, apply? Explain.

12. Stephen bought \$48 worth of tapes and records at the sale prices shown.

a. Write an equation to represent his purchase, using x to represent the number of records he bought, and y the number of tapes.
b. Determine the x- and y-intercepts. Give an interpretation of each value.
c. Graph the equation.
d. If Stephen bought four records, how many tapes did he buy?

Record Breaking Prices!		
Records	**Reg.**	**\$9.00**
	Only	**\$6.00**
Tapes	**Reg.**	**\$11.00**
	Only	**\$8.00**

13. At the Racquet Squash Club, the membership fee for one year is \$165. In addition, a fee of \$3.50 is charged each time a court is booked.

a. Define a pair of variables and write an equation that relates the total cost per year for playing squash at the club, and the number of times a court is booked.
b. Graph the equation.
c. If the total cost for one year was \$277, how many times were courts booked?

Historical Note

Srinivasa Ramanujan (1887-1920)

Ramanujan was a remarkable Indian mathematician with an uncanny understanding of number systems. Despite intense poverty and very limited formal education, he made lasting contributions to the study of number theory, pursuing his mathematical interests until his early death from tuberculosis at age 33.

A colleague of Ramanujan, G.H. Hardy, once mentioned on a visit that he had come in a taxi numbered 1729—a number he thought uninteresting. Ramanujan quickly replied that, on the contrary, 1729 is quite a surprising number, as it is the smallest number that can be written as the sum of two cubes in two different ways.

Find the two pairs of cubes.

Find out if there are numbers greater than 1729 that can be written as the sum of two cubes in two different ways.

4-2 Slope

In downhill skiing, one factor to consider is the **slope** or steepness of hills. If a number is used to represent the slope of a beginner's hill, it will be less than the slope of a more advanced hill.

The slope of a line is defined to be $\frac{\text{rise}}{\text{run}}$. On the coordinate plane, the slope of a line through two points can be calculated by finding the ratio of the change in *y*-values to the change in *x*-values. The letter *m* is often used to represent slope.

For $\overline{PQ}$ at the right: $m = \frac{\text{rise}}{\text{run}}$

$= \frac{\text{change in } y}{\text{change in } x}$

$= \frac{5}{6}$

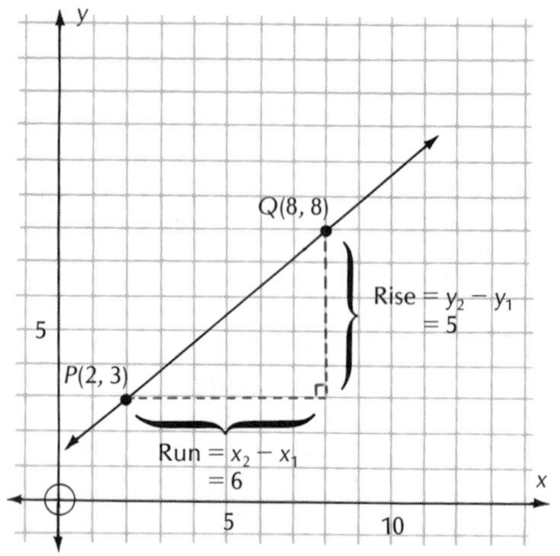

In general, for $\overleftrightarrow{P_1P_2}$: $m = \frac{\text{change in } y}{\text{change in } x}$

$= \frac{y_2 - y_1}{x_2 - x_1}$

EXAMPLE: Find the slope of each segment shown.

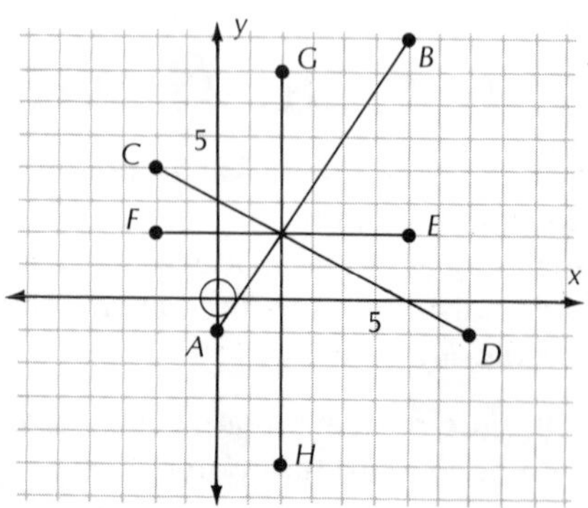

For $\overline{AB}$, $m = \frac{y_2 - y_1}{x_2 - x_1}$

$= \frac{8 - (-1)}{6 - 0}$

$= \frac{3}{2}$

For $\overline{EF}$, $m = \frac{2 - 2}{-2 - 6}$

$= 0$

For $\overline{CD}$, $m = \frac{-1 - 4}{8 - (-2)}$

$= \frac{-1}{2}$

For $\overline{GH}$, $m = \frac{-5 - 7}{2 - 2}$

$= \frac{-12}{0}$

For $\overline{GH}$, *m* is undefined.

Notice how the line segments above illustrate the following descriptions:

A line that slopes upward to the right has a positive slope. A line that slopes upward to the left has a negative slope. A line parallel to the *x*-axis has a slope of zero, and a line parallel to the *y*-axis has an undefined slope, since division by zero is undefined.

EXERCISE 4-2

A 1. Find the slope of the line segment that joins each pair of points.

a. (6, 8) and (5, 3) b. (8, 4) and (7, 0) c. (10, −1) and (8, 8)
d. (3, 3) and (4, 2) e. (−3, 6) and (9, −4) f. (9, −7) and (6, −7)
g. (−8, −4) and (−5, 3) h. (1, −5) and (1, 4) i. (0, 0) and (−5, −6)

2. For the graph at the right, identify lines with the given type of slope.

a. positive slope
b. negative slope
c. slope equal to zero
d. slope undefined

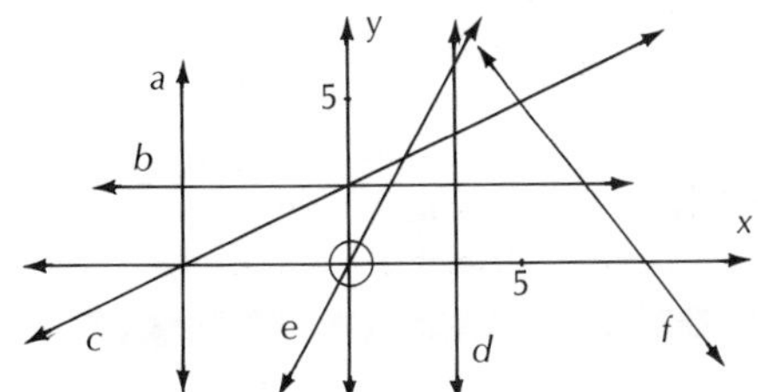

B 3. $R(-8, 9)$ and $S(5, 2)$ are the endpoints of $\overline{RS}$. Show that the slope of $\overline{RS}$ is the same as the slope of $\overline{SR}$.

4. Find the slope of the line containing each pair of points.

a. $\left(\frac{1}{2}, \frac{2}{3}\right)$ and $\left(\frac{3}{4}, \frac{7}{9}\right)$ b. $\left(\frac{4}{5}, \frac{5}{12}\right)$ and $\left(\frac{3}{10}, -\frac{2}{3}\right)$

5. A line through $A(3, -2)$ has a slope $\frac{3}{4}$. Plot the point A and find other points on the line by using the fact that rise : run = 3 : 4. Graph the line by joining the points.

6. Graph the line that passes through the given point P and has the given slope m.

a. $P(4, 2)$, $m = -1$ b. $P(-2, -4)$, $m = 4$ c. $P(3, 0)$, $m = \frac{1}{2}$
d. $P(-1, 3)$, $m = 0$ e. $P(0, 0)$, $m = -\frac{4}{5}$ f. $P(2, -3)$, m undefined

7. Graph the line that passes through $P(1, -2)$ and has slope −2. Identify the x- and y-intercepts of the line.

8. Find the x-intercept of the line that passes through $A(3, 4)$ and has slope 2.

9. A line with slope $-\frac{6}{7}$ passes through the point $C(8, -1)$. Find the point on this line that has a y-coordinate of 5.

10. A line with slope $\frac{4}{5}$ passes through the point $B(-2, 3)$. Find the point on this line that has an x-coordinate of −6.

C 11. Graph each equation.

a. $\frac{y-0}{x-0} = 3$ b. $\frac{y-5}{x-4} = -2$ c. $\frac{y+4}{x-1} = 2$ d. $\frac{y-3}{x+2} = -\frac{3}{5}$

12. Describe how exercises 9 and 10 could be solved without first graphing.

4-3 Slopes of Parallel and Perpendicular Lines

In the graph at the right, $\overline{AB}$ and $\overline{CD}$ are parallel.

For $\overline{AB}$, $m = \dfrac{6 - (-2)}{3 - (-3)} = \dfrac{4}{3}$

For $\overline{CD}$, $m = \dfrac{4 - (-4)}{5 - (-1)} = \dfrac{4}{3}$

Notice that the slopes are equal.

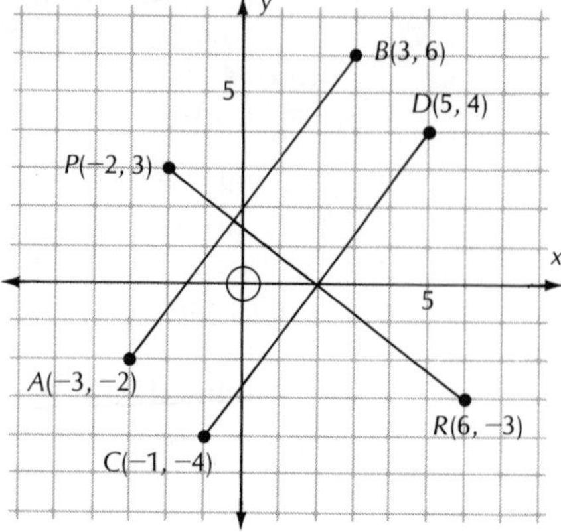

> Parallel lines have equal slopes.
> Lines with equal slopes are parallel.

In the graph, $\overline{PR}$ is drawn perpendicular to both $\overline{AB}$ and $\overline{CD}$.

For $\overline{PR}$, $m = \dfrac{-3 - 3}{6 - (-2)} = -\dfrac{3}{4}$

Notice that $\frac{4}{3} \times (-\frac{3}{4}) = -1$.

> Perpendicular lines have slopes that are negative reciprocals. Two lines whose slopes have a product of −1 are perpendicular.

EXAMPLE 1: Determine whether each pair of line segments is parallel, perpendicular, or neither.

a. $\overline{AB}$ has endpoints $A(-1, 1)$ and $B(3, 3)$; $\overline{CD}$ has endpoints $C(1, -2)$ and $D(9, 2)$.

For $\overline{AB}$, $m = \dfrac{3 - 1}{3 - (-1)}$
$= \frac{1}{2}$

For $\overline{CD}$, $m = \dfrac{2 - (-2)}{9 - 1}$
$= \frac{1}{2}$

Since the slopes are equal, $\overline{AB} \parallel \overline{CD}$.

b. $\overline{AB}$ has endpoints $A(7, 5)$ and $B(-3, 1)$; $\overline{CD}$ has endpoints $C(2, 3)$ and $D(4, -2)$.

For $\overline{AB}$, $m = \dfrac{1 - 5}{-3 - 7}$
$= \frac{2}{5}$

For $\overline{CD}$, $m = \dfrac{-2 - 3}{4 - 2}$
$= -\frac{5}{2}$

Notice that $\left(\frac{2}{5}\right)\left(-\frac{5}{2}\right) = -1$

Since the slopes are negative reciprocals, $\overline{AB} \perp \overline{BC}$.

EXAMPLE 2: Show that $\overline{PQ}$ containing $P(-3, 2)$ and $Q(1, 2)$ is perpendicular to $\overline{RS}$ containing $R(3, 4)$ and $S(3, -1)$.

For $\overline{PQ}$, $m = \frac{2-2}{1-(-3)}$
$= \frac{0}{4}$
$= 0$

For $\overline{RS}$, $m = \frac{-1-4}{3-3}$
$= \frac{-5}{0}$
m is undefined.

Since the slope of $\overline{PQ}$ is 0, $\overline{PQ}$ is parallel to the x-axis.

Since the slope of $\overline{RS}$ is undefined, $\overline{RS}$ is parallel to the y-axis. Since the x- and y-axes are perpendicular to each other, a line parallel to one axis will be perpendicular to the other axis.

$\therefore \overline{PQ} \perp \overline{RS}$

EXAMPLE 3: Given that $\overline{AB}$ with endpoints $A(6, -4)$ and $B(-2, 6)$ is parallel to $\overline{CD}$ with endpoints $C(5, 3)$ and $D(1, y)$, find the value of y.

$\frac{6-(-4)}{-2-6} = \frac{y-3}{1-5}$

Since $\overline{AB} \parallel \overline{CD}$, their slopes must be equal.

$\frac{10}{-8} = \frac{y-3}{-4}$

$y - 3 = -4\left(\frac{10}{-8}\right)$

$y - 3 = 5$

$\therefore y = 8$

Points that lie on the same line are called **collinear points**. The equal slope property of parallel lines can be applied to prove that points are collinear.

EXAMPLE 4: Show that $A(-2, -3)$, $B(0, 1)$ and $C(2, 5)$ are collinear.

For $\overline{AB}$, $m = \frac{1-(-3)}{0-(-2)}$
$= 2$

For $\overline{BC}$, $m = \frac{5-1}{2-0}$
$= 2$

Since their slopes are equal, $\overline{AB}$ is parallel to $\overline{BC}$. But B is a common point to both $\overline{AB}$ and $\overline{BC}$; therefore all three points must lie on the same line. That is, points A, B, and C are collinear.

In general, to prove that three points are collinear, show that two line segments with one common point have the same slope.

EXERCISE 4-3

A **1.** State the slope of any line that would be parallel to the line passing through each pair of points.

a. $A(3, -2), B(4, 6)$ **b.** $E(-2, 5), F(-5, 7)$
c. $X(0, -3), Y(0, 4)$ **d.** $C(6, -2), D(-1, -2)$

2. State the slope of any line that would be perpendicular to the line passing through each pair of points.

a. $A(2, 8), B(5, 9)$ **b.** $D(-2, -5), E(2, -5)$
c. $X(4, -2), Y(5, 3)$ **d.** $F(-4, 6), G(3, 4)$

B **3.** For each given set of points, determine whether $\overline{AB}$ and $\overline{CD}$ are parallel, perpendicular, or neither.

a. $A(-5, 0), B(7, -4), C(-2, 3), D(4, 1)$ **b.** $A(4, -2), B(8, -7), C(-2, 2), D(2, -3)$
c. $A(-2, 2), B(4, 4), C(1, 3), D(3, -3)$ **d.** $A(7, -2), B(-3, -2), C(-6, 1), D(-6, 3)$

4. The vertices of a right-angled triangle are $A(-2, 4)$, $B(5, -3)$, and $C(11, 3)$.

a. Find the slope of each side of the triangle.
b. Name the right angle.

5. Determine which set of points are the vertices of a right-angled triangle.

a. $P(-3, 2), Q(-2, 4), R(4, 1)$ **b.** $X(4, 6), Y(-2, -2), Z(-5, 2)$
c. $A(-4, 4), B(4, 4), C(-4, 1)$ **d.** $S(-3, 2), T(4, 3), U(3, -2)$

6. Given that $\overline{PQ}$ is perpendicular to $\overline{RS}$, find the value of x if the endpoints of the two line segments are $P(-5, 3)$, $Q(3, 1)$ and $R(-1, 2)$, $S(x, -2)$.

7. A line containing $(-3, 1)$ and $(2, y)$ is parallel to the line through $(-1, 3)$ and $(4, -3)$. Find the value of y.

8. Determine whether the given set of points is collinear.

a. $(-3, -3), (3, 1), (6, 3)$ **b.** $(1, -9), (0, -4), (-2, 4)$
c. $(-4, -2), (-1, 1), (2, 4)$ **d.** $(-1, 0), (1, -5), (-3, 5)$

9. Determine the value of x so that $A(-4, 2)$, $B(3, 5)$, and $C(x, 9)$ are collinear.

10. Determine the value of y so that $P(-8, 7)$, $Q(4, -3)$, and $R(0, y)$ are collinear.

11. Find a point on the x-axis collinear with each pair of points.

a. $A(-2, 3), B(8, -2)$ **b.** $C(3, 5), D(-5, -5)$

12. Find a point on the y-axis collinear with each pair of points.

a. $A(-1, 5), B(3, -3)$ **b.** $C(1, 5), D(-6, -2)$

13. Show that $ABCD$, with vertices $A(-3, 2)$, $B(2, 3)$, $C(0, 0)$, and $D(-5, -1)$, is a parallelogram.

C 14. Show that each figure with the given vertices is a trapezoid.

a. $A(2, 2), B(-2, 5), C(-4, 2), D(4, -4)$

b. $A(-2, 3), B(4, 5), C(4, -1), D(1, -2)$

15. Determine the value of a so that the points $X(-2, 2)$, $Y(9, 4)$, and $Z(1, a)$ are the vertices of a right-angled triangle with the right angle at Y.

16. Given the points $A(4, 1)$, $B(-2, 2)$, and $C(4, -2)$ as three vertices of parallelogram $ABCD$, find the fourth vertex. Find all possible solutions.

17. Given that $P(6, -1)$, $Q(4, 2)$, and $R(-3, -5)$ are three vertices of a parallelogram, find a fourth vertex.

18. The vertices of a right-angled triangle are $A(-1, 2)$, $B(2, 5)$ and $C(7, y)$. Find all possible values of y.

19. Given that $\overline{CD}$ has endpoints $C(3, k)$ and $D(k + 1, 12)$, that $\overline{CD}$ and $\overline{AB}$ are parallel, and $\overline{AB}$ has slope -4, find the value of k.

20. The vertices of $\triangle DEF$ are $D(4, 5)$, $E(-2, -1)$, and $F(10, -3)$. $M(1, 2)$ is a point on $\overline{DE}$ and $N(x, 1)$ is a point on $\overline{DF}$ so that $\overline{MN}$ and $\overline{EF}$ are parallel.

a. Find the value of x.

b. Find the coordinates of a point G on $\overline{EF}$ so that $MNGE$ is a parallelogram.

21. Show that the figure with vertices $A(-4, 1)$, $B(-4, -5)$, $C(2, -5)$, and $D(2, 1)$ has diagonals which are perpendicular.

22. Let $m = \dfrac{y_2 - y_1}{x_2 - x_1}$ and show that the slope of line ② is $-\dfrac{1}{m}$ by rotating line ① through 90° counter-clockwise.

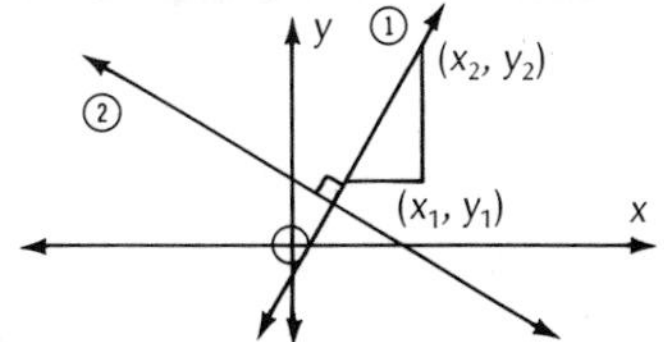

EXTRA

Plane Logic

Which of the following statements is a direct result of one or more of the other statements?

1. A, B and C are collinear.
2. $AB = BC$
3. $AC = BD$
4. B is the midpoint of AC.
5. A, B, C, and D are collinear.
6. $\triangle EAD$ is a right-angled triangle.
7. The slope of $\overline{AE}$ is $\frac{2}{5}$ and the slope of $\overline{AD}$ is $-\frac{5}{2}$.

4-4 Distance Between Two Points

Formulas can sometimes be developed to simplify problems in geometry. The Pythagorean Theorem can be used to develop a formula for the distance between two points.

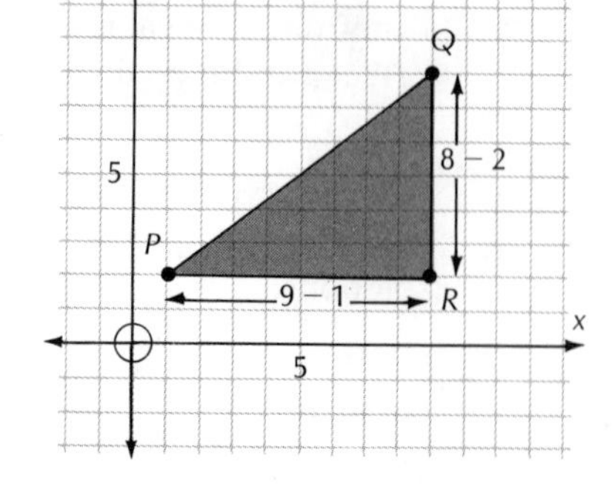

To find the distance between $P(1, 2)$ and $Q(9, 8)$, consider the right-angled triangle PQR, where R is at $(9, 2)$.

$$PQ^2 = PR^2 + QR^2$$
$$PQ^2 = (\text{change in } x)^2 + (\text{change in } y)^2$$
$$PQ^2 = (9 - 1)^2 + (8 - 2)^2$$
$$PQ^2 = 100$$
$$PQ = 10$$

The method used above to find the distance between P and Q can be generalized to a formula for finding the distance between $P_1(x_1, y_1)$ and $P_2(x_2, y_2)$.

$$(P_1P_2)^2 = (\text{change in } x)^2 + (\text{change in } y)^2$$
$$P_1P_2 = \sqrt{(\text{change in } x)^2 + (\text{change in } y)^2}$$

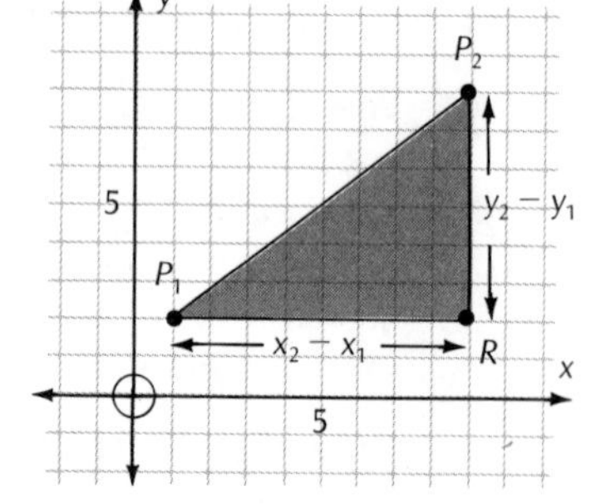

In general, the distance between $P_1(x_1, y_1)$ and $P_2(x_2, y_2)$ is given by:

$$P_1P_2 = \sqrt{(x_2 - x_1)^2 + (y_2 - y_1)^2}$$

EXAMPLE: Determine the type of triangle with the given vertices by finding the length of each side.

a. $P(1, 1)$, $Q(-6, 8)$, $R(-5, 2)$

$$PQ = \sqrt{[(-6) - 1]^2 + [8 - 1]^2} = \sqrt{(-7)^2 + 7^2} = \sqrt{98} = 7\sqrt{2}$$

$$QR = \sqrt{[(-5) - (-6)]^2 + [2 - 8]^2} = \sqrt{1^2 + (-6)^2} = \sqrt{37}$$

$$PR = \sqrt{[(-5) - 1]^2 + [2 - 1]^2} = \sqrt{(-6)^2 + 1^2} = \sqrt{37}$$

Check that $QR + PR \neq PQ$, so that the vertices are not collinear.

Since $\triangle PQR$ has two equal sides, it is an isosceles triangle.

b. $A(-5, 1)$, $B(-1, 4)$, $C(5, -4)$

$$AB = \sqrt{[-1 - (-5)]^2 + [4 - 1]^2} = \sqrt{4^2 + 3^2} = \sqrt{25} = 5$$

$$BC = \sqrt{[5 - (-1)]^2 + [-4 - 4]^2} = \sqrt{6^2 + (-8)^2} = \sqrt{100} = 10$$

$$AC = \sqrt{[5 - (-5)]^2 + [-4 - 1]^2} = \sqrt{10^2 + (-5)^2} = \sqrt{125} = 5\sqrt{5}$$

Notice that $AB^2 + BC^2 = 25 + 100$, or 125, and $AC^2 = 125$; that is, $AB^2 + BC^2 = AC^2$. Therefore $\triangle ABC$ is a right-angled triangle.

EXERCISE 4-4

B 1. Calculate the distance between each pair of points. Express radical answers in simplest form.

a. $(-2, -7)$ and $(3, 5)$
b. $(9, -5)$ and $(9, 6)$
c. $(2, 7)$ and $(6, 7)$
d. $(1, 2)$ and $(4, -2)$
e. $(1, 0)$ and $(-3, 5)$
f. $(8, 9)$ and $(6, -1)$
g. $(-4, -3)$ and $(8, 13)$
h. $(13, 0)$ and $(-1, -5)$
i. $(7, -4)$ and $(-2, -5)$
j. $(4, -1)$ and $(1, 3)$
k. $(2\sqrt{3}, 5)$ and $(\sqrt{3}, 1)$
l. $(8\sqrt{2}, \sqrt{5})$ and $(6\sqrt{2}, 3\sqrt{5})$

2. Given a circle with centre C, find the length of the radius with endpoints P and C.

a. $C(0, 0)$, $P(5, 6)$ **b.** $C(2, 3)$, $P(5, -3)$ **c.** $C(-1, -1)$, $P(8, -7)$

3. Find the distance between the origin and the given point.

a. $A(4, 3)$ **b.** $B(3, -4)$ **c.** $C(5, -12)$ **d.** $D(-8, -6)$ **e.** $E(6, 9)$
f. $F(6, 4)$ **g.** $G(-7, -4)$ **h.** $H(-6, 4)$ **i.** $I(a, b)$ **j.** $J(x_1, y_1)$

4. Develop a formula for the distance between $O(0, 0)$ and a point $P_1(x_1, y_1)$.

5. Find the perimeter of the triangle with the given vertices.

a. $X(-4, -2)$, $Y(5, -10)$, $Z(0, 2)$
b. $P(0, 0)$, $Q(3, 3)$, $R(5, 1)$
c. $A(2, -4)$, $B(10, 12)$, $C(6, 5)$
d. $D(-3, 2)$, $E(1, 4)$, $F(4, -2)$

6. Use the Pythagorean Theorem to show that the triangle with the given verticles is a right-angled triangle.

a. $A(-2, 2)$, $B(-4, -1)$, $C(-1, -3)$ **b.** $R(-5, 3)$, $S(-1, -2)$, $T(9, 6)$

7. Given the three points $A(-6, -4)$, $B(0, -2)$, and $C(3, -1)$, answer the following:

a. Find the lengths of $\overline{AB}$, $\overline{BC}$, and $\overline{AC}$.
b. Explain why the results of part **a** show that A, B, and C are collinear.

8. Show that $P(-2, 6)$, $R(4, -2)$, and $S(7, -6)$ are collinear.

9. Find an expression to represent the distance between A and B.

a. $A(p - q, p + q)$, $B(p + q, p - q)$
b. $A(m, 2n)$, $B(5m, -n)$
c. $A(x^2, y)$, $B(2x^2, y)$
d. $A(2a + 3b, -4b)$, $B(a - b, 3a)$

C 10. The distance between $P(3, 10)$ and $Q(a, -2)$ is 13 units. Find the value of a. There are two possible solutions.

11. Given that the distance between $Q(5, b)$ and $R(2, 5)$ is the same as the distance between R and $S(-2, 2)$, find the value of b. There are two solutions.

12. Given $\overline{FG}$ with endpoints $F(10, 8)$ and $G(-4, 2)$, and point $M(3, 5)$ on $\overline{FG}$, show that M is half-way between F and G.

4-5 Midpoint of a Line Segment

The formula used in lesson 4-4 to find the distance between two points can be used to prove that a point is the midpoint of a given line segment.

EXAMPLE 1: Show that $M(-1, 2)$ is the midpoint of $\overline{PQ}$ with endpoints $P(4, 6)$ and $Q(-6, -2)$.

$$PM = \sqrt{[4-(-1)]^2 + [6-2]^2} = \sqrt{5^2+4^2} = \sqrt{41}$$

$$MQ = \sqrt{[-1-(-6)]^2 + [2-(-2)]^2} = \sqrt{5^2+4^2} = \sqrt{41}$$

$$\therefore PM = MQ$$

It is also necessary to verify that M does in fact lie on $\overline{PQ}$.

$$\text{For } \overline{PM},\ m = \frac{6-2}{4-(-1)} = \frac{4}{5} \qquad \text{For } \overline{MQ},\ m = \frac{2-(-2)}{-1-(-6)} = \frac{4}{5}$$

Since the slopes are equal, the points are collinear and $\overline{PM} = \overline{MQ}$. Therefore, M is the midpoint of $\overline{PQ}$.

Given two endpoints of a line segment, you can find the midpoint. The midpoint is the average of the x- and y-coordinates of the endpoints.

> In general, for points $P_1(x_1, y_1)$ and $P_2(x_2, y_2)$, the midpoint of $\overline{P_1P_2}$, is:
>
> $$M = \left(\frac{x_1+x_2}{2}, \frac{y_1+y_2}{2}\right).$$

EXAMPLE 2: Find the midpoint of $\overline{AB}$ with endpoints $A(1, 2)$ and $B(-3, 4)$.

Applying the formula, $M = \left(\frac{1+(-3)}{2}, \frac{2+4}{2}\right)$.

The midpoint of $\overline{AB}$ is $M(-1, 3)$.

The midpoint formula can be applied to find unknown endpoints of a line segment.

EXAMPLE 3: If $M(3, -5)$ is the midpoint of $\overline{AB}$ with $A(4, 2)$, find $B(x, y)$.

$$(3, -5) = \left(\frac{4+x}{2}, \frac{2+y}{2}\right) \longrightarrow 3 = \frac{4+x}{2} \text{ and } -5 = \frac{2+y}{2}$$

Solving the two equations gives $x = 2$ and $y = -12$.

EXERCISE 4-5

A 1. Find the midpoint of the line segment joining each given pair of points.

a. $A(3, 6), B(7, 2)$ b. $C(-1, 0), D(9, 8)$ c. $E(7, 6), F(5, -6)$
d. $G(3, -4), H(-5, 2)$ e. $I(-8, -5), J(7, 6)$ f. $K(-3, 0), L(8, -2)$
g. $M(9, 4), N(9, -1)$ h. $P(-7, 3), Q(8, 3)$ i. $R\left(\frac{1}{2}, \frac{3}{5}\right), S\left(\frac{3}{4}, -\frac{1}{10}\right)$

B 2. Given that $M(a, 7)$ is the midpoint of the segment joining $A(4, -9)$ to $B(-5, b)$, find the values of a and b.

3. Given that $T(-8, q)$ is the midpoint of $\overline{CD}$ joining $C(-9, 6)$ to $D(p, -5)$, find the values of p and q.

4. The vertices of a triangle are $A(6, 8)$, $B(-10, 4)$, and $C(2, -4)$.
   a. Draw the graph of $\triangle ABC$.
   b. Find the midpoint P of $\overline{AB}$ and the midpoint Q of $\overline{BC}$.
   c. Find the slopes of $\overline{PQ}$ and $\overline{AC}$.
   d. Find the lengths of $\overline{PQ}$ and $\overline{AC}$.
   e. Use the results of parts **c** and **d** to state how $\overline{PQ}$ and $\overline{AC}$ are related.
   f. Repeat for two other triangles, using vertices of your own choice.

5. The endpoints of a diameter of a circle are $H(-9, -6)$ and $M(3, 12)$. Find the centre of the circle.

6. Find the midpoint of the segment joining the given pair of points.
   a. $R(a, b), S(c, d)$ b. $T(2a, 3b), U(-5a, 8b)$ c. $V(x^2, -x), W(5x^2, 7x)$

7. a. Show that the quadrilateral with vertices $A(1, 3)$, $B(7, -5)$, $C(2, -7)$, and $D(-4, 1)$ is a parallelogram.
   b. Prove that the diagonals of $ABCD$ bisect each other.

C 8. Find the midpoint of the segment joining $T(x^2 + 2x, -3x^2 - 2x)$ to $V(5x^2 - 8x, 7x^2 + 10x)$.

9. The vertices of a quadrilateral are $P(2, 5)$, $Q(6, 1)$, $R(-2, -5)$, and $S(-6, -3)$.
   a. Find the vertices of quadrilateral $ABCD$, formed by joining the midpoints of the sides $PQRS$.
   b. Prove that quadrilateral $ABCD$ is a parallelogram.

10. The vertices of a quadrilateral are $A(-1, 1)$, $B(2, -3)$, $C(10, 3)$, and $D(7, 7)$.
    a. Prove that $ABCD$ is a rectangle.
    b. Find the vertices of quadrilateral $PQRS$, formed by joining the midpoints of the sides of $ABCD$.
    c. Prove that $PQRS$ is a rhombus.

4-6 Internal Division of a Line Segment

Finding the midpoint of a line segment can be thought of as finding the point that divides the segment in the ratio 1:1. This skill can be extended to finding points that divide a segment in other ratios.

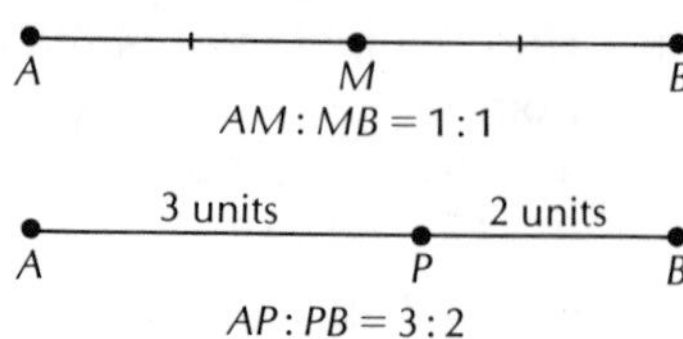

The point P **divides $\overline{AB}$ internally** in the ratio $3:2$.
(P divides $\overline{BA}$ internally in the ratio $2:3$.)

When working with divided line segments on the coordinate plane, ratios can often be easily determined by counting.

For the graph at the right:

Q divides $\overline{PR}$ in the ratio $5:8$;
R divides $\overline{PS}$ in the ratio $13:6$;
Q divides $\overline{SP}$ in the ratio $14:5$;
Q divides $\overline{PS}$ in the ratio $5:14$.

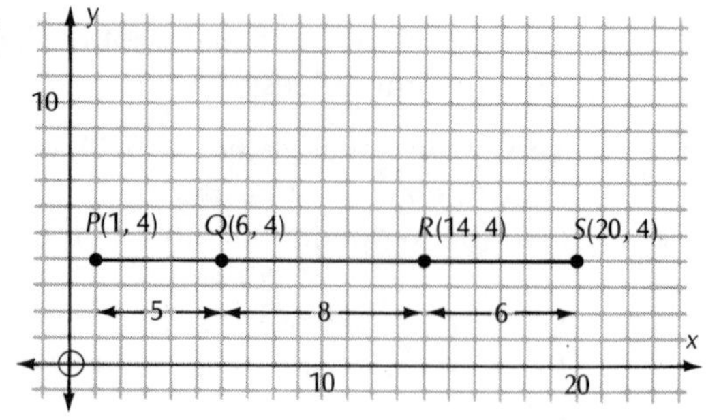

EXAMPLE 1: $\overline{AB}$ has endpoints $A(2, 3)$ and $B(17, 12)$. Find the point that divides $\overline{AB}$ in the ratio $1:2$.

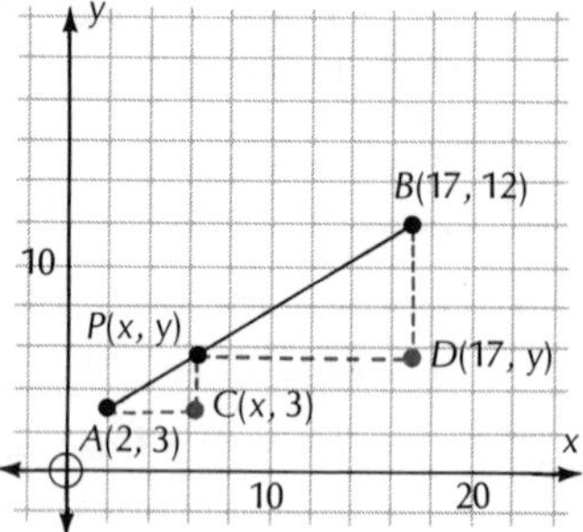

Let $P(x, y)$ be the point of division. Then $AP : PB = 1:2$.

Look at $\triangle APC$ and $\triangle PBD$. $\triangle APC$ is a *reduction* of $\triangle PBD$. Since the reduction factor affects all dimensions equally, then corresponding sides are in proportion. ($\triangle APC$ and $\triangle PBD$ are **similar triangles.**)

That is, $\dfrac{AC}{PD} = \dfrac{PC}{BD} = \dfrac{AP}{PB} = \dfrac{1}{2}$

$\therefore \quad \dfrac{x-2}{17-x} = \dfrac{1}{2}$ and $\dfrac{y-3}{12-y} = \dfrac{1}{2}$

$$2x - 4 = 17 - x \qquad 2y - 6 = 12 - y$$
$$3x = 21 \qquad 3y = 18$$
$$x = 7 \qquad y = 6$$

Therefore, the point of division is $(7, 6)$.

The method used in example 1 can be applied in general to find an internal point of division of a line segment on the coordinate plane.

EXAMPLE 2: $\overline{RS}$ has endpoints $R(-4, 5)$ and $S(6, -10)$. Find the point that divides $\overline{RS}$ in the ratio 2 : 3.

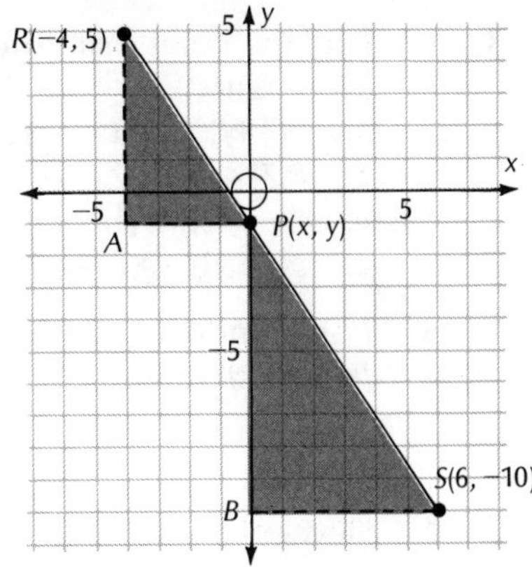

Let the point of division be $P(x, y)$. Then $RP : PS = 2 : 3$, and $\triangle RPA$ is similar to $\triangle PSB$, with corresponding sides in proportion.

$$\frac{RA}{PB} = \frac{AP}{BS} = \frac{RP}{PS} = \frac{2}{3}$$

$$\therefore \frac{5 - y}{y - (-10)} = \frac{2}{3} \qquad \text{and} \qquad \frac{-4 - x}{x - 6} = \frac{2}{3}$$

$$3(5 - y) = 2(y + 10) \qquad 3(-4 - x) = 2(x - 6)$$

$$15 - 3y = 2y + 20 \qquad -12 - 3x = 2x - 12$$

$$5y = -5 \qquad 5x = 0$$

$$y = -1 \qquad x = 0$$

Therefore, the point of division is $(0, -1)$.

EXERCISE 4-6

A **1.** Find the midpoint of the segment joining each pair of points.

a. $(7, -8), (6, 3)$ **b.** $(-5, -9), (-1, 0)$ **c.** $(11, 4), (0, -12)$ **d.** $(-5, 8), (5, -8)$

2. Plot each pair of points, A and B, and find the point P that divides $\overline{AB}$ in the given ratio.

a. $A(4, 9), B(-6, 9)$; 2 : 3 **b.** $A(5, 7), B(5, -2)$; 4 : 1

c. $A(-8, 4), B(4, 4)$; 1 : 3 **d.** $A(-4, 12), B(-4, -3)$; 3 : 2

3. State the ratio in which P divides $\overline{AB}$ in each case.

a.

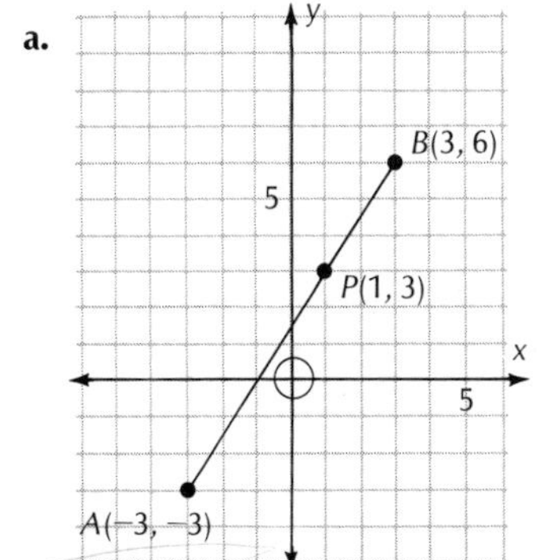

b.

c.

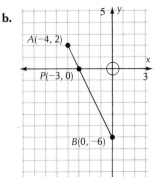

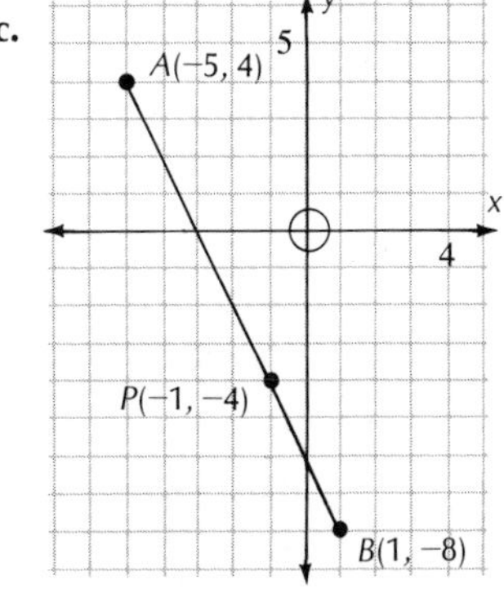

4. For each part in exercise 3, state the ratio in which P divides $\overline{BA}$.

B 5. Find the point that divides $\overline{PQ}$ with the given endpoints in the given ratio.

a. $P(-4, 2)$, $Q(4, 2)$; $3:5$
b. $P(-3, 6)$, $Q(-3, -4)$; $2:3$
c. $P(7, 4)$, $Q(-2, -2)$; $2:1$
d. $P(-5, 6)$, $Q(5, 1)$; $1:4$
e. $P(-5, 2)$, $Q(10, -3)$; $3:2$
f. $P(-5, -3)$, $Q(4, 8)$; $1:2$
g. $P(-5, 2)$, $Q(7, 4)$; $3:1$
h. $P(-6, 5)$, $Q(1, -9)$; $4:3$

6. $\overline{JK}$ has endpoints $J(-5, 5)$ and $K(10, -3)$. Find the point that divides $\overline{JK}$ in each ratio.

a. $3:5$
b. $3:1$
c. $7:1$
d. $1:1$
e. $5:3$
f. $1:7$
g. $2:3$
h. $3:2$

7. Develop a general formula for the point of division of a line segment. Let the endpoints of the segment be $P_1(x_1, y_1)$ and $P_2(x_2, y_2)$. Find the point $D(x, y)$ that divides $\overline{P_1P_2}$ in the ratio $a:b$.

8. Apply the formula developed in exercise 7 to determine the point that divides $\overline{AB}$ in each ratio.

a. $A(2, 5)$, $B(-3, 1)$; $2:3$
b. $A(-1, 4)$, $B(2, -3)$; $5:2$
c. $A(-6, 8)$, $B(3, 2)$; $6:7$
d. $A(0, 7)$, $B(-2, -5)$; $2:7$

9. The line segment joining $J(3, 2)$ to $K(-6, -4)$ is divided into three equal parts by the points $L(m, n)$ and $R(s, t)$. Find the points L and R.

10. $P(q, 3)$ divides $\overline{AB}$ joining $A(-5, 4)$ to $B(7, r)$ in the ratio $1:3$. Find the values of r and q.

11. $E(3, 1)$ divides the segment joining $F(s, t)$ to $G(9, 5)$ in the ratio $3:2$. Find s and t.

C 12. $X(-1, 6)$, $Y(-6, -4)$, and $Z(14, 1)$ are the vertices of $\triangle XYZ$.

a. Draw the graph of $\triangle XYZ$.
b. Find the point L that divides $\overline{XY}$ in the ratio $2:3$.
c. Find the point N that divides $\overline{XZ}$ in the ratio $2:3$.
d. Find the slope of $\overline{YZ}$.
e. Find the slope of $\overline{LN}$.
f. What is the relationship between $\overline{YZ}$ and $\overline{LN}$?

13. $A(3, 11)$, $B(-9, 3)$, and $C(7, -5)$ are the vertices of $\triangle ABC$. L and N divide $\overline{AB}$ and $\overline{AC}$, respectively, in the ratio $1:3$. Prove that $\overline{LN} \parallel \overline{BC}$.

14. L and N are points which divide two sides of a triangle in the same ratio. How is $\overline{LN}$ related to the third side of the triangle? Prove your answer.

15. In the diagram, point P is said to divide $\overline{AB}$ **externally** in the ratio $p:q$. Determine P for the given points and ratios.

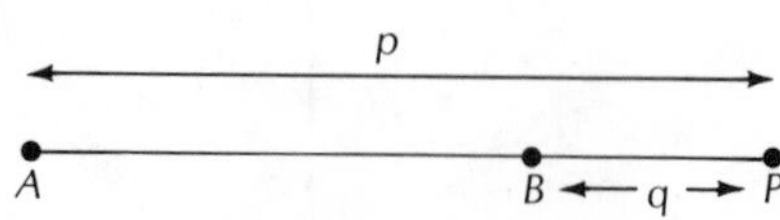

a. $A(0, 0)$, $B(4, 2)$; $5:3$

b. $A(-1, -2)$, $B(3, 1)$; $2:1$

Review

1. Find the x- and y-intercepts of the graph represented by each equation.
   a. $4x - 3y - 12 = 0$ b. $y = 2x - 4$ c. $x - 5y + 5 = 0$
   d. $2x + y = 0$ e. $x + 3 = 0$ f. $y = 4$
2. Graph each equation in exercise 1.
3. Given that the endpoints of $\overline{PQ}$ are $P(-3, 1)$ and $Q(9, 6)$, answer the following:
   a. Find the length of $\overline{PQ}$. b. Find the slope of $\overline{PQ}$.
   c. Find the midpoint of $\overline{PQ}$.
4. Determine the value of p so that $A(2, 8)$, $B(p, -1)$ and $C(-1, 3)$ are collinear.
5. Show that $ABCD$ with vertices $A(2, 1)$, $B(10, 3)$, $C(5, 0)$, and $D(-3, -2)$ is a parallelogram.
6. Find the value of q so that $\overline{ST}$ with endpoints $S(-3, 2)$ and $T(2, 4)$ is perpendicular to $\overline{SU}$, with $U(7, q)$.
7. Show that $A(1, 2)$, $B(-3, -1)$, and $C(7, -6)$ are the vertices of a right-angled triangle.
8. Find the radius of a circle with centre $C(8, -4)$ that passes through $D(2, -10)$.
9. Find the centre of a circle if the endpoints of its diameter are $G(9, -6)$ and $H(-7, 5)$.
10. Prove that $\triangle ABC$ with vertices $A(2, 0)$, $B(-2, -3)$, and $C(5, -4)$ is isosceles.
11. Find the point that divides $\overline{PQ}$ with endpoints $P(1, 7)$ and $Q(-2, -2)$ in the ratio $1:2$.
12. a. Find the point C on the x-axis for which the segment joining $A(-2, 4)$ to C is perpendicular to the segment joining A to $B(-5, -2)$.
    b. Find the midpoint M of $\overline{BC}$.
    c. Find the lengths of $\overline{MB}$, $\overline{MA}$, and $\overline{MC}$.
13. a. Show that $P(1, 4)$, $Q(8, 2)$, $R(4, -1)$, and $S(-3, 1)$ are the vertices of a parallelogram.
    b. Show that the diagonals of $PQRS$ bisect each other.
14. A rental car is available at a cost of \$25/day plus \$0.20/km.
    a. Write an equation relating the cost, C dollars, of renting the car for one day if you travel d kilometres.
    b. Draw a graph showing the relationship between C and d for one day if you travel d kilometres.
    c. From the graph, find the cost of renting a car if you travel 75 km.
    d. If a customer paid \$49 to rent the car for one day, how many kilometres did the customer drive?

4-7 Graphing Equations and Inequalities

Larry wants to invest two amounts of money, x dollars at 8%/a and y dollars at 9%/a. The simple interest he would earn in a year can be calculated by applying the formula $I = 0.08x + 0.09y$. If he has a target of earning $260 interest in a year, then an equation representing how he can meet that target is $260 = 0.08x + 0.09y$.

EXAMPLE 1: Graph the equation

$$260 = 0.08x + 0.09y.$$

Find the intercepts and a third point to check.

x	y
0	2888.9
3250	0
1000	2000

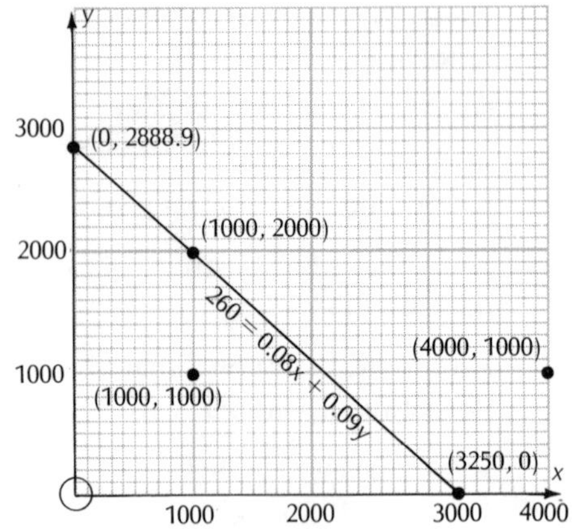

The graph is restricted to the first quadrant since only positive amounts can be invested.

Larry can read points from the graph to see the combinations of amounts that could be invested to earn $260. For instance, investing $1000 at 8% and $2000 at 9% would yield $260 simple interest in one year.

If Larry's target is to earn *more* than $260, still investing two amounts at 8%/a and 9%/a, then the same line graph can be used to represent the situation. Consider any point *above* the line, such as (4000, 1000), and substitute into the original formula, $I = 0.08x + 0.09y$.

$$\begin{aligned} I &= 0.08(4000) + 0.09(1000) \\ &= 320 + 90 \\ &= 410 \qquad 410 > 260 \end{aligned}$$

The situation of earning more than $260, then, could be represented by indicating all points above the line, possibly by shading.

If the amounts invested correspond to a point *below* the line, the interest earned will be less than $260. Consider the point (1000, 1000) and apply the formula for I.

$$\begin{aligned} I &= 0.08(1000) + 0.09(1000) \\ &= 80 + 90 \\ &= 170 \qquad 170 < 260 \end{aligned}$$

The line can be thought of as a **boundary line** for each of the two situations.

EXAMPLE 2: Graph the inequality $x - 3y \geq 6$, for $x, y \in \boldsymbol{R}$.

First graph the boundary line $x - 3y = 6$.

x	y
0	−2
6	0
9	1

The table summarizes the calculations for the intercepts and a third point to check.

Then use a test point to determine which side of the line corresponds to $x - 3y \geq 6$.

Test (0, 0): L.S. = 0; R.S. = 6.
L.S. < R.S., so (0, 0) is not part of the solution.

Test a point on the other side, say (3, −2): L.S. = 9; R.S. = 6.
L.S. > R.S., so (3, −2) satisfies the inequality $x - 3y \geq 6$.
Shade the area below the boundary line.

As an alternative to using test points, you might find that careful observation will help you identify which region to shade.

EXAMPLE 3: Draw the graph of $y > 2x - 1$, for $x, y \in \boldsymbol{R}$.

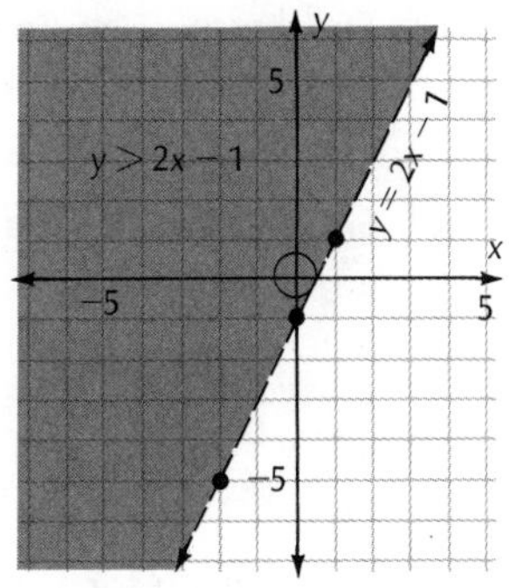

First graph the boundary line, $y = 2x - 1$.
Use a broken line to show that $y = 2x - 1$ is not part of the answer.

The line goes through all points for which the value of y *equals* $2x - 1$. Since y increases as you move in a positive direction up, then the value of y is increased in points above the line. Shade the region *above* the boundary line.

The concept applied in example 2 can be used to graph other inequalities if you isolate y before graphing the boundary line.

EXAMPLE 4: Draw the graph of $3x + y \leq 0$, for $x, y \in \boldsymbol{R}$.

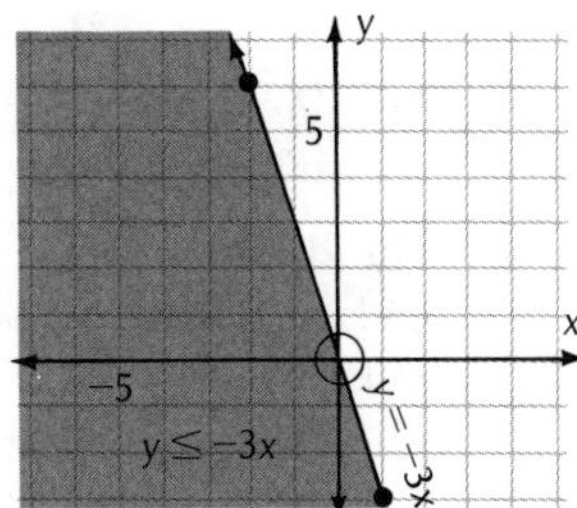

First isolate y: $y \leq -3x$.
Then graph $y = -3x$, using a solid line.

Since the value of y decreases as you move to points *below* the line in this case, shade the region below the boundary line to show $y \leq -3x$.

EXERCISES 4-7

A **1.** Write an inequality to represent each shaded area.

a.

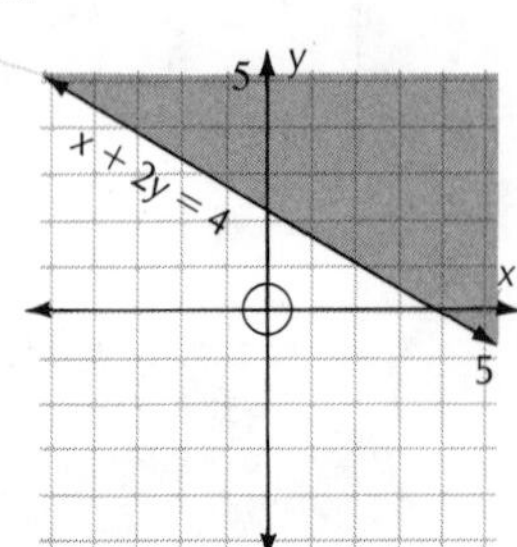

b.

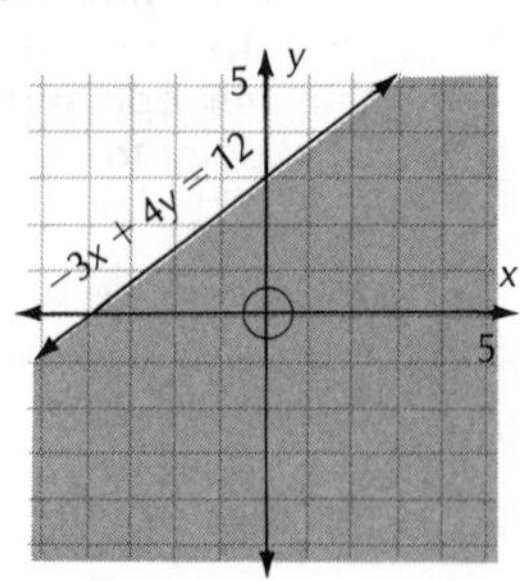

c.

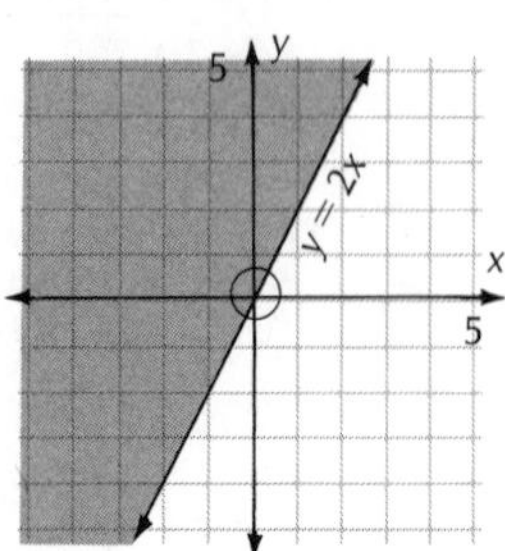

2. Test to see if $O(0, 0)$ lies in the region defined by each inequality.

a. $y \geq 5x - 6$ **b.** $2x - 4y > 6$ **c.** $y + 2x < 0$
d. $3x - 7y \leq 21$ **e.** $x < 3y - 2$ **f.** $4x + 3y < 12$

B **3.** Find the *x*- and *y*-intercepts of each equation and draw each graph.

a. $4x + y = 8$ **b.** $5x - 2y = 15$ **c.** $y = 7x - 7$
d. $y = \frac{1}{2}x + 1$ **e.** $3x + 9 = 2y$ **f.** $7x - 2y = 0$

4. For the two regions formed by each graph in exercise 3, write an appropriate equation or inequality corresponding to the region containing the origin.

5. Graph each inequality for $x, y \in \mathbf{R}$.

a. $x + y > 3$ **b.** $x - y < 4$ **c.** $x + 2y \geq 6$
d. $x - 3y \leq 3$ **e.** $x + 4y < -4$ **f.** $y > x - 5$
g. $y \geq -x + 3$ **h.** $y < -2x + 2$ **i.** $y \leq 4x - 4$
j. $y - 3 < x$ **k.** $2x + 3y < 6$ **l.** $5x - 4y \leq 20$
m. $6x - 7y > 42$ **n.** $2x - 5y \geq 10$ **o.** $8x - 5y < 20$

6. Graph each for $x, y \in \mathbf{R}$.

a. $\{(x, y) | x = 4\}$ **b.** $\{(x, y) | y = 3\}$ **c.** $\{(x, y) | x + 2 = 0\}$
d. $\{(x, y) | x \geq -1\}$ **e.** $\{(x, y) | y < 2\}$ **f.** $\{(x, y) | x + 5 \leq 0\}$
g. $\{(x, y) | y \geq -2\}$ **h.** $\{(x, y) | y - 4 \leq 0\}$ **i.** $x + 5y > 0$
j. $x - 2y \leq 0$ **k.** $3x + y \geq 0$ **l.** $y < 3x$

7. Graph each pair of inequalities on the same set of axes for $x, y \in \mathbf{R}$.

a. $\{(x, y) | x > 2\}$ and $\{(x, y) | y > -1\}$
b. $\{(x, y) | x + 1 \geq 1\}$ and $\{(x, y) | y + 2 < 0\}$
c. $\{(x, y) | x + 2y < -1\}$ and $\{(x, y) | y > x - 2\}$

8. The distance Lisa travelled while driving at an average speed of 80 km/h can be given by the equation $d = 80t$, where d is distance in kilometres and t is travelling time in hours.

a. Draw the graph representing the relation between d and t.
b. How far would she have travelled in 5 h?

9. a. Referring to the opening examples for this lesson, write an inequality to represent the situation in which two amounts are invested at 8%/a and 9%/a, and more than \$260 simple interest is earned in one year.
   b. Graph the inequality for $x, y \in \mathbf{R}$.

C 10. A two-digit number can be represented by the expression $10x + y$.
   a. Write an inequality to represent the relation between x and y if the number is less than 20.
   b. Graph the inequality for $x, y \in \mathbf{Z}$, with $1 \leq x \leq 9$ and $0 \leq y \leq 9$.
   c. From the graph, determine all two-digit numbers that satisfy the relation.

11. Movie tickets cost \$6.00 for adults and \$5.00 for students. The total receipts for an evening can be calculated by the equation $T = 6x + 5y$, where x is the number of adult tickets sold and y is the number of student tickets sold.
   a. Write an inequality to represent total receipts greater than or equal to \$3300.
   b. What restrictions would you place on x and y in order that the inequality accurately reflects the application?
   c. Graph the inequality for values of x and y as described in answer to part **b**.

12. The points in a football game were scored by x touchdowns worth 7 points each plus y field goals worth 3 points each.
   a. Write an equation relating the number of touchdowns and field goals if the total point score is 63.
   b. What restrictions would you place on the variables in order that the equation accurately reflect the application?
   c. Find the x-intercept of the graph corresponding to the equation. What does the intercept represent in terms of field goals and touchdowns?
   d. When the Tigers played their last game, they made more than 63 points from both touchdowns and field goals. Write an inequality to represent this situation. State restrictions on the variables and graph the inequality.

13. The perimeter of a rectangle can be calculated using the formula $P = 2l + 2w$.
   a. Write an inequality relating the length and width of a rectangle with a perimeter less than 40 units.
   b. State any restrictions on the variables.
   c. Graph the inequality for variables as described in answer to part **b**.
   d. If the width of a rectangle is greater than 12 units, and the perimeter is less than 40 units, graph the relation and give two examples of rectangles that satisfy the requirements of this relation.

4-8 Graphing $y = mx + b$

By noticing general patterns, your work in mathematics can sometimes be simplified.

Each line below can be represented by an equation of the form $y = 2x + b$.

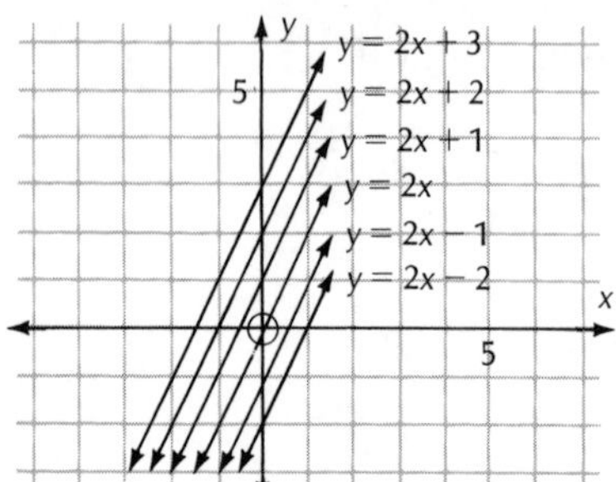

Each of the lines has slope 2.
The lines are all parallel.

Each line below can be represented by an equation of the form $y = mx + 3$.

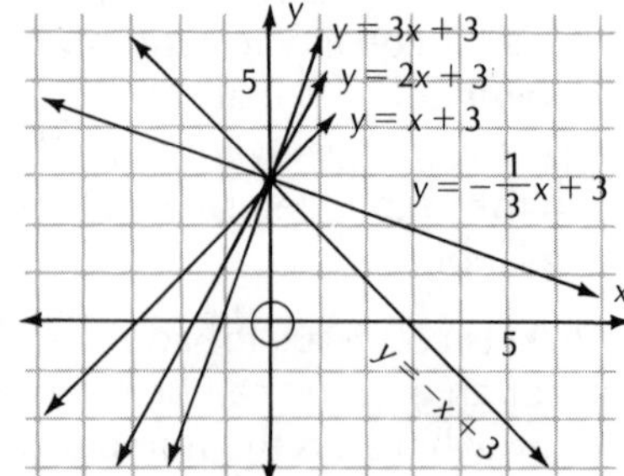

Each of the lines has y-intercept +3.
The lines are **concurrent** at (0, 3).

> In general, the equation $y = mx + b$ represents a line with slope m and y-intercept b.

If two facts are known about a line, such as two points, or the slope and one point, or the slope and one intercept, then the line can be graphed. The general result above, then, can be applied to graph an equation that can be written in the form $y = mx + b$.

EXAMPLE 1: Graph the line represented by $y = \frac{1}{2}x + 4$.

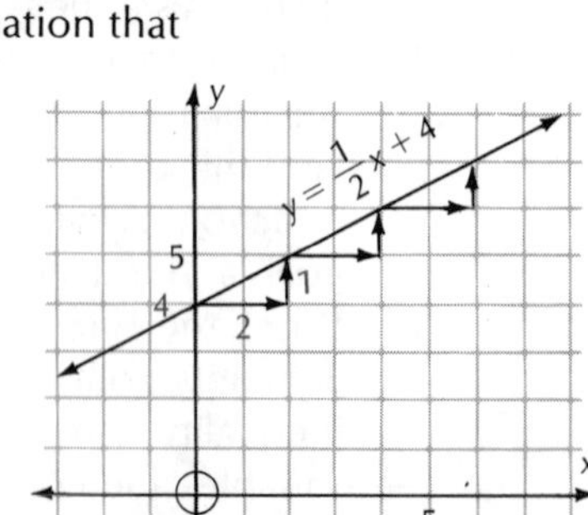

The line has slope $\frac{1}{2}$ and y-intercept 4. To graph the line, plot the point (0, 4), then draw a line starting from (0, 4) and having $\frac{\text{rise}}{\text{run}} = \frac{1}{2}$.

EXAMPLE 2: Find the slope and the y-intercept of the line represented by $2x + 3y = 3$. Graph the line.

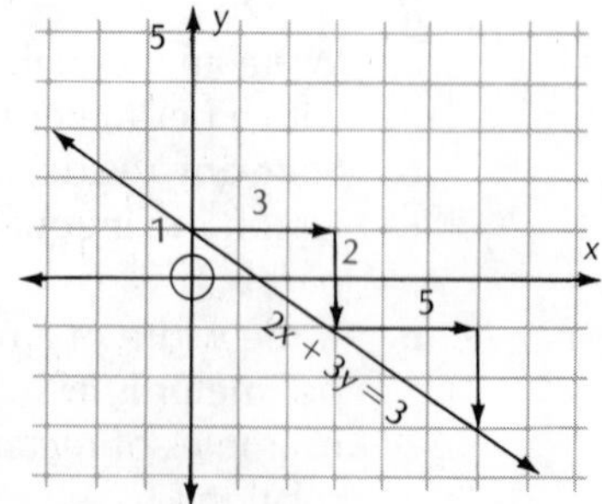

Isolate y and compare with $y = mx + b$.

$$2x + 3y = 3$$
$$3y = -2x + 3$$
$$y = -\frac{2}{3}x + 1$$

The line has slope $-\frac{2}{3}$ and y-intercept 1.

EXERCISE 4-8

A **1.** State the slope and *y*-intercept of each line.

a. $y = -2x + 4$ **b.** $y = -x - 6$ **c.** $y - 1 = 5x$ **d.** $y = 8$

2. Draw the line with the given slope m and *y*-intercept b.

a. $m = 5, b = 2$ **b.** $m = \frac{2}{3}, b = 3$ **c.** $m = -\frac{1}{2}, b = -1$ **d.** $m = -\frac{5}{4}, b = -2$

3. Determine the slope and *y*-intercept of each line and write an equation of the line.

a.

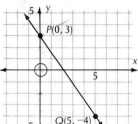

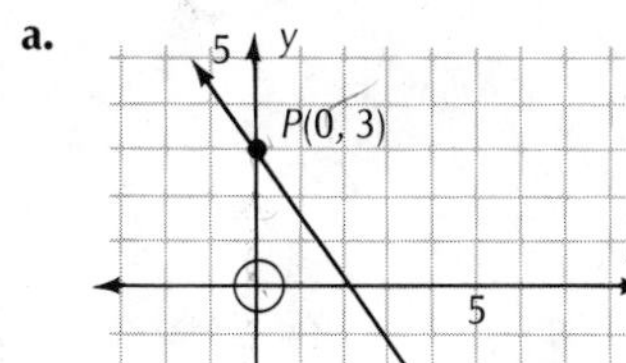

b.

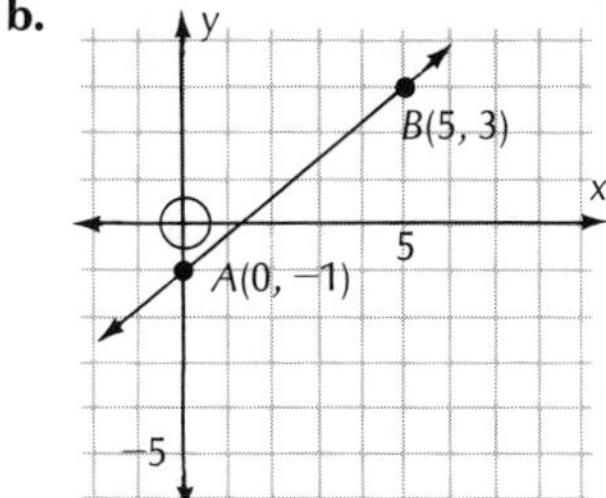

c.

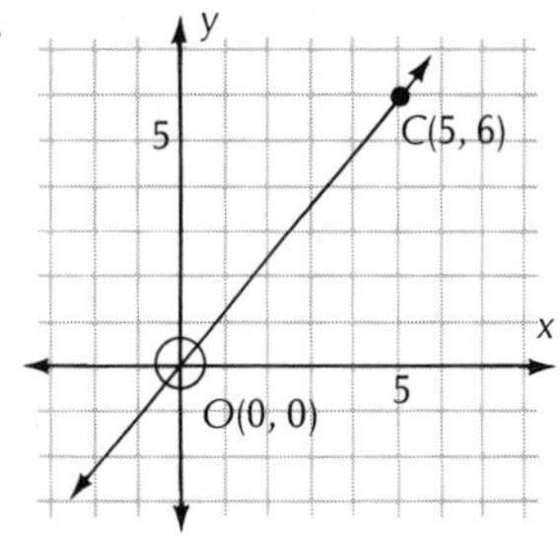

B **4.** Write an equation of the line with the given slope and *y*-intercept.

a. slope 4, *y*-intercept 6 **b.** slope −3, *y*-intercept 5 **c.** slope $-\frac{1}{3}$, *y*-intercept $\frac{1}{2}$

5. Graph the line represented by each equation.

a. $y = 4x - 3$ **b.** $y = -3x + 1$ **c.** $y = \frac{2}{3}x - 3$

d. $y = -\frac{5}{3}x + 2$ **e.** $2y = 3x + 1$ **f.** $3y = x - 4$

6. What is the slope of any line parallel to the line represented by $y = 8x - 6$?

7. Find the slope of the line represented by each equation.

a. $4x - y = 6$ **b.** $3x + 5y = 15$ **c.** $2x - 7y + 14 = 0$

d. $8x = 3y - 12$ **e.** $x = 5$ **f.** $y + 6 = 0$

C **8.** Write an equation of the line that is parallel to the line represented by $y = 3x + 2$ and has the same *y*-intercept as the line represented by $y = 7x - 5$.

9. Find an equation of the line that passes through the origin and has the given slope.

a. 4 **b.** −5 **c.** $\frac{4}{5}$ **d.** $-\frac{6}{7}$ **e.** 0

10. Find the slope of a line that is perpendicular to the line represented by the given equation.

a. $y = -x + 6$ **b.** $y = \frac{1}{3}x - 7$ **c.** $y = 6x - 8$

d. $5x - y + 6 = 0$ **e.** $4x + 3y = 24$ **f.** $3x = 4y + 7$

11. Find an equation of the line that is perpendicular to the line represented by $6x - 5y + 30 = 0$ and has the same *y*-intercept as the line represented by $8x - 3y - 24 = 0$.

4-9 Linear Equations in Standard Form

Tickets to the school band concert were priced at \$2 for students and \$3 for adults. The band hopes to sell \$1200 worth of tickets. An equation to represent this situation is $2x + 3y - 1200 = 0$, where x is the number of student tickets sold and y is the number of adult tickets sold.

An equation in the form $Ax + By + C = 0$, where A, B, and C are real numbers, is said to be in **standard form**. An equation in standard form can be written in $y = mx + b$ form, so that the slope and y-intercept can be readily identified.

$$\begin{aligned} Ax + By + C &= 0 \\ By &= -Ax - C \\ y &= -\frac{A}{B}x - \frac{C}{B} \end{aligned}$$

Isolate y and compare with $y = mx + b$.

> For equations in standard form, $Ax + By + C = 0$, slope m is represented by $-\frac{A}{B}$, and y-intercept b is represented by $-\frac{C}{B}$.

EXAMPLE 1: Find the slope and y-intercept of the line represented by $2x + 3y - 1200 = 0$.

The equation $2x + 3y - 1200 = 0$ is in standard form, so $A = 2$, $B = 3$, and $C = -1200$. From the general result above:

$$m = -\frac{A}{B} = -\frac{2}{3} \quad \text{and} \quad b = -\frac{C}{B} = -\frac{(-1200)}{3} = 400$$

Therefore, the line has slope $-\frac{2}{3}$ and y-intercept 400.

EXAMPLE 2: Find the slope of a line that is perpendicular to the line represented by $x + 7y + 3 = 0$.

From the general result, the equation $x + 7y + 3 = 0$ represents a line with slope $-\frac{A}{B}$, or $-\frac{1}{7}$.

Since the slopes of perpendicular lines are negative reciprocals, then a line perpendicular to the given line will have slope 7.

EXERCISE 4-9

A **1.** State the values of A, B, and C in each equation.

a. $3x + 6y + 6 = 0$ **b.** $5x - 2y - 10 = 0$ **c.** $x - y - 6 = 0$
d. $7x + y - 7 = 0$ **e.** $y - 3 = 0$ **f.** $x + 3 = 0$
g. $4x - 7y = 28$ **h.** $2x + y = 6$ **i.** $6x - 30 = 5y$

2. **a.** State the slope and y-intercept of each line represented in exercise 1.
b. Graph each line represented in exercise 1.

B **3.** Graph the line represented by each equation.

a. $x - 2y = 8$ **b.** $7x - 2y + 14 = 0$ **c.** $9x - y - 9 = 0$
d. $6x + 5y + 15 = 0$ **e.** $4x - 9y = 36$ **f.** $2x + 3y + 6 = 0$

4. Find the slope of a line parallel to the line represented by the given equation.

a. $7x - y - 8 = 0$ **b.** $3x + y = 7$ **c.** $x - 8y + 5 = 0$
d. $6x + 3y - 4 = 0$ **e.** $9x - 4y - 9 = 0$ **f.** $5x + 6y + 1 = 0$

5. Find the slope of a line perpendicular to the line represented by the given equation.

a. $4x - 5y + 3 = 0$ **b.** $2x + 7y - 8 = 0$ **c.** $x - 3y - 7 = 0$
d. $5x + y - 6 = 0$ **e.** $9x - 5y = 6$ **f.** $6x - y + 7 = 0$

6. Which pairs of equations represent parallel lines?

a. $3x - 8y - 7 = 0,\ 2x - 8y - 7 = 0$ **b.** $2x + 5y - 7 = 0,\ 2x + 5y - 1 =$
c. $x - 6y - 4 = 0,\ 6x - y + 3 = 0$ **d.** $y = \frac{2}{3}x + 2,\ 2x - 3y + 5 = 0$

7. Which pairs of equations represent perpendicular lines?

a. $4x - 5y + 3 = 0,\ 5x + 4y - 2 = 0$ **b.** $6x - y = 7,\ x - 6y - 3 = 0$
c. $y = -\frac{5}{6}x + 4,\ 6x - 5y - 5 = 0$ **d.** $x + 3y - 8 = 0,\ y = 3x + 4$

8. **a.** The line given by $ax + 5y - 10 = 0$ has slope $\frac{2}{5}$. Find the value of a.
b. The line given by $6x - py + 3 = 0$ has y-intercept -1. Find the value of p.
c. The line defined by $ax + by = 8$ has slope $\frac{3}{2}$ and y-intercept -4. Find the values of a and b.

9. **a.** Graph the triangle whose sides lie in the lines represented by: $3x - 2y + 6 = 0$; $2x + 3y + 6 = 0$; $y = -3$.
b. What type of triangle is this?

C **10.** Describe the graph of $Ax + By + C = 0$ for the given restrictions on A, B, and C.

a. $A = 0;\ B, C \neq 0$ **b.** $B = 0;\ A, C \neq 0$
c. $A, C = 0;\ B \neq 0$ **d.** $B, C = 0;\ A \neq 0$

4-10 Linear Equations in Point-Slope Form

In lesson 4-8 it was established that often two pieces of information about a line are enough to graph the line. Similarly, two pieces of information are often sufficient to find an equation of the line.

A point $P(x, y)$ is on a line if and only if x and y satisfy the equation of the line.

EXAMPLE 1: A line with slope $\frac{4}{5}$ passes through the point $A(1, 3)$. Sketch the line and find an equation to represent the line.

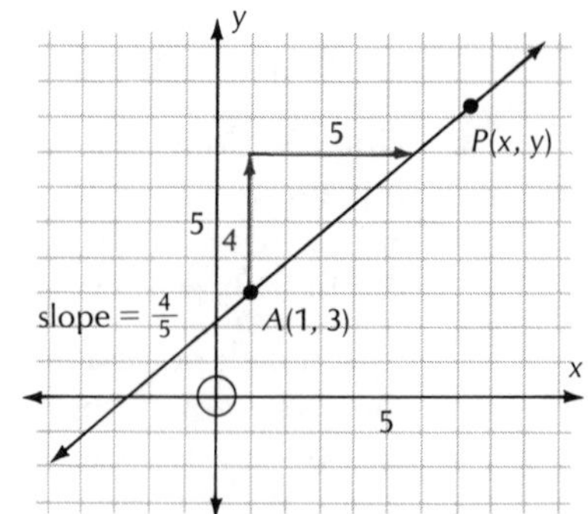

$A(1, 3)$ is a known point on the line. Let $P(x, y)$ be another point on the line. Since it is given that the line has slope $\frac{4}{5}$, then you know that AP has slope $\frac{4}{5}$. Apply the slope formula and substitute known values for slope and one point.

$$m = \frac{y_2 - y_1}{x_2 - x_1} \longrightarrow \frac{4}{5} = \frac{y - 3}{x - 1}$$

$$4x - 4 = 5y - 15$$

$$4x - 5y + 11 = 0$$

An equation of the line, in standard form, is $4x - 5y + 11 = 0$.

The method applied to solve example 1 can be generalized to a formula for finding an equation of a line, given the slope and one point on the line. To find an equation of a line with slope m that passes through $P_1(x_1, y_1)$, first let $P(x, y)$ be any other point on the line.

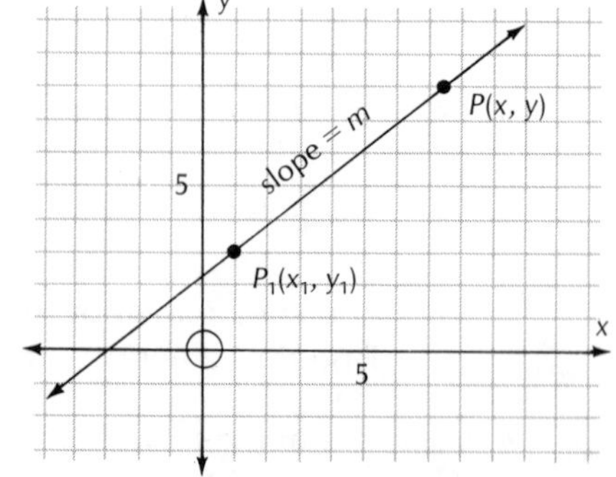

Then: $m = \frac{y - y_1}{x - x_1}$

That is: $y - y_1 = m(x - x_1)$

Point-Slope Form of a Linear Equation

Any line with slope m that passes through $P_1(x_1, y_1)$ can be represented by the equation $y - y_1 = m(x - x_1)$.

EXAMPLE 2: Find an equation of the line with slope 6 that passes through $A(5, 3)$.

Apply the general formula, substituting $A(5, 3)$ for P_1 and 6 for m.

$$y - y_1 = m(x - x_1)$$
$$y - 3 = 6(x - 5)$$
$$y - 3 = 6x - 30$$
$$0 = 6x - y - 27$$

An equation of the line in standard form is $6x - y - 27 = 0$.

EXAMPLE 3: Find an equation of the line that is perpendicular to the line represented by $3x + 2y - 8 = 0$ and passes through $D(6, -4)$.

The slope of the given line is $-\frac{A}{B}$, or $-\frac{3}{2}$.

The slope of a perpendicular line would be $\frac{2}{3}$.

Substitute known values into $y - y_1 = m(x - x_1)$.

$$y - (-4) = \tfrac{2}{3}(x - 6)$$
$$3(y + 4) = 2(x - 6)$$
$$3y + 12 = 2x - 12$$
$$0 = 2x - 3y - 24$$

An equation of the line in standard form is $2x - 3y - 24 = 0$.

EXAMPLE 4: Find an equation of the line that is parallel to the y-axis and passes through $F(-3, 1)$.

Any line parallel to the y-axis consists of points whose x-coordinates are all the same. Therefore, any line parallel to the y-axis has an equation of the form $x = k$, where k is a constant. Since the line goes through $F(-3, 1)$, where $x = -3$, then an equation of the line is $x = -3$.

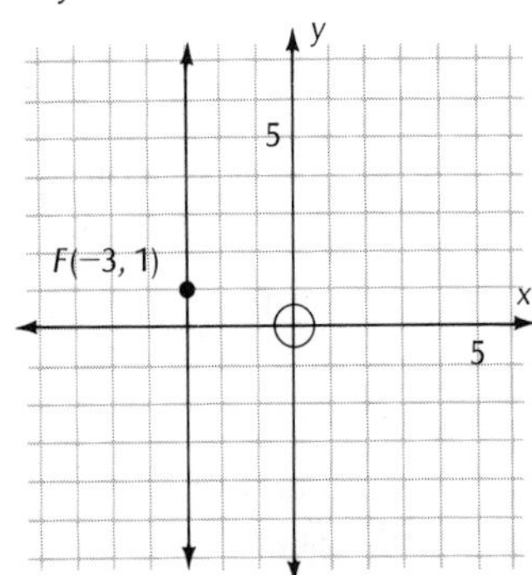

An equation of the line in standard form is $x + 3 = 0$.

EXERCISE 4-10

A **1.** Determine the slope and one point on the line represented by the given equation.

a. $y-8=3(x-7)$ **b.** $y-3=-5(x+4)$ **c.** $y+2=\frac{1}{4}(x-6)$

d. $4(y-5)=-7(x+5)$ **e.** $2(y+1)=3(x-8)$ **f.** $3(y-2)=\frac{1}{2}(x+1)$

2. Find an equation of the line with the given slope m and passing through the given point.

a. $m=6$, $P(7, 2)$ **b.** $m=-3$, $T(-4, 8)$ **c.** $m=5$, $S(-5, -6)$

d. $m=-2$, $U(0, 0)$ **e.** $m=\frac{1}{2}$, $A(4, 0)$ **f.** $m=-\frac{3}{4}$, $B(1, 1)$

g. $m=\frac{7}{6}$, $C(5, 1)$ **h.** $m=-\frac{2}{5}$, $D(-9, 3)$ **i.** $m=\frac{2}{3}$, $Q(0, -7)$

B **3.** Find an equation of the line parallel to the x-axis that passes through the given point.

a. $A(4, 7)$ **b.** $B(-6, 9)$ **c.** $C(-3, 0)$ **d.** $D(-8, -2)$ **e.** $E\left(\frac{1}{2}, -\frac{6}{5}\right)$

4. Find an equation of the line parallel to the y-axis that passes through the given point.

a. $F(-3, 8)$ **b.** $G(6, 9)$ **c.** $H(-1, 0)$ **d.** $J(-3, -5)$ **e.** $K(2, -5)$

5. Find an equation of the line with the given characteristics.

a. perpendicular to the x-axis, passing through $R(4, -1)$
b. perpendicular to the y-axis, passing through $S(-6, 5)$
c. parallel to the line given by $x-7y+8=0$, passing through $T(2, 9)$
d. parallel to the line given by $6x+y-5=0$, passing through $U(-3, -1)$
e. perpendicular to the line given by $3x+y-5=0$, passing through $V(4, 0)$
f. perpendicular to the line given by $3x-4y+8=0$, passing through $W(7, 2)$
g. parallel to the line given by $y=-\frac{5}{2}x+7$, passing through $A(-1, 8)$
h. perpendicular to the line given by $y=\frac{3}{5}x-3$, passing through $B(3, 2)$
i. parallel to the line given by $x-5y-6=0$, passing through the origin
j. perpendicular to the line given by $6x-y+8=0$, passing through the origin

6. Find an equation of the line that has the same x-intercept as the line given by $4x-3y+12=0$ and is parallel to the line given by $2x+5y-8=0$.

7. Find an equation of the line that passes through the midpoint of the segment joining $R(5, 8)$ to $S(-11, 12)$ and is perpendicular to the line given by $y=-5x+7$.

8. Find an equation of the line that is parallel to the line given by $6x + 7y - 5 = 0$ and passes through the midpoint of the segment joining $T(-5, 5)$ to $U(3, 9)$.

9. Does the point $W(-4, 3)$ lie on the line that is parallel to the line represented by $3x - 4y - 8 = 0$ and passes through $T(4, 3)$? Explain.

C 10. Find an equation of the line that is perpendicular to the line given by $3x + 7y - 5 = 0$ and passes through the point that divides the segment joining $A(-5, 1)$ to $B(4, 7)$ in the ratio $1:2$.

11. Find an equation of the line that is parallel to $y = -\frac{6}{5}x + 3$ and passes through the point that divides the segment joining $C(-3, 5)$ to $D(2, -5)$ in the ratio $3:2$.

12. The vertices of a triangle are $A(5, -3)$, $B(11, 9)$ and $C(-7, -1)$.
   a. Find an equation of the line that contains the median from A to $\overline{BC}$.
   b. Find an equation of the line that contains the perpendicular bisector of $\overline{BC}$.
   c. Find an equation of the line that contains the altitude from A to $\overline{BC}$.

13. A line passes through the point $D(5, 4)$. The x-intercept of the line is double its y-intercept. Find an equation of the line.

14. The x- and y-intercepts of a line are equal. Given that the line passes through the point $E(-7, -4)$, find an equation of the line.

15. Find a general equation for a line that has slope m and x-intercept a. (With an x-intercept equal to a, a known point on the line is $(a, 0)$.)

16. Apply the general equation you developed in answer to exercise 15 to find an equation of the line with the given x-intercept a and slope m.
   a. $a = 8, m = -4$
   b. $a = -7, m = \frac{3}{4}$
   c. $a = \frac{2}{3}, m = -\frac{1}{2}$
   d. $a = -\frac{5}{2}, m = -7$

17. Find a general equation of a line, given its intercepts, by following the steps below.
   a. Let the x-intercept be a and the y-intercept be b. Name two points on the line.
   b. Use the two points to find the slope of the line.
   c. Use the slope and one of the points to find a general equation.

18. Use the general equation developed in answer to exercise 17 to find an equation of the line with the given intercepts.
   a. x-intercept 3, y-intercept 4
   b. x-intercept -6, y-intercept -5
   c. x-intercept $\frac{2}{3}$, y-intercept $-\frac{1}{2}$
   d. x-intercept $-\frac{1}{5}$, y-intercept -4

4-11 Finding an Equation of a Line Through Two Point

Two points on a line are sufficient to find an equation of the line. Add one step to the procedure used in lesson 4-10.

EXAMPLE 1: Find an equation of the line through $A(2, -3)$ and $B(4, 7)$.

Start by finding the slope of the line.

$$\text{For } \overline{AB},\ m = \frac{7-(-3)}{4-2} = \frac{10}{2} = 5$$

Apply the slope m and either point to substitute known values into $y - y_1 = m(x - x_1)$.

$$y - 7 = 5(x - 4)$$
$$y - 7 = 5x - 20$$
$$0 = 5x - y - 13$$

A standard form equation of the line is $5x - y - 13 = 0$.

EXAMPLE 2: A triangle has vertices $P(3, 5)$, $Q(-1, 4)$, and $R(4, -3)$. Find an equation to represent the line containing the altitude, $\overline{PS}$, from P to $\overline{QR}$.

$$\text{For } \overline{QR},\ m = \frac{-3-4}{4-(-1)} = \frac{-7}{5}$$

$\therefore$ For $\overline{PS}$, $m = \frac{5}{7}$.

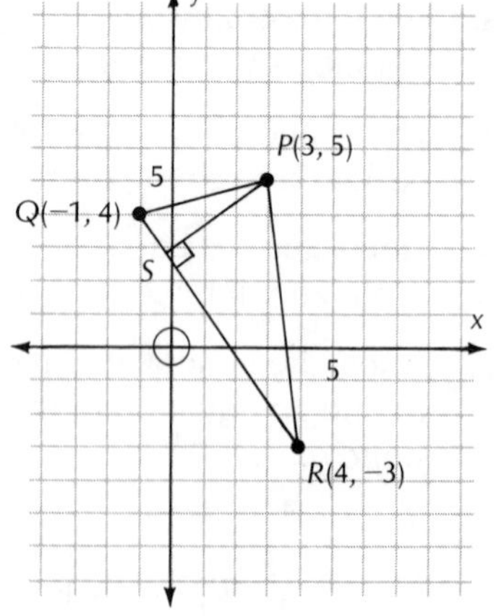

Since $\overline{PS}$ has slope $\frac{5}{7}$, and $P(3, 5)$ is on $\overline{PS}$, the point-slope form can be used.

$$y - 5 = \frac{5}{7}(x - 3)$$
$$7y - 35 = 5x - 15$$
$$0 = 5x - 7y + 20$$

The standard form equation of the line is $5x - 7y + 20 = 0$.

EXERCISE 4-11

A 1. Find an equation of the line that passes through each pair of points.

a. $A(2, 8)$, $B(-1, 2)$ **b.** $C(-5, 8)$, $D(0, 6)$ **c.** $E(7, -4)$, $F(12, 9)$

d. $G(0, -3)$, $H(5, 3)$ **e.** $J(6, 7)$, $K(-4, -4)$ **f.** $O(0, 0)$, $L(-5, -4)$

g. $M\left(\frac{1}{2}, \frac{1}{3}\right)$, $N(1, 1)$ **h.** $P\left(\frac{3}{4}, 6\right)$, $Q\left(\frac{1}{2}, -2\right)$ **i.** $R(a, b)$, $S(2a, 2b)$

2. The vertices of $\triangle ABC$ are $A(2, -4)$, $B(5, 7)$, and $C(-3, 10)$. Find equations of the lines that contain the sides of $\triangle ABC$.

B 3. $X(8, 6)$, $Y(12, -2)$, and $Z(5, 6)$ are the vertices of $\triangle XYZ$.

   a. Find the midpoint of $\overline{XY}$.
   b. Find an equation of the line containing the median from Z to $\overline{XY}$.
   c. Find an equation of the line containing the perpendicular bisector of $\overline{XY}$.

4. The vertices of a triangle are $P(4, 5)$, $Q(-2, 2)$, and $R(6, y)$. The altitude, $\overline{PS}$, from P to $\overline{QR}$, has slope $-\frac{5}{8}$.

   a. Find an equation of the line containing $\overline{QR}$.
   b. Find y.

5. Find an equation of the line with the given x-intercept a and y-intercept b.

   a. $a = 5, b = -3$ b. $a = -1, b = -3$
   c. $a = \frac{1}{2}, b = \frac{1}{3}$ d. $a = \frac{3}{4}, b = -\frac{1}{4}$

6. $C(5, -9)$ is the centre and $P(8, 2)$ is a point on the circle. Find an equation of the line containing radius $\overline{CP}$.

7. A triangle has vertices $P(3, 7)$, $Q(11, -9)$ and $R(-5, -1)$.

   a. Find M, the midpoint of $\overline{PQ}$.
   b. Write an equation to represent the line containing $\overline{MN}$, where N is the midpoint of $\overline{PR}$.

8. Quadrilateral $ABCD$ has vertices $A(-5, 2)$, $B(-3, -2)$, $C(6, 4)$, and $D(4, 8)$.

   a. Prove that $ABCD$ is a parallelogram.
   b. Write an equation to represent the line passing through the midpoints of $\overline{AB}$ and $\overline{CD}$.

C 9. $P(-1, 7)$, $Q(-6, -3)$, and $R(5, -2)$ are the vertices of $\triangle PQR$.

   a. Find the equations of the lines containing the sides of $\triangle PQR$.
   b. S divides $\overline{PQ}$ in the ratio $2:3$. Find an equation of the line containing $\overline{RS}$.
   c. T divides $\overline{PR}$ in the ratio $1:2$. Find an equation of the line containing $\overline{QT}$.
   d. Find an equation of the line containing $\overline{ST}$.

10. a. Graph $\triangle ABC$ with vertices $A(2, 5)$, $B(-2, -3)$, and $C(6, 1)$.
   b. Find the point D that divides $\overline{AB}$ in the ratio $1:3$.
   c. Find the point E that divides $\overline{AC}$ in the ratio $1:3$.
   d. Find the slopes of $\overline{DE}$ and $\overline{BC}$.

4-12 Direct and Partial Variation

The Canadarm is manipulated by means of electro-mechanical devices, including electric motors. The speed of an electric motor can be varied by varying the voltage applied to the motor, as tabulated below.

Voltage Applied (*v* volts)	25	50	75	100	125
Motor Speed (*s* revolutions per minute)	100	200	300	400	500

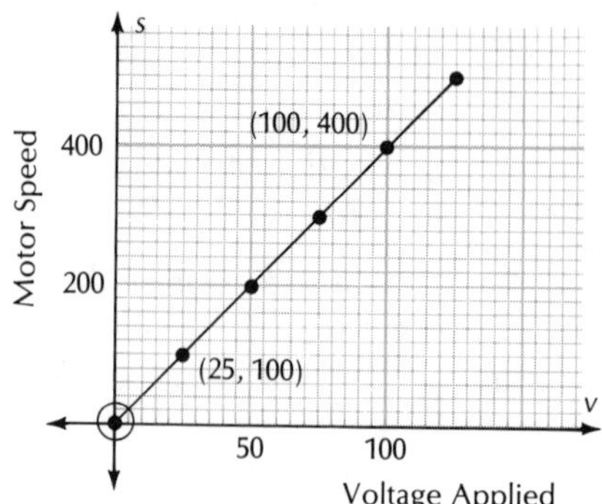

Because the variables *s* and *v* increase or decrease together, the relationship between them is called a **direct variation**. Here, *s* varies directly as *v*; written $s \alpha v$. Graphing the data from the table results in a straight line with slope 4 passing through the origin: *s* and *v* exhibit a **linear direct variation.**

For each ordered pair (v, s), the variation, $\frac{s}{v}$, is equal to 4, a constant. And, since $\frac{s}{v} = 4$, then $s = 4v$.

> A **linear direct variation** is defined by an equation of the form $y = kx$, $k \neq 0$, where the constant k is called the **constant of variation.** For any two ordered pairs (x_1, y_1) and (x_2, y_2) in the variation, the following proportion is true:
> $\frac{y_1}{x_1} = \frac{y_2}{x_2}$ $(= k)$. k is the slope of the line $y = kx$.

EXAMPLE 1: The time interval between a lightning flash and the sound of thunder varies directly as the distance from the source of the lightning. The thunder from a lightning strike 6.1 km away was heard 18.5 s after the flash was seen. How far away is lightning that can be heard 28 s after the flash is seen?

Let *t* represent the time in seconds; let *d* be the distance in kilometres. Since $d \alpha t$, then $d = kt$. Substitute known values for *d* and *t* to find *k*.

$d = kt \longrightarrow (6.1) = k(18.5)$

$k = 0.33 \longrightarrow \therefore d = 0.33t$

Now apply the equation $d = 0.33t$ to find *d* when $t = 28$.

$$d = 0.33(28)$$
$$= 9.24$$

The lightning is about 9.24 km away.

Sometimes one quantity depends *partially* on another. The cost of renting a truck for a day, for instance, includes a fixed cost plus a charge for each kilometre driven. The graph at the right, illustrating a typical rental structure, is linear, but does not pass through the origin.

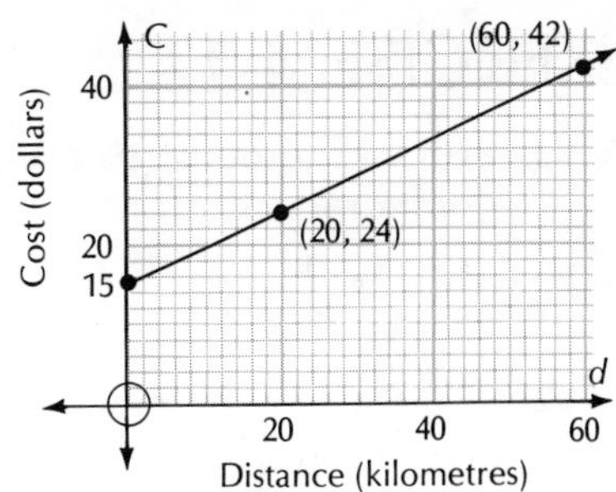

The relationship between cost and distance contains two parts: a constant part, plus an amount that varies directly as the distance. Cost and distance are in **partial variation**.

EXAMPLE 2: Find an equation of the line representing the relationship between cost, C dollars, and distance travelled, d kilometres, in the form $C = kd + b$.

To determine the value of k, find the slope of the line using the points (60, 42) and (20, 24). The slope of the line corresponds to the charge per kilometre, 45¢.

$$k = \frac{42 - 24}{60 - 20} = \frac{18}{40} = 0.45$$

k is also called the **constant of proportionality.**

The value of b is the y-intercept, which is 15 in this case. The y-intercept corresponds to the fixed charge for the day.

The cost, in dollars, of renting the truck is given by $C = 0.45d + 15$.

Variables in direct variation are not necessarily related by a *linear* equation. The following example illustrates two variables in **quadratic** direct variation.

EXAMPLE 3: Many satellites are equipped with stationary cameras. The area that can be photographed by a camera with a fixed lens varies directly as the square of the camera's height above the ground. A camera 200 km above the ground can cover an area of 1000 km². How large an area is covered by a camera 500 km high?

Let h be height in kilometres; let A be the corresponding area. Then $A \alpha h^2$, or $A = kh^2$. Substitute known values for A and h.

$$A = kh^2 \longrightarrow \begin{aligned} 1000 &= k(200)^2 \\ 1000 &= 40\,000k \\ k &= 0.025 \end{aligned} \longrightarrow A = 0.025\,h^2$$

Find the value of A when $h = 500$.

$$A = 0.025(500)^2 = 6250$$

A camera at a height of 500 km will photograph an area of 6250 km².

EXERCISE 4-12

A 1. For each ordered pair (x, y), $x \alpha y$. Find k, the constant of proportionality.

a. (5, 10) **b.** (7, 3.5) **c.** (7, 21) **d.** (4, 6)
e. (9, 3) **f.** (8, 1.6) **g.** (7, 3) **h.** (15, 9)

2. For each of the following, write a general equation describing the relationship between the two variables.

a. $y \alpha x$
b. r varies directly with t.
c. L varies partially with x.
d. Cost varies partially with mass.
e. $I \alpha C^2$
f. Distance varies partially with time.

3. Graph each set of ordered pairs (x, y) and determine whether they could result from a linear direct variation in which $x \alpha y$. If they could, find the constant of proportionality and an equation to represent the relationship. If not, assume they result from a partial variation and, again, find an equation to represent the relationship.

a. (6, 15), (8, 20) **b.** (2, 8), (5, 17) **c.** (6, 9), (2, 4) **d.** (6, 4), (9, 6)
e. (8, 6), (12, 9) **f.** (1, 6), (2, 11) **g.** (7, 6.5), (4, 5) **h.** (1.5, 0.9), (2.8, 1.5)

B 4. **a.** Given that $y \alpha x$, and that $y = 7.5$ when $x = 3$, find y when $x = 8$.
b. Given that $y \alpha x$, and that $y = 2.5$ when $x = 9$, find x when $y = 3.5$.
c. Given that $r \alpha t$, and that $t = 1.25$ when $r = 3.75$, find r when $t = 8$.
d. Given that $A \alpha l$, and $A = 180$ when $l = 24$, find l when $A = 300$.
e. Given that $V \alpha T$, and $T = 0.3$ when $V = 120$, find V when $T = 1.0$.

5. The current in an electric circuit varies directly as the voltage. When the voltage is 60 V, the current is 1.5 A. Find the current when the voltage is 150 V.

6. As a car travels at a constant speed, the distance travelled is directly proportional to the time travelled. Given that the distance travelled after 8 s is 90 m, answer the following:

a. What is the constant of proportionality?
b. What does the constant of proportionality correspond to in this situation?
c. How far would the car travel in 10 s?

7. Fuel consumption varies directly as distance travelled. Jan's car consumes 15 L of gas in 180 km.

a. How much gas is consumed in 500 km?
b. What is the rate of fuel consumption in litres per 100 km?

8. At a fixed interest rate, interest earned on an investment is directly proportional to the amount invested. An investment of \$3500 earns \$280 in interest. What amount is needed to earn \$500 interest?

9. A caterer supplies meals for a fixed charge plus an additional charge for each person served. The cost of serving 75 people is $525.00. The cost of serving 120 people the same meal is $795.00. Find the fixed charge and cost per meal.

10. The power dissipated in an electrical circuit varies as the square of the applied voltage. A heating element produces 150 W when 50 V is applied. How much heat will be produced when 80 V is applied?

11. The length of a metal wire varies partially with temperature. At 5°C a copper wire has a length of 200 m. When the temperature rises to 25°C, the wire has a length of 200.36 m. What would be the length of the wire if the temperature were 40°C?

12. For each graph below, find an equation relating the variables.

a.

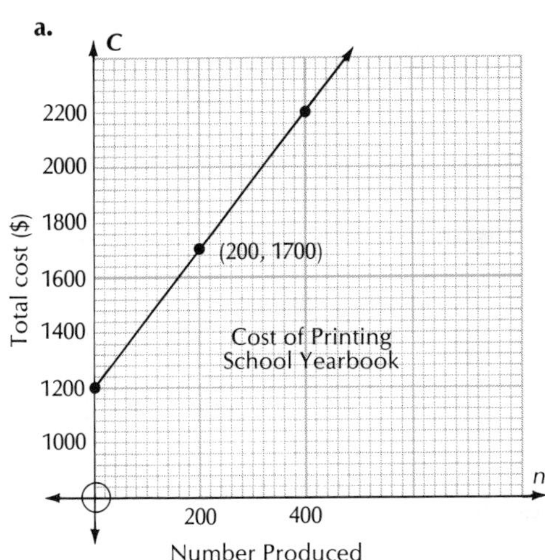

b.

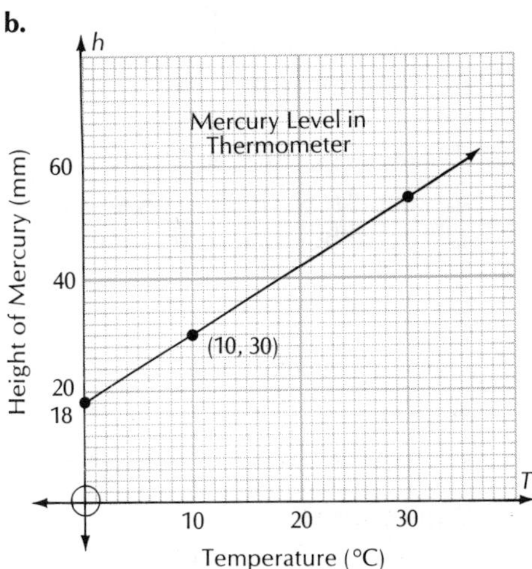

13. The stage area illuminated by a spotlight is proportional to the square of the distance of the spotlight from the stage. At a distance of 3 m, a light illuminates 12 m².
   a. What area will be illuminated if the light is 5 m from the stage?
   b. How far away should the light be placed to illuminate 48 m²?

C 14. The surface area of a hemispherical building varies as the square of the diameter of the building. The cost of the building varies directly as the surface area. If the diameter of the building is increased by 50%, how does the cost change?

15. If $y \alpha x$, then which statements are true?

a. $y = kx$ **b.** $x = ry$ **c.** $x_1 : x_2 = y_1 : y_2$

d. $x_2 : y_1 = x_1 : y_2$ **e.** $x_1x_2 = y_1y_2$ **f.** $x_1y_2 = x_2y_1$

Review

1. State the slope and y-intercept of each line.
   a. $y = 7x - 14$ b. $3x - y = 6$ c. $4x + 3y + 12 = 0$ d. $5x - 2y - 10 = 0$

2. Sketch the graph of each equation in question 1.

3. a. Draw the graphs of $3x + y = 11$ and $x - 2y = 6$ on the same set of axes.
   b. State the coordinates of the point of intersection of the two lines in part **a.**

4. Draw the graph of each equation.
   a. $\frac{y-0}{x-0} = 2$ b. $\frac{y-6}{x+2} = -3$ c. $\frac{y+4}{x-1} = \frac{2}{3}$ d. $\frac{y-5}{x+3} = -\frac{3}{4}$

5. Find the slope of each line described below.
   a. parallel to the line given by $y = 6x - 7$
   b. parallel to the x-axis
   c. parallel to the y-axis
   d. perpendicular to the line given by $y = \frac{1}{2}x + 4$
   e. parallel to the line given by $5x - 3y = 7$
   f. perpendicular to the line given by $6x + 5y + 30 = 0$

6. Show that the points $A(1, 3)$, $B(-2, -3)$, and $C(-3, -5)$ are collinear.

7. Graph each relation for $x, y \in \mathbf{R}$.
   a. $2x - 3y \geq 6$ b. $y > 2x - 4$ c. $y \leq 3x$ d. $y \leq 5x + 5$
   e. $6x - 7y < 42$ f. $x + 3 \geq 0$ g. $2x - 5y < 0$ h. $y - 3 \leq 0$

8. Write an equation of the line that fits each description.
   a. slope 4, y-intercept 6
   b. slope -9, y-intercept -5
   c. slope $\frac{2}{3}$, y-intercept 3
   d. slope $-\frac{1}{2}$, y-intercept 5
   e. slope 3, passing through $A(-4, 2)$
   f. slope $\frac{5}{4}$, passing through $B(-1, -2)$
   g. passing through $C(6, 7)$ and $D(-5, -7)$
   h. passing through $P(-6, 4)$ and $Q(5, -8)$

9. Find an equation of the line fitting each description.
   a. parallel to the line given by $y = 8x - 7$ and passing through $A(-2, 3)$
   b. parallel to the x-axis and passing through $B(-4, 8)$
   c. perpendicular to the x-axis and passing through $C(7, 6)$
   d. perpendicular to the line given by $x - 4y + 4 = 0$ and with the same y-intercept as the line given by $2x + 3y = 6$
   e. passing through the midpoint of the segment joining $D(4, -7)$ and $E(10, 11)$ and perpendicular to the segment joining D and $F(-4, -2)$
   f. passing through the origin and the midpoint of the segment joining $T(-3, 18)$ and $U(15, -2)$
   g. having x-intercept 6 and y-intercept -4

10. In what ratio does the point $R(-2, -5)$ divide the segment joining $A(-8, 4)$ and $B(2, -11)$?

11. Find an equation of the line whose y-intercept is double its x-intercept, given that the point $Q(-5, -3)$ is on the line.

12. **a.** Graph $\triangle PQR$ with vertices $P(8, 5)$, $Q(-4, 9)$, and $R(0, -3)$.
    b. Find an equation of the line containing side $\overline{PQ}$.
    c. Find an equation of the line containing the median $\overline{PM}$.
    d. Find an equation of the line containing the altitude $\overline{PD}$.
    e. Find an equation of the line containing the perpendicular bisector of $\overline{PQ}$.
    f. Prove that the segment joining the midpoints of sides $\overline{PQ}$ and $\overline{PR}$ is parallel to $\overline{QR}$ and equal to half its length.

13. Movie tickets cost \$5.50 for adults and \$4.50 for students.
    a. Let x represent the number of adult tickets sold and y represent the number of student tickets sold. Write an expression to represent the total proceeds from ticket sales.
    b. Write an equation to represent that the total proceeds for one showing were \$1640.
    c. State any necessary restrictions that should be placed on the variables and graph the equation given in answer to part **b**.
    d. Is it possible that only students attended the showing? Explain. How is this information reflected in the graph?

14. For each ordered pair (x, y), $x \alpha y$. Find each constant of proportionality.
    a. $(3, 8)$ **b.** $(12, 7)$ **c.** $(5, 2)$ **d.** $(9, 6)$

15. **a.** Graph the triangle with vertices $A(3, 7)$, $B(-5, -1)$ and $C(9, -9)$.
    b. Find the midpoints M and N of $\overline{BC}$ and $\overline{AB}$, respectively.
    c. Graph the point of intersection of the medians, I, and find AM and CN.
    d. Find the ratio in which I divides median $\overline{CN}$.
    e. Find the ratio in which I divides median $\overline{AM}$.

16. **a.** Repeat the instructions in exercise 17 for a triangle with vertices $A(11, 10)$, $B(-9, 0)$, and $C(7, 2)$.
    b. Write a general statement describing the results of question 15 and part **a** of question 15.

Test

Unit 4

1. Graph each for $x, y \in \boldsymbol{R}$.

   a. $4x - 3y - 12 = 0$ **b.** $y = 2x + 2$ **c.** $y > \frac{1}{2}x - 3$ **d.** $2x + 5y + 10 \leq 0$

2. Find the slope and y-intercept of each line and draw its graph.

   a. $y = \frac{1}{3}x - 5$ **b.** $3x - y + 6 = 0$ **c.** $4x + 7y - 28 = 0$

3. Given the points $A(8, 0)$, $B(4, -3)$, $C(12, -11)$, $D(12, 5)$, and $E(6, -3)$, find the slope of each segment.

   a. $\overline{BE}$ **b.** $\overline{CD}$
   c. a segment parallel to $\overline{DE}$ **d.** a segment perpendicular to $\overline{BC}$

4. Find the lengths of $\overline{BE}$, $\overline{CD}$, and $\overline{BC}$ from question 3.

5. Find an equation of each line, using the points from question 3.

   a. $\overline{BE}$ **b.** $\overline{CD}$
   c. a line parallel to DE through $F(8, 2)$
   d. a line perpendicular to BC through the origin

6. Prove that $H(-7, 4)$, $J(5, -4)$, and $K(-4, 2)$ are collinear.

7. A circle with centre $C(5, -4)$ passes through $P(8, -8)$. Find the following:

   a. the length of radius CP **b.** an equation of $\overline{CP}$

8. $R(6, 4)$, $S(-4, 10)$ and $T(12, -8)$ are the vertices of $\triangle RST$. Find an equation of each line containing the indicated segment.

   a. the altitude from R to $\overline{ST}$
   b. the perpendicular bisector of $\overline{RS}$
   c. the line through R parallel to $\overline{ST}$

9. Find the point that divides the segment joining $A(-1, 6)$ to $B(-6, -4)$ in the ratio $3:2$.

10. Carrie delivers a weekly community magazine, *The West End News*, and other assorted fliers once a week to 150 customers. She earns 3¢ for each *West End News* and 1¢ for each flier delivered. Her receipts for the week can be calculated by the equation $y = (150)(0.03) + (150)(0.01)x$, where x is the number of fliers delivered and y is the total receipts in dollars.

    a. Graph this relation for $0 \leq x \leq 10$.
    b. What is the y-intercept and what does it represent in this situation?
    c. How much would Carrie earn if she delivered 4 different types of fliers?

11. The volume of a sphere varies directly as the cube of its diameter. A sphere with diameter 6 cm has volume 36π cm^3. What is the diameter of a sphere with volume 56.25π cm^3?

Cumulative Review

1. Evaluate.
   a. $(x + 1)(x + 3)$
   b. $(10x - 9)(10x + 9)$
   c. $(x^3 + 2x^2 + x)(2x - 3)$
   d. $(2x^2 + 3x + 1) \div (x + 1)$
   e. $(2x^5 + 5x^3 + 10x^2 + 3x + 15) \div (2x^2 + 3)$
   f. $(x^5 + 2x^4 + 3x^3 + 3x^2 + 3x + 2) \div (x^2 + 1)$

2. Simplify by removing perfect squares, if possible.
   a. $\sqrt{63}$ b. $2\sqrt{72}$ c. $\sqrt{1024}$ d. $2\sqrt{1026}$ e. $\sqrt{2341}$ f. $\sqrt{7803}$

3. Solve, verifying answers if necessary.
   a. $x^2 + 3x + 2 = 0$
   b. $3(x - 4) + 2(x + 3) = 13$
   c. $\sqrt{x + 4} + \sqrt{x - 5} = 9$
   d. $\sqrt{x + 2} - \sqrt{x - 2} = \sqrt{2}$
   e. $2x^2 - x\sqrt{3} - 3 = 0$
   f. $\dfrac{x^2 + x + 1}{x - 2} = x - 2$

4. Solve and graph the inequalities on a number line.
   a. $3x - 2 > 7$
   b. $|4x + 2| \leq 6$
   c. $3w + 4 \leq 2(w + 5) + 1$
   d. $|5x - 9| \geq 4$

5. Evaluate.
   a. $4^{\frac{3}{2}}$ b. 3^{-1} c. 2^{-3} d. $9^{-\frac{3}{2}}$ e. $6^{\frac{2}{3}}$ f. $27^{\frac{2}{3}}$

6. The population of a certain species of insects doubles every week. The starting population is 300.
   a. How many weeks will it take for the population to reach 9600?
   b. How many weeks ago was the population 75?
   c. After 3 weeks, a flock of insect-eating birds wipe out 40% of the population. How many weeks does it take for the population to surpass 10 000?

7. Kim can consume a medium pizza in 30 min, while it takes Chris 40 min to complete the same meal. Eating together, how long does it take them to finish a medium pizza?

8. Assuming a constant 4.5% inflation rate, answer the following:
   a. In 1986 a pair of shoes costs $40.00. How much would the same pair of shoes cost in the year 2000?
   b. In 1986, a calculator costs $100.00 How much did it cost in 1984?
   c. In 1986, a book costs $5.00. In what year does it surpass $6.00?

9. A train derails, spilling 100 000 L of toxic waste into a lake. The lake has a volume of 6.6×10^7 L.
   a. What percent concentration is the toxic waste?
   b. The concentration halves every 6 months, due to the flow of water into and out of the lake. After two years, what is the concentration of toxic waste in the lake?

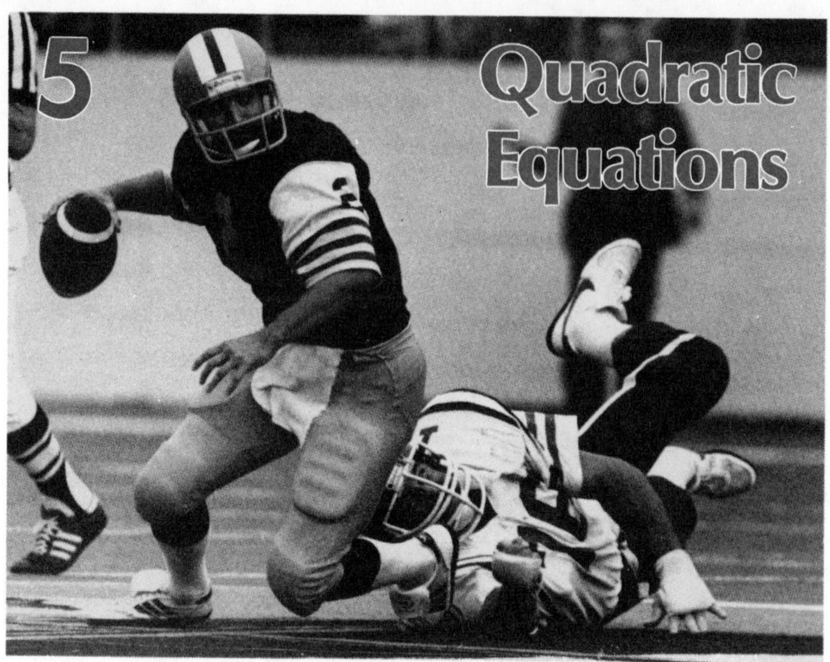

5-1 Graphing Quadratic Equations

When Tom Clements throws a touchdown pass, the ball follows a curved path. The relationship between the height of the ball, h metres, and the time, t seconds, can be represented by an equation like

$$h = -4.9t^2 + 10t + 1.75.$$

Such an equation, with the highest degree of any of its terms being two, is called **quadratic**.

Quadratic equations in x and y can be graphed on the coordinate plane to show how the variables are related. The quadratic equation $y = x^2$, for $x, y \in \boldsymbol{R}$, is graphed below from a table of values.

x	y
0	0
1	1
−1	1
2	4
−2	4
±3	9

Notice that opposite values of x give the same value of y. Write ±3 to represent "positive or negative 3".

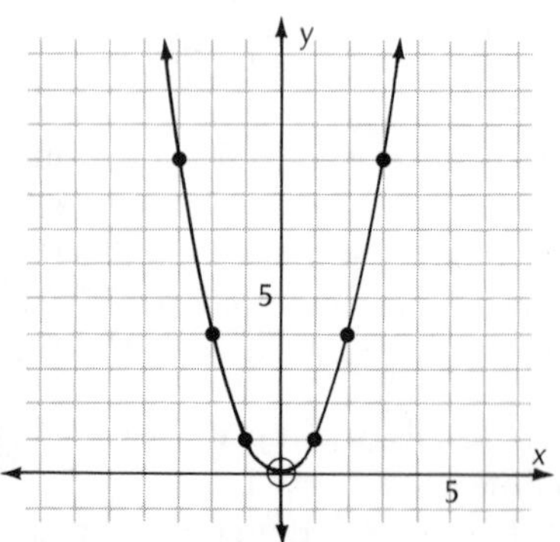

A smooth curve joins the points.

The graph of the equation $y = x^2$ is a **parabola**.

Here are some examples of equations that graph to give parabolas.

$x = 2y^2$ $\qquad y + 3x^2 - 2x = 0 \qquad$ $y = 5x^2 - 7x + 3$

EXAMPLE 1: Graph each equation for $x, y \in \mathbf{R}$.

a. $x = y^2$

x	y
0	0
1	±1
4	±2
9	±3

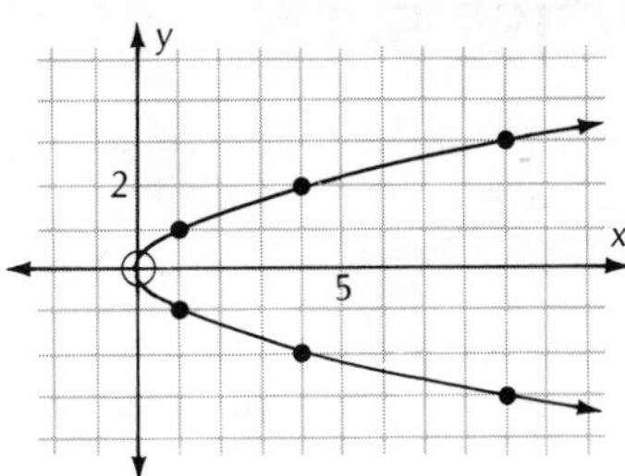

b. $y = -x^2$

x	y
0	0
±1	−1
±2	−4
±3	−9

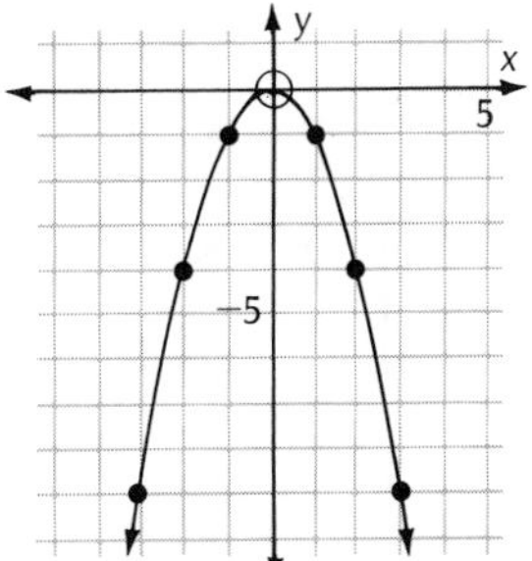

Look again at the graph of $y = x^2$.

The graph is a parabola that **opens upward**. The parabola is symmetric about the y-axis, which can be represented by the equation $x = 0$. The parabola's **axis of symmetry** is the line $x = 0$.

Since the value of y is never less than zero, $y = x^2$ is said to have a **minimum** y-value of zero. The point at which the minimum y-value occurs is called the **vertex** of the parabola. For $y = x^2$, the vertex is (0, 0).

By contrast, the graph of $y = -x^2$, above, is a parabola that opens downward. For $y = -x^2$, the **maximum** y-value is zero. Like the graph of $y = x^2$, it has axis of symmetry $x = 0$ and vertex (0, 0).

EXAMPLE 2: Graph $y = x^2 + 3$. State the axis of symmetry, the vertex and the maximum or minimum y-value.

x	y
0	3
±1	4
±2	7
±3	12

The parabola has axis of symmetry $x = 0$, vertex (0, 3), and the minimum y-value is 3.

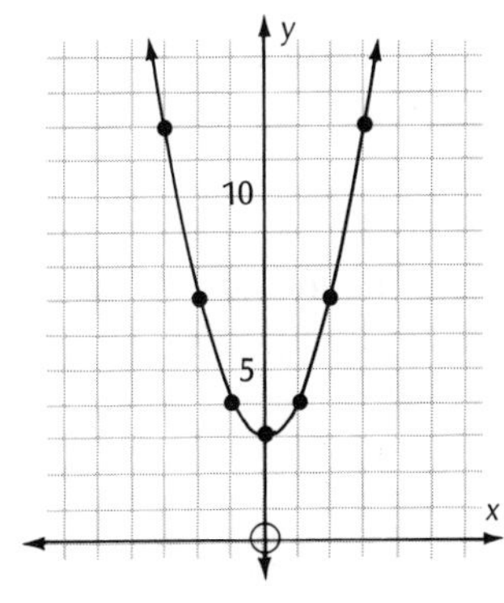

EXERCISE 5-1

A 1. Which of the following equations represent parabolas?

a. $y = 6x^2$ **b.** $x = y^2 - 8$ **c.** $y = 3x^2 + 6x$
d. $5x - y = 7$ **e.** $A = \pi r^2$ **f.** $x^2 + y^2 = 16$

2. For each parabola graphed below, state the direction of opening, name the vertex, and give an equation of the axis of symmetry.

a.

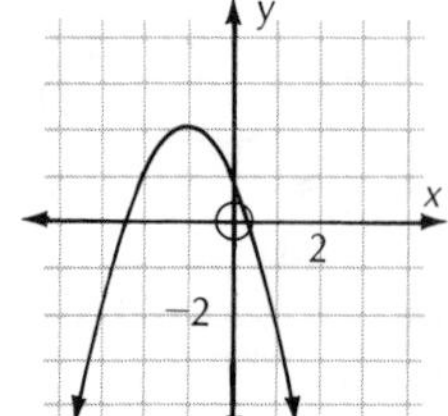

b.

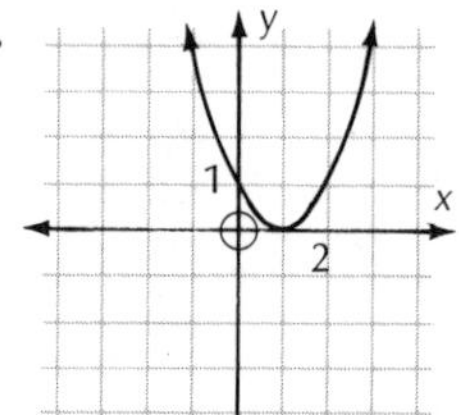

c.

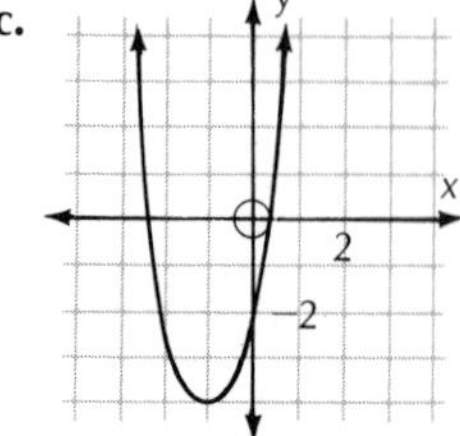

d.

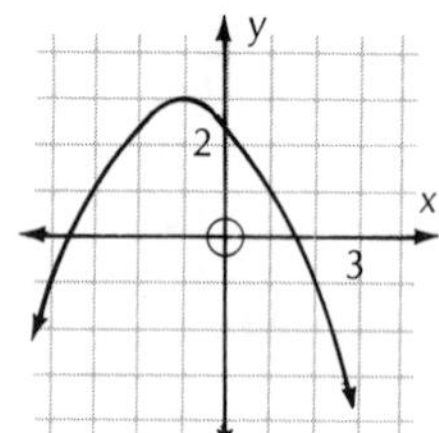

e.

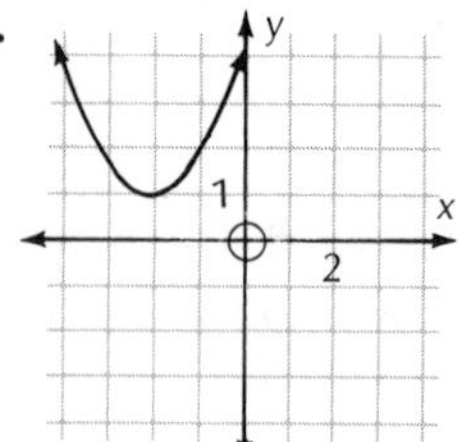

f.

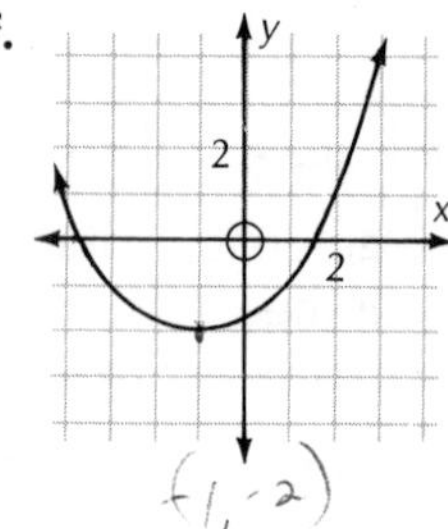

3. The axis of symmetry of a parabola that opens upward is $x = 0$. If one point on the parabola is (2, 12), name another point on the parabola.

B 4. Graph the parabola defined by each quadratic equation, using a coordinate grid that extends from −10 to 10 on each axis.

a. $y = x^2$ **b.** $y = 2x^2$ **c.** $y = 3x^2$
d. $y = \frac{1}{2}x^2$ **e.** $y = \frac{1}{3}x^2$ **f.** $y = -2x^2$
g. $y = -3x^2$ **h.** $y = -0.5x^2$ **i.** $y = -4x^2$

5. For each parabola graphed in exercise 4, state the direction of opening, give an equation of the axis of symmetry, name the vertex, and give the maximum or minimum y-value.

6. Graph each quadratic equation on a separate set of axes. State the direction of opening of each parabola, and give the vertex and an equation of the axis of symmetry. State each maximum or minimum y-value.

a. $y = x^2 + 1$ **b.** $y = x^2 - 3$ **c.** $y = x^2 + 4$
d. $y = -x^2 + 1$ **e.** $y = -x^2 - 2$ **f.** $y = 2x^2 + 1$

7. Does the given point lie on the parabola defined by $y = -x^2 + 2x - 3$?

a. (−1, −6) **b.** (2, −3) **c.** (−1, −4)
d. (−3, −18) **e.** (−3, 0) **f.** (0, −3)

8. Given that $y = x^2 + 2x - 3$ for $x \in \mathbf{R}$, answer the following:

   a. Find the value of y when $x = -4, -3, -2, \dots, 2$.

   b. Graph the equation.

C 9. **a.** Using the equation given in the introduction to this lesson, $h = -4.9t^2 + 10t + 1.75$, find (h, t) for integer values of t from 0 to 5.

   b. Explain why, in this application, it is appropriate to restrict t to positive values.

   c. Using the table of values from part **a**, graph the parabola defined by the equation. Note that the parabola does *not* represent the path of the ball; rather, it shows the relationship between height and time elapsed, (not height and distance covered).

   d. From the graph, give the height from which the ball was originally thrown.

   e. From the graph, give the maximum height attained by the ball.

10. Some familiar formulas relate two variables in an equation that represents a parabola. Graph each quadratic equation. State any necessary restrictions on the variables as appropriate for a measurement application.

   a. Area of a circle: $A = \pi r^2$ **b.** Surface area of a sphere: $S = 4\pi r^2$

11. The axis of symmetry of a parabola that opens upward is $x = 2$. If one point on the parabola is (4, 4), name another point on the parabola.

12. Graph each quadratic equation. For each parabola, name the vertex and give an equation of the axis of symmetry.

   a. $x = 4y^2$ **b.** $x = y^2 + 1$ **c.** $x = -2y^2 + 3$

Application

Conic Sections

Picture a right circular cone like the one at the right. If a cut is made along a plane passing through the cone, then the curve formed when the plane intersects the surface of the cone is called a **conic section**. A parabola is formed when the plane is parallel to the side of the cone.

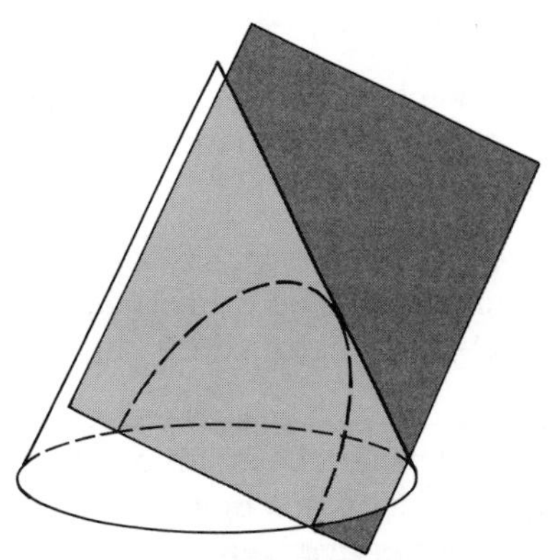

Describe three other possible positions of the plane, and the curve that would be formed by a cut along such a plane.

5-2 Sketching the Graph of $y = a(x - h)^2 + k$

By analysing parabolas and comparing to the graph of $y = x^2$, general results can be established that will help you work more efficiently when graphing quadratic equations.

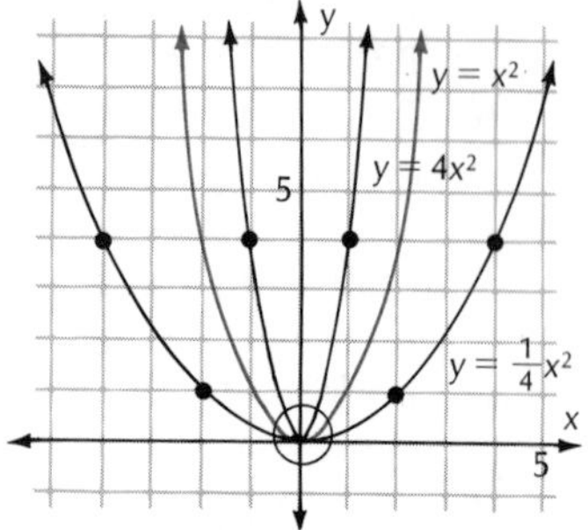

The diagram at the right contains the graphs of $y = x^2$, $y = 4x^2$, and $y = \frac{1}{4}x^2$.

The parabolas all open *upward*. All have the same axis of symmetry and the same vertex as the parabola defined by $y = x^2$. The *minimum* y-values are also the same.

For coefficients of x^2 greater than 1, the graph is narrower than that of $y = x^2$; for coefficients less than 1, the graph is wider.

The following diagram contains the graphs of $y = -x^2$, $y = -3x^2$, and $y = -\frac{1}{3}x^2$.

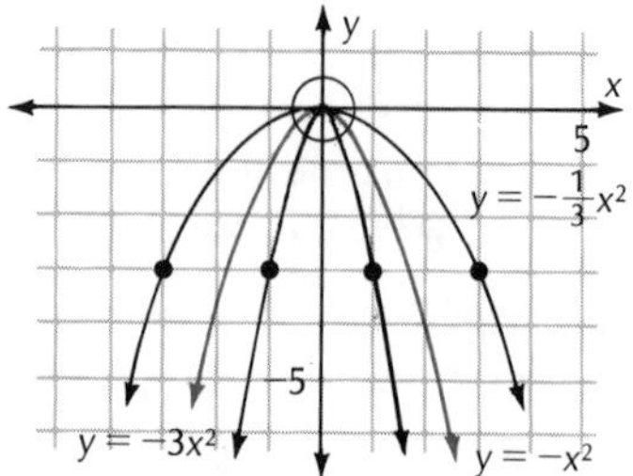

The parabolas all open *downward*. All have the same axis of symmetry and the same vertex as the parabola defined by $y = -x^2$. The *maximum* y-values are also the same.

For coefficients of x^2 with absolute value greater than 1, the parabola is narrower; for coefficients with absolute value less than 1, the parabola is wider.

In general, the graph of $y = ax^2$ opens upward if $a > 0$, downward if $a < 0$.

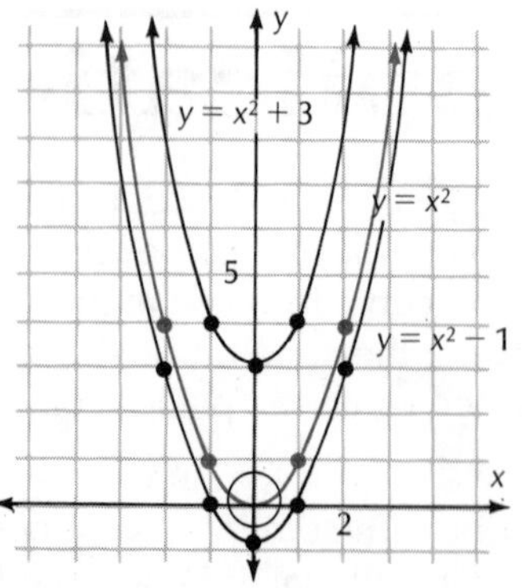

Compare the graphs of $y = x^2 + 3$ and $y = x^2 - 1$ to the graph of $y = x^2$. The parabolas are both congruent to the parabola defined by $y = x^2$ and open in the same direction, but the vertex of each parabola and each minimum y-value is different.

The graph of $y = x^2 + 3$ has vertex (0, 3) and the minimum y-value is 3. The parabola is a vertical translation of $y = x^2$, by positive 3.

The graph of $y = x^2 - 1$ has vertex (0, −1) and the minimum y-value is −1. The parabola is a vertical translation of $y = x^2$, by negative 1.

In general, the graph of $y = x^2 + k$ can be found by performing a vertical translation of k units to the graph of $y = x^2$.

Finally, compare the graphs of $y = (x - 3)^2$ and $y = (x + 2)^2$ to that of $y = x^2$.

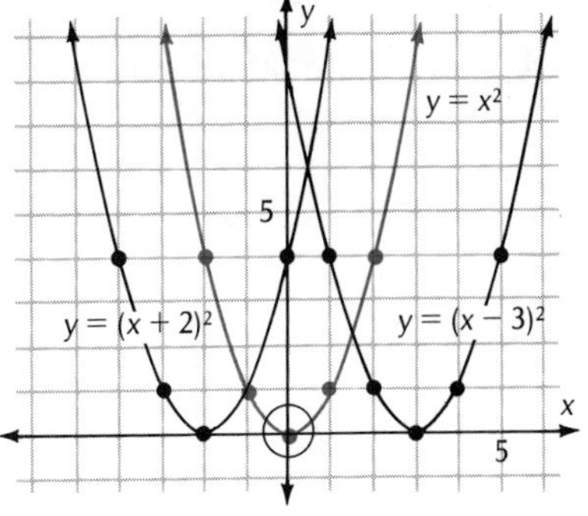

The parabolas are both congruent to the parabola defined by $y = x^2$, with the same general characteristics, except for the axis of symmetry and the vertex.

The graph of $y = (x - 3)^2$ has axis of symmetry $x = 3$ and vertex (3, 0). The parabola is a horizontal translation of $y = x^2$, by positive 3 units.

The graph of $y = (x + 2)^2$ has axis of symmetry $x = -2$ and vertex (−2, 0). This parabola is a horizontal translation of $y = x^2$, by negative 2.

> In general, the graph of $y = (x - h)^2$ can be found by performing a horizontal translation of h units to the graph of $y = x^2$.

The three general results stated above can be combined to predict the characteristics of the parabola defined by $y = a(x - h)^2 + k$.

> **Sketching $y = a(x - h)^2 + k$, $a \neq 0$**
>
> The graph of $y = a(x - h)^2 + k$ can be found by performing a vertical translation of k units and a horizontal translation of h units to the graph of $y = ax^2$.

EXAMPLE 1: Sketch the graph of $y = -(x - 1)^2 - 2$.

Starting with the graph of $y = -x^2$, perform a translation of −2 units vertically (2 units down) and 1 unit horizontally (1 unit to the right).

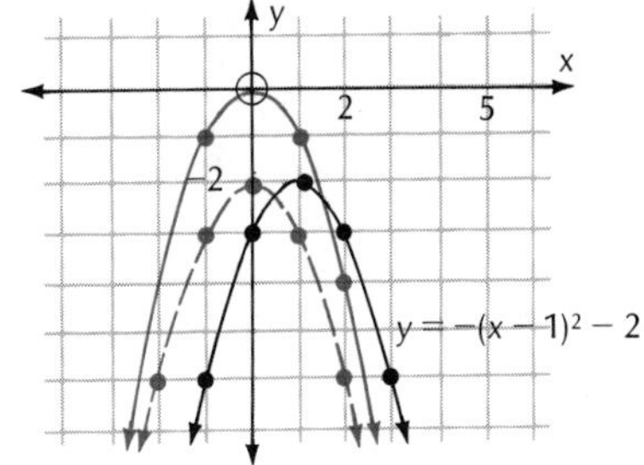

EXAMPLE 2: Describe the graph of $y = -3(x + 2)^2 - 4$ and sketch it.

$$y = -3(x + 2)^2 - 4$$

- The parabola opens downward.
- The parabola is "narrow".
- Its maximum y-value is −4.
- The axis of symmetry is $x = -2$.
- The vertex is (−2, −4).

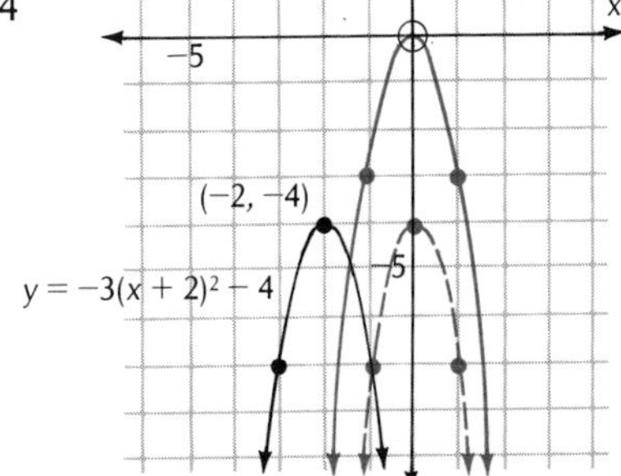

EXERCISE 5-2

A **1.** State the direction of opening of the parabola defined by each given equation.

a. $y = x^2$ **b.** $y = -2x^2$ **c.** $y = -4x^2 - 5$
d. $y = 3x^2 + 6$ **e.** $y = -3(x + 7)^2$ **f.** $5y = 3x^2 + 6$

2. Give an equation in the form $y = ax^2$ which defines a parabola that is congruent to the parabola defined by each given equation.

a. $y = 3x^2 + 1$ **b.** $y = -4x^2 + 5$ **c.** $y = \frac{1}{2}x^2 - 4$
d. $y = -(x - 4)^2 + 6$ **e.** $y = -2(x + 1)^2 + 4$ **f.** $y = (3x - 1)^2$

3. State the horizontal and vertical translations that are performed upon $y = x^2$ to yield the parabola defined by each equation.

a. $y = (x - 4)^2 + 3$ **b.** $y = (x - 1)^2 - 2$ **c.** $y = (x + 7)^2 - 5$
d. $y = (x + 1)^2 + 6$ **e.** $y = (x - 3)^2$ **f.** $y = x^2 + 7$

4. Does the order in which you perform the translations for exercise 3 make a difference in the resulting parabola? Explain.

5. By applying the stated translations to the point $O(0, 0)$, the vertex of $y = x^2$, find the vertex of each parabola in exercise 3.

6. Answer the following for the parabolas in question 3.

a. State an equation of the axis of symmetry for each parabola.
b. State each maximum or minimum y-value.

B **7.** For the equation $y = a(x - h)^2 + k$, find the following:

a. the vertical translation performed upon $y = ax^2$.
b. the horizontal translation performed upon $y = ax^2$.
c. the vertex of the parabola.
d. an equation of the axis of symmetry.
e. the minimum or maximum y-value.

8. For the equation $y = (x - 3)^2 + 2$:

a. Sketch the graph of the equation.
b. Give the vertex of the parabola.
c. Write an equation of the axis of symmetry.
d. What is the minimum or maximum y-value?

9. Repeat each part of exercise 8 for each given equation.

a. $y = (x - 2)^2 - 1$ **b.** $y = -(x + 4)^2 - 2$ **c.** $y = 2(x - 1)^2$
d. $y = -\frac{1}{2}(x - 3)^2$ **e.** $y = -3(x + 2)^2$ **f.** $y = (x + 1)^2 + 3$
g. $y = -(x + 3)^2 - 1$ **h.** $y = 4(x - 4)^2 - 3$ **i.** $y = -\frac{1}{3}(x - 2)^2 - 1$

10. Sketch the graph of the parabola defined by each quadratic equation.

a. $y = (x + 2)^2 - 3$ **b.** $y = -(x - 1)^2 + 2$ **c.** $y = 2(x + 1)^2$
d. $y = -\frac{1}{2}(x - 3)^2$ **e.** $y = 3(x - 2)^2 + 1$ **f.** $y = \frac{1}{3}(x - 1)^2$

11. Give an equation of a parabola congruent to $y = 2x^2$, which opens in the same direction and has the given property.
   a. The parabola is 2 units to the right of $y = 2x^2$.
   b. The parabola is 3 units to the left of $y = 2x^2$.
   c. The parabola is 5 units below $y = 2x^2$.
   d. The parabola is 1 unit to the left and 4 units above $y = 2x^2$.
   e. The parabola is 3 units to the right and 1 unit below $y = 2x^2$.

12. A parabola that is congruent to the parabola defined by $y = 4x^2$, also opens upward and has vertex $V(0, -2)$. Find an equation of the parabola.

13. The point $P(2, 7)$ lies on the parabola defined by $y = 2(x - a)^2 + 5$. Find the value of a.

14. The points $G(-3, 4)$ and $H(-4, 13)$ lie on the parabola defined by $y = a(x + 2)^2 + b$. Find the values of a and b.

15. The points $(3, -10)$ and $(-2, -25)$ lie on the parabola defined by $y = a(x - 1)^2 + b$. Find the values of a and b.

C 16. A parabola opening upward has vertex V and contains point P. Write an equation of the parabola.
   a. $V(0, 2)$, $P(2, 6)$
   b. $V(0, -1)$, $P(2, 3)$
   c. $V(2, 0)$, $P(3, 1)$
   d. $V(1, 2)$, $P(4, 4)$
   e. $V(1, -2)$, $P(-1, 6)$
   f. $V(-2, 2)$, $P(-1, 4)$

17. A parabola opening downward has vertex V and contains point P. Write an equation of the parabola.
   a. $V(0, 0)$, $P(1, -2)$
   b. $V(0, -1)$, $P(1, -2)$
   c. $V(0, 0)$, $P(2, -2)$
   d. $V(2, -1)$, $P(-3, -2)$
   e. $V(0, 2)$, $P(-1, 0)$
   f. $V(3, 1)$, $P(1, -3)$

Application

Parabolic Mirrors

The parabola has special reflector properties that make it useful in the manufacture of automobile headlights. The mirror in a headlight has a curved surface which can be formed by rotating a parabola about its axis of symmetry. The resulting three-dimensional figure is called a **paraboloid**.

A light placed at exactly the right point, called the **focus** of the paraboloid, will be reflected from the mirrored surface in parallel rays. Thus a straight beam of light is formed.

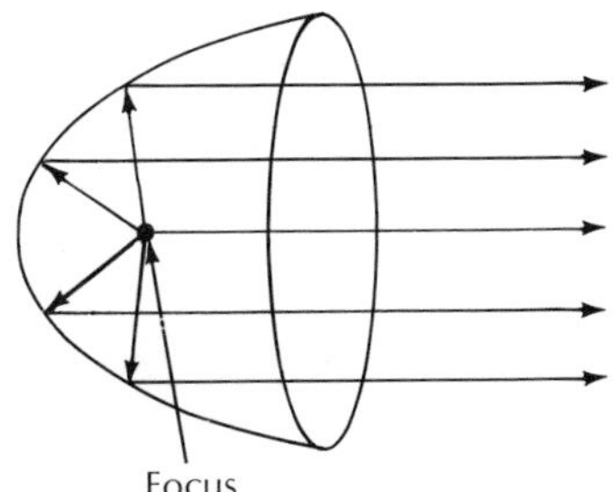

Paraboloids are also used as giant mirrors in reflecting telescopes and in antennas used to collect light and radio waves from outer space. In these cases, the waves are travelling towards the mirror, and all converge at the focus.

5-3 Completing the Square to Sketch $y = ax^2 + bx + c$

The general results established in lesson 5-2 can assist you in sketching the graph of $y = a(x - h)^2 + k$.

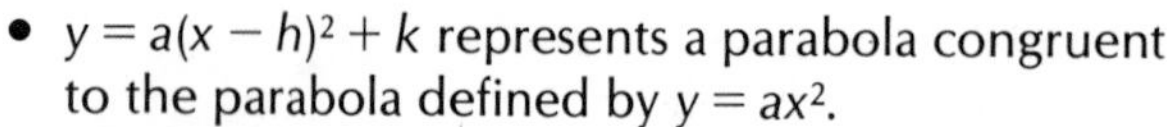

- $y = a(x - h)^2 + k$ represents a parabola congruent to the parabola defined by $y = ax^2$.
- If $a > 0$, the parabola opens upward; if $a < 0$, it opens downward.
- The maximum or minimum y-value is k.
- The axis of symmetry is $x - h = 0$.
- The vertex is (h, k).

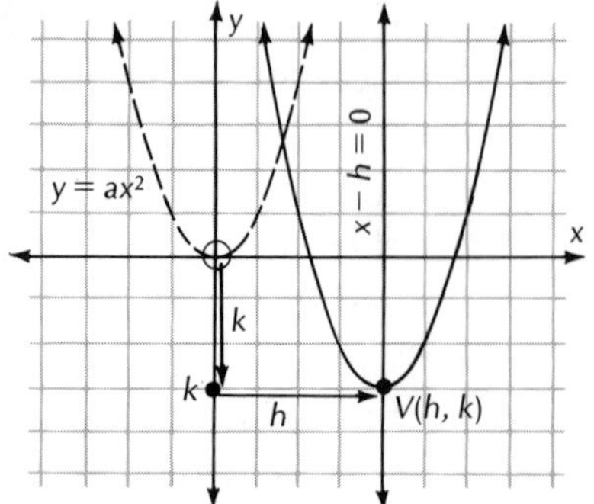

These results could also be applied to graph quadratic equations in the form $y = ax^2 + bx + c$, where $a \neq 0$, if this equation were rewritten in the form $y = a(x - h)^2 + k$, where $a \neq 0$. The following examples illustrate this process.

EXAMPLE 1: Rewrite $x^2 - 6x + 10$ in the form $(x - h)^2 + k$. That is, rewrite the trinomial to reveal a trinomial square, which can then be factored.

First, consider that $(x - h)^2 = x^2 - 2hx + h^2$. The last term is the *square* of *half* the coefficient of x.

To find the last term of the trinomial square $x^2 - 6x + \blacksquare$, take *half* the coefficient of x (half of 6 is 3) and *square* it (3^2 is 9). So $x^2 - 6x$ are the first two terms of trinomial square $x^2 - 6x + 9$.

Now rewrite $x^2 - 6x + 10$ to reveal the trinomial square $x^2 - 6x + 9$.

$$\begin{aligned} x^2 - 6x + 10 &= (x^2 - 6x) + 9 + (10) - 9 && \text{9 is added to complete the square, and subtracted to balance the expression.} \\ &= (x^2 - 6x + 9) + 1 \\ &= (x - 3)^2 + 1 && \text{This is in the desired form.} \end{aligned}$$

Rewriting an expression to reveal a trinomial square is called **completing the square**. There is an additional step required when the coefficient of the x^2 term is not 1.

EXAMPLE 2: Rewrite each equation in the form $a(x - h)^2 + k$.

a. $2x^2 - 16x + 11 = 2(x^2 - 8x) + 11$ — Factor 2 from $2x^2 - 16x$

$= 2(x^2 - 8x + 16) + 11 - 2(16)$ — Complete the square: $\left(\frac{1}{2} \text{ of } 8\right)^2$.

$= 2(x - 4)^2 - 21$

b. $3x^2 - 5x - 1 = 3\left(x^2 - \frac{5}{3}x\right) - 1$

$= 3\left(x^2 - \frac{5}{3}x + \frac{25}{36}\right) - 1 - 3\left(\frac{25}{36}\right)$

$= 3\left(x - \frac{5}{6}\right)^2 - 1 - \frac{25}{12}$ — $\left(\frac{1}{2} \text{ of } \frac{5}{3}\right)^2$ is $\frac{25}{36}$

$= 3\left(x - \frac{5}{6}\right)^2 - \frac{37}{12}$

Given an equation in the form $y = ax^2 + bx + c$, where $a \neq 0$, you can now sketch its graph by completing the square to obtain the form $y = a(x - h)^2 + k$, where $a \neq 0$, and then applying the general results summarized at the beginning of this lesson.

EXAMPLE 3: Sketch the graph of $y = x^2 - 6x + 10$.

From example 1,
$x^2 - 6x + 10 = (x - 3)^2 + 1$,
so $y = x^2 - 6x + 10$ is equivalent to
$y = (x - 3)^2 + 1$.

The graph of $y = (x - 3)^2 + 1$ is a parabola congruent to $y = x^2$ with axis of symmetry $x - 3 = 0$ and vertex (3, 1). The minimum y-value is 1.

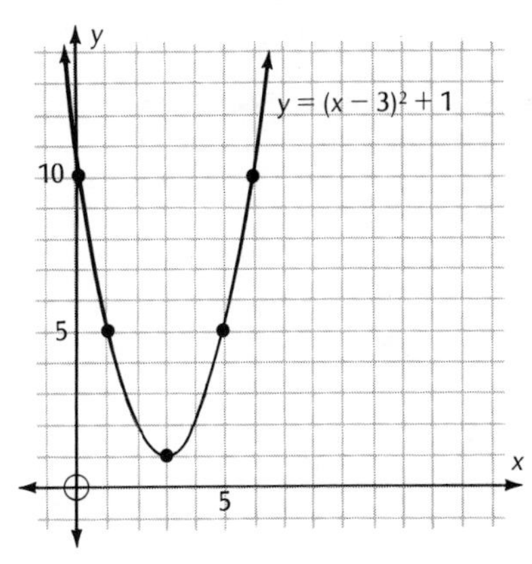

EXAMPLE 4: Sketch the graph of $y = -3x^2 + 3x - 5$.

Rewrite in the form $y = a(x - h)^2 + k$.

$y = -3(x^2 - x) - 5$

$y = -3\left(x^2 - x + \frac{1}{4}\right) - 5 + 3\left(\frac{1}{4}\right)$

$y = -3\left(x - \frac{1}{2}\right)^2 - \frac{17}{4}$

This equation defines a parabola congruent to $y = 3x^2$ with axis of symmetry $x - \frac{1}{2} = 0$ and vertex $(0.5, -4.25)$. The maximum y-value is -4.25.

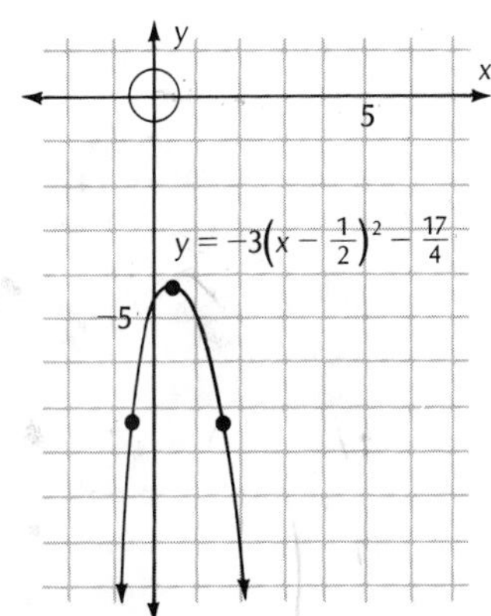

EXERCISE 5-3

A **1.** For the graph of each given quadratic equation, state an equation of its axis of symmetry, give its vertex, and state the maximum or minimum y-value.

a. $y = x^2 - 5$ **b.** $y = 2x^2 + 1$ **c.** $y = (x - 3)^2$

d. $y = 2(x + 1)^2 + 4$ **e.** $y = \frac{1}{2}(x - 2)^2 - 1$ **f.** $y = -3(x + 3)^2 - 2$

2. Expand each expression.

a. $(x - 3)^2$ **b.** $(x + 5)^2$ **c.** $(x - 7)^2$

d. $(x + 4)^2$ **e.** $3(x - 1)^2$ **f.** $-2.5(x - 6)^2$

3. Find the term that must be added to each binomial to complete the square.

a. $x^2 - 6x$ **b.** $x^2 + 10x$ **c.** $x^2 - 5x$

d. $x^2 + 7x$ **e.** $4x^2 - 8x$ **f.** $25x^2 - 10x$

4. State the vertex of the parabola defined by each quadratic equation.

a. $y = (x - 4)^2 + 3$ **b.** $y = 3(x - 1)^2 - 2$ **c.** $y = -4(x + 1)^2 + 6)$

B **5.** Rewrite each expression in the form $(x - h)^2 + k$.

a. $x^2 - 6x + 7$ **b.** $x^2 + 10x - 15$ **c.** $x^2 - 5x + 3$

d. $2x^2 - 12x + 3$ **e.** $3x^2 - 9x - 1$ **f.** $5x^2 - 8x$

6. For each given equation, describe the curve it defines and sketch the graph.

a. $y = 2x^2 - 4x + 5$ **b.** $y = -x^2 + 5x - 7$ **c.** $y = x^2 + 6x - 1$

d. $y = -4x^2 - 8x + 3$ **e.** $y = \frac{1}{2}x^2 - x$ **f.** $y = -\frac{1}{2}x^2 + 5x$

g. $y = -2x^2 - 6x - 3$ **h.** $y = x^2 + x + 2$ **i.** $y = 3x^2 + 9x + 4$

7. For the parabola defined by each quadratic equation in exercise 6:

a. State the vertex.

b. State an equation of the axis of symmetry.

c. State the maximum or minimum y-value.

8. A parabola facing upwards has vertex $V(3, 4)$ and passes through the point $P(-2, 29)$. Find an equation of the parabola.

9. A parabola facing upwards has vertex $V(-1, -10)$ and passes through $P(-3, -22)$. Find an equation of the parabola.

C **10.** A projectile is shot straight up from a height of 2 m with an initial velocity of 65 m/s. Its height, h metres, after t seconds, is given by the equation $h = 2 + 65t - 4.9t^2$.

a. Sketch a graph of the equation, with height along the vertical axis and time along the horizontal axis.

b. After how many seconds does the projectile reach its maximum height?

c. What is the maximum height?

Review

1. Graph each quadratic equation.
   a. $y = 3x^2$ b. $y = \frac{1}{2}x^2$ c. $y = x^2 - 1$ d. $x = y^2$
   e. $x = 2y^2$ f. $y = 2x^2$ g. $y = 2x^2 + 5$ h. $x = -y^2$

2. State the vertex and axis of symmetry of the parabola defined by each equation. Sketch each parabola.
   a. $y = (x - 4)^2 + 5$ b. $y = -(x + 5)^2 - 6$ c. $y = 7(x - 2)^2$ d. $y = -3(x + 2)^2 + 11$

3. Answer the following for the parabola defined by $y = ax^2 + bx + c$:
   a. Under what condition will the parabola open upward?
   b. Under what condition will the parabola open downward?
   c. Under what conditions does the parabola pass through the origin?
   d. Under what condition will the parabola have y-intercept -5?

4. Solve for c in order that the given point is on the parabola.
   a. $y = cx^2 + 3x - 7$; $(-2, 6)$ b. $y = -3x^2 + cx - 1$; $(2, -3)$

5. Find an equation of the graph of each given parabola.

a.

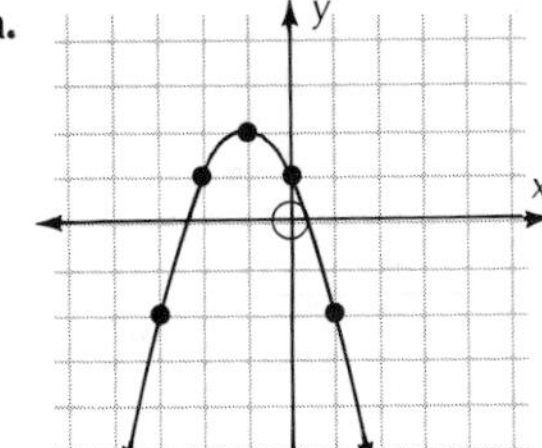

b.

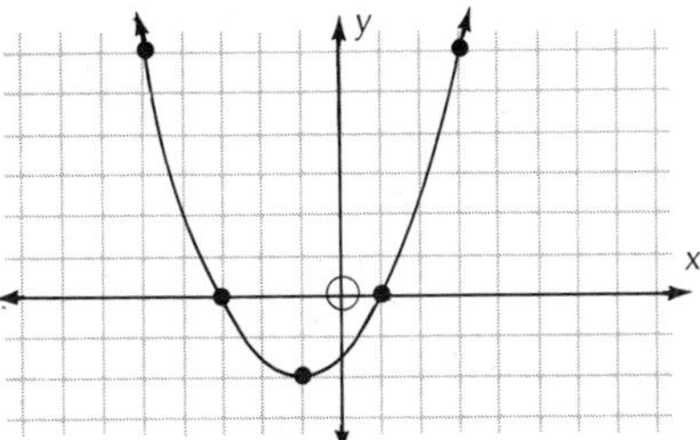

c.

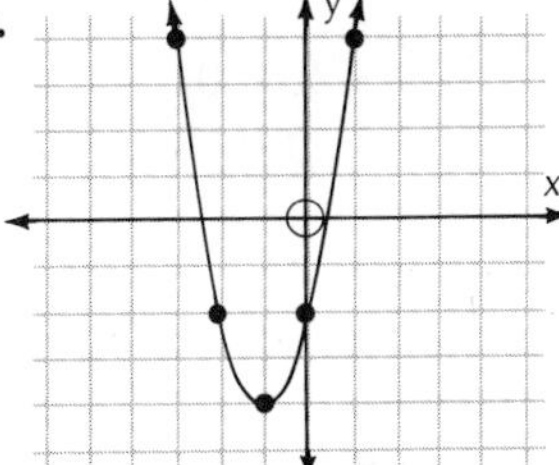

6. Complete the square to determine the vertex, the maximum or minimum y-value, and the axis of symmetry. Sketch the parabola defined by each equation.
   a. $y = x^2 + 6x + 9$ b. $y = x^2 - x + 12$ c. $y = 2x^2 + 6x$ d. $y = x^2 + 8x + 12$
   e. $y = 3x^2 + 6x + 7$ f. $y = 2x^2 - x - 10$ g. $y = x^2 + 3x + 9$ h. $y = -2x^2 + 4x - 3$

7. The vertex of a parabola is $(-4, 8)$. If the parabola opens upward, what is its axis of symmetry?

8. The x-intercepts of a parabola are 5 and -1. If the parabola opens upward, what is its axis of symmetry?

9. A parabola that opens downward has vertex $(-3, 5)$ and passes through the point $(-5, 3)$. Find an equation of the parabola.

10. The equation $h = -4.9t^2 + 12t + 1.5$ describes the path of a football, where t is the time in flight in seconds and h is the height of the football in metres.
    a. What is the maximum height of the football?
    b. At what time is the maximum height reached?
    c. How long is the football in the air?

5-4 The Roots of a Quadratic Equation

A helicopter, rising vertically at 14.7 m/s, reaches a height of 343 m when a relief package is thrown from it. A quadratic equation relating the height of the package (y metres) to time elapsed (t seconds) is

$$y = -4.9t^2 + 14.7t + 343.$$

When the package hits the ground, its height is zero. The time t at which the height h is zero satisfies the equation $-4.9t^2 + 14.7t + 343 = 0$. The values of t which satisfy the equation are called the **roots** of the equation.

To solve the problem, set y equal to zero and find the roots of the resulting quadratic equation.

$$-4.9t^2 + 14.7t + 343 = 0$$

$$t^2 - 3t - 70 = 0 \quad \text{Divide by } -4.9.$$

$$(t - 10)(t + 7) = 0 \quad \text{Factor the trinomial.}$$

$$\therefore t - 10 = 0 \quad \text{or} \quad t + 7 = 0$$

$$t = 10 \quad \text{or} \quad t = -7 \quad \text{Set each factor equal to zero and solve.}$$

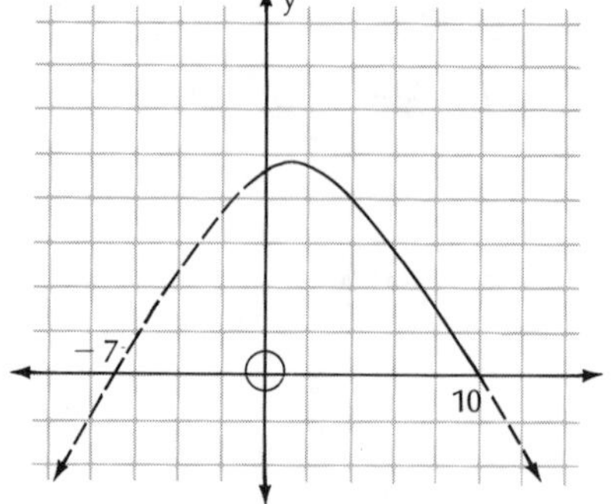

Although $t = -7$ is a solution of the equation, it has no meaning in the context of this application and so it is an **inadmissible** root. The only appropriate root for this example is $t = 10$, indicating that the package hits the ground after 10 s.

> The roots of the quadratic equation $ax^2 + bx + c = 0$ are the x-intercepts of the parabola defined by $y = ax^2 + bx + c$, where $a \neq 0$.

EXAMPLE 1: Find the x-intercepts of the parabola defined by $y = x^2 - 10x + 25$.

Set y equal to zero and solve the quadratic equation.

$$x^2 - 10x + 25 = 0$$

$$(x - 5)(x - 5) = 0$$

$$\therefore x - 5 = 0 \quad \text{or} \quad x - 5 = 0$$

$$x = 5$$

The equation has "two equal roots" of 5. The graph of the equation is a parabola with one x-intercept, 5, corresponding to its vertex (5, 0).

In cases where the quadratic equation contains a trinomial that cannot be factored, complete the square to solve the equation.

EXAMPLE 2: Find the x-intercepts of the parabola defined by $y = 2x^2 - 8x + 1$.

$$2x^2 - 8x + 1 = 0$$ Set y equal to zero.

$$2(x^2 - 4x + 4) + 1 - 8 = 0$$ Complete the square and factor the resulting trinomial square.

$$2(x - 2)^2 = 7$$

$$(x - 2)^2 = \frac{7}{2}$$ Isolate the squared term.

$$\therefore x - 2 = \pm\sqrt{\frac{7}{2}}$$ $\frac{7}{2}$ has two square roots, one negative, the other positive.

$$x = 2 \pm \sqrt{\frac{7}{2}}$$

$$x = 2 \pm \frac{\sqrt{14}}{2}$$ Rationalize the denominator.

The x-intercepts are $x = 2 + \dfrac{\sqrt{14}}{2}$ and $x = 2 - \dfrac{\sqrt{14}}{2}$

The following example illustrates the solution of an equation that corresponds to a parabola that does not cross the x-axis.

EXAMPLE 3: Find the x-intercepts of the parabola defined by $y = 2x^2 - x + 4$.

$$2x^2 - x + 4 = 0$$

$$2\left(x^2 - \frac{1}{2}x + \frac{1}{16}\right) + 4 - \frac{1}{8} = 0$$

$$2\left(x + \frac{1}{4}\right)^2 = -3\frac{7}{8}$$

Since the left side must be positive but the right side is negative, there is no real-number solution. The graph has no x-intercepts.

EXERCISE 5-4

A

1. Find the roots of each equation.
   - **a.** $(x + 6)(x - 4) = 0$
   - **b.** $(x - 3)(x - 8) = 0$
   - **c.** $(x + 4)(x + 8) = 0$
   - **d.** $4x(3x + 2) = 0$
   - **e.** $x(5x + 8)(2x - 3) = 0$
   - **f.** $2x(x - 6)(5x + 4) = 0$

2. Solve each equation. Answers should have rational denominators.
   - **a.** $(x - 3)^2 = 16$
   - **b.** $(x + 3)^2 = 25$
   - **c.** $(x - 6)^2 = 9$
   - **d.** $(x + 7)^2 = 1$
   - **e.** $4(x - 1)^2 = 8$
   - **f.** $-2(x - 7)^2 = 5$
   - **g.** $\frac{1}{2}(x + 1)^2 = 8$
   - **h.** $(x - 5)^2 = -4$
   - **i.** $7(x - 3)^2 = 5$

3. Find the x-intercepts of the parabola defined by each equation.
   - **a.** $y = (x - 7)(x + 4)$
   - **b.** $y = (x - 4)(x - 5)$
   - **c.** $y = 2(x - 1)(x - 8)$
   - **d.** $y = 3x(x + 9)$
   - **e.** $y = (3x - 7)(5x + 4)$
   - **f.** $y = -2(x + 1)(3x - 5)$
   - **g.** $y = (4x - 1)(6x + 4)$
   - **h.** $y = (2x - 5)(7x - 3)$
   - **i.** $y = -5(x + 3)(x + 1)$

4. What do you know about the roots of the quadratic equation corresponding to each parabola graphed below?

a. 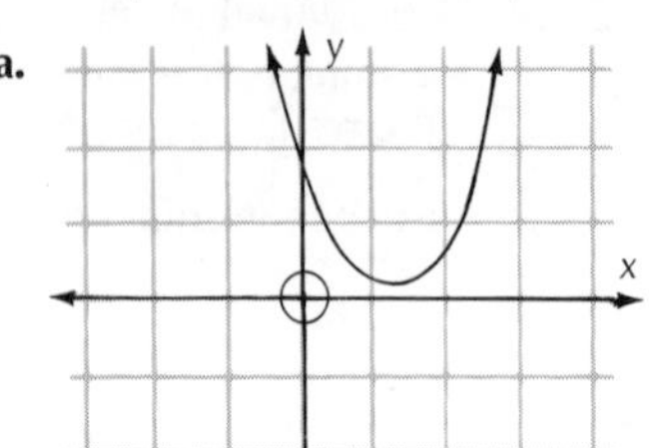

b. 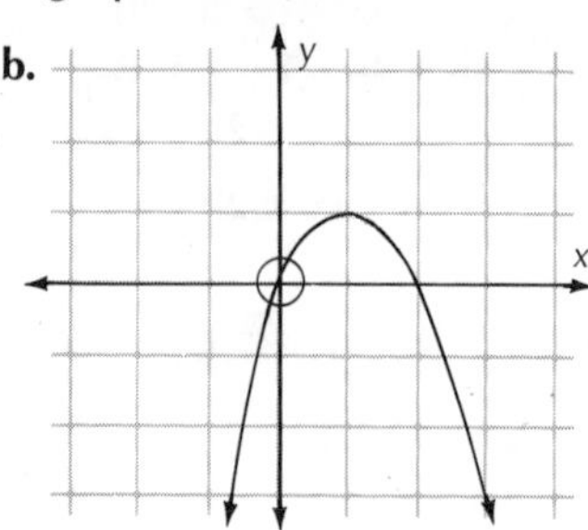

c. 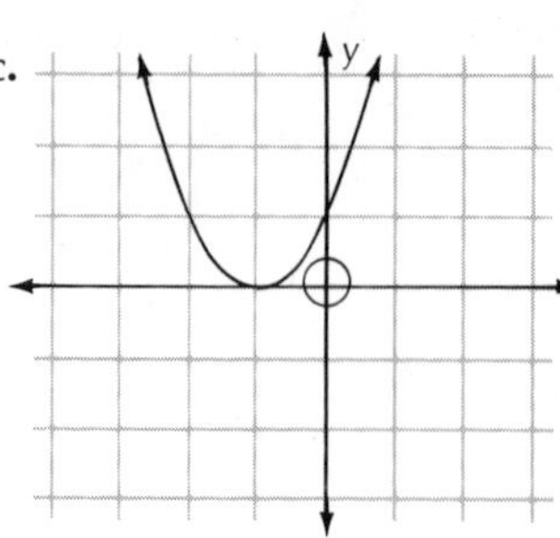

B 5. Find the x-intercepts of the parabola defined by each equation.

a. $y = x^2 - x - 12$ b. $y = x^2 + 8x + 12$ c. $y = x^2 - 2x - 35$
d. $y = x^2 - 13x + 36$ e. $y = 3x^2 - 12x$ f. $y = 5x^2 - 10x$
g. $y = x^2 - 16$ h. $y = x^2 - 49$ i. $y = 16x^2 - 46x - 35$

6. Solve each equation by completing the square.

a. $x^2 + 2x - 1 = 0$ b. $x^2 - 2x - 4 = 0$ c. $x^2 + 3x - 5 = 0$
d. $x^2 + x + 5 = 0$ e. $2x^2 - 6x - 1 = 0$ f. $3x^2 + 9x + 1 = 0$
g. $-2x^2 + 2x + 5 = 0$ h. $5x^2 + 20x - 2 = 0$ i. $7x^2 + 3x - 1 = 0$

7. Find the x-intercepts of the parabola defined by each equation.

a. $y = x^2 + 2x - 8$ b. $y = x^2 - x - 12$ c. $y = x^2 + 6x + 3$
d. $y = x^2 - 2x - 5$ e. $y = 2x^2 + 2x - 1$ f. $y = 3x^2 + 6x - 5$
g. $y = -2x^2 + 3x + 3$ h. $y = -4x^2 + 2x - 7$ i. $y = 5x^2 + x + 1$

8. For the parabola defined by $y = 3x^2 - x - 2$, find its vertex, give an equation of the axis of symmetry, and sketch the graph.

9. Repeat the instructions in exercise 8 for each given quadratic equation.

a. $y = 2x^2 - 9x - 5$ b. $y = x^2 - 4x + 2$ c. $y = 3x^2 - 3x + 2$

10. Given a parabola defined by $y = ax^2 + bx + c$, what does each given statement tell you about the roots of the equation $ax^2 + bx + c = 0$?

a. There are two distinct x-intercepts.
b. There are two equal x-intercepts.
c. There are no x-intercepts.

C 11. Find two consecutive integers, the sum of whose squares is 545.

12. A parabola facing upwards with vertex $(2, -3)$ has 5 as one of its x-intercepts.

a. What is the other intercept of the parabola?
b. Find an equation of the parabola.

13. Given that the lengths of the sides of two squares are consecutive integers, write an equation which represents the combined area of the squares.

Maximum/Minimum Problems

We have discovered how to find the maximum value of y when $y = a(x - h)^2 + k$, $a < 0$, and the minimum value of y when $y = a(x - h)^2 + k$, $a > 0$. Use this knowledge to solve the problems in this exercise.

EXAMPLE: A rectangular field is to be fenced in on three sides with the fourth side bounded by a river. If 1000 m of fencing are to be used, what is the maximum size of the field? What are the dimensions of the field of maximum area?

Let A represent the area of the field of in square metres.
Let x represent the width of the field in metres.
$\therefore(1000 - 2x)$ represents the length of the field in metres.

$A = x(1000 - 2x)$ Form an equation using $A = l \times w$
$\quad = 1000x - 2x^2$
$\quad = -2(x^2 - 500x)$ Complete the square.
$\quad = -2(x^2 - 500x + 62\,500) + 125\,000$
$\quad = -2(x - 250)^2 + 125\,000$

The vertex of the corresponding parabola is $(250, 125\,000)$.

$\therefore$The maximum area is 125 000 m^2 when the width is 250 m and the length is 500 m.

Solve.

1. Two integers have a sum of 12. What is their maximum product?
2. Find values for two positive integers whose sum is 10 if the sum of their squares is a minimum.
3. Find two numbers which differ by 6 if the sum of their squares is a minimum.
4. Find the dimensions of the rectangle of maximum area having a perimeter of 40 m.
5. Find a number which exceeds its square by the largest possible amount.
6. The sum of two numbers is k. Show that the sum of one number and the square of the other is at least $\left(k - \frac{1}{4}\right)$.
7. Three sides of a garden are to be fenced with 100 m of fencing, the fourth side being against the house. Find the dimensions of the garden of greatest possible area. State the total area.
8. A rectangular dog run is to be enclosed by a fence and then divided into two smaller rectangular areas by a fence parallel to one of the sides. If 54 m of fence is available, find the dimensions of the dog run of greatest possible area. State the total area.

5-5 The Quadratic Formula

By completing the square to solve the *general* quadratic equation $ax^2 + bx + c = 0$, $a \neq 0$, a general formula for solving quadratic equations can be derived.

$$ax^2 + bx + c = 0$$

$$x^2 + \frac{b}{a}x = -\frac{c}{a}$$ Divide by a and subtract the constant from both sides.

$$x^2 + \frac{b}{a}x + \frac{b^2}{4a^2} = \frac{b^2}{4a^2} - \frac{c}{a}$$ Complete the square using $\left(\frac{1}{2} \text{ of } \frac{b}{a}\right)^2$.

$$\left(x + \frac{b}{2a}\right)^2 = \frac{b^2 - 4ac}{4a^2}$$ Factor the left side; find a common denominator on the right side.

$$x + \frac{b}{2a} = \frac{\pm\sqrt{b^2 - 4ac}}{2a}$$ Take the square root of both sides.

$$x = \frac{-b \pm \sqrt{b^2 - 4ac}}{2a}$$ Isolate x.

The Quadratic Formula

The two roots of $ax^2 + bx + c = 0$, where $a \neq 0$, are

$$x = \frac{-b + \sqrt{b^2 - 4ac}}{2a} \text{ and } x = \frac{-b - \sqrt{b^2 - 4ac}}{2a}.$$

A quadratic equation has two distinct real roots, two equal real roots, or no real roots.

EXAMPLE 1: Use the quadratic formula to find the roots of $x^2 + 4x - 2 = 0$.

$$x = \frac{-b \pm \sqrt{b^2 - 4ac}}{2a}$$ Substitute $a = 1$, $b = 4$, $c = -2$.

$$x = \frac{-4 \pm \sqrt{16 - 4(1)(-2)}}{2(1)}$$

$$x = \frac{-4 \pm \sqrt{24}}{2}$$

$$x = -2 \pm \sqrt{6}$$

Normally, answers are left in radical form. If a decimal answer is needed, a calculator can be used to approximate $\sqrt{6}$.

EXAMPLE 2: Find the roots of $4x^2 - 2x + 1 = 0$.

$$x = \frac{-b \pm \sqrt{b^2 - 4ac}}{2a}$$ Substitute $a = 4$, $b = -2$, $c = 1$.

$$x = \frac{-(-2) \pm \sqrt{4 - 4(4)(1)}}{2(4)}$$

$$x = \frac{2 \pm \sqrt{-12}}{8}$$

There is no real number solution since the radicand of $\sqrt{-12}$ is negative.

The following results can be applied to double-check the roots of a quadratic equation.

Given the general quadratic equation $ax^2 + bx + c = 0, a \neq 0$:

The sum of its roots is $\dfrac{-b + \sqrt{b^2 - 4ac}}{2a} + \dfrac{-b - \sqrt{b^2 - 4ac}}{2a} = -\dfrac{2b}{2a}$ or $-\dfrac{b}{a}$.

The product of its roots is $\dfrac{-b + \sqrt{b^2 - 4ac}}{2a} \times \dfrac{-b - \sqrt{b^2 - 4ac}}{2a} = \dfrac{(-b)^2 - (b^2 - 4ac)}{4a^2}$

$= \dfrac{4ac}{4a^2}$ or $\dfrac{c}{a}$.

EXAMPLE 3: Check the roots found for $x^2 + 4x - 2 = 0$ in example 1 by checking whether their sum and product satisfy the results above.

The roots found in example 1 were $x = -2 + \sqrt{6}$, $x = -2 - \sqrt{6}$.

Find the sum: $(-2 + \sqrt{6}) + (-2 - \sqrt{6}) = -4$

Check: $\dfrac{-b}{a} = \dfrac{-4}{1}$ or -4 ✓

Find the product: $(-2 + \sqrt{6})(-2 - \sqrt{6}) = 4 - 6$ A difference of squares

$= -2$

Check: $\dfrac{c}{a} = \dfrac{-2}{1}$ or -2 ✓

EXERCISE 5-5

A 1. State the values of a, b and c for each equation.

a. $2x^2 - 6x + 4 = 0$ b. $x^2 + \dfrac{5x}{3} - 6 = 0$ c. $-\dfrac{x^2}{2} - x = 0$

2. Solve, expressing answers with radicals in simplest radical form.

a. $3x^2 + x - 14 = 0$ b. $2x^2 - 6x + 3 = 0$ c. $5x^2 - x - 2 = 0$

d. $x^2 - 8x + 4 = 0$ e. $2x^2 - x + 4 = 0$ f. $2x^2 + x - 7 = 0$

g. $\dfrac{1}{2}x^2 - 4x + 1 = 0$ h. $5x^2 - \dfrac{7x}{3} - 2 = 0$ i. $x^2 = 6x + 7$

j. $3x^2 - 5x = -4$ k. $7x^2 = -4x + 6$ l. $-3x + 2 = 6x^2$

B 3. Solve each equation.

a. $x(x - 8) = -16$ b. $-3x(2x + 5) + 4 = 0$ c. $x^2 + (x + 1)^2 = 13$

d. $4x^2 - (3x + 1)^2 = 5$ e. $2x^2 = 3 - (x + 5)^2$ f. $(2x + 1)(3x - 1) = 1$

g. $x - \dfrac{2x - 1}{3} = x^2 - \dfrac{1}{2}$ h. $16x + 16 = \dfrac{16x + 4}{x}$ i. $\dfrac{x + 3}{2x - 7} = \dfrac{2x - 1}{x - 3}$

4. Solve, answering correct to two decimal places and using a calculator as necessary.

a. $5x^2 - 4x + 7 = 0$ b. $3x^2 + 6x - 7 = 0$ c. $x^2 - 8x - 7 = 0$

5. Find the sum and product of the roots without solving the equation.

a. $7x^2 - 6x - 9 = 0$ b. $3x^2 + 5x + 4 = 0$ c. $3x^2 + 8x + 1 = 0$
d. $7x^2 + 5x = 9$ e. $x^2 + 1 = 0$ f. $2x^2 = 5x - 6$

6. One root of $8x^2 + bx - 5 = 0$ is $\frac{1}{2}$. Find the other root and the value of b.

7. One root of $ax^2 + 19x - 6 = 0$ is -3. Find the other root and the value of a.

8. What can be deduced about the coefficients of a quadratic equation, $ax^2 + bx + c = 0, a \neq 0$, from each piece of information? *opposites

a. The product of the roots is zero. b. The roots are additive inverses.
c. One of the roots is one. d. The roots are reciprocals.

9. Given the parabola defined by $y = 3x^2 + 6x - 7$, find the vertex and the axis of symmetry. Find the x-intercepts, correct to one decimal place, and the y-intercept. Sketch the graph.

10. Repeat each part of exercise 9 for $y = -2x^2 + 8x - 2$.

C 11. Show that any quadratic equation, $ax^2 + bx + c = 0, a \neq 0$, can be expressed in the following form:
$x^2 - (\text{sum of roots})x + (\text{product of roots}) = 0$.

12. Use the result from exercise 11 to find the quadratic equation with the given roots.

a. $5, -7$ b. $8, 9$ c. $-4, -6$ d. $\frac{1}{2}, \frac{1}{3}$
e. $\sqrt{3}, -2\sqrt{3}$ f. $6, -6$ g. $3 - \sqrt{3}, 4 + \sqrt{3}$ h. $5\sqrt{2} + 6, 5\sqrt{2} - 6$

13. Using the form $y = ax^2 + bx + c$ of a quadratic equation, derive general formulas for the vertex and axis of symmetry of any parabola. (Hint: use the "completing the square" method.)

Historical Note

Diophantus of Alexandria

Diophantus, a Greek mathematician of the third century B.C., introduced symbolism into Greek algebra. Although, unfortunately, this part of his writing has been lost, his works are said to have contained a version of the quadratic formula.

Diophantus devoted much time to studying equations, where he insisted that solutions were, ideally, whole numbers. Roots that were irrational or even negative were regarded as impossible. The study of **Diophantine equations**, such as $y^3 = x^2 + 2$, where *all* solutions must be whole numbers, has been of interest to many mathematicians.

Find a solution to $y^3 = x^2 + 2$, where $x, y \in W$. Can you find a second solution to the equation? Compare your solutions with those of other students in your class.

Using the Calculator

To solve quadratic equations with a calculator, you must first be familiar with the way your calculator handles order of operations.

To find the roots of a quadratic equation on a calculator, first ensure that your calculator has the following:

- a memory
- a [±] key
- an [x^2] key
- a [$\sqrt{\ }$] key
- the capacity to handle order of operations.

You can then evaluate the roots of an equation like $4x^2 - 6x - 3 = 0$ by using the following method and the quadratic formula.

First, evaluate $\sqrt{b^2 - 4ac}$.

To enter negative numbers, like −6, first enter the numeral, then press the [±] key.

[6] [±] [x^2] [−] [4] [×] [4] [×] [3] [±] [=] 84, and $\sqrt{84} = 9.1651514$

[9.1651514] [M+] Since this value will be used to find both roots, it will save time to have it in the memory.

Now evaluate the first root: $\dfrac{-b + \sqrt{b^2 - 4ac}}{2a}$

[6] [±] [±] [+] [MR] [=] [÷] [2] [÷] [4] [=] 1.8956439

Evaluate the second root: $\dfrac{-b - \sqrt{b^2 - 4ac}}{2a}$

[6] [±] [±] [−] [MR] [=] [÷] [2] [÷] [4] [=] −0.3956439

Therefore, the roots are 1.90 and −0.40, correct to two decimal places.

Note that the two operations ± ± cancel each other out; it would save time to calculate −(−6) mentally first and enter only [6] [x^2] etc.

---

1. Solve the following quadratic equations using your calculator. Express your answers correct to two decimal places.

a.	$5x^2 - 6x - 9 = 0$	**b.**	$4x^2 + 3x - 8 = 0$	**c.**	$7x^2 + 10x - 2 = 0$
d.	$3x^2 - x - 20 = 0$	**e.**	$0.5x^2 + 0.25x - 1.5 = 0$	**f.**	$1.2x^2 + 3.1x + 1.7 = 0$
g.	$3.14x^2 - 2.2x - 5.2 = 0$	**h.**	$-7.6x^2 + 1.1x + 0.66 = 0$	**i.**	$0.82x^2 - 0.53x - 2.1 = 0$

2. If your calculator does not perform the order of operations in the correct order, what changes would you have to make in the sequence of operations described above?

5-6 The Discriminant

The parabola defined by $y = ax^2 + bx + c$, where $a \neq 0$, has x-intercepts given by $x = \dfrac{-b \pm \sqrt{b^2 - 4ac}}{2a}$.

Knowing that $\sqrt{n}$ has no real value when $n < 0$, one real value when $n = 0$, and two values when $n > 0$, consider the radical portion of the quadratic formula, $\sqrt{b^2 - 4ac}$. The sign of $b^2 - 4ac$ reflects the *nature* of the roots of $ax^2 + bx + c = 0$, and the *number* of x-intercepts for the graph of the equation $y = ax^2 + bx + c$.

When $b^2 - 4ac$ is negative, there are *no* real roots for the quadratic equations; the parabola has no x-intercepts.

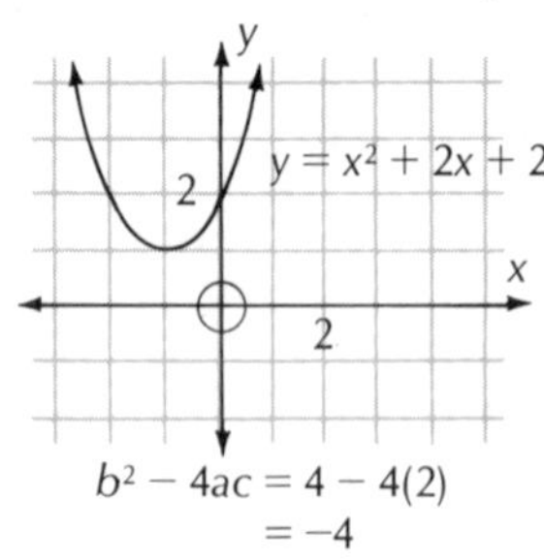

$$b^2 - 4ac = 4 - 4(2) = -4$$

When $b^2 - 4ac$ equals 0, the equation has two *equal* real roots; the parabola has one x-intercept.

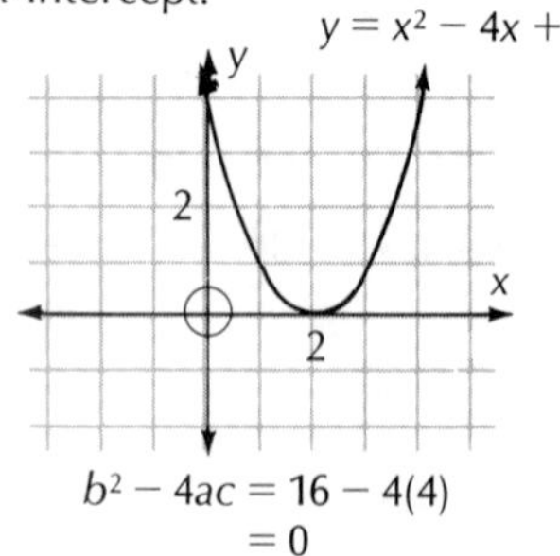

$$b^2 - 4ac = 16 - 4(4) = 0$$

When $b^2 - 4ac$ is positive, the equation has two *distinct* real roots; the parabola has two x-intercepts.

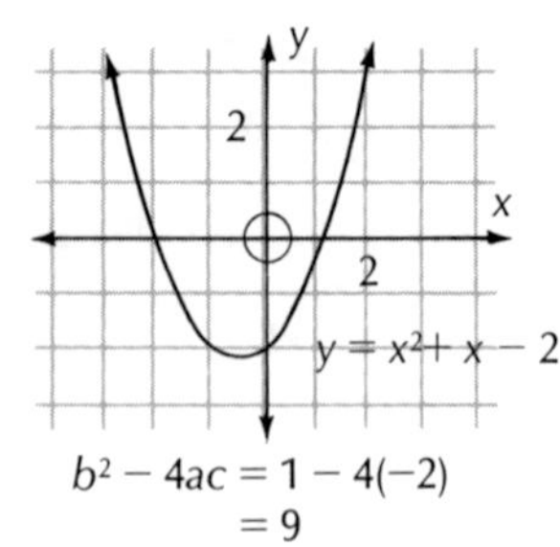

$$b^2 - 4ac = 1 - 4(-2) = 9$$

Because the value of $b^2 - 4ac$ can be used to distinguish the three cases outlined above, it is called the **discriminant, *D*,** of the quadratic.

EXAMPLE 1: Find the number of x-intercepts of each parabola.

a. $y = 3x^2 + x + 8$

$$\begin{aligned} b^2 - 4ac &= (1)^2 - 4(3)(8) \\ &= 1 - 96 \\ &= -95 \end{aligned}$$

Since $-95 < 0$, there are no x-intercepts.

b. $y = 16x^2 - 40x + 25$

$$\begin{aligned} b^2 - 4ac &= (-40)^2 - 4(16)(25) \\ &= 1600 - 1600 \\ &= 0 \end{aligned}$$

Since $b^2 - 4ac = 0$, there is one x-intercept.

EXAMPLE 2: For what values of p will $3x^2 - px + 4 = 0$ have two real and distinct roots?

For two real and distinct roots, the discriminant must be positive.

$$\begin{aligned} (-p)^2 - 4(3)(4) &> 0 \\ p^2 - 48 &> 0 \\ p^2 &> 48 \end{aligned}$$

$$\therefore p > \sqrt{48} \quad \text{or} \quad p < -\sqrt{48}$$

EXERCISE 5-6

A **1.** Calculate the discriminant, D, and state the nature of the roots of each quadratic equation.

a. $x^2 - 8x + 16 = 0$ **b.** $5x^2 - 6x - 9 = 0$ **c.** $4x^2 + x + 8 = 0$

d. $7x^2 = 6 - 3x$ **e.** $x^2 - 9 = 0$ **f.** $8x^2 - 4x = 0$

2. Determine the number of x-intercepts of each parabola.

a. $y = 3x^2 - 7x - 6$ **b.** $y = 4x^2 + 12x + 9$ **c.** $y = 9x^2 - 16$

d. $y = -x^2 - 6x - 2$ **e.** $y = -9x^2 + 6x + 1$ **f.** $y = -16x^2 + 9$

B **3.** For what real values of q do these quadratic equations have one real root?

a. $x^2 - qx - 9 = 0$ **b.** $4x^2 + qx + 25 = 0$ **c.** $qx^2 - 24x + 64 = 0$

d. $9x^2 - 42x + q = 0$ **e.** $4x^2 - 5qx + 25 = 0$ **f.** $3qx^2 + 12x + 4 = 0$

4. For what real values of k do these quadratic equations have no real roots?

a. $kx^2 + 4x - 9 = 0$ **b.** $4x^2 + kx + 1 = 0$ **c.** $5x^2 + 10x + k = 0$

d. $2kx^2 - 6x - 1 = 0$ **e.** $4x^2 - 5kx + 25 = 0$ **f.** $3x^2 - 4x + 2k = 0$

5. For what real values of p do these quadratic equations have two distinct real roots?

a. $px^2 + 6x + 9 = 0$ **b.** $3x^2 + px - 4 = 0$ **c.** $5x^2 = 4x + p$

d. $6x^2 - 3px = 4$ **e.** $x^2 - 6px + 5 = 0$ **f.** $2px^2 - x = 4$

6. For what values of n will the graph of $y = -2x^2 - nx - 7$ intersect the x-axis in two distinct points?

7. Prove that the parabola defined by $y = -4x^2 + kx + 5$ will not intersect the x-axis for any real value of k.

8. Find the value of n such that the graph defined by $y = -4x^2 - nx - 144$ has one x-intercept only.

C **9.** Find the values of s such that the x-intercepts of the parabola defined by $y = 3x^2 + 8x + s$ will be rational.

10. Show that the parabola defined by $y = (a + 2)x^2 - x - (a + 1)$ has at least one x-intercept for all values of a.

11. At what point(s) on the parabola defined by $y = 6 - x^2$ is the sum of the distances to the coordinate axes the greatest?

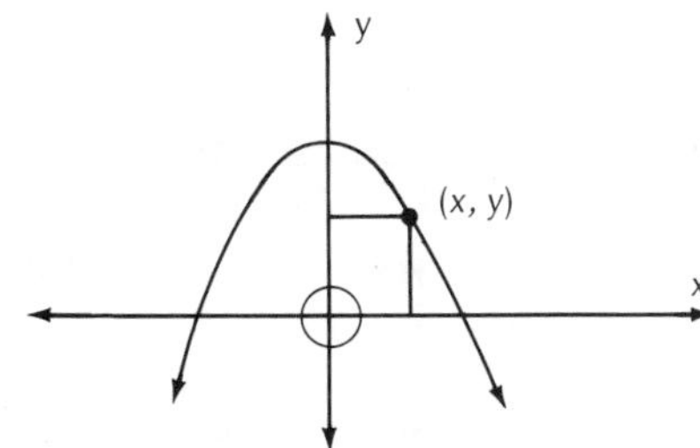

5-7 Graphing Quadratic Inequalities

Like graphs of linear equations, graphs of quadratic equations divide the plane into two regions. The **interior region** contains the points lying within the arms of the parabola. $A(2, 5)$ lies in the interior of the parabola defined by $y = x^2$.

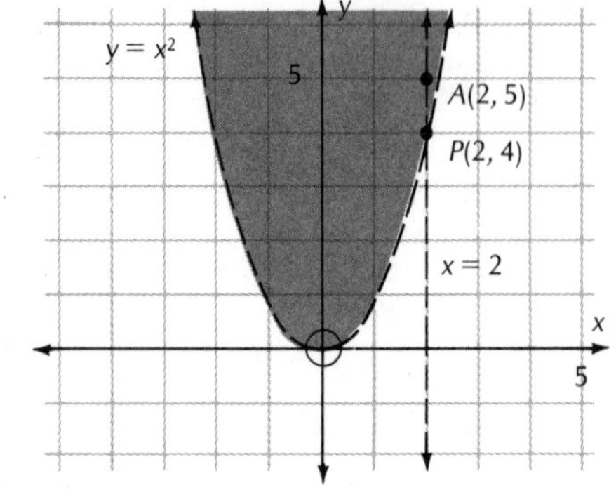

Consider the set of points lying along the line defined by $x = 2$. The point $P(2, 4)$ is on the line $x = 2$ and on the parabola defined by $y = x^2$.

Points on the line $x = 2$ that lie in the interior of the parabola have y values greater than $(2)^2$. That is, they satisfy $y > x^2$. In fact, the inequality $y > x^2$ represents the entire interior region of the parabola, shaded in the diagram at the right. The parabola itself is not included since $y > x^2$ does not include equality.

EXAMPLE 1: Graph the region represented by $y < -2x^2 + 6x + 8$.

Start by graphing $y = -2x^2 + 6x + 8$, using a broken line. Find the intercepts of the parabola.

When $x = 0$, $y = 8$

The y-intercept is 8.

When $y = 0$, $-2x^2 + 6x + 8 = 0$

$-2(x - 4)(x + 1) = 0$

$\therefore x = 4$ or $x = -1$

The x-intercepts are 4 and -1.

Find the vertex and axis of symmetry.

$y = -2x^2 + 6x + 8$

$y = -2\left(x^2 - 3x + \frac{9}{4}\right) + 8 + \frac{9}{2}$

$y = -2\left(x - \frac{3}{2}\right)^2 + \frac{25}{2}$

The vertex is $\left(\frac{3}{2}, \frac{25}{2}\right)$ and the axis of symmetry is $x = \frac{3}{2}$.

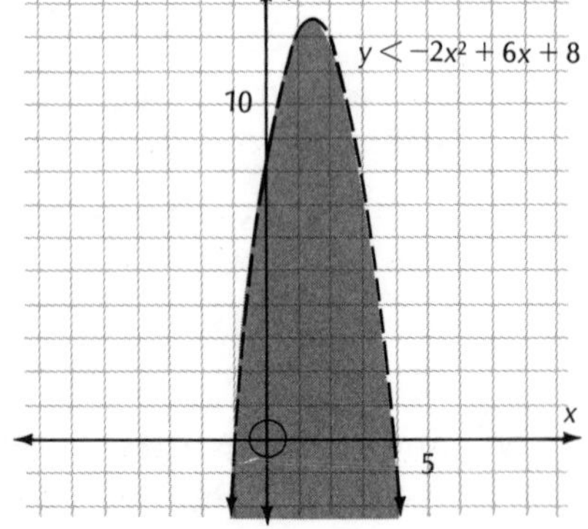

The broken line represents

$y = -2x^2 + 6x + 8$.

Since $y < -2x^2 + 6x + 8$, shade the interior region of the graph.

You can verify that the correct region has been shaded by selecting a test point (x, y) and checking that $y < -2x^2 + 6x + 8$ for that point.

Test $(0, 0)$. L.S. $= y$ $= 0$ R.S. $= -2x^2 + 6x + 8$ $= 8$

Since L.S. < R.S., the correct region has been shaded.

In general, for graphs of $y = ax^2 + bx + c$, where $a \neq 0$, that open upward, the interior region is given by $y > ax^2 + bx + c$. For parabolas that open downward, the interior region is given by $y < ax^2 + bx + c$.

Compound inequalities can also be graphed.

EXAMPLE 2: Graph the region represented by the compound inequality $y > 2x^2 + 4x - 6$ or $y < x + 3$.

First graph the boundaries, $y = 2x^2 + 4x - 6$ and $y = x + 3$, using broken lines to start.

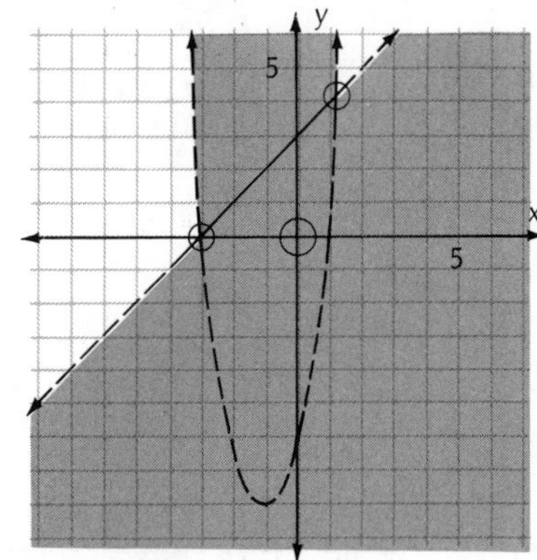

The inequality $y > 2x^2 + 4x - 6$ represents the interior region of the parabola, and does not include the parabola itself. The inequality $y < x + 3$ represents the region below the line $y = x + 3$.

Any point that satisfies *either* one inequality, *or* the other, *or both*, satisfies the compound inequality $y > 2x^2 + 4x - 6$ or $y < x + 3$.

The shaded region displays the solution set. Notice that the intersection points of the two equations are *not* in the solution set, as neither $y > 2x^2 + 4x - 6$ nor $y < x + 3$ includes equality.

EXAMPLE 3: Graph the compound inequality $y \leq -x^2 + 2x + 8$ and $y \geq x^2 - 1$.

First graph the boundaries, $y = -x^2 + 2x + 8$ and $y = x^2 - 1$, using broken lines to start.

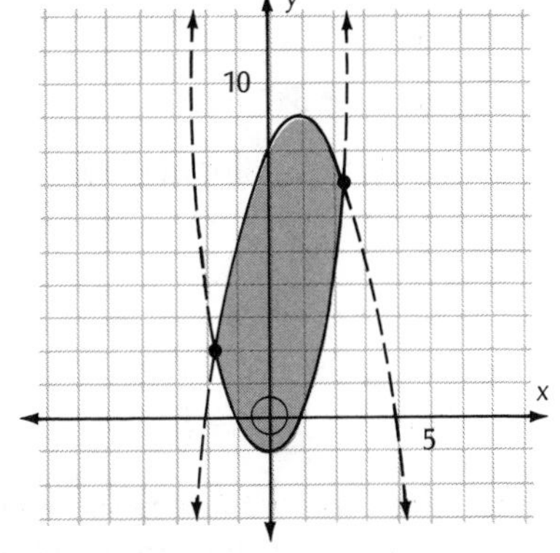

The inequality $y \leq -x^2 + 2x + 8$ represents the interior region of the parabola and includes the parabola itself; $y \geq x^2 - 1$ also represents the interior region of the corresponding parabola as well as the parabola itself.

A point must satisfy *both* inequalities in order to satisfy the compound inequality $y \leq -x^2 + 2x + 8$ and $y \geq x^2 - 1$.

The shaded region in the diagram displays the solution set. The intersection points are included, and the boundaries of the region are now drawn solid, but the portions of the parabolas outside the region are not solid.

EXERCISE 5-7

A 1. Write an inequality to represent the shaded region, using the equation of the boundary given below each graph.

a. 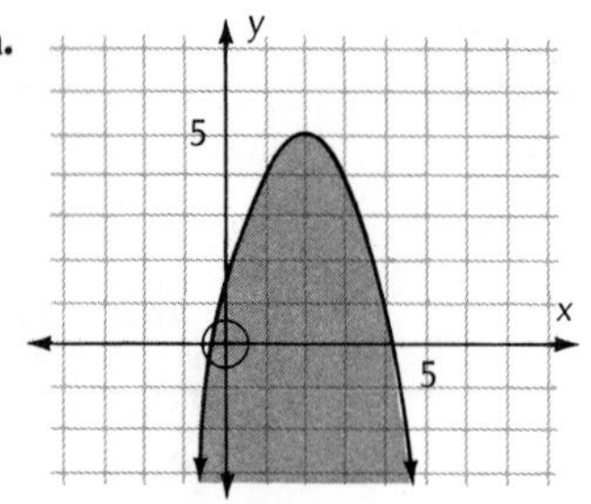

$y = -x^2 + 4x + 1$

b. 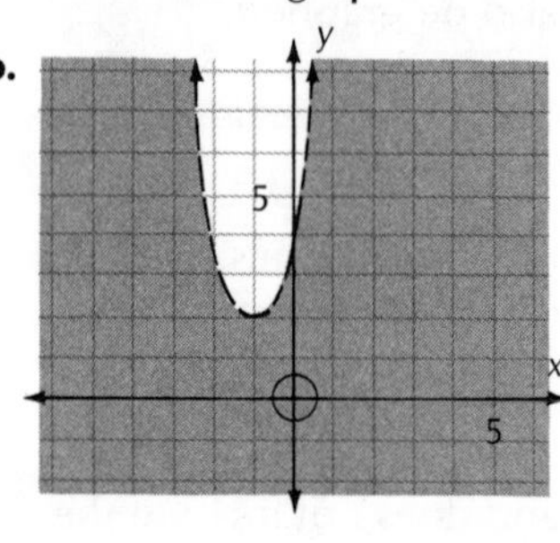

$y = 2x^2 + 4x + 4$

c. 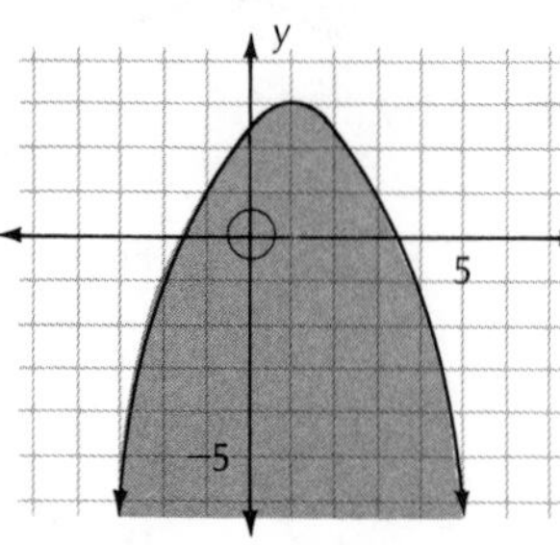

$y = -\frac{1}{2}x^2 + x + \frac{5}{2}$

d. 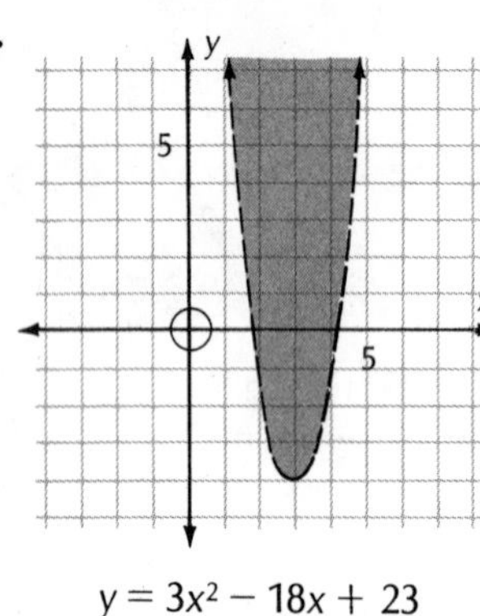

$y = 3x^2 - 18x + 23$

e. 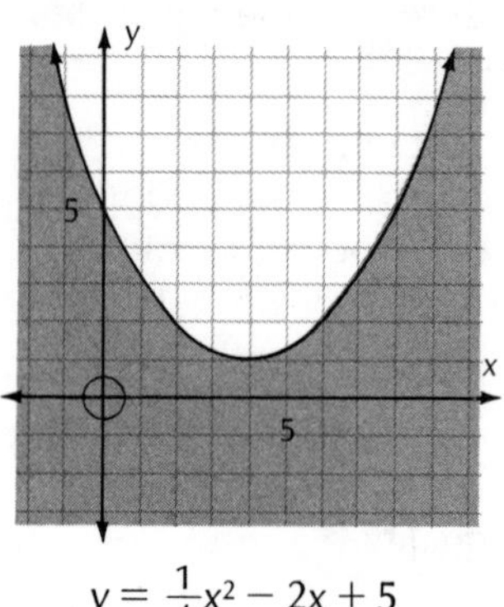

$y = \frac{1}{4}x^2 - 2x + 5$

f. 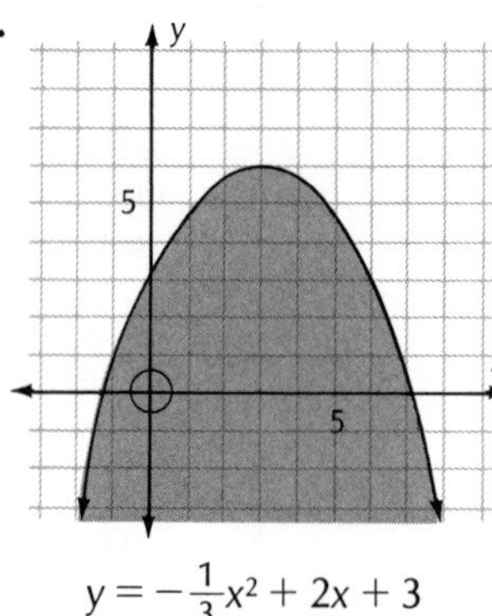

$y = -\frac{1}{3}x^2 + 2x + 3$

2. Graph each inequality. Name a test point for each region and use it to check.

a. $y > x^2 + 1$	b. $y \leq -x^2 - 3$	c. $y < 2x^2 + 3$
d. $y \geq -\frac{1}{2}x^2 - 2$	e. $y > \frac{1}{3}x^2 + 2$	f. $y < -2x^2$
g. $y \geq 3x^2$	h. $y > -(x + 2)^2$	i. $y \leq (x + 3)^2$

B 3. Graph each inequality.

a. $y > 4x^2 - 2x$	b. $y < -2x^2 + 2x$	c. $y \geq x^2 - 9$
d. $y \leq -x^2 + 16$	e. $y < x^2 - 2x - 3$	f. $y \leq -x^2 + 5x - 6$
g. $y > 2x^2 - 5x - 3$	h. $y \geq x^2 + 8x + 12$	i. $y < 2(x + 3)^2 - 1$
j. $y > -3(x - 1)^2 + 2$	k. $y \leq \frac{1}{2}(x + 1)^2 - 1$	l. $y > -(x + 3)^2 + 1$
m. $y > \frac{1}{3}(x - 2)^2$	n. $y \leq -2(x + 1)^2 - 3$	o. $y \geq 4(x - 1)^2 + 2$

4. Write an inequality to represent the interior of the graph of each quadratic equation, then graph the inequality given.

a. $y = (x - 2)^2$	b. $y = -(x + 5)^2$	c. $y = 2(x - 4)^2$
d. $y = -\frac{1}{2}x^2 - 4$	e. $y = 2x^2 + x + 4$	f. $y = -x^2 - 4x + 2$
g. $y = -\frac{1}{2}x^2 - 4x$	h. $y = 4x^2 + 4x - 1$	i. $y = -2x^2 + 3x - 2$

5. Write a system of inequalities to describe each given region.

a.
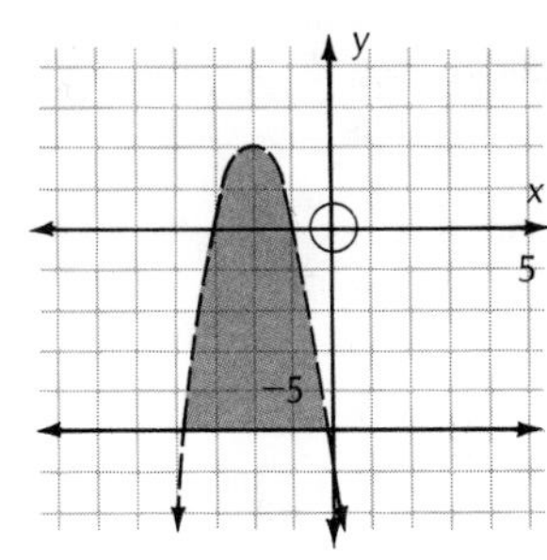

$y = -6$, $y = -2x^2 - 8x - 6$

b.
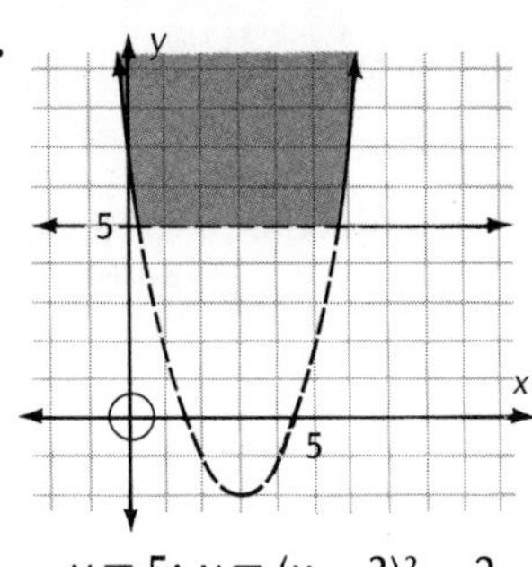

$y = 5$; $y = (x - 3)^2 - 2$

c.
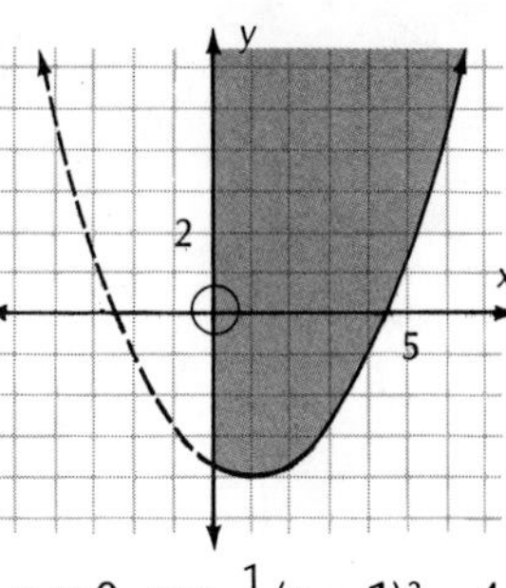

$x = 0$, $y = \frac{1}{3}(x - 1)^2 - 4$

d.
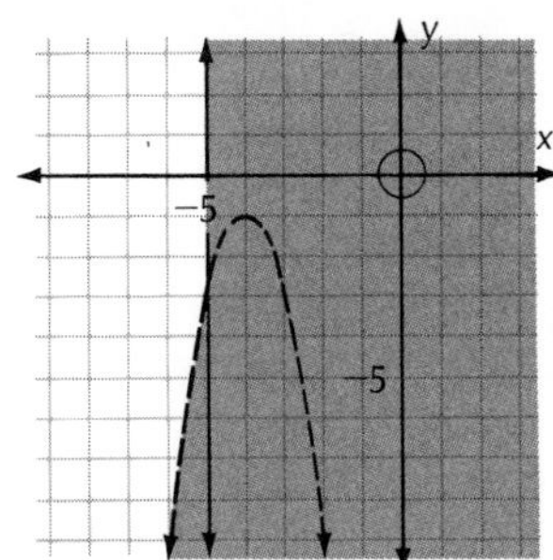

$x = -5$; $y = -2(x + 4)^2 - 1$

e.
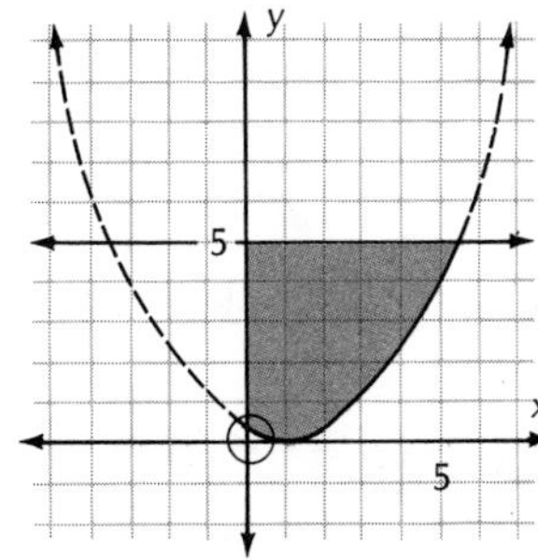

$y = 5$; $x = 0$; $y = \frac{1}{4}(x - 1)^2$

f.
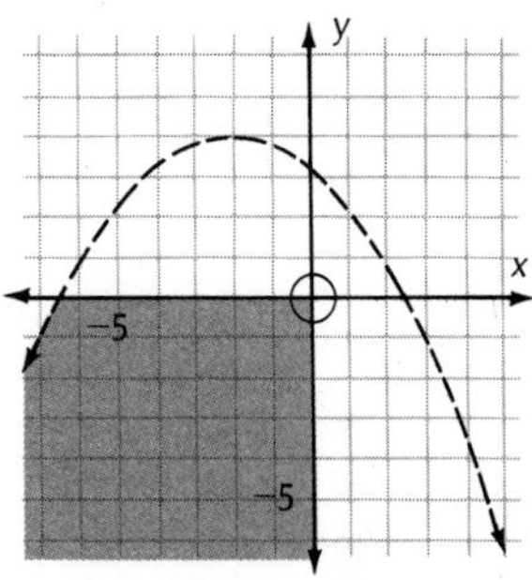

$x = 0$; $y = 0$; $y = -\frac{1}{5}(x + 2)^2 + 4$

6. Graph each system of inequalities.

a. $y > 2(x - 3)^2 + 4$ and $y \leq 6$

b. $y \leq -\frac{1}{2}(x + 1)^2 + 3$ or $x > 1$

c. $y < -(x + 3)^2 - 2$ or $x \leq -1$

d. $y \geq 3(x - 2)^2 - 1$ and $y \leq 4$

e. $y > x^2 - 2x + 1$ and $y \geq 2$

f. $y < 2x^2 - 4x + 5$ and $x > 1$

g. $y > -x^2 - 4x - 5$ or $x \geq -3$

h. $y \leq \frac{1}{2}x^2 + 4x + 7$ and $x < -3$

i. $y > x^2$ and $y \leq 2x + 5$

j. $y \leq -x^2 + 1$ and $y \geq -2x - 3$

k. $y > 2x^2 + 4x$ and $x + 2y \leq 4$

l. $y > -3x^2 + 9x$ and $x - 3y - 3 > 0$

m. $y \geq 3x^2 - 6x + 7$ and $y < x + 5$

n. $y < -x^2 - 6x - 10$ and $y < x$

C 7. Write a system of inequalities to describe each shaded region.

a.
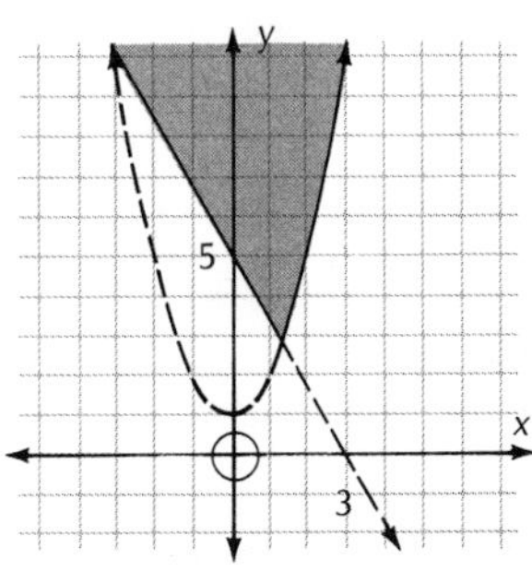

b.
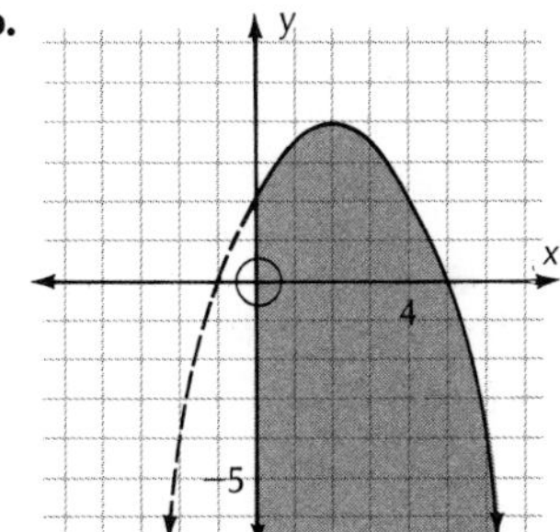

c.
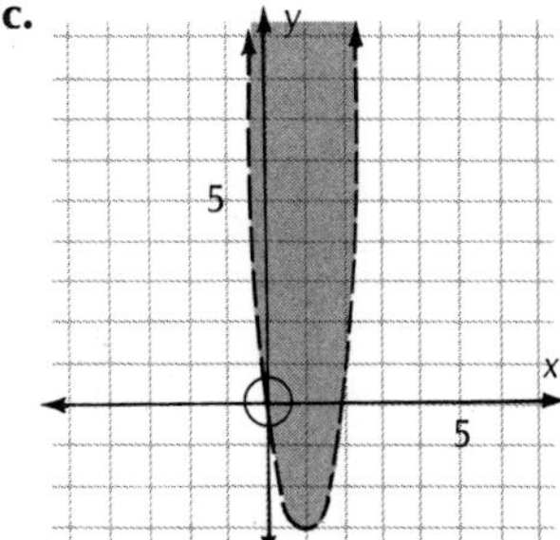

5-8 Applying Quadratics to Solve Problems

The following examples illustrate some of the many applications of quadratic equations.

EXAMPLE 1: The height of a projectile, h metres, t seconds after being shot into the air, is given by $h = -5t^2 + 29t + 2$. When, to the nearest 0.1 s, is the projectile 10 m above the ground?

$$10 = -5t^2 + 29t + 2$$

$$5t^2 - 29t + 8 = 0$$

Use the given equation and substitute $h = 10$.

$$t = \frac{29 \pm \sqrt{29^2 - 4(5)(8)}}{2(5)}$$

Apply the quadratic formula.

$$t \doteq \frac{29 \pm 26.1}{10}$$

$$\therefore t \doteq 5.51 \text{ or } 0.29$$

The object is 10 m high at 0.3 s and then again at 5.5 s.

In some cases, a quadratic equation must be derived before the problem can be solved.

EXAMPLE 2: A picture with an area of 424 cm² has a frame of uniform width with outside dimensions 50 cm by 30 cm. How wide is the frame, to the nearest 0.1 cm?

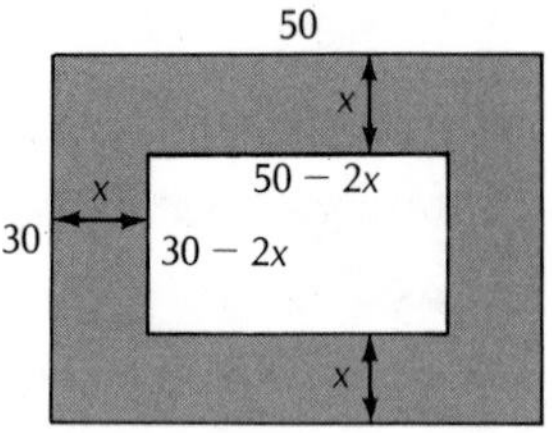

The diagram shows that the picture must be $(30 - 2x)$ by $(50 - 2x)$. Its area is 424 cm².

$$(30 - 2x)(50 - 2x) = 424$$ Write an equation.

$$1500 - 160x + 4x^2 = 424$$ Expand.

$$4x^2 - 160x + 1076 = 0$$ There is a common factor of 4.

$$x^2 - 40x + 269 = 0$$

$$\therefore x = \frac{40 \pm \sqrt{40^2 - 4(269)}}{2(1)}$$

Apply the quadratic formula.

$$= \frac{40 \pm \sqrt{524}}{2}$$

$$x \doteq 31.45 \text{ or } 8.55$$

The units are centimetres.

The root 31.45 is inadmissible, as it exceeds the dimensions of the framed picture, so the root 8.55 is the only solution appropriate in this case.

Therefore, the frame has a uniform width of about 8.6 cm.

If a description of a parabolic curve is given and an equation must be found, position the curve on the coordinate plane in such a way that finding an equation is simplified. Typically, this is done by putting the vertex at the origin.

EXAMPLE 3: A bridge arches over a highway in a parabolic curve. The maximum height of the parabola is 8 m; its width at ground level is 20 m, as shown. There is 4.5 m clearance for any traffic passing under the bridge. About how far from the centre of the highway do the shoulders start? Answer to the nearest centimetre.

8 m
4.5 m
20 m

Start by finding an equation of the parabola.

Draw a parabola with its vertex at the origin that opens downward and passes through the points $(\pm 10, -8)$.

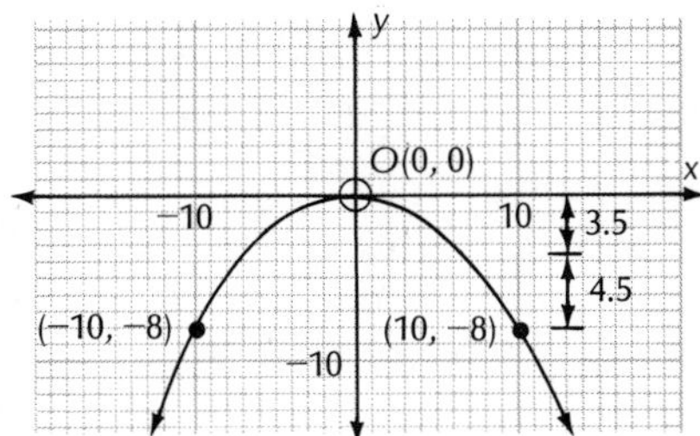

An equation of the parabola is $y = ax^2$.

Since $(10, -8)$ is on the parabola, its coordinates must satisfy the equation. Substitute and solve for a.

$$-8 = a(10^2)$$
$$a = \frac{-8}{100}$$
$$= \frac{-2}{25}$$

Therefore, an equation of the parabola is $y = \frac{-2}{25}x^2$.

Now find the points that correspond to a clearance of 4.5 m. Find the value of x when $y = -3.5$ (since $8.0 - 4.5 = 3.5$).

When $y = -3.5$:
$$-3.5 = \frac{-2}{25}x^2$$
$$(25)(3.5) = 2x^2$$
$$x^2 = 43.75$$
$$x \doteq 6.6$$

Therefore, the shoulders start about 6.6 m from the centre of the highway.

EXERCISE 5-8

A

1. The sum of the squares of two consecutive integers is 2813. Find the integers.

2. The sum of the squares of three odd consecutive integers is 875. Find the integers.

3. A rectangle with area 108 cm^2 is 3 cm longer than it is wide. Find its dimensions.

B

4. A basketball court is 2 m longer than it is wide. If its area is 364 m^2, find the lengths of its sides.

5. This year, Marilyn planted a garden 12 m by 8 m. She plans to double the size of the garden next year by increasing the width and length by the same amount. What will the dimensions of her garden be next year?

6. The lengths of three sides of a right-angled triangle are consecutive integers. Find the values of the sides.

7. The sum of two whole numbers is 33 and the sum of their squares is 549. Find the numbers.

8. A box is to be made by cutting squares measuring 10 cm on a side from each corner of a square piece of cardboard and folding up the sides. The box is to have a volume of 1440 cm^3. What must be the dimensions of the original piece of cardboard?

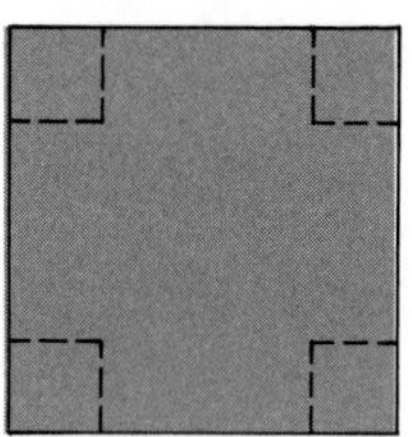

9. A group of students at a class party ordered pizzas and shared the bill for $45.00 equally. If there had been five more students, each would have had to pay 30 cents less. How many students were at the party?

10. The sum of the first n consecutive integers can be found using the expression $\frac{n(n+1)}{2}$. If the sum of the first k consecutive integers is 1176, find the value of k.

11. The lengths of the parallel sides of a trapezoid differ by 8 cm. The distance between the parallel sides is equal to the shorter of the two parallel sides. If the area of the trapezoid is 96 cm^2, find the lengths of the parallel sides.

12. A square lawn is surrounded by a walk 1 m wide. If the area of the walk is equal to half the area of the lawn, what are the dimensions of the lawn?

13. A bridge arches over a river in a parabolic curve so that its maximum height above the river's bank is 25 m and its width is 100 m. A boat is to sail under the bridge and needs a clearance of 15 m. Given that the water surface is 1 m below the river's banks at the time, how far from the centre of the river can the boat safely pass?

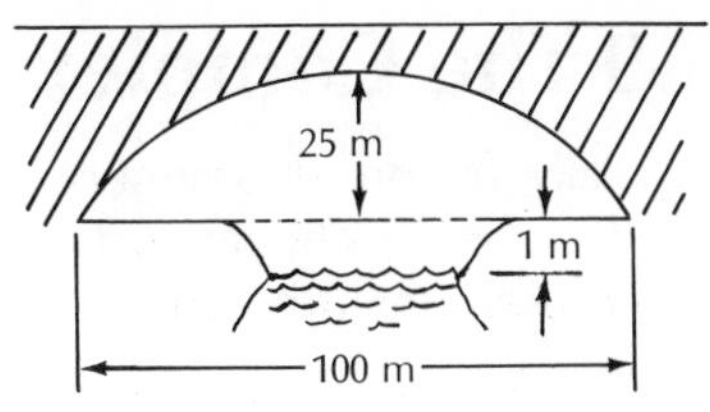

14. A football is kicked so that its height, h metres, after t seconds is given by the equation $h = 22t - 5t^2$.
   a. When is the football 8 m high? Explain why you get two answers.
   b. What is the maximum height reached?
   c. How long does the ball stay in the air?

15. Mineral deposits formed a coating 4 mm thick on the inside of a water pipe, reducing its cross-sectional area by 50%. Find the original diameter of the pipe.

Historical Note

Falling Objects and Projectiles

Galileo Galilei is recognized among physicists for his study of falling objects. He is said to have conducted experiments from the top of the leaning tower of Pisa, simultaneously releasing two iron balls of different masses. Since they both reached the ground at the same time, Galileo concluded that all objects, regardless of mass, accelerate at the same rate under free fall near the Earth's surface.

Galileo Galilei (1564-1642)

This conclusion, which directly contradicted Aristotle's earlier theory, was demonstrated by Robert Boyle shortly after Galileo's death. Using his newly developed air pump to create a vacuum, Boyle showed that, once the effects of air resistance were removed, a lead ball and a feather would fall at the same rate.

If one rock is dropped from a cliff at the same instant that another rock is thrown horizontally from the cliff, the two rocks will fall at the same rate and hit the ground at the same time. The diagram shows that they both accelerate, moving through greater distances in each successive one-second interval. You can see that the second rock follows a parabolic path.

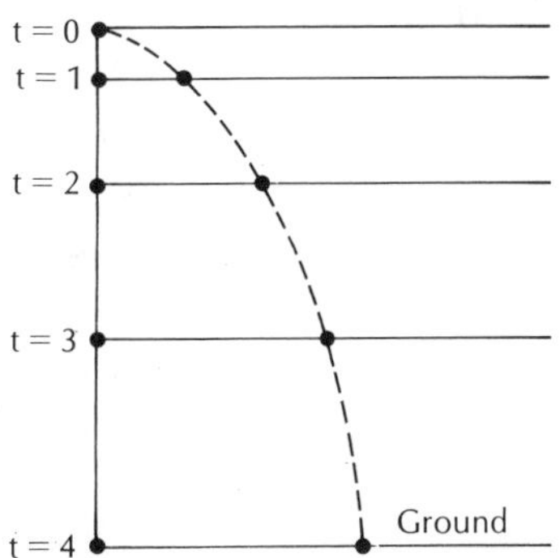

Galileo was the first to realize that a projectile, if unaffected by outside forces such as wind, would in fact follow such a path.

5-9 The Complex Number System

Typically, the development of a new number system originates from the need to solve problems and, particularly, to solve the equations being used to represent the problems.

- The integers were introduced so that an equation like $x + 3 = 0$ would have a meaningful root: $x = -3$.
- The rational numbers were introduced so that an equation like $2x + 7 = 0$ would have a meaningful root: $x = -3.5$.
- The irrational numbers were introduced so that an equation like $x^2 - 2 = 0$ has meaningful roots: $x = \pm\sqrt{2}$.

The rational and irrational numbers together form the set of *real* numbers. In this unit, however, there have been equations that cannot be solved in the set of real numbers.

The equation $x^2 + 1 = 0$, with discriminant $D = -4$, has no real solution.

$$x^2 + 1 = 0$$
$$x^2 = -1$$
$$x = \pm\sqrt{-1}$$

Yet, there are important applications in physics, engineering, and technology, where problems must be solved using equations that have non-real roots. This need has led to the development of the **complex numbers**, which are based on defining $\sqrt{-1}$ to be i.

The use of i to represent $\sqrt{-1}$ stems from the belief, at the time of its introduction, that $\sqrt{-1}$ was an "imaginary" number. This has been called "the great algebraic calamity", as there is nothing imaginary about the number i and the concrete results of applying complex numbers in the science and technology fields.

A **complex number** is defined to be a number that can be written in the form $a + bi$, where $a, b \in \boldsymbol{R}$ and $i^2 = -1$. **C** represents the set of complex numbers.

EXAMPLE 1: Show that each of the following is a complex number.

a. $\sqrt{3} + 4i$ **b.** -7 **c.** $-2i$ **d.** $\sqrt{5}$

a. Since $\sqrt{3}$ and 4 are real numbers, and $\sqrt{3} + 4i$ is in the form $a + bi$, $\sqrt{3} + 4i \in \mathbf{C}$.

b. Since -7 can be rewritten as $-7 + 0i$, it is a complex number.

c. Since $-2i$ can be rewritten as $0 - 2i$, it is a complex number.

d. Since $\sqrt{5}$ can be rewritten $\sqrt{5} + 0i$, it is a complex number.

Generalizing from parts **b** and **d** of example 1, it is clear that the set of complex numbers includes the entire set of real numbers, which can be rewritten as $a + bi$, where $b = 0$.

Each complex number $a + bi$ is made up of a **real component**, a, and an **imaginary component**, b. When the real component is zero, the complex number is called a **pure imaginary number**.

The representation of complex numbers requires the use of two dimensions. The complex numbers can be graphed on the **Argand plane**, named after Swiss mathematician Jean Robert Argand, who introduced its use.

Complex numbers $a + bi$ are graphed as ordered pairs (a, b) on the Argand plane. The vertical axis, I, represents the imaginary component of the complex number; the horizontal axis, R, represents the real component.

The numbers $A(2 + 3i)$, $B(-3 - 5i)$, $C(-6i)$, and $D(4)$ are graphed at the right.

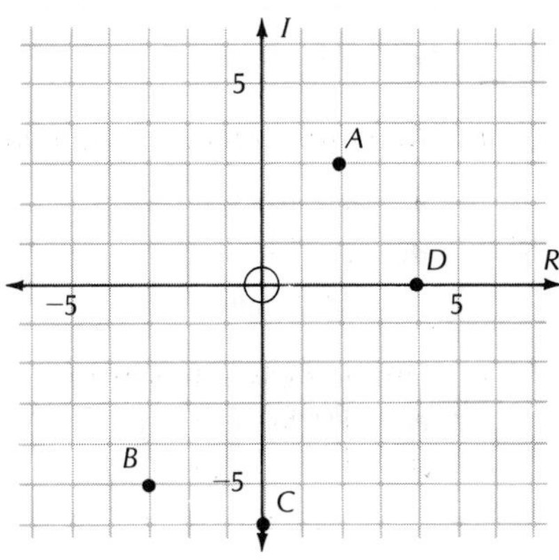

A complex number is in **simplest form** if it is expressed as $a + bi$.

EXAMPLE 2: Rewrite $5 - \sqrt{-32}$ in simplest form.

$$5 - \sqrt{-32} = 5 - \sqrt{(16)(2)(-1)}$$
$$= 5 - 4\sqrt{2}i.$$

To add or subtract complex numbers, add or subtract corresponding real and imaginary components.

$$(a + bi) + (c + di) = (a + c) + (b + d)i$$
$$(a + bi) - (c + di) = (a - c) + (b - d)i$$

EXAMPLE 3: Simplify each expression.

a. $(3 + 2i) + (4 - 5i) = (3 + 4) + (2i - 5i)$
$= 7 - 3i$

b. $(6 - 3i) - (7 + 2i) = (6 - 7) + (-3i - 2i)$
$= -1 - 5i$

To multiply complex numbers, use the distributive property, as necessary.

EXAMPLE 4: Simplify each expression.

a. $3i(2 - 4i) = 6i - 12i^2$
$= 6i - 12(-1)$
$= 12 + 6i$

b. $(2 + 4i)(3 - 5i) = 6 - 10i + 12i - 20i^2$
$= 6 + 2i - 20(-1)$
$= 26 + 2i$

c. $i^5 = (i^2)(i^2)(i)$
$= (-1)^2 i$
$= i$

d. $(3 + 2i)(3 - 2i) = 9 - 6i + 6i - 4i^2$
$= 9 - 4(-1)$
$= 13$

Every complex number $a + bi$ has a **conjugate** complex number $a - bi$. A complex number and its conjugate multiply to give $a^2 + b^2$, a real number.

EXAMPLE 5: Simplify so that the denominator does not contain an imaginary component.

a. $\frac{-5}{7i} = \frac{-5}{7i} \times \frac{i}{i}$

$= \frac{-5i}{7i^2}$

$= \frac{5i}{7}$

b. $\frac{2-i}{(3+2i)} = \frac{(2-i)}{(3+2i)} \times \frac{(3-2i)}{(3-2i)}$ Multiply by the conjugate of the denominator.

$= \frac{6 - 4i - 3i + 2i^2}{9 - 6i + 6i - 4i^2}$

$= \frac{4-7i}{13}$

EXERCISE 5-9

A **1.** Rewrite each of the following in the form $a + bi$.

a. $\sqrt{-16}$ **b.** $\sqrt{-49}$ **c.** $\sqrt{-100}$

d. $\sqrt{-36}$ **e.** $\sqrt{-12}$ **f.** $\sqrt{-24}$

g. $-2\sqrt{-48}$ **h.** $6 - 5\sqrt{-75}$ **i.** $\frac{1}{2}\sqrt{-98}$

2. Simplify each expression.

a. $(5 + 6i) + (4 - 6i)$ **b.** $(-4 + 6i) + (7 - 3i)$ **c.** $(8 - 2i) + (7i - 3)$

d. $\frac{1}{2}i + (i - 8)$ **e.** $(9 - 4i) - (-4 + 6i)$ **f.** $(2i + 7) - (5 + 9i)$

g. $(-6 - 8i) - (-3i - 7)$ **h.** $\left(\frac{3}{2} + i\right) - (7 - 2i)$ **i.** $(8i - 3) - (-6i + 5)$

3. **a.** For each point graphed at the right, write the complex number represented by the point.

b. Which points represent pure imaginary numbers?

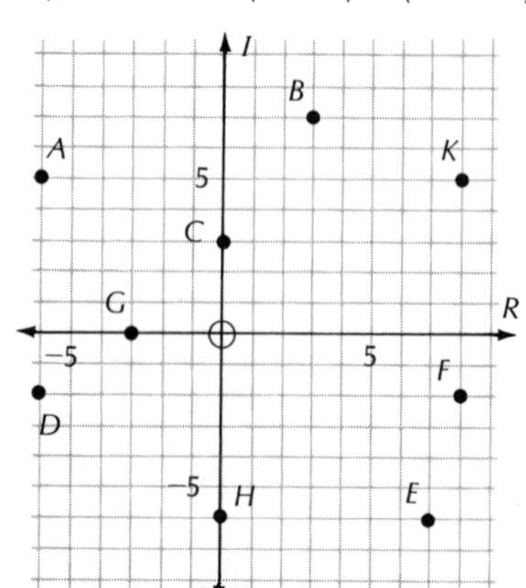

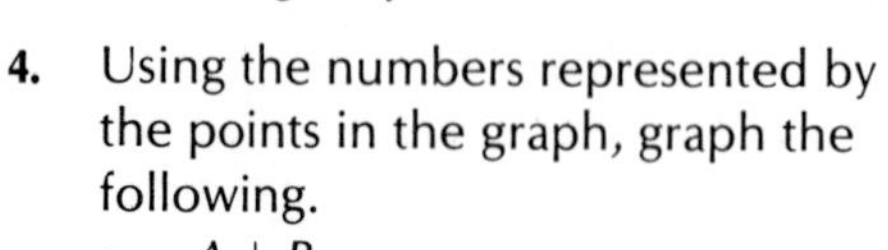

4. Using the numbers represented by the points in the graph, graph the following.

a. $A + B$

b. $C - D$

c. $-E$

d. $C - A + B$

B **5.** Express each complex number in simplest form.

a. $6 - \sqrt{-12}$ **b.** $4 + \sqrt{-50}$ **c.** $\sqrt{-125}$ **d.** $\sqrt{16 - 36}$

e. $12 + \sqrt{-27}$ **f.** $-8 - 2\sqrt{-98}$ **g.** $i(3 - 5\sqrt{-300})$ **h.** $\sqrt{5^2 - 6^2}$

6. Simplify each expression.

a. $3(5 + 2i)$ **b.** $7i(2 + 3i)$ **c.** $-3i(6 - 2i)$

d. $(2 + 4i)(3 - 6i)$ **e.** $(7 + 2i)(3 - 8i)$ **f.** $(i - 7)(i + 7)$

g. $(5 + 2i)^2$ **h.** $(3i - 2)^2$ **i.** $2(4 - 3i)(5 + 2i)$

7. a. Simplify: $i^3, i^4, i^5, i^6, i^7, i^8, i^9, i^{10}$.
   b. Use the results of part **a** to determine the simplest form of i^k.

8. State the reciprocal of each complex number and rewrite in the form $a + bi$.
   a. $2i$ b. $-5i$ c. $4 + 2i$
   d. $2 - i$ e. $3 + 5i$ f. $-1 + 4i$
   g. $-6 - 2i$ h. $7 + 6i$ i. $-3 - i$

9. Rewrite so that the denominator contains no imaginary component.
   a. $\frac{2}{i}$ b. $\frac{-3}{5i}$ c. $\frac{5 + i}{3i}$ d. $\frac{1}{1 - i}$ e. $\frac{2}{3 + 2i}$ f. $\frac{-4i}{5 - 2i}$
   g. $\frac{1 + i}{1 - i}$ h. $\frac{2 - 3i}{2 + 3i}$ i. $\frac{6 - 4i}{6 + i}$ j. $\frac{2 - 5i}{3 + 2i}$ k. $\frac{7 + 3i}{6 - i}$ l. $\frac{4 + \frac{1}{2}i}{3 - \frac{1}{2}i}$

C 10. Rewrite each expression in simplified form.
   a. $i + i^2 + i^3 + i^4$ b. $\frac{1}{i} + \frac{1}{i^2} + \frac{1}{i^3} + \frac{1}{i^4}$ c. $i^{102} \times i^{98}$

11. Solve for $x \in \mathbf{C}$.
   a. $(4 - 5i)x = 3$ b. $(3 + 2i)x = 5 - 4i$ c. $5x - 7 = 6ix + 8i$

12. a. Show that $1 - i\sqrt{3}$ is a cube root of -8.
   b. Find the two other cube roots of -8.

13. a. Show that $\frac{3}{2} + \frac{3\sqrt{3}}{2}i$ is a cube root of -27.
   b. Find the other two cube roots of -27.

EXTRA The Magnitude of a Complex Number

Mathematicians have shown that, unlike real numbers, it is impossible to find a method for defining order in the set of complex numbers. However, it is possible to consider the relative distance of a complex number from the origin on the Argand plane.

$AO = \sqrt{3^2 + 4^2}$ $BO = \sqrt{(-4)^2 + 2^2}$ $CO = \sqrt{(-5)^2 + (-3)^2}$
$= 5$ $= 2\sqrt{5}$ $= \sqrt{34}$

The real-number value is called the **magnitude** of a complex number and is written as follows:

$$|a + bi| = \sqrt{a^2 + b^2}$$

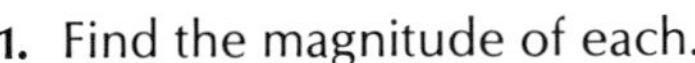

1. Find the magnitude of each.
   a. $|2 + 3i|$ b. $|-3 - 5i|$ c. $|\frac{1}{2} + 3i|$ d. $|-2 + 6i|$

2. Describe geometrically, for $z \in \mathbf{C}$.
   a. $|z| = 3$ b. $2 < |z| < 3$ c. $|z| < 4$

5-10 The Quadratic Formula and Complex Roots

Quadratic equations that could not be solved over the set of real numbers can be solved over the set of complex numbers. In fact, *all* polynomial equations, even those with complex coefficients, can be solved over the set of complex numbers.

EXAMPLE 1: Find the complex roots of $x^2 - 2x + 7 = 0$.

$$x = \frac{-b \pm \sqrt{b^2 - 4ac}}{2a} \qquad x = \frac{-(-2) \pm \sqrt{4 - 4(1)(7)}}{2}$$

$$x = \frac{2 \pm \sqrt{-24}}{2}$$

$$x = \frac{2 \pm 2\sqrt{6}i}{2}$$

$$x = 1 \pm \sqrt{6}i$$

EXAMPLE 2: Find k so that $5x^2 - 2kx + 3 = 0$, with discriminant D, has two distinct complex roots.

If $D > 0$, there are two distinct real roots; if $D < 0$, there are two distinct non-real roots. In either case, the roots are complex. The only case in which there will not be two distinct complex roots occurs when $D = 0$, and there are two equal roots.

Let $b^2 - 4ac = 0$. $\quad (-2k)^2 - 4(5)(3) = 0$

$$4k^2 - 60 = 0$$

$$k^2 = 15 \qquad \therefore k = \pm\sqrt{15}$$

The equation $5x^2 + 2kx + 3 = 0$ will have two distinct complex roots for *all* complex values of k *except* $k = \pm\sqrt{15}$.

If a quadratic equation with real coefficients has non-real complex roots, those roots are complex conjugates.

$$x = \frac{-b \pm \sqrt{b^2 - 4ac}}{2a}$$

If $b^2 - 4ac < 0$, then it can be written as ki.

$$x = \frac{-b}{2a} + \frac{k}{2a}i,\ x = \frac{-b}{2a} - \frac{k}{2a}i$$

These are complex conjugates.

EXAMPLE 3: Find real values of b and c so that $x^2 + bx + c = 0$ has $2 + 3i$ as one of its roots.

If $2 + 3i$ is one root, then the other root is $2 - 3i$, and the equation is $[x - (2 + 3i)][x - (2 - 3i)] = 0$.

$$[x - (2 + 3i)][x - (2 - 3i)] = 0$$

Rewrite to reveal a difference of squares.

$$[(x - 2) - 3i][(x - 2) + 3i] = 0$$

$$(x - 2)^2 - 9i^2 = 0$$

$$x^2 - 4x + 13 = 0$$

Therefore $b = -4$, $c = 13$.

EXERCISE 5-10

A **1.** Solve for x where $x \in C$.

a. $x^2 - 5x + 6 = 0$ **b.** $x^2 - x + 2 = 0$ **c.** $2x^2 - 3x + 1 = 0$
d. $3x^2 + 4x + 6 = 0$ **e.** $4x^2 - 3x = 7$ **f.** $2x^2 = 5x + 6$
g. $6x^2 = 4x - 1$ **h.** $x^2 + x + 3 = 0$ **i.** $2x^2 - 6x = -3$

2. Find the quadratic equation with the given roots.

a. $3i, -3i$ **b.** $2 + i, 2 - i$ **c.** $2\sqrt{2}i, -2\sqrt{2}i$ **d.** $5 - 2i, 5 + 2i$

B **3.** Solve for x, where $x \in C$.

a. $x(3 - 4x) = 7$ **b.** $3x^2 - \sqrt{2}i + 1 = 0$ **c.** $3x^2 + 2ix - 1 = 0$
d. $ix^2 - 4x + 2i = 0$ **e.** $3ix^2 + 4x - 5i = 0$ **f.** $2\sqrt{3}x^2 - x - 3 = 0$
g. $5x^2 + ix - 4 = 0$ **h.** $\sqrt{2}x^2 - x + 4\sqrt{2} = 0$

4. One root of a quadratic equation with real coefficients is given. Find the other root and the quadratic equation.

a. $5 + 2i$ **b.** $i - 4$ **c.** $2\sqrt{3} + i$ **d.** $4i - \sqrt{5}$

5. Find a quadratic equation with the given roots.

a. $\pm i$ **b.** $3 + i, 2 - i$ **c.** $5 - 3i, 7 + 4i$ **d.** $-2 \pm 6i$

6. Find the value of k so that the given equation has two distinct complex roots.

a. $kx^2 - 5x + 8 = 0$ **b.** $3x^2 + 2kx - 9 = 0$ **c.** $4x^2 + 3x + k = 0$
d. $5x^2 + (k + 1)x + 3 = 0$ **e.** $2x^2 - 3x + (k + 1) = 0$ **f.** $3x^2 + (k + 2)x + 3 = 0$

C **7.** Solve for x where $x \in C$.

a. $x^2 - (3 + 2i)x + (1 + 3i) = 0$ **b.** $\dfrac{2x + i}{x - i} = \dfrac{3x + 4i}{x + 3i}$ **c.** $\dfrac{1}{2x + i} + \dfrac{1}{2x - i} = \dfrac{4}{x + 2i}$

EXTRA

Express x in terms of y

It is sometimes necessary to rearrange an equation in order to perform the calculation required in a problem.

Express x in terms of y given that $y = 4x - 3$.

Isolate the term containing x. $y + 3 = 4x$

Solve for x. $\dfrac{y + 3}{4} = x$

Consider the difference in solving for x in the equation: $y = \dfrac{3}{x} \quad x \neq 0$

$yx = 3 + x^2$

$0 = x^2 - yx + 3$

Use the quadratic formula to express x in terms of y.

$$x = \frac{y \pm \sqrt{y^2 - 4(3)}}{2} = \frac{y \pm \sqrt{y^2 - 12}}{2}$$

Use the quadratic formula to express x in terms of y:

1. $y = \dfrac{2}{x} - x$ **2.** $y = \dfrac{5 + x^2}{x}$ **3.** $y = 4x - \dfrac{1}{2x}$ **4.** $y = \dfrac{7 - 2x^2}{3x}$

Review

1. Graph each quadratic equation.

   a. $y = x^2 - 4$ b. $y = 2(x + 3)^2 - 1$ c. $y = -x^2 + 3$

2. Find the vertex, an equation of the axis of symmetry, and the x and y-intercepts of the graph of each equation in exercise 1.

3. State an equation of the parabola congruent to the parabola defined by $y = 3x^2$, having the given properties.

   a. The graph is two units to the right of the given parabola.

   b. The graph is three units to the left and one unit down from the given parabola.

4. The vertex of a parabola which opens upward is $(7, -8)$. If $(3, 2)$ is one point on the parabola, find another point on the parabola.

5. Find the roots of each quadratic equation.

   a. $y = x^2 - 5$ b. $y = x^2 - 7x + 12$ c. $y = 2x^2 - 7x - 15$

   d. $y = -3x^2 - 4x + 15$ e. $y = 4x^2 + 12x$ f. $y = 6x^2 - 11x - 7$

6. Solve each equation by completing the square.

   a. $x^2 + 2x + 8 = 0$ b. $x^2 - 4x - 1 = 0$ c. $36x^2 - 12x + 1 = 0$

   d. $6x^2 + 9x + 3 = 0$ e. $2x^2 + 8x - 1 = 0$ f. $3x^2 - 3x + 2 = 0$

7. For the parabola defined by each given equation, find the vertex, an equation of the axis of symmetry, and the x and y-intercepts. Graph each equation and state the maximum or minimum y-value.

   a. $y = (x - 2)(x + 5)$ b. $y = -(x + 3)(x - 1)$ c. $y = -2x(x - 5)$

   d. $y = 2x(x + 2)$ e. $y = 2x^2 - 4x - 3$ f. $y = -x^2 - 3x - 3$

8. A parabola that opens upward has vertex $(4, -6)$; one of its x-intercepts is 7. Find the other intercept and an equation of the parabola.

9. Use the quadratic formula to find the roots of each equation.

   a. $x^2 - 6x - 4 = 0$ b. $2x^2 - 6x - 5 = 0$ c. $3x^2 - x - 1 = 0$

   d. $x^2 - 3x + 1 = 0$ e. $5x^2 + x - 2 = 0$ f. $4x^2 - 7x + 2 = 0$

10. Without solving the given equation, find the sum and product of its roots.

    a. $5x^2 - 6x - 3 = 0$ b. $x^2 - 7 = 0$ c. $3x^2 - 8x = 0$

    d. $2x^2 - 3x + 4 = 0$ e. $3x^2 + 1 = 0$ f. $5x^2 + x = 8$

11. The equation $ax^2 - 5x - 8 = 0$ has 2 real roots, one of which is -2. Find the value of a and find the other root.

12. The roots of $12x^2 - 25x - k = 0$ are reciprocals. Find the value of k and the roots of the equation.

13. Without solving the given equation, state the nature of its roots.

a. $2x^2 - 6x - 3 = 0$ b. $3x^2 + x + 4 = 0$ c. $16x^2 - 24x + 9 = 0$

d. $5x^2 - 6x = 0$ e. $4x^2 + 3x + 1 = 0$ f. $7x^2 = x + 1$

g. $-2x^2 + 6x = 7$ h. $2x^2 = 5$ i. $-3x^2 = x - 2$

14. For what real values of k does the parabola defined by $y = 2x^2 - kx + 4$ have two distinct real roots?

15. For what real values of k does the parabola defined by $y = kx^2 - 12x + 9$ have two equal real roots?

16. For what real values of k does the parabola defined by $y = 2x^2 - 3x + k$ have no real roots?

17. Graph each inequality.

a. $y > -2(x - 3)^2 + 1$ b. $y < \frac{1}{2}(x + 1)^2 - 2$ c. $y \geq x^2 + 2x - 3$

d. $y \leq -2x^2 - 2x + 4$ e. $y < x^2 - 4x + 7$ f. $y \geq -2x^2 - 12x - 11$

18. Graph the combined inequality $y > 3(x - 2)^2 + 2$ and $y \leq 4$.

19. Graph $y > x^2 - 4x - 5$ and $x \geq 1$ on the same set of axis.

20. A parabola is defined by $y = 3x^2 + 11x - 4$.

a. Find the vertex of the parabola.

b. Find the axis of symmetry.

c. Find the x- and y-intercepts of the parabola.

d. Sketch the parabola.

21. Repeat the instructions in exercise 20 for the parabola defined by $y = -2x^2 + 2x + 12$.

22. A lidless box is made by cutting a 3 cm square from each corner of a square piece of cardboard and then bending up the sides. If the volume of the box is 60 cm^3, find the size of the original piece of cardboard.

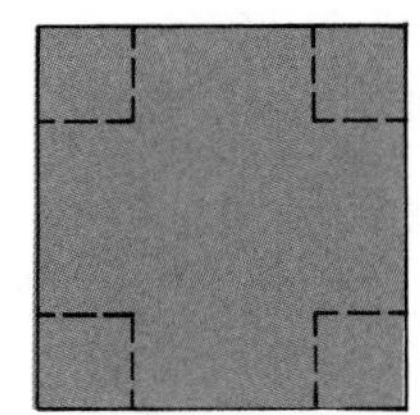

23. A gutter with an open top and rectangular cross section is to be formed from a sheet of metal 40 cm wide by bending up equal strips along the edges. In order to carry the maximum amount of water, the area of the cross section must be at its maximum possible value. What should the dimensions of the gutter be?

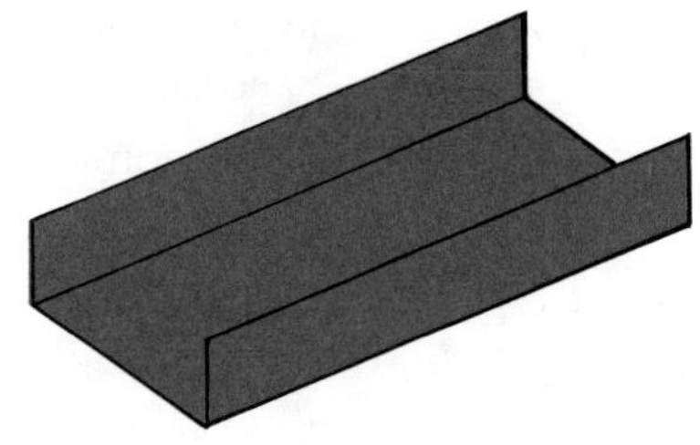

Test

1. For the parabola defined by each quadratic equation, find the vertex, the axis of symmetry, the x- and y-intercepts, and the maximum or minimum y-value. Sketch each graph.

   a. $y = 2x^2 - 3$ **b.** $y = 2x(x + 5)$

   c. $y = 2x^2 - x - 3$ **d.** $y = -x^2 + 5x - 4$

2. Graph the inequality $y \leq 3x^2 - 10x - 8$.

3. For what values of p does the equation $x^2 - px + 6 = 0$ have two real, distinct roots?

4. For what values of k does the equation $kx^2 + (k + 4)x - 1 = 0$ have two real, equal roots?

5. Without solving each given equation, find the sum and product of its roots.

   a. $x^2 - 4x - 5 = 0$ **b.** $7x^2 - x = 0$ **c.** $3x^2 - 2x + 4 = 0$

6. Find the quadratic equation that has the given roots.

   a. $5, -3$ **b.** $2 + \sqrt{3}, 4 - 2\sqrt{3}$ **c.** $6 - i, 6 + i$

7. One root of the quadratic equation $x^2 + 4kx - 5 = 0$ is $\frac{1}{2}$. Find the value of k and the other root.

8. Simplify each of the following:

   a. $(4 + 3i) - (6 + 2i)$ **b.** $-2i(3 + 5i)$ **c.** $(3 - 7i)^2$

9. Solve for $x \in \mathbf{C}$: $4x^2 + 1 = 3x$.

10. What information is revealed about a parabola, given that its equation has the type of roots indicated?

    a. two real equal roots

    b. two non-real roots

    c. two distinct real roots

11. The sum of the first n integers is $\dfrac{n(n + 1)}{2}$. If the sum of the first k integers is 3741, find the value of k.

12. Susan kicked a soccer ball in such a way that the relationship between the height h of the ball in metres and the elapsed time t in seconds, from the instant of kicking the ball, can be expressed by the equation $h = -4.9t^2 + 28t + 0.5$.

    a. Graph the equation.

    b. Determine the maximum height of the ball.

    c. How long is the ball in the air?

Cumulative Review

1. Find the slope of the line segment between each given pair of points.
   a. $(-2, 4), (4, -3)$ **b.** $(1, 3), (1, 1)$ **c.** $(2, 2), (4, 6)$
   d. $(7, 4), (3, 5)$ **e.** $(2, 2), (3, 5)$ **f.** $(2, 4), (3, 2)$

2. Does the given line contain the point P?
   a. $2x + y - 2 = 0$; $P(3, -4)$ **b.** $5x - 11y + 19 = 0$; $P(16, -9)$
   c. $x - y - 1 = 0$; $P(2, 1)$ **d.** $7x + 13y - 64 = 0$; $P(11, -1)$

3. For each given pair of points, find an equation of the line containing them.
   a. $(4, 1), (5, 2)$ **b.** $(2, 1), (9, 7)$ **c.** $(2, 3), (-6, 3)$
   d. $(-5, -4), (0, 0)$ **e.** $(4, -3), (-6, 1)$ **f.** $(-2, -4), (-3, 0)$

4. Find the midpoint of the line segment joining each pair of points given in exercise 3.

5. In a horse race between the four horses, Nearctic, Dancer's Image, Northern Dancer, and Sunny's Halo, the following was observed: Nearctic got a bad start, started 2 s behind the rest, and ran at 17 m/s. Dancer's Image started 1 m behind the starting line and ran at 16 m/s. Northern Dancer ran at 17 m/s and Sunny's Halo started 1 s late, 1 m behind the starting line, and ran at 19 m/s.
   a. Write equations to represent the distance covered by each horse at time t.
   b. Plot each equation on the same grid.
   c. Find all times when one horse is passing another.
   d. The course is 2000 m long. Rank each horse in order of arrival at the finish line, and make a note of each time.

6. One photocopier can do a job in 10 min. Another, newer model can do the same job in 7 min. If the job is split between the two copiers, how long does it take?

7. Solve and graph each inequality.
   a. $x + 3y \geq 5$ **b.** $2x - y < 1$ **c.** $5x - 7y > 6$
   d. $7x + 3 \geq 5$ **e.** $4x + 9y < 2$ **f.** $2x + y > 1$

8. Find an equation of the line that fits the given description.
   a. y-intercept -6, passes through $(4, -3)$
   b. slope 2, x-intercept 3
   c. passes through $(1, 1)$ and $(2, 6)$
   d. x-intercept 2, y-intercept -3
   e. slope 5, passes through $(2, 1)$

9. Carbon-14 has a half-life of 5770 years. Determine how much carbon-14 is left from 10 kg after the indicated amount of time.
   a. 6 months **b.** 1 year **c.** 10 years
   d. 1800 years **e.** 200 centuries **f.** 2 000 000 years

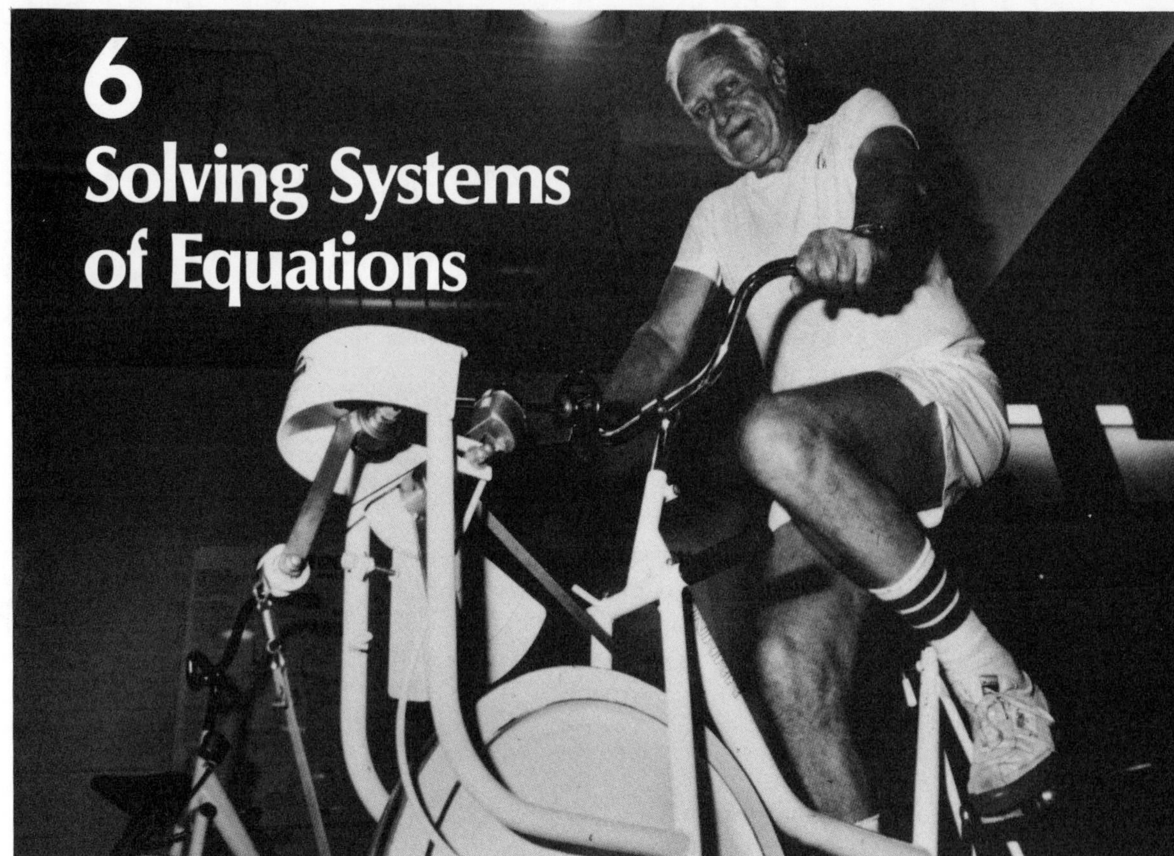

6 Solving Systems of Equations

6-1 Graphing Linear Systems

The managing partners of U-Tone Fitness Club can qualify for a discount from their equipment supplier if they place an order with a total value of \$18 000 at regular wholesale prices. They want to order 14 new exercise bicycles, some computerized exercise bicycles, which wholesale at \$3000, and some non-computerized stationary bicycles, which wholesale at \$600.

This situation can be represented algebraically: let the number of computerized models be x and the number of non-computerized models be y. Two equations can be written from the given information.

$x + y = 14$ — The partners are ordering 14 bicycles altogether.
$3000x + 600y = 18\,000$ — The total value of the order is \$18 000.

The second equation can be simplified by dividing through by 600 to obtain an *equivalent* equation: $5x + y = 30$.

$$x + y = 14$$
$$5x + y = 30$$

This pair of equations in two unknowns is called a linear **system of equations**.

The graphs of the equations intersect at one point. The coordinates of this point satisfy *both* equations. Hence, the point corresponds to values of x and y for which $x + y = 14$ *and* $5x + y = 30$.
The common point appears to be (4, 10).

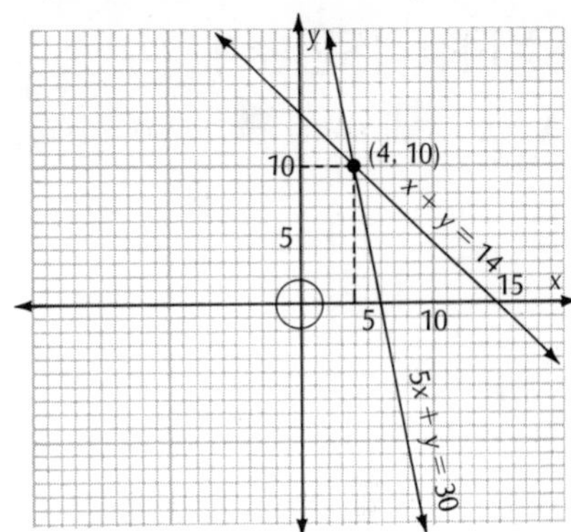

In the context of the opening example, this estimated solution would indicate that the partners should order 4 computerized models and 10 non-computerized models.

By substituting $x = 4$ and $y = 10$ into both equations, you can verify that $(x, y) = (4, 10)$ is indeed the exact solution.

A system like the one above which has at least one solution, is called a **consistent** system of equations. A linear system which has no points of intersection and hence no solution is **inconsistent**.

When graphing two linear equations in two unknowns, there are three possibilities.

EXAMPLE 1: $\begin{cases} x + y = 10 \\ x - y = 4 \end{cases}$

This system has one point of intersection hence one solution. Therefore, the system is consistent.

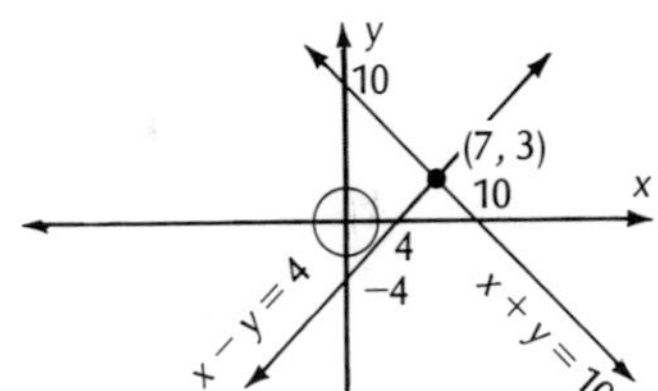

Mathematicians call systems of this type **independent systems**.

EXAMPLE 2: $\begin{cases} x + y = 10 \\ 2x + 2y = 20 \end{cases}$

This system involves two coincident lines. There are infinitely many common points and hence many solutions. This system is consistent, but not independent.

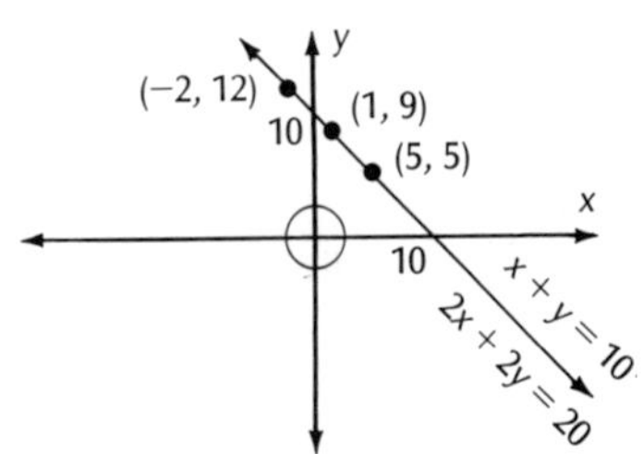

Example 2 demonstrates a **dependent system**. The two equations are equivalent because one is a multiple of the other.

EXAMPLE 3: $\begin{cases} x + y = 10 \\ 3x + 3y = 12 \end{cases}$

This system involves two parallel lines and hence no common points and therefore no solutions. This is an independent system that is inconsistent.

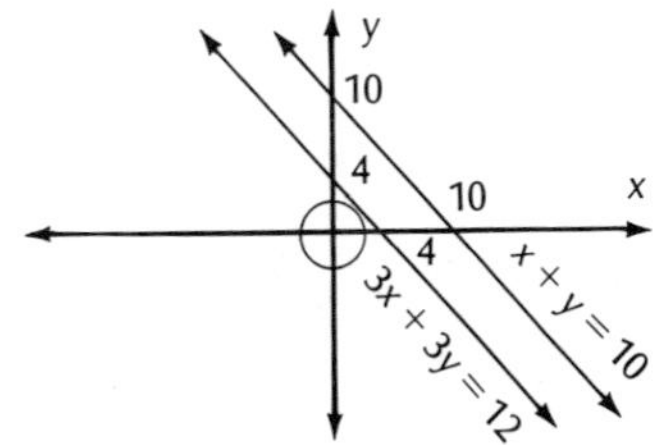

In Example 3, the coefficients of the variables in one equation are exact multiples of those in the other (same slope). The constant has *not* been multiplied by the same factor (different y-intercepts).

EXERCISE 6-1

A **1.** Name the point where the lines appear to intersect.

a.

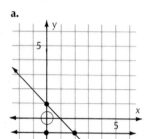

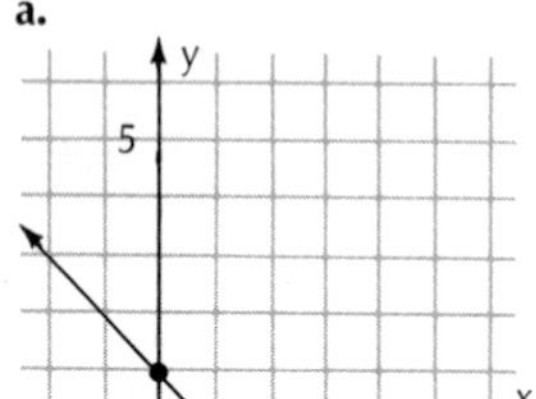

b.

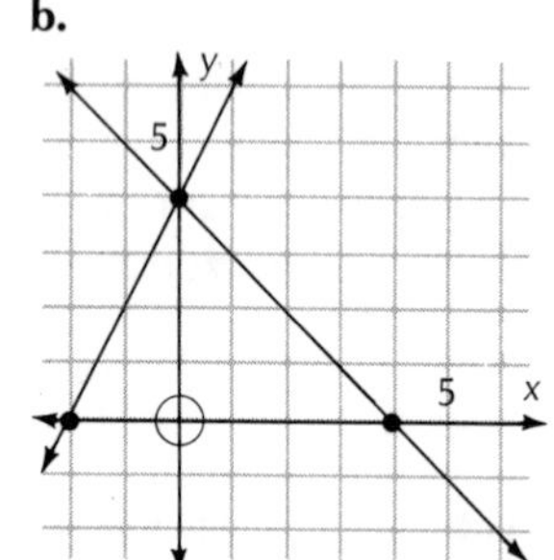

c.

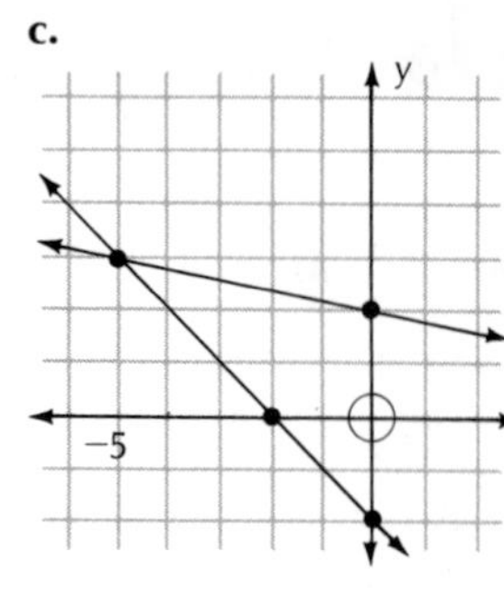

2. Estimate the ordered pair solution of each system of linear equations represented below.

a.

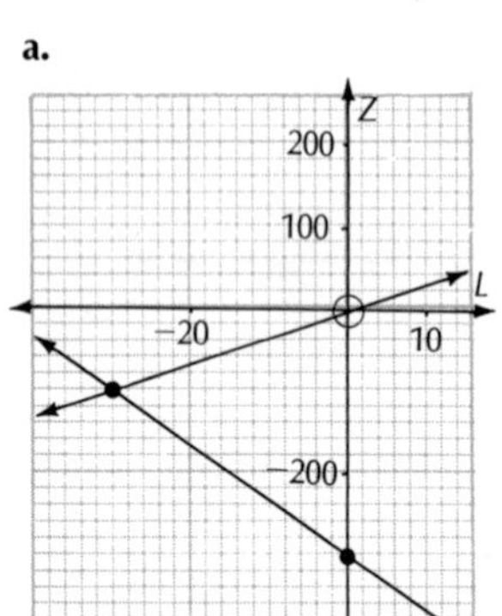

b.

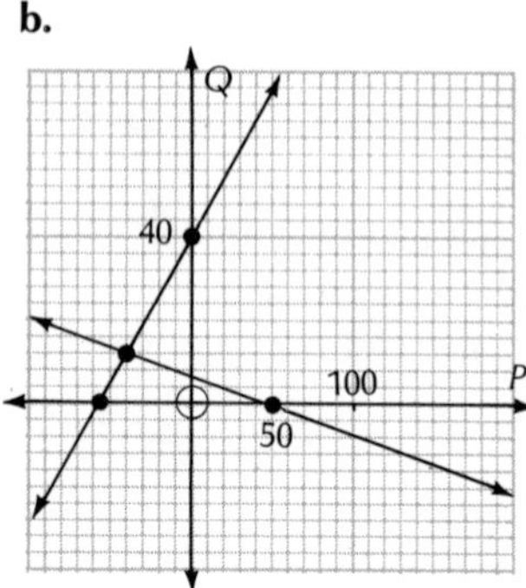

c.

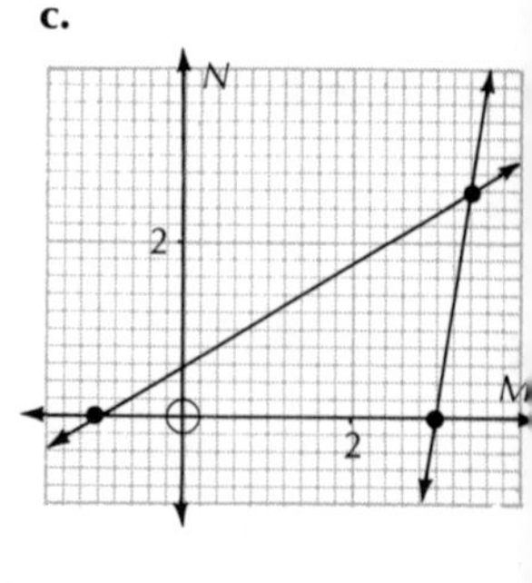

3. Classify each given system as dependent, independent, or inconsistent.

a. $2x - 3y = 6$
$4x + 6y = 12$

b. $4x - 5y + 7 = 0$
$5y - 4x = 7$

c. $3x - 4y = 12$
$4x - 3y = 12$

d. $12x - 9y - 15 = 0$
$3y - 4x = 5$

e. $3x - 4y = 12$
$4x - 3y = 12$

f. $2x + 3y = 0$
$4x + 6y = 0$

B **4.** Solve each system of equations by graphing. Verify your answer by substitution.

a. $x - y = 6$
$x + y = 10$

b. $x - 7 = 0$
$x + y = 5$

c. $x - 2y = 6$
$x + 3y = -9$

d. $2x - 5y = -10$
$4x - 10y = 20$

e. $3x + y = 0$
$y - x = 8$

f. $2x - 8 = y$
$6x - 3y = 24$

g. $x + y = 40$
$x - y = -10$

h. $x + 2y = 4$
$x - 2y = 32$

i. $y - x = 25$
$12x + 13y = 0$

5. For each of the following, define a pair of variables, write a pair of equations to represent the given information, and graph the equations to answer the question.
   a. A branch of the Humane Society is holding a total of 60 dogs and cats. If there are 30 more dogs than cats, how many of each are there?
   b. One pen and one pencil together cost 50¢. Ten pencils and two pens cost $2.20. Find the cost of each pencil and pen.
   c. A car dealership ordered 70 cars, some sedans at $10 000 and the others sports cars at $20 000. The total invoice was for $950 000. How many of each type of car was ordered?
   d. While on tour, a school band of 44 members went into a restaurant where each was given the choice of a deluxe hamburger and fries at $4 or a small pizza at $5. If the total bill came to $200, how many hamburgers were ordered?
   e. A garden is 3 m longer than it is wide. If the perimeter of the garden is 26 m, find its dimensions.
   f. Ahmed invests a sum of money at an interest rate of 9% per annum and a second sum, $520 greater, at 10% per annum. He earns a total of $90 in one year. How much did he invest at each rate?

C 6. Systems of three or even more equations can be solved by graphing. Graph each system of three linear equations and state each solution.

a.	b.	c.
$x + y = 1$	$x + y = 5$	$2y - x = 6$
$y - x = 5$	$3x - y = 3$	$x + y = 9$
$x + 2y = 4$	$2x - 7y = 14$	$x - 2y + 6 = 0$

7. The cost of a reception for a family reunion is based on a fixed cost for the hall rental, R, plus a charge per person for the food served, p. The total cost C, which is a partial variation, can be written as $C = np + R$, where n represents the number of people. If a reception for 20 people costs $500 and for 50 people costs $1100, find the amount charged for the hall rental and the amount charged per person for the food.

8. The cost of purchasing school sweatshirts ("one-size") is partly constant, due to the cost of the silk screen, and partly variable, due to the cost of each sweatshirt. If 20 students order sweatshirts, the total cost will be $340; if 50 students place orders, then the total cost will be $700. Find the fixed cost of making the silk screen and the individual price of each sweatshirt before printing.

9. The fee a repairperson charges is partly constant, due to the fixed charge for the service call, and partly variable, due to the time spent on the repair. A repair that takes 1.5 h costs $70, while a repair that takes 2 h costs $85. Find the fixed rate for the service call and the hourly rate for repairs.

6-2 Solving by Elimination

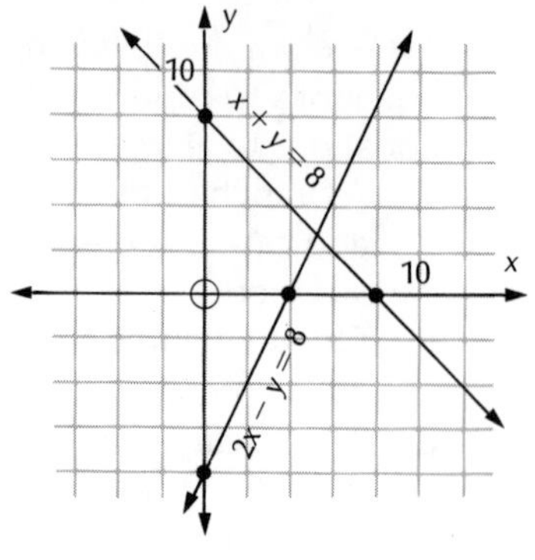

Graphing to solve systems of equations is not always reliable. For the system of equations graphed at the right, for instance, the solution does not have integer values for either x or y.

Example 1 illustrates a fast, reliable method of solving systems of equations algebraically, which leads to an exact solution even in the case of fractional values.

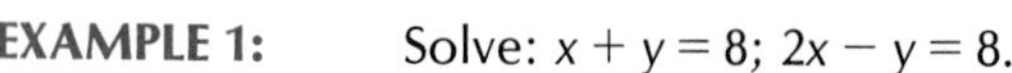

EXAMPLE 1: Solve: $x + y = 8$; $2x - y = 8$.

Adding the left and right sides of the equations yields one equation in one unknown, x. Solve for x.

$$\begin{aligned} x + y &= 8 \\ 2x - y &= 8 \\ \hline 3x \quad &= 16 \\ x \quad &= \tfrac{16}{3} \end{aligned}$$

Add the equations to *eliminate* y.

Substitute one of the original equations to find the remaining variable.

$$\begin{aligned} \tfrac{16}{3} + y &= 8 \\ y &= \tfrac{8}{3} \end{aligned}$$

Substitute into *both* of the original equations to check the solution.

For $x + y = 8$: $\quad \text{L.S.} = \frac{16}{3} + \frac{8}{3}$
$= 8$
$= \text{R.S.}$ ✓

For $2x - y = 8$: $\quad \text{L.S.} = 2\left(\frac{16}{3}\right) - \frac{8}{3}$
$= \frac{32}{3} - \frac{8}{3}$
$= 8$
$= \text{R.S.}$ ✓

$\therefore (x, y) = \left(\frac{16}{3}, \frac{8}{3}\right)$

The system of equations above was solved by **elimination**. In some cases, a multiplication step is required before adding or subtracting will eliminate a variable.

EXAMPLE 2: Solve by elimination: $3x - 2y = 18$; $2x + y = -2$.

Multiplying the first equation through by 2 and the second by 3 will yield an *equivalent* system of equations with equal coefficients of x.

$$\begin{aligned} 3x - 2y &= 18 \xRightarrow{\times 2} & 6x - 4y &= 36 \\ 2x + y &= -2 \xRightarrow{\times 3} & 6x + 3y &= -6 \\ \hline & & -7y &= 42 \\ & & y &= -6 \end{aligned}$$

Subtract left sides and right sides to eliminate x.

and so
$$\begin{aligned} 2x + y &= -2 \\ 2x - 6 &= -2 \\ 2x &= 4 \\ x &= 2 \end{aligned}$$

On your own, check that $(x, y) = (2, -6)$ is the correct solution.

You could repeat example 2, eliminating y first.

EXERCISE 6-2

A **1.** Which of the given systems of equations contain equivalent equations?

a. $2x + y = 3$
$2x - y = 3$

b. $3x + 2y = 15$
$x + \frac{2}{3}y = 5$

c. $-28x + 12y = -80$
$7x - 3y = 20$

d. $4x - 9 = 3y$
$9y - 27 = 12x$

e. $5x - y = 10$
$\frac{5}{2}x - 2y = 5$

f. $-3x = 7y + 12$
$21y - 9x = -36$

2. Solve each system of equations.

a. $x + y = 3$
$x - y = 5$

b. $2x + y = -1$
$x - 2y = -8$

c. $x + y = 6$
$4x - 2y = 7$

d. $3x - y = 4$
$6x + y = 17$

e. $x + 4y = 12$
$2x - 8y = -12$

f. $x + 3y = -7$
$3x + 6y = -10$

3. Find any points of intersection for the pairs of lines defined by the given equations.

a. $2x - 3y = 0$
$4x + y = 14$

b. $2x + 5y = 10$
$10y + 20 = -4x$

c. $5x - 2y = 0$
$3x + 4y = 0$

B **4.** Solve.

a. $3x + 4y = 6$
$5x - 3y = -19$

b. $5x + 7y = -10$
$3x - 5y = -6$

c. $4x + 3y = 1$
$6x - 5y = 30$

d. $6x + 5y = 21$
$2y + 9x = -7$

e. $3y + 11 = 5x$
$2x - 33 = 9y$

f. $6x - 35 = 6y$
$4y + 40 = 9x$

5. Solve.

a. $\frac{2}{3}x - \frac{1}{2}y = 10$
$\frac{1}{2}x + \frac{2}{3}y = -5$

b. $\frac{3}{2}x + \frac{3}{5}y = -6$
$\frac{3}{4}x - \frac{1}{2}y = -11$

c. $\frac{1}{3}x - \frac{2}{3}y = \frac{5}{6}$
$\frac{2}{3}x + \frac{1}{3}y = -\frac{5}{6}$

C **6.** Solve.

a. $\frac{1}{x} + \frac{2}{y} = 8$
$\frac{3}{x} + \frac{1}{y} = 9$

b. $\frac{4}{x} - \frac{6}{y} = 10$
$\frac{2}{x} + \frac{9}{y} = -3$

c. $\frac{3}{x} - \frac{2}{y} = 9$
$\frac{9}{x} + \frac{4}{y} = 2$

7. Solve each system of three equations by first eliminating one of the variables to establish a system of equations in two unknowns.

a. $5x + 4y + z = 36$
$2x - 2y + z = 9$
$3x - 2y + z = 14$

b. $5x + 4y + z = 28$
$2x - 2y + z = -5$
$3x - 2y + z = -2$

c. $5x + y - 2z = 6$
$3x + y + z = 6$
$2x + y + 2z = 5$

6-3 Solving by Substitution

Solving by elimination is not the only algebraic method available for solving a system of equations. You can also find the intersection point of two lines using the **substitution** method.

EXAMPLE 1: Solve: $y = 5 - 2x$; $3x - 2y = 11$.

If there is a solution (x, y), then the first equation tells you that y *equals* $5 - 2x$, so you can *substitute* this expression for y in the second equation.

The equations wo[rk] have y in commo[n]

Substitution results in one equation in one unknown, which is readily solved.

$$3x - 2(5 - 2x) = 11$$
$$3x - 10 + 4x = 11$$
$$7x - 10 = 11$$
$$x = 3$$

Substitute the value for x in one of the original equations.

$$y = 5 - 2x$$
$$y = 5 - 2(3)$$
$$y = -1$$

$\therefore (x, y) = (3, -1)$

You can always verify a solution by substitution into both of the original equations.

EXAMPLE 2: Solve by substitution: $2x + 3y = -11$; $4x - 5y = 33$.

Rewrite the first equation to isolate $2x$. Then write an equivalent equation by multiplying by 2.

$$2x + 3y = -11$$
$$2x = -3y - 11$$
$$4x = -6y - 22$$

Substitute for $4x$ in the second equation. Simplify.

$$4x - 5y = 33$$
$$(-6y - 22) - 5y = 33$$
$$-11y = 55$$
$$y = -5$$

Substitute for y in the first equation.

$$2x + 3y = -11$$
$$2x + 3(-5) = -11$$
$$2x = 4$$
$$x = 2$$

The solution is $(2, -5)$. On your own, check that $(2, -5)$ is indeed the solution.

EXERCISE 6-3

A **1.** Rewrite the given equation to isolate x; to isolate y.

a. $x - y + 8 = 0$ **b.** $y - x + 4 = 0$ **c.** $2x + y = 7$

d. $x - 3y + 12 = 0$ **e.** $4x + 3y = 7$ **f.** $5x - 2y - 6 = 0$

2. Given that $x = -3y + 4$, substitute for x in the given equation and solve for y.

a. $x = -5$ **b.** $x = 1$ **c.** $x = 8 + y$

d. $x = 2y - 6$ **e.** $x = 7 - y$ **f.** $x = \frac{1}{2}$

3. Solve by substitution.

a. $y = 10 - x$, $2x + y = 17$ **b.** $y = x + 7$, $3x + y = -1$ **c.** $y = x$, $3x + y + 16 = 0$

d. $x = 3$, $2x - 3y = 9$ **e.** $2x = y - 1$, $x + 2y = 11$ **f.** $x - 2y + 7 = 0$, $x + 3y = 13$

B **4.** Solve by substitution.

a. $x + y = 4$, $3x + 2y = 14$ **b.** $y - 2x = 9$, $3y - 5x = 22$ **c.** $x + 2y = 3$, $3x - 5y = 64$

d. $x + y = 2$, $2y - x = 5$ **e.** $y + 3x = 5$, $6x + 2y = -10$ **f.** $x + 2y = 5$, $5x - 4y = -24$

5. Using the substitution method, find the point of intersection of the lines defined by the given pair of equations.

a. $2x + 3y = -4$, $3y + 5x = 17$ **b.** $3y + 2x = 3$, $5x - 3y = -45$ **c.** $3x - 7y = -10$, $7y - 2x = 2$

d. $5x + 6y = -10$, $10x - 3y + 8 = 0$ **e.** $-2x + 4y - 7 = 0$, $5x = 6y - 3$ **f.** $-3x - 5y = 12$, $9x + 7y = -6$

C **6.** Solve each system of equations by substitution.

a. $2x = 3y - 35$, $4x - 3y = -25$ **b.** $3y = 6 - 2x$, $5x + 6y = 21$ **c.** $3x - 2y = 29$, $6x + 5y = -5$

7. Solve by substitution.

a. $y = 2x - 4$, $\frac{1}{3}x + \frac{1}{2}y = 6$ **b.** $x = 2y - 8$, $\frac{1}{2}x - \frac{3}{4}y = -1$ **c.** $x - 5y = 8$, $x - \frac{3}{4}y = -9$

8. Solve by substitution.

a. $y = 7$, $y = x^2 + 3$ **b.** $y = \frac{12}{x}$, $x - \frac{36}{y} = -4$ **c.** $y = 6x - 11$, $y = x^2 - 2$

6-4 Solving Problems Using Systems of Equations

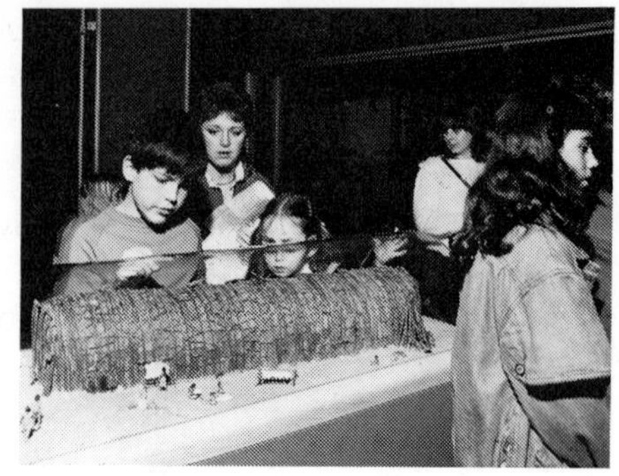

A possible approach to use when solving word problems that involve two unknowns is to write an appropriate system of equations and solve it. Example 1 establishes the steps to follow.

EXAMPLE 1: A museum charges different admission fees for students and adults. The admission fee for 2 students and 3 adults is \$14.00 and the fee for 3 students and 2 adults is \$12.25. Find the unit cost of each ticket.

Define a pair of variables.
Let the cost of a student ticket be x dollars and an adult ticket be y dollars.

Write a pair of equations from the information given.

$$2x + 3y = 14.00$$
$$3x + 2y = 12.25$$

Solve the system of equations.

$$\begin{aligned} 2x + 3y = 14.00 &\overset{\times 3}{\Rightarrow} 6x + 9y = 42.00 \\ 3x + 2y = 12.25 &\underset{\times 2}{\Rightarrow} 6x + 4y = 24.50 \end{aligned} \quad \text{Subtract.}$$

$$5y = 17.50$$
$$y = 3.50$$

$$\Rightarrow \quad \begin{aligned} 2x + 3y &= 14.00 \\ 2x + 3(3.50) &= 14.00 \\ 2x &= 3.50 \\ x &= 1.75 \end{aligned}$$

$$\therefore (x, y) = (1.75, 3.50)$$

Write a conclusion.
A student ticket costs \$1.75 and an adult ticket costs \$3.50.

Check in the original word problem.
Two student tickets at \$1.75 and 3 adult tickets at \$3.50 cost \$3.50 + \$10.50, or \$14.00.
Three student tickets at \$1.75 and 2 adult tickets at \$3.50 cost \$5.25 + \$7.00, or \$12.25.

Some applications involving direct or partial variation, as described in example 2, can be solved using two equations in two unknowns.

EXAMPLE 2: The cost of printing a school yearbook is based on a fixed cost plus a cost per book. Given that an order for 500 books would cost $7500, and an order for 600 books would cost $8650, find the fixed cost and the cost per book.

This partial variation can be written as $C = nc + k$, where C dollars is the total cost, n is the number of books ordered, c dollars is the cost per book, and k dollars is the fixed cost.

Substituting the information from the problem gives two equations in two unknowns.

$$
\begin{aligned}
7500 &= 500c + k \\
8650 &= 600c + k \\
\hline
1150 &= 100c \\
c &= 11.50
\end{aligned}
$$

Substituting $c = 11.50$ in the first equation gives $k = 1750$.

The fixed cost is $1750 and the cost per book is $11.50.

Check.
500 books would cost $1750 + $11.50(500), or $7500;
600 books would cost $1750 + $11.50(600), or $8650. ✓

EXERCISE 6-4

A

1. The sum of two numbers is 37. Twice the smaller number, decreased by the larger, is 2. Find the numbers.
2. Two numbers differ by four. Twice the smaller, increased by the larger is 25. Find the numbers.
3. One number exceeds another by 5. Three more than the smaller number, doubled, is equal to the larger number increased by 7. Find the numbers.
4. One number is 5 less than a second number. If the smaller number is tripled the result is the same as when the larger number is doubled and then increased by 8. Find the sum of the two numbers.

B

5. A community hall is 9.5 m longer than it is wide. Its perimeter is 61 m. Find its dimensions.
6. An isosceles triangle has a perimeter of 24 cm. Each of its congruent sides is 3 cm longer than the base. Find the length of each side.
7. Two circles have radii that differ by 2 cm. The sum of their circumferences is 16π cm. Find the radius of each circle.

8. The perimeters of two squares add up to 34 m. Each side of one of the squares measures 2 m longer than each side of the other. Find the dimensions of each square.

9. If 4 pairs of socks and 3 ties cost \$54, and 6 pairs of socks and 2 ties cost \$51, find the unit cost of each.

10. If 4 packages of mixed nuts and 6 packages of dried fruit cost \$68, and 6 packages of mixed nuts and 4 packages of dried fruit cost \$69.50, then how much will it cost to buy 3 packages of mixed nuts and 5 packages of dried fruit?

11. Deb takes 2 h to travel 60 km downstream in a small motor boat and then 6 h to return. Find the speed of the boat in still water, x km/h, and the speed of the river, y km/h.

12. When Dale cycles, he goes 15 km/h faster than when he jogs. One Saturday, Dale jogged for 2 h and then cycled for 4 h, covering a total of 120 km. Find his rates of jogging and cycling.

13. Two friends, one walking and one jogging, who are 6 km apart will meet in $\frac{1}{2}$ h if they head toward each other; they will meet in $1\frac{1}{2}$ h if they head in the same direction. Find their rates of jogging and walking.

14. Caterina invested \$12 600, part at 8% per annum and part at 9% per annum. She earned \$1089 in one year. How much did she invest at each rate?

15. Fred invested one sum of money at 9% per annum and a second sum, \$1200 greater than the first, at 11% per annum, making \$278 more on his second investment in the first year. How much did he invest at each rate?

16. The cost of renting a car is based on a fixed fee plus a charge for each kilometre driven. A one-day rental costs \$33 if the car is driven 150 km and \$39 if the car is driven 200 km. Find the fixed fee and the charge per kilometre driven.

17. A box contains \$1.01 in nickels and pennies. If each nickel were replaced by a dime and each penny were replaced by a quarter, then the value of the coins would be \$4.55. Find the total number of coins in the box.

C 18. The sum of the digits of a two digit number is 11. If the digits are reversed, the new number is 7 more than twice the original number. Find the original number.

Review

1. Solve by graphing.

a. $x + y = -5$, $3x - 2y = 0$

b. $y = 2x - 4$, $6x - 3y + 12 = 0$

c. $y = 4x + 8$, $2x + 4 - \frac{y}{2} = 0$

2. Classify each of the systems in question 1 as dependent, independent, or inconsistent.

3. Solve by elimination.

a. $3x + 5y = -21$, $4x + 3y = -6$

b. $4x - 3y = 22$, $10x + 2y = 74$

c. $5x - 2y = -6$, $6y + 18 = 15x$

d. $4x - 7y = -24$, $5x + 6y = -30$

e. $2x - 8y = 9$, $6x - 27 = 24y$

f. $4x + 3y = 1$, $6y - 8x = -10$

g. $\frac{3}{4}y + \frac{2}{5}x = -5$, $\frac{2}{3}y - \frac{1}{2}x = -13$

h. $\frac{3}{2}x - \frac{1}{3}y = 15$, $\frac{1}{4}x + \frac{2}{3}y = -4$

i. $\frac{4}{x} - \frac{1}{y} = 10$, $\frac{2}{x} + \frac{3}{y} = -9$

4. Solve the following by substitution.

a. $y = x + 11$, $x + y = -7$

b. $y - x = 4$, $2x - y = 18$

c. $x + y = 3$, $3x - 2y = -26$

d. $3y = 2x + 19$, $5x + 3y = 5$

e. $2x + 3y = -9$, $4x + 3y = -3$

f. $4x - 3y = -3$, $8x + 6y = -2$

5. If 4 mechanics and 2 apprentices earn \$364 in one day and 5 mechanics and 3 apprentices earn \$476 in one day, then what would 3 mechanics and 3 apprentices earn in 5 days?

6. A sum of \$6000 was invested, part at 10% per annum and part at 8% per annum. In one year a total of \$576 was earned in interest. How much was invested at each rate?

7. A machinist earns \$60 per week less than twice the wage of an apprentice. Together they earn \$900 per week. How much does each earn in one week?

8. If 2 is added to both the numerator and denominator of a fraction, the result is $\frac{1}{3}$. If 1 is subtracted from both numerator and denominator of the same fraction, the result is $\frac{1}{6}$. Find the fraction.

9. A light aircraft takes 3 h to fly 720 km with the wind and 4 h flying back into the wind. Find the wind speed.

10. The cost of a ferry trip for a vehicle with passengers is partly constant and partly varies as the number of passengers. A vehicle with 4 passengers is charged \$31; one with 6 passengers is charged \$32.50. If a van was charged \$46.75, how many people were in the van?

6-5 Solving Linear-Quadratic Systems

A solution of a *linear* system of equations can be interpreted as a point of intersection of two lines. But a system of equations may also contain non-linear equations. Three possibilities arise in a system consisting of a linear equation and a quadratic equation representing a parabola.

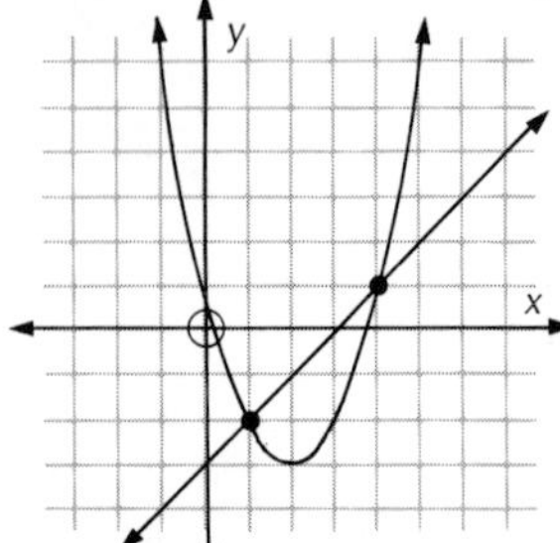

Two solutions: the system is consistent.

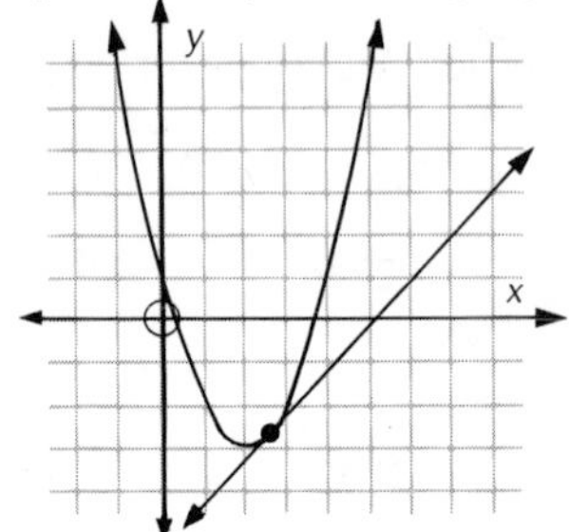

One solution: the system is consistent.

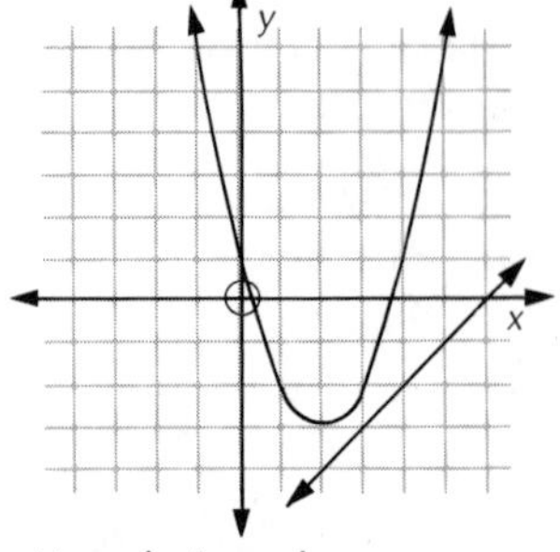

No solution: the system is inconsistent.

Linear-quadratic systems of equations can be solved by substitution.

EXAMPLE 1: Solve and graph: $x - y = -2$; $y = x^2$.

Isolate x in the linear equation and substitute into $y = x^2$.

$x - y = -2$

$x = y - 2 \Rightarrow y = (y - 2)^2$

$y = y^2 - 4y + 4$

$0 = y^2 - 5y + 4$

$0 = (y - 4)(y - 1)$

$\therefore y = 4$ or $y = 1$

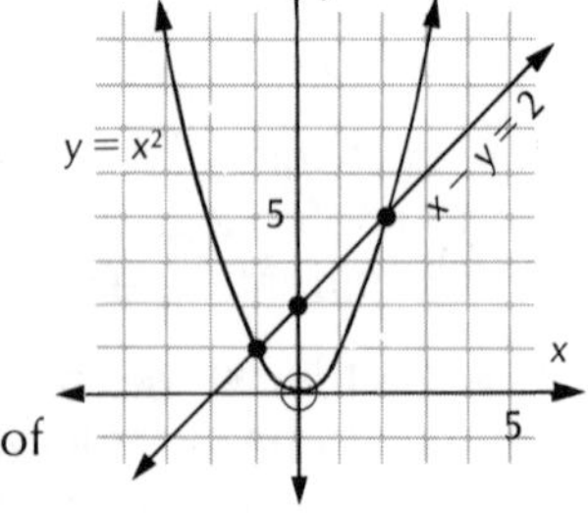

Substitute for y in the linear equation.

Substituting $y = 4$ gives $x = 2$, so $(2, 4)$ is a point of intersection.

Substituting $y = 1$ gives $x = -1$, so $(-1, 1)$ is a point of intersection.

Some word problems, when represented algebraically, will contain a quadratic equation.

EXAMPLE 2: A bungalow has a rectangular interior foundation with a perimeter of 42 m. The total floor area is 104 m^2. Find the dimensions of the foundation.

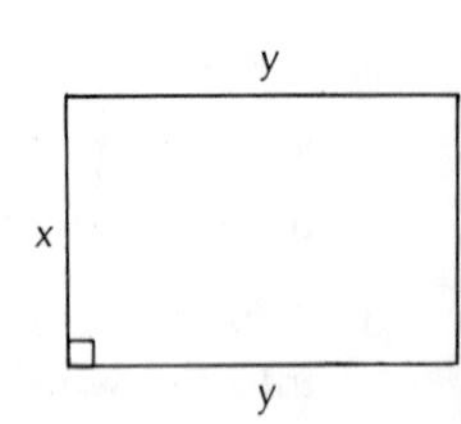

Let the width be x metres and the length y metres.

Then: $2x + 2y = 42$

$xy = 104$ The term xy has degree 2.

Although you have not yet graphed equations like $xy = 104$, an algebraic approach will yield a solution to the system of equations without the necessity of graphing.

Isolating x in the linear equation yields $x = 21 - y$; substitute into $xy = 104$.

$$\begin{aligned} xy = 104 \quad \Rightarrow \quad (21 - y)(y) &= 104 \\ 21y - y^2 &= 104 \\ y^2 - 21y + 104 &= 0 \\ (y - 8)(y - 13) &= 0 \quad \Rightarrow \quad \therefore y = 8 \text{ or } y = 13 \end{aligned}$$

Substitute for each value of y in the linear equation: if $y = 8$, then $x = 13$; if $y = 13$, then $x = 8$.
The two solutions are (13, 8) and (8, 13).
With respect to the word problem, both solutions represent the same answer, that the foundation is 8 m by 13 m.

EXAMPLE 3: Solve: $y - 2x = 0$; $y = x^2 + 3$.

Since $y - 2x = 0$, then $y = 2x$; substitute in $y = x^2 + 3$.

$$2x = x^2 + 3$$

$$x^2 - 2x + 3 = 0$$ This quadratic equation cannot be solved by factoring.

$$x = \frac{2 \pm \sqrt{4 - 12}}{2}$$ Apply the quadratic formula.

$$= \frac{2 \pm \sqrt{-8}}{2}$$ $\sqrt{-8}$ is not a real number.

There are no real number solutions, and therefore no points of intersection for the graphs defined by the given pair of equations.

EXAMPLE 4: Solve: $x^2 + y^2 = 25$; $3x - 4y = 25$.

Isolate x in the linear equation: $x = \frac{4y + 25}{3}$; substitute in $x^2 + y^2 = 25$.

$$\begin{aligned} \left(\frac{4y + 25}{3}\right)^2 + y^2 &= 25 \\ 16y^2 + 200y + 625 + 9y^2 &= 225 \\ 25y^2 + 200y + 400 &= 0 \\ y^2 + 8y + 16 &= 0 \\ (y + 4)(y + 4) &= 0 \quad \Rightarrow \quad \therefore y = -4 \text{ or } y = -4 \end{aligned}$$

Substituting $y = -4$ in the linear equation yields $x = 3$, so $(x, y) = (3, -4)$.

When substituting to find the remaining unknown, it is best to substitute into the *linear* equation. Substituting into an equation of higher degree in the unknown may lead to extraneous roots. Look again at example 4: substituting $y = -4$ into the quadratic equation would yield two answers for x, representing two points of intersection, which is incorrect. *Only* the point (3, −4) will satisfy *both* of the original equations. Try substituting on your own to verify.

EXERCISE 6-5

A **1.** Use tables of values to graph each of the systems presented in examples 3 and 4 to illustrate the solution of each system.

2. Solve by graphing.

a. $y = x^2 - 9$
$y - 7 = 0$

b. $y = x^2 - 3$
$2x + y + 4 = 0$

c. $x = 4 - y^2$
$2y + x - 5 = 0$

d. $y = (x - 3)^2$
$y + 3x = 13$

e. $y = (x + 2)^2 + 2$
$x + y = 0$

f. $x^2 - 2y = 0$
$2x - y = 0$

3. Classify each system in exercise 2 as dependent, independent, or inconsistent.

4. Give an algebraic solution of each system in exercise 2.

B **5.** Find the coordinates of any points of intersection.

a. $y = x^2 + 6x + 5$
$x - y + 1 = 0$

b. $x^2 + y^2 = 25$
$7x - y = 25$

c. $2x + y = 2$
$xy = -12$

d. $9x^2 + 4y^2 = 36$
$x + 2y + 2 = 0$

e. $x^2 + y^2 = 169$
$5x - y = 13$

f. $xy = 20$
$2y + x + 2 = 0$

g. $y = -x^2 - 6x$
$3x + y = 0$

h. $y = x^2 + 5$
$6x + y + 4 = 0$

i. $y = x^2 - 2x + 3$
$8x + y + 6 = 0$

6. Solve for x and y.

a. $x^2 + y^2 = 169$
$12x - 5y = 0$

b. $xy = 36$
$4x - 3y = -6$

c. $y = x^2 - 3$
$9x - 2y = 15$

d. $xy = x - 12$
$3x + 2y = 8$

e. $5x - 2y + 3 = 0$
$y = x^2 + 3$

f. $x^2 - y^2 = 25$
$3y - 2x = 10$

7. Two square gardens have a total perimeter of 128 m. The difference in their areas is 64 m². Find their total area.

8. A right-angled triangle has a hypotenuse 45 cm long. Given that the perimeter of the triangle is 108 cm, find the lengths of the other two sides.

9. Two circular pizzas have a total area of 41π cm², and a total circumference of 18π cm. Find the diameter of each pizza.

10. Find the dimensions of a rectangular garden that has an area of 24 m², given that twice the width, increased by the length is 14 m.

11. A house property is landscaped with a square garden in the back yard and a rectangular garden across the front property line. The rectangular garden is 2 m longer than it is wide. Given that the total area of the two gardens is 220 m², find the dimensions of each garden. (Assume that the width of the back yard is equal to the width of the front yard.)

C 12. Find the points of intersection.

a.	$(x + y)^2 - 9 = 0$ $x - 2y = 0$	**b.**	$x^2 - (y + 3)^2 = 0$ $x + 3y + 5 = 0$
c.	$(2x + y)^2 - 16 = 0$ $y = 8 - 2x$	**d.**	$x^2 - (2y + 1)^2 = 0$ $x = 2y + 1$
e.	$(x - y)^2 - (x - y) - 12 = 0$ $3x + 4y = 12$	**f.**	$(2x - y)^2 - (2x - y) - 20 = 0$ $2x - y = 5$

13. Identify each system of equations in exercise 12 as dependent, independent, or inconsistent.

14. On a separate set of axes, graph each system of equations given in question 12. First factor each quadratic equation to reveal two linear equations.

EXTRA

Paper Parabolas

A parabolic curve can be constructed by paper folding. Cut an unlined piece of ordinary paper in half width-wise, as shown. From the centre of the bottom edge, mark a point approximately 2.54 cm up from the edge. Fold the bottom edge up, as shown, so that it intersects the point. Make about ten such folds from each side of the bottom edge, using a different angle each time and ensuring that the edge of the paper intersects the point. Then trace the resulting curve.

1. Try this method with other points located at different places on the paper. What do you notice?
2. Can you create other curves by paper folding?

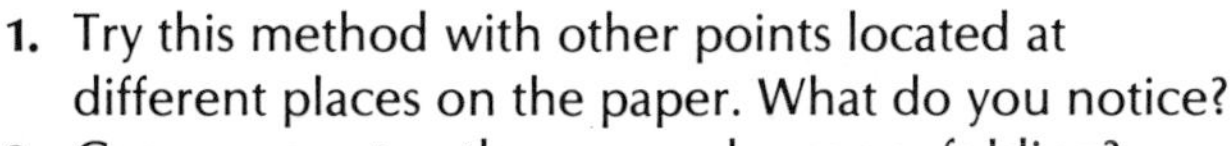

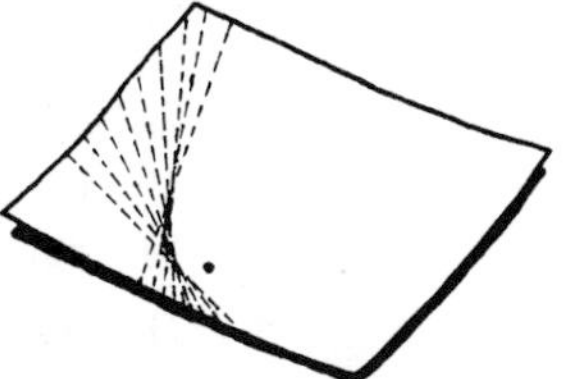

6-6 Solving Quadratic-Quadratic Systems

Two square bulletin boards have a total surface area of 14 500 cm². The area of one is 1700 cm² greater than the area of the other. If x centimetres represents the length of one bulletin board, and y centimetres represents the length of the other, then two equations can be written to represent the information given.

$x^2 + y^2 = 14\,500$ Total area, 14 500 cm²

$x^2 = y^2 + 1700$ The area of one board is 1700 cm² greater.

This system of equations, containing two quadratic equations, is called a **quadratic-quadratic** system of equations.

EXAMPLE 1: Solve the system above to find the dimensions of the two bulletin boards.

Rewriting the equations reveals that the system can be solved by elimination. Adding eliminates the y^2 term.

$$\begin{aligned} x^2 + y^2 &= 14\,500 \\ x^2 - y^2 &= 1\,700 \\ \hline 2x^2 &= 16\,200 \\ x^2 &= 8100 \\ x &= \pm 90 \end{aligned}$$

Since length must be positive, $x = -90$ is an inadmissible root.
$\therefore x = 90$

Substituting $x = 90$ in the first equation yields $y = \pm 80$. Again, the negative root is inadmissible.

An algebraic solution to the system of equations is $(x, y) = (90, 80)$.

The bulletin boards are 90 cm by 90 cm and 80 cm by 80 cm.

Check the solution in the original word problem:

The areas of the bulletin boards are (90 cm)² and (80 cm)², or 8100 cm² and 6400 cm².

The total surface area, then, is 8100 + 6400, or 14 500 cm². ✓

The difference in area is 8100 − 6400, or 1700 cm². ✓

Not all quadratic-quadratic systems can be solved by elimination.

EXAMPLE 2: Solve: $xy = 12$; $x^2 + y^2 = 25$.

Isolate y in the first equation. $y = \frac{12}{x}$

Substitute in the second equation. $x^2 + \frac{144}{x^2} = 25$

Multiply by $x^2 (x \neq 0)$. $x^4 + 144 = 25x^2$

$x^4 - 25x^2 + 144 = 0$

Simplify. $(x^2 - 9)(x^2 - 16) = 0$

Factor. $(x - 3)(x + 3)(x - 4)(x + 4) = 0$

$\therefore x = 3, x = -3, x = 4, \text{ or } x = -4$

Substituting for x in the first equation yields the following ordered-pair solutions: (3, 4), (−3, −4), (4, 3), (−4, −3).

EXAMPLE 3: Solve: $x^2 - 2y = 10$; $x^2 + y^2 = 25$.

Isolate x^2 in the first equation: $x^2 = 10 + 2y$.

Substitute in the second equation. $10 + 2y + y^2 = 25$

$y^2 + 2y - 15 = 0$

$(y + 5)(y - 3) = 0$

$\therefore y = -5 \text{ or } y = 3$

Substituting into the first equation: if $y = -5$, then $x = 0$; if $y = 3$, then $x = \pm 4$.

The ordered-pair solutions are (0, −5), (4, 3), and (−4, 3).

EXERCISE 6-6

A **1.** Solve by graphing.

a. $y = x^2 + 3$
$y = 3 - x^2$

b. $y = x^2 - 4$
$y = 4 - x^2$

c. $y = x^2 + 2$
$x = y^2 + 2$

d. $y = 2x^2 + 1$
$y = \frac{1}{2}x^2 + 1$

e. $y = (x - 2)^2$
$y = 4 - x^2$

f. $y = 2x^2 + 4$
$y = -\frac{1}{2}x^2 + 2$

g. $y = x^2$
$x = \frac{1}{8}y^2$

h. $y = -(x + 4)^2 + 8$
$y = x^2$

i. $y = x^2 - 1$
$y = 2 - 2x^2$

B **2.** Give an algebraic solution of each system in exercise 1.

3. Repeat example 3, changing the first step by isolating y in the first equation and then substituting for y in the second equation.

4. Solve algebraically.

a. $x^2 + y^2 = 58$
$x^2 - y^2 = 40$

b. $x^2 + y^2 = 16$
$4x^2 + 9y^2 = 36$

c. $y = x^2 - 5$
$y = -2x^2 - 2$

d. $xy = -48$
$x^2 + y^2 = 100$

e. $x^2 + y^2 = 4$
$9x^2 + 4y^2 = 36$

f. $y = x^2 - 5$
$y = -x^2 + 11$

g. $x^2 + y^2 = 14$
$x^2 - y^2 = 4$

h. $2x^2 + 3y^2 = 30$
$xy = -6$

i. $x^2 + y^2 = 7$
$x^2 - y^2 = 3$

j. $x^2 + y^2 = 100$
$x^2 - 2y = 20$

k. $x^2 - y^2 = 72$
$x - y^2 = 0$

l. $y^2 = 8x$
$y = x^2$

5. A right-angled triangle with an area of 54 cm^2 has a hypotenuse 15 cm long. Find the lengths of the other two sides.

6. A square garden has an area 4 m^2 greater than the area of a nearby rectangular garden. The rectangular garden is twice as long as it is wide. Given that the total area of the two gardens is 68 m^2, find the dimensions of each garden.

7. A rectangular swimming pool and a square swimming pool, in neighbouring yards, have equal widths. The total surface area of the two pools is 126 m^2. Given that the difference in their surface areas is 28 m^2, find the dimensions of each pool.

8. A pilot, flying a distance of 2000 km, can reduce the flying time by 1 h with an increase in speed of 100 km/h. Find the original flying time and speed.

9. As the manager of his basketball team, Cliff is responsible for ordering uniforms and equipment. When he places an order for knee-high sports socks for the team, he learns that the price has just gone up by 90¢ a pair. With $54 to buy socks for the team, he will now find that he can afford 3 fewer pairs than at the old price. Find the new price for a pair of socks.

10. A right-angled triangle has a hypotenuse $4\sqrt{2}$ cm long. Given that the area of the triangle is 8 cm^2, find the dimensions of the triangle.

11. Last week, a cafeteria purchased $180 worth of coffee. This week, the same $180 will purchase 10 fewer kilograms, because the price has increased by $3/kg. Find the new price of 1 kg of coffee.

12. A community hall has a rectangular floor plan with an area of 160 m^2. If the hall were 2 m wider and 1 m shorter, the area would be 20 m^2 greater. Find the actual dimensions of the hall.

13. Solve.

a. $(x - y)^2 - 9 = 0$
$x^2 + y^2 = 9$

b. $9x^2 - (y + 9)^2 = 0$
$y = x^2 - 9$

c. $x^2 + y^2 = 25$
$9x^2 - (4y - 25)^2 = 0$

d. $(x + y)^2 - 36 = 0$
$y = x^2$

e. $(x - y)^2 - 9 = 0$
$(x + y)^2 - 25 = 0$

f. $(x - y)^2 - 2(x - y) - 24 = 0$
$x^2 + y^2 = 16$

EXTRA

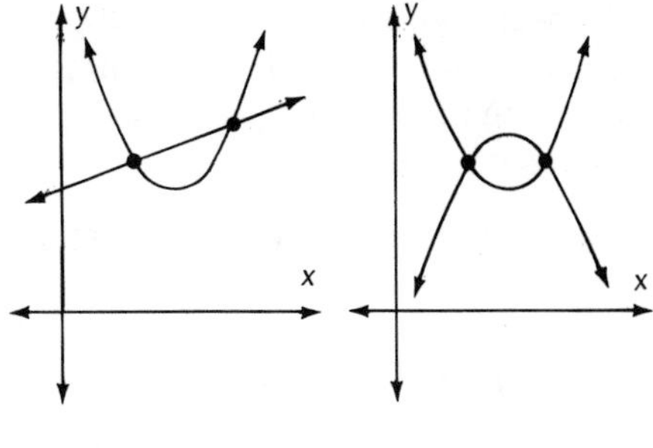

The systems of equations you've graphed so far in this text have had at most 2 solutions. A straight line and a parabola can have 2 points of intersection, as can 2 parabolas.

Other systems of equations, however, can have 3 or even 4 solutions.

Consider the system of equations: $xy = 12$; $x^2 + y^2 = 25$.

Make a table of values to graph $xy = 12$.

x	1	2	3	4	−1	−2	−3	−4
y	12	6	4	3	−12	−6	−4	−3

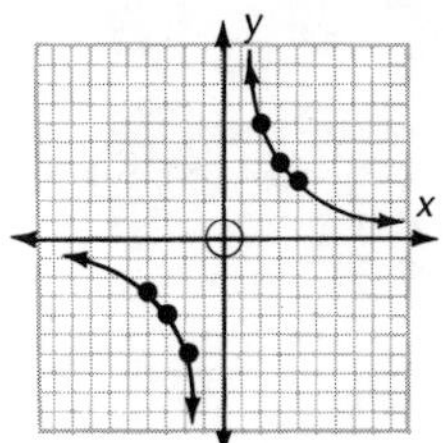

The graph of $xy = 12$ is a **hyperbola**, as shown above.

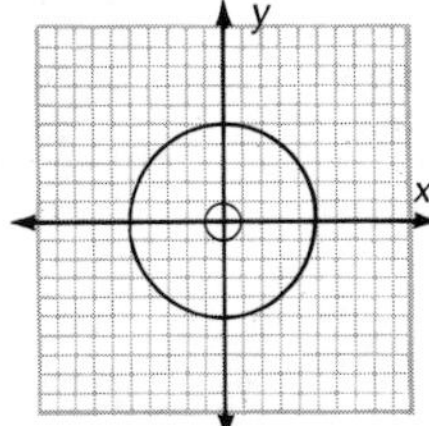

The graph of $x^2 + y^2 = 25$ is a **circle**, with centre at the origin, as shown above.

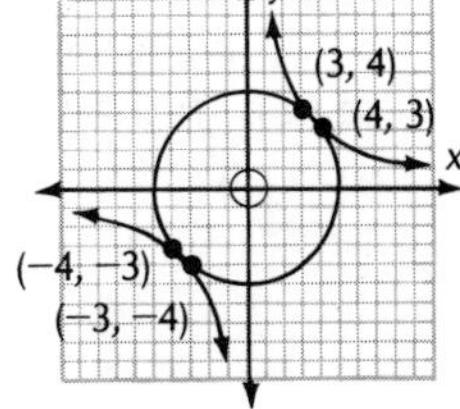

The system of equations can be solved graphically, on the same set of axes. Doing so reveals there are 4 solutions.

1. Graph each system of equations on a separate set of axes. State the number of solutions for each system. (The graph of $x^2 + y^2 = 25$ is given above.)

   a. $x^2 + y^2 = 25$
   $y = x^2 + 5$

   b. $x^2 + y^2 = 16$
   $xy = 16$

   c. $x^2 + y^2 = 25$
   $y = (x - 5)^2$

   d. $x^2 + y^2 = 32$
   $xy = -16$

   e. $x^2 + y^2 = 16$
   $4x^2 + y^2 = 64$

Some quadratic equations can be factored to result in graphs of *linear* equations.

For example, $(x + y)^2 - 36 = 0$ can be factored as a difference of squares. Verify, by graphing, that $x + y = 6$ and $x + y = -6$ represent parallel lines.

$$(x + y)^2 - 36 = 0$$
$$[(x + y) - 6][(x + y) + 6] = 0$$
$$\therefore x + y = 6 \text{ and } x + y = -6$$

2. Solve each system of equations by graphing. Factor equations as necessary before graphing.

   a. $(x + y)^2 - 36 = 0$
   $y = x^2$

   b. $(x + y)^2 - 16 = 0$
   $xy = 3$

   c. $(x - y)^2 - 9 = 0$
   $(x + y)^2 - 25 = 0$

   d. $9x^2 - (y + 9)^2 = 0$
   $y = x^2 - 9$

6-7 Solving Systems of Inequalities

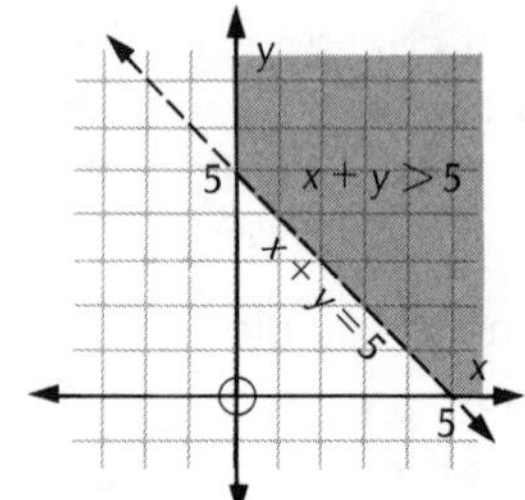

A linear inequality in two variables can be represented as a region of the coordinate plane, as established in Unit 4 of this text. In the graph at the right, the shaded region represents $x + y > 5$.

Some inequalities involve quadratics.

EXAMPLE 1: Graph $y \leq (x - 2)^2 + 1$.

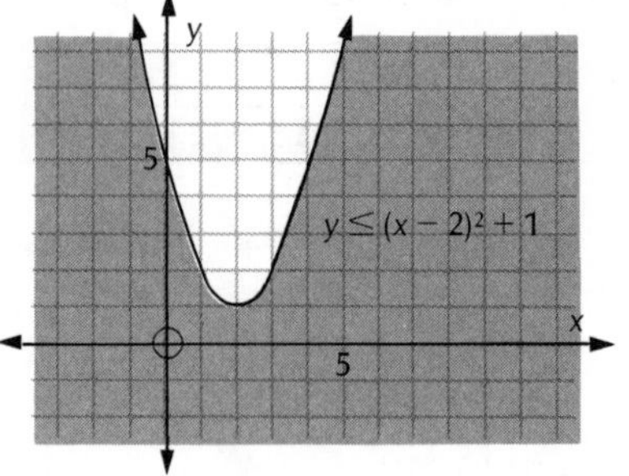

Start by graphing the boundary line, $y = (x - 2)^2 + 1$. A solid boundary indicates that the points *on* the curve are also a part of the solution set.

Select a test point to determine which region to shade. When possible, select (0, 0) to simplify calculations.

Test (0, 0): L.S. = 0 $\quad$ R.S. = $(0 - 2)^2 + 1$
$= 4 + 1$
$= 5$

Since L.S. < R.S., the origin is in the solution set: shade the region containing the origin.

A **system of inequalities** in two variables consists of two or more inequalities in two variables. The solution set of a system of inequalities can be represented by the *intersection* of the graphs corresponding to the inequalities.

EXAMPLE 2: Show the solution set of: $2x - 5y \geq 10$; $2x + 5y \leq 10$.

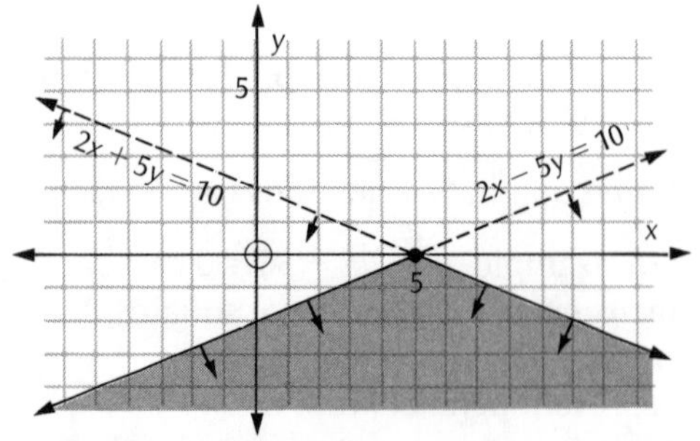

First, graph $2x - 5y = 10$ and $2x + 5y = 10$. Use broken lines to start.

As an intermediate step, use small arrows to mark the side of each line that would represent the solution of the individual inequality.

Then, shade the region containing points that satisfy *both* inequalities. In this example, the boundaries of the region should be solid lines; their point of intersection is a solid dot.

EXAMPLE 3: Show the solution set of: $2x - 3y < 6$; $4x + 5y > 20$

Again, start by plotting the boundary lines, using broken lines. Small arrows indicate the appropriate side to shade for each individual inequality.

Shade the region marking the points that satisfy *both* inequalities. Here, the boundary lines remain as broken lines, and their point of intersection is an open dot, as it is not a part of the solution set.

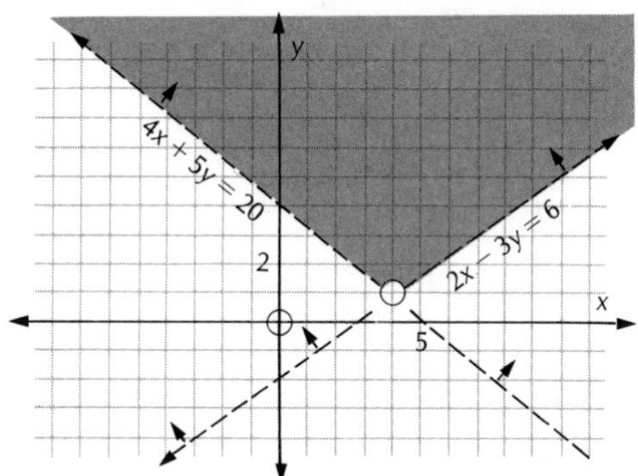

Notice that a point of intersection of two boundary lines will be marked as a solid dot only when it lies on two solid lines.

A system of inequalities may also contain one or more quadratic inequalities.

EXAMPLE 4: Show the solution set of: $y < x + 4$; $y \geq (x + 2)^2 - 4$.

Plot the boundaries, using a broken line for the graph of $y < x + 4$ and a solid line for the graph of $y \geq (x + 2)^2 - 4$. Again, the small arrows indicate the appropriate side to shade for each inequality.

The points that satisfy both inequalities are shaded in the graph. Since the two points of intersection of the line with the parabola are not included in the solution, they are marked with open dots.

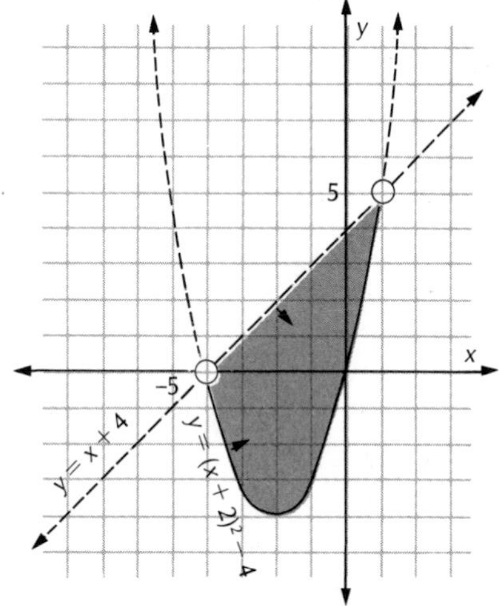

EXERCISE 6-7

A **1.** Graph each inequality.

a. $2x - 5y < 10$ **b.** $5x + 7y \geq 35$ **c.** $2x + 6 \leq 0$

d. $3x + 12 \geq -4y$ **e.** $4x - 7y > 0$ **f.** $2x - 6 < -3y$

g. $5y - 20 \geq 0$ **h.** $3y - 5x < 15$ **i.** $5x \leq 0$

j. $4x + 3y \leq 0$ **k.** $3y \geq 0$ **l.** $7y - 2x < -14$

2. For each inequality in exercise 1, name one pair of values for x and y that satisfies the given condition.

3. Graph each quadratic inequality.

a. $y \leq x^2$ **b.** $y > x^2 - 2$ **c.** $y < 4 - x^2$

d. $y \geq -x^2 - 1$ **e.** $y - 3 > x^2$ **f.** $y + 5 \leq -x^2$

g. $y < (x - 3)^2$ **h.** $y \geq (x + 2)^2$ **i.** $y \geq -(x - 1)^2 - 2$

j. $y < 3 - (x + 4)^2$ **k.** $y + 2 > (x + 3)^2$ **l.** $y + 5 > -(x + 1)^2$

B **4.** Plot the region defined by the given system of inequalities.

a. $x \geq 5$, $y \leq 2$ **b.** $x \geq 0$, $3x - 4y \leq 12$ **c.** $y \leq 0$, $3x + 5y \geq -15$

d. $x < -3$, $3x - 7y \geq 21$ **e.** $y \geq 0$, $5x - 10 < 2y$ **f.** $y < -1$, $5x - 2y \geq 0$

g. $3x - 6 < 0$, $5x + 8y > 40$ **h.** $4y < 20$, $5x < 6y$ **i.** $2x + 6 < 0$, $3y - 12 > 0$

j. $5x - 3y \geq -15$, $2x + 6y \geq -6$ **k.** $5x - 3y > 15$, $5x + 3y \leq -15$ **l.** $2x - 7y < 0$, $4x - 12 > 0$

5. For each system of inequalities in exercise 4, name one pair of values for x and y that satisfies the given condition.

6. Graph each linear-quadratic system of inequalities.

a. $y \leq 4$, $y \leq x^2 + 1$ **b.** $x < 2$, $y > x^2 - 4$ **c.** $x - y > -4$, $y \geq -x^2 + 2$

d. $2x - y < 4$, $y < (x + 2)^2$ **e.** $x - y \leq 0$, $y > (x - 2)^2$ **f.** $y \leq -x^2$, $x - y \leq 4$

g. $y \geq -x^2 - 2$, $y + 5 < 0$ **h.** $y \geq x^2$, $2x - y + 3 > 0$ **i.** $y - 2 < x^2$, $y - 4 \geq 0$

7. Graph each quadratic-quadratic system of inequalities.

a. $y < x^2 + 1$, $y \geq x^2 - 1$ **b.** $y \leq x^2 - 2$, $y \geq 2 - x^2$ **c.** $y > x^2 - 3$, $y \geq -x^2 + 1$

d. $y < x^2 + 4$, $y > -x^2 - 4$ **e.** $y < (x + 3)^2$, $y \leq (x - 2)^2$ **f.** $y \leq (x + 2)^2$, $y > -(x - 3)^2$

8. A system of inequalities in two variables may contain more than two inequalities. Graph each system below.

a. $x - 3y \leq 6$
$2x - 6y > -6$

b. $2x - 3y \geq 0$
$2x \leq 8$
$y \geq 0$

c. $x \geq 0$
$y \geq 0$
$5x + 4y \geq 20$

d. $x \geq 0$
$y \geq 0$
$7x + 2y \geq 14$
$5x + 4y \geq 20$
$3x + 10y \geq 20$

e. $x \geq 0$
$y \geq 0$
$10x + 8y \leq 80$
$3x + y \leq 18$

f. $2x - 5y > -10$
$5x + 3y < 15$
$2x + 7y > -14$

g. $3x - 5y \geq -30$
$y \leq 6$
$6x - 10y \leq 0$
$x + y \geq -3$

h. $x \geq 0$
$y \geq 0$
$10x + 3y \geq 30$
$6x + 5y \geq 30$
$2x + 8y \geq 16$

i. $x \geq 0$
$y \geq 0$
$x + y \leq 16$
$2x + y \leq 20$
$x + 3y \leq 30$

9. Which of the systems in exercise 8 define a closed polygonal region?

C 10. Graph each inequality. Substitute the coordinates of a test point into each inequality to determine the appropriate region to shade.

a. $xy > 24$
b. $xy < 16$
c. $x^2 + y^2 > 25$
d. $xy \geq -20$
e. $xy < -12$
f. $x^2 + y^2 \leq 25$

11. Graph each system of inequalities.

a. $xy > 12$
$x - y + 1 < 0$

b. $y \geq x^2 - 4$
$xy \geq 4$

c. $x^2 + y^2 \geq 25$
$y - 3 \geq 0$

d. $xy \leq -6$
$x^2 < y + 2$

e. $x^2 + y^2 \leq 25$
$xy \geq -12$

f. $y^2 - 3 \leq x^2$
$xy \leq 4$

g. $x^2 + y^2 > 36$
$3x + 5y \leq 0$

h. $xy \leq 16$
$x^2 + y^2 \geq 4$

i. $x^2 + y^2 \leq 36$
$x^2 + y^2 \geq 16$

12. State a system of inequalities that will define the following regions.

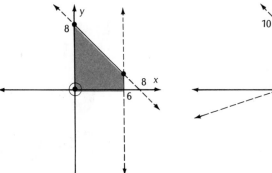

a.

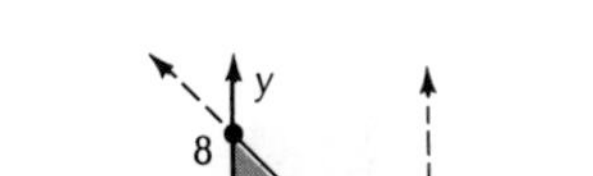

b.

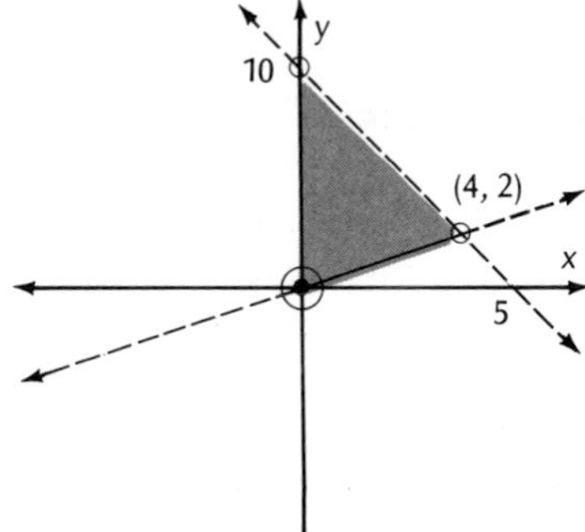

6-8 Linear Programming

The production levels at a car manufacturing plant reflect such factors as distribution and availability of parts. The mathematics of systems of inequalities can be applied to make intelligent, long-term production decisions that will minimize costs while maximizing profits.

The following discussion establishes the basic concept involved.

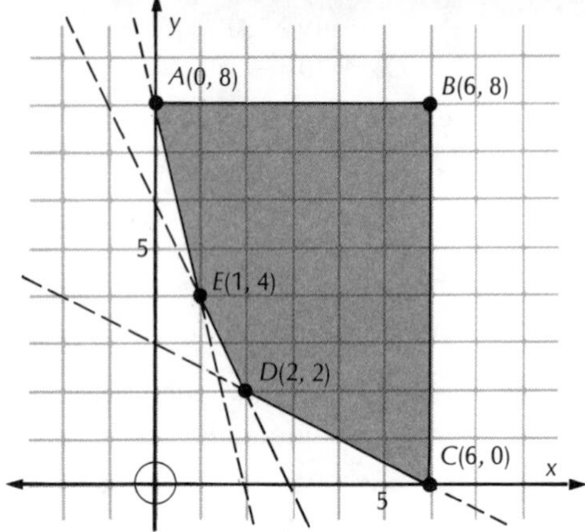

The graph at the right displays the given system of inequalities which, in an application setting, are called the **constraints** of the problem. Any point in the shaded polygonal region belongs to the solution set, and will satisfy *all* of the constraints.

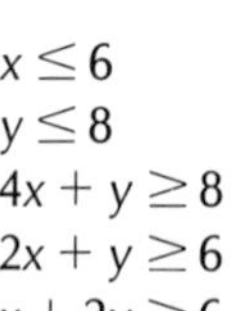

$x \leq 6$
$y \leq 8$
$4x + y \geq 8$
$2x + y \geq 6$
$x + 2y \geq 6$

Therefore the shaded area is called the **feasible region**.

The coordinates of any vertex can be found by solving the appropriate pair of equations for x and y. The vertices of the polygon have been labelled on the graph.

A production manager, having to work within the constraints of a practical application, would consider questions of the following type. Is there a point in the region that would maximize an expression like $x + y$? Is there a point that would minimize the expression $x + y$?

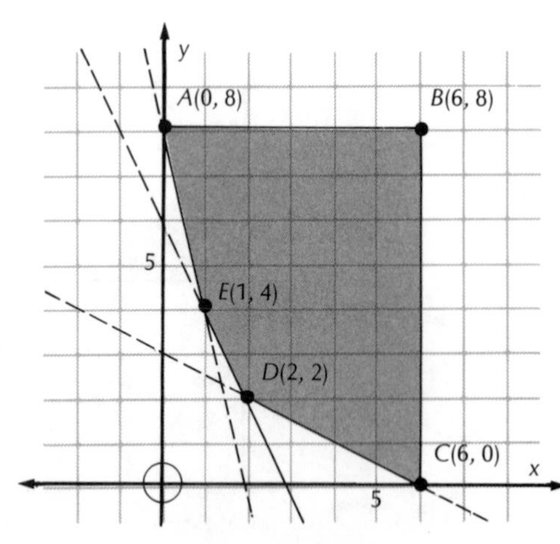

The answers can be found graphically by plotting a sequence of lines of the form $x + y = a$. There are many points in the polygonal region that satisfy the equation for some a. But, there is only one point, $D(2, 2)$, which minimizes the expression $x + y$ with a value of 4.
Also, there is only one point, $B(6, 8)$, which maximizes the expression $x + y$ with a value of 14. Therefore, within the constraints, $x + y$ is a maximum when $x = 6$ and $y = 8$, and $x + y$ is a minimum when $x = 2$ and $y = 2$.

Notice that both the maximum and the minimum occur at a vertex of the polygonal region. In fact, for any linear expression to have a maximum or minimum value within the constraints, that maximum or minimum will occur at one of the vertices of the feasible region.

The process of determining the maximum or minimum value of a linear expression subject to linear constraints on the variables is called **linear programming**.

EXAMPLE 1: For the constraints given above, find the values of x and y that will maximize the expression $2x - y + 3$; find the values that will minimize $2x - y + 3$.

Since both the maximum and minimum will occur at one of the vertices of the feasible region, make a table giving the value of $2x - y + 3$ at each vertex.

Point (x, y)	$2x - y + 3$
$A(0, 8)$	-5
$B(6, 8)$	7
$C(6, 0)$	15
$D(2, 2)$	5
$E(1, 4)$	1

The expression has a maximum value of 15 when $x = 6$ and $y = 0$ and a minimum value of -5 when $x = 0$ and $y = 8$.

Example 2 demonstrates a typical application of linear programming.

EXAMPLE 2: An assembly line can produce up to 6000 vehicles per month. Because of their size, the maximum number of trucks that can be shipped in a month is 5000. The number of cars ordered in one month never exceeds 3000. The contractors that supply transmissions need twice as long to produce a car transmission as a truck transmission.

If nothing but truck transmissions are ordered, they can supply 8000 in a month, but if their production is shifted entirely to car transmissions, they can supply only 4000.

Given that \$500 profit is made on each car assembled and \$400 on each truck, how many of each should be assembled in one month in order to maximize profit?

Start by identifying the constraints of the situation. Let x be the number of cars and y the number of trucks produced, and write a system of inequalities from the information given.

$x + y \leq 6000$	The maximum number of vehicles produced is 6000.
$y \leq 5000$	The maximum number of trucks shipped per month is 5000.
$x \leq 3000$	The number of cars ordered per month never exceeds 3000.

To derive a fourth constraint, use the information on transmissions. Let t be the fraction of the month spent producing car transmissions. Then $(1 - t)$ of the month is spent producing truck transmissions.

$x \leq 4000t$ ①
$y \leq 8000(1 - t)$ ②

$\therefore y \leq 8000 - 8000t$
$\leq 8000 - 2x$ from inequality ①

$\therefore 2x + y \leq 8000$

Since the number of cars or trucks must be positive, there are two additional constraints: $x \geq 0$ and $y \geq 0$.

Graph the constraints and identify the vertices of the feasible region.

Once the constraints have been graphed, find an expression to represent the quantity to be minimized or maximized. Let $\$P$ represent total profit. With \$500 profit on each car and \$400 profit on each truck, $P = 500x + 400y$.

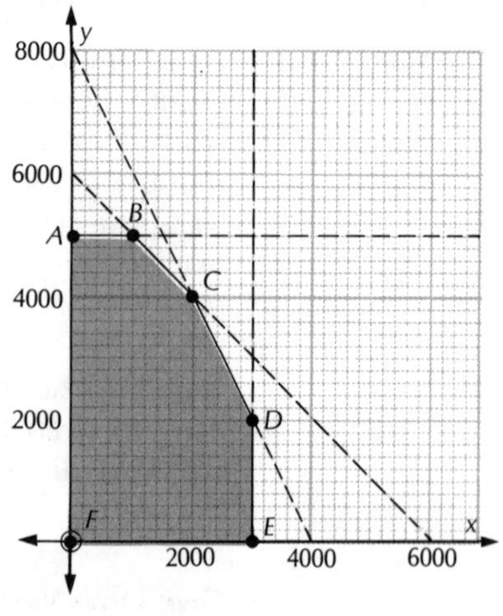

Make a table.

Vertices	$P = 500x + 400y$ (\$)
$A(0, 5000)$	\$2 000 000
$B(1000, 5000)$	\$2 500 000
$C(2000, 4000)$	\$2 600 000
$D(3000, 2000)$	\$2 300 000
$E(3000, 0)$	\$1 500 000
$F(0, 0)$	\$0

The maximum value is \$2 600 000, when $x = 2000$ and $y = 4000$.

Therefore, the assembly line should produce 2000 cars and 4000 trucks in a month, to give a maximum profit of \$2 600 000.

EXERCISE 6-8

A **1.** Graph each polygonal region defined by the given constraints, given that each item includes the constraints $x \geq 0$ and $y \geq 0$. Find the coordinates of the vertices of the feasible region.

a. $y \leq 4$
$x \leq 6$
$2x + y \leq 14$

b. $x \leq 12$
$2x + y \leq 30$
$x + 3y \leq 45$

c. $y \leq 20$
$2x + 5y \leq 120$
$4x + y \leq 96$

2. For each of the following expressions, find its maximum value for each set of constraints given in question 1.

a. $x + y$ **b.** $3x + y$ **c.** $5x - 4y$

3. Graph the following unbounded regions and find the coordinates of the vertices of the feasible region. Include the contraints $x \geq 0$ and $y \geq 0$ in each graph.

a. $3x + y \geq 9$
$x + 2y \geq 8$

b. $3x + y \geq 12$
$x + y \geq 8$
$x + 2y \geq 12$

c. $x + y \geq 16$
$5x + y \geq 20$
$x + 5y \geq 40$

4. For each of the following expressions, finds its minimum value for each set of constraints given in question 3.

a. $4x + y$ **b.** $2x + y$ **c.** $x + 5y$

5. Are there any other solutions to part (c) of question 4? Explain.

B **6.** **a.** Graph the polygonal region defined by the constraints listed at the right.

$y \leq 15$ $2x + 5y \geq 20$ $x \geq 0$
$x \leq 14$ $x - y \leq 10$ $y \geq 0$
$x + y \leq 20$

b. Find the vertices of the feasible region.

c. Within the given constraints, find the maximum and minimum values of $y + 5x$.

d. Find the maximum and minimum values of $y - 2x$.

7. **a.** Graph the polygonal region defined by the constraints at the right.

$x + 4y \geq 80$ $x \geq 0$
$x + 2y \geq 50$ $y \geq 10$
$2x + y \geq 40$

b. Find the vertices of the feasible region.

c. Within the given constraints, find the minimum value of $x + 3y$ and under what conditions it occurs.

d. Within the given constraints, find the minimum value of $5x + y$ and under what conditions it occurs.

8. Bill can do 3 oil changes and 2 tire repairs in 1 h and Mike can do 3 oil changes and 3 tire repairs in 1 h. If Bill is paid \$4/h and Mike \$5/h, for how many hours should each be hired if the manager anticipates at least 39 oil changes and 36 tire repairs, and wants to minimize costs? Answer the following to find the solution.

   a. Let x be the number of hours Bill works and y be the number of hours Mike works. Together they do $3x + 3y$ oil changes. Write an inequality to show that they do at least 39 oil changes.
   b. Together they do $2x + 3y$ tire repairs. Write an inequality to show that they do at least 36 tire repairs.
   c. Graph the constraints from parts **a** and **b**, and include the constraints $x \geq 0$ and $y \geq 0$.
   d. If \$C represents cost, then $C = 4x + 5y$. Find the number of hours that the manager should have each of Bill and Mike work to minimize cost.

9. A manager of a bakery anticipates orders for at least 120 birthday cakes and 180 layer cakes. Molly can ice 12 birthday cakes and 15 layer cakes in 1 h and Syd can ice 8 birthday cakes and 20 layer cakes in 1 h. Neither can work more than 12 h on the weekend.

   a. How many hours should each be employed to minimize costs?
   b. If each bakery assistant earns \$5/h, how much would the manager have to pay in order to have the cakes iced?

10. A cabinet manufacturer makes two styles of buffet, model A and model B. The table gives the number of hours each labourer works to produce one buffet.

	Cutter	Assembler	Finisher
Model A	0.5	1	0.8
Model B	1	0.5	0.8

None of the labourers can be asked to work more than 8 h a day. If the profit on model A is \$80 and on model B is \$60, how many of each should be made each day to maximize profits? Answer the following to find the solution.

   a. Let x be the number of model As and y be the number of model Bs. Then the time required of the cutter is $0.5x + y$ hours. Write an inequality to show that the cutter does not work more than 8 h in one day. Simplify the inequality so that it does not contain decimal coefficients.
   b. The time required of the assembler is $x + 0.5y$ hours. Write an inequality to show that the assembler does not work more than 8 h in one day.
   c. Write an inequality showing the time the finisher works.
   d. Graph the constraints for this application.
   e. Let \$$P$ represent profit. Then $P = 80x + 60y$. Apply this equation to find how many of each style buffet should be manufactured to maximize profit.

C 11. Mari plans to invest up to $60 000 in either term deposits, bonds, or both. She wants to purchase at least $10 000, but not more than $30 000 worth of bonds. The maximum amount she wants to invest in term deposits is $40 000.

  a. Given that the interest rate is 9% for bonds and 10% for term deposits, how should she invest her money in order to maximize her yearly return from interest?

  b. What is the maximum amount of interest Mari could make in the first year of investment?

12. Noah intends to invest between $50 000 and $70 000 in two different banks, bank A and bank B. At bank A, he must invest at least $20 000, but not more than $50 000 to receive an 8% interest rate. At bank B, he can receive a 9% interest rate by investing up to $40 000.

  a. How much money should he invest in each bank in order to maximize the amount of interest he would make in the first year of investment?

  b. How much money from interest would he make in the first year of investment?

13. If the interest rates described in question 12 were reversed for the banks (that is, bank A pays 9% interest and bank B pays 8% interest), then how much money should be invested at each bank in order to maximize the amount of money made from interest each year, and what amount of money from interest would be made in the first year of investment?

14. In order to stay in business, a fast-food restaurant needs to sell at least 10 hamburgers and 20 hot dogs during lunch hour. The employees can prepare a maximum of 60 hamburgers and 80 hot dogs per hour, but not more than 100 of any combination altogether. The restaurant makes a profit of 60 cents on each hamburger and 40 cents on each hot dog.

  a. How many hot dogs and hamburgers must be sold each hour in order to maximize profits?

  b. What is the maximum profit that can be made during a lunch hour?

15. For the fast-food restaurant described in question 14, the manager wants to make a profit of 50 cents per hamburger and 60 cents per hot dog.

  a. Find the number of hot dogs and hamburgers that would have to be sold in order to maximize profit.

  b. What would be the profit made from part **a**?

Review

1. Solve algebraically and illustrate the solution graphically.

   a. $2x + y = 10$, $4x - 3y = 0$

   b. $x = y^2 + 12$, $x + 6y = 3$

   c. $y = x^2$, $y = -\frac{1}{4}x^2 + 5$

   d. $\frac{1}{3}x + \frac{1}{4}y = 0$, $\frac{1}{2}x - \frac{1}{2}y = 7$

   e. $y - 3x + 1 = 0$, $y = x^2 - 5$

   f. $y = 2x^2 + 1$, $y = -2x^2 - 3$

2. Solve algebraically to find any points of intersection.

   a. $y - 5 = 0$, $y = x^2 + 4$

   b. $x + y = 0$, $y = x^2 - 6$

   c. $y + 4x - 2 = 0$, $y = -2x^2 + 8$

   d. $y = -x^2 + 9$, $x + 2y - 3 = 0$

   e. $y = x^2 - 8$, $y - 2x + 9 = 0$

   f. $y = -x^2 - 2$, $x - 3y = 0$

3. Solve algebraically.

   a. $x = y^2 - 5$, $x^2 + y^2 = 25$

   b. $xy = 4$, $x^2 + y^2 = 10$

   c. $y = -x^2$, $xy = 64$

   d. $x^2 + y^2 = 16$, $y = \frac{1}{4}x^2 - 4$

   e. $x^2 + y^2 = 18$, $xy = 9$

   f. $y = (x - 3)^2 + 2$, $y = -(x - 7)^2 + 10$

4. Graph each system of inequalities.

   a. $x + y \geq 0$, $5x - 2y \leq 0$

   b. $5x - 3y \leq 15$, $3y + 6 < 0$

   c. $x + y - 4 < 0$, $x + y + 1 > 0$

5. Graph each system of inequalities.

   a. $y \leq x^2 - 3$, $x - y < 0$

   b. $y \geq x^2 - 2$, $y - 2 \geq 0$

   c. $y > x + 1$, $x \geq y^2 - 3$

   d. $y \leq (x + 3)^2 + 1$, $y \leq (x - 2)^2 - 1$

   e. $y \leq -x^2 + 6$, $y > -x^2 + 2$

   f. $y < x^2 + 4$, $y \geq -x^2 - 4$

6. A farmer used 48 m of fencing to enclose a rectangular pen against the side of a barn which is 25 m long. The area of the pen is 270 m^2. Given that no fencing was required on the fourth side of the pen, running along the side of the barn, find the dimensions of the pen.

7. As one of the sales representatives for her firm, Cary makes a regular trip of 400 km from her office headquarters to a client in Annapolis. She found that the trip took 1 h longer than usual when poor weather conditions caused her to slow her speed by 20 km/h. What is her usual speed and travelling time?

8. George made two investments; one for \$4200 and the other \$6800. The larger amount was invested at a rate 2% greater than that obtained for the smaller amount. If the total interest obtained for the first year of investment was \$906, find the rates of interest.

9. Plot the polygonal region defined by the given constraints and find the coordinates of the vertices of the feasible region.

a.	**b.**	**c.**
$x \geq 0$	$x \geq 0$	$x \geq 0$
$y \geq 0$	$y \geq 0$	$y \geq 0$
$x + y \leq 400$	$x + 2y \geq 120$	$x + y \geq 4$
$5x + 3y \leq 1500$	$x + y \geq 100$	$x + y \leq 10$
$x \leq 225$	$3x + y \geq 120$	$x + 3y \geq 6$
		$y \leq 8$

10. For each expression given below, find its maximum and minimum for each set of constraints given in question 9.
    a. $2x + y + 20$ **b.** $x - 2y$

11. Under what condition will linear programming yield more than one solution point as a maximum or minimum?

12. A furniture manufacturer can produce a maximum of 160 sofas and a maximum of 100 loveseats. A sofa costs \$500 to manufacture and a loveseat costs \$400 to manufacture. The company has \$100 000 to invest in furniture production. If the profit made on a sofa is \$200 and the profit made on a loveseat is \$150, how many of each should they produce to maximize profits?

13. When storing Physics textbooks, it was found that the grade 11 text was 4 cm thick with a mass of 1 kg and the grade 12 text was 3 cm thick with a mass of 1.5 kg. The storage shelves are 180 cm long and can support at most 60 kg of books. How many of each grade level of textbook should be stored on each shelf so that the maximum number of books are stored?

14. A lumber yard sells two models of picnic tables, model A and model B. Below the number of hours each labourer works to produce one picnic table is given.

	Cutter	Assembler
Model A	$\frac{1}{4}$	$\frac{1}{2}$
Model B	$\frac{1}{2}$	$\frac{1}{3}$

Neither labourer can be required to work more than 8 h/day. The number of model As produced cannot exceed 12. If the profit on model As is \$20 per table and the profit on model Bs is \$24 per table, how many tables of each model should be produced each day to maximize profit?

15. If the picnic table manufacturer described in exercise 14 raises prices so that prices now mean a profit of \$25 for model As and a profit of \$55 for model Bs, how many tables of each model should be produced daily to maximize profit?

Test

1. Solve graphically.

a. $x + y + 5 = 0$ $x - 2y + 8 = 0$	**b.** $x - y - 1 = 0$ $y = -x^2 + 5$	**c.** $y = -x^2 + 5$ $y = (x + 3)^2$

2. Solve algebraically.

a. $3x + y + 1 = 0$ $y = 6x + 5$	**b.** $xy = -12$ $x - 2y = 0$	**c.** $x + 4y + 9 = 0$ $x = y^2 - 6$
d. $y = (x + 4)^2 + 2$ $y = -(x + 2)^2 + 4$	**e.** $xy = -12$ $x^2 + y^2 = 25$	**f.** $4x - 3y + 25 = 0$ $x^2 + y^2 = 25$
g. $x^2 + y^2 = 36$ $x^2 + 9y^2 = 36$	**h.** $y - 2 = (x + 3)^2$ $y + 3 = (x - 2)^2$	**i.** $9x^2 + 4y^2 = 72$ $x^2 + y^2 = 13$

3. Graph each system of inequalities.

a. $x - 5y < 0$ $x + y \leq 2$	**b.** $y - x^2 - 2 < 0$ $x - y \leq 2$	**c.** $y < x^2 - 6$ $y > -x^2 + 1$
d. $2x + 3y \leq 6$ $2x + 3y > -12$	**e.** $y \leq -x^2 + 4$ $y - x > 2$	**f.** $y \leq (x - 2)^2$ $y \leq (x + 2)^2$

4. If 4 shirts and 3 ties together cost \$144, and 3 shirts and 4 ties cost \$129, find the unit price of each.

5. The hypotenuse of a right-angled triangle measures 41 cm. If the perimeter of the triangle is 90 cm, find the length of the other two sides.

6. Graph the polygonal region defined by the given constraints and find the coordinates of the vertices of the feasible region.
   $10 \leq x \leq 40$; $10 \leq y \leq 40$; $x + y \leq 60$; $2x + 3y \geq 75$

7. Using the set of constraints given in question 6, find the maximum and minimum value of each given expression.
   a. $3x + 2y$ **b.** $x - y$

8. A car ferry has 800 m² of deck space. Each car needs 8 m² of space and each van needs 10 m². If the cost for transporting a car on the ferry is \$20 and the cost for a van is \$22, how many of each would maximize receipts?

9. A charter aircraft can carry almost 200 passengers. A first-class passenger is allowed 20 kg of luggage; an economy-fare passenger, 12 kg of luggage. The maximum load of luggage that the aircraft can carry is 3000 kg. If a first class ticket costs \$350 and an economy ticket costs \$310, then how many first-class seats should be installed to maximize receipts from fares? What will be the total receipts if all the seats are sold?

Cumulative Review

1. Factor.
   a. $2x^3 + y^4 + 2x^2y + xy^3$
   b. $10xy + 35x + 6y^2 + 21y$
   c. $108x^2 + 231x - 245$
   d. $5xy^2 + 12y^3 - 2x^2y$

2. Find the number of real roots of each quadratic equation.
   a. $x^2 + 3x + 1 = 0$
   b. $3x^2 - 2x + 4 = 0$
   c. $x^2 - 2x + 1 = 0$
   d. $5x^2 + 5x + 2 = 0$
   e. $3x^2 + 7x - 1 = 0$
   f. $2x^2 + 3x + 1 = 0$

3. In a tractor pull, one tractor can pull its load at a rate of 6 m/s. Another tractor in the same contest can pull at a rate of 5 m/s. The first tractor stalls at the beginning of the race, and loses 9 s.
   a. At what time does the first tractor pass the second?
   b. The course is 60 m long. Plot the race on a distance-time graph.

4. Divide as indicated.
   a. $(x^4 + 2x^3 + 5x + 2) \div (x^2 + 1)$
   b. $(x^3 + 4x^2 + 25) \div (x + 4)$
   c. $(6x^5 + 4x^4 + 3x + 2) \div (x^3 + x^2 + x + 1)$
   d. $(12x^4 + 11x^3 + x^2 + x - 1) \div (3x - 1)$
   e. $(3x^5 - 1) \div (3x + 1)$
   f. $(x^2 + 4x + 7) \div (x - 1)$

5. The population of a certain bacterium doubles every 2 h. The colony starts with a population of 8 cells.
   a. What is the population after 5 h?
   b. What is the population after 2 days?
   c. To the nearest hour, how long does it take for the population to reach 1 000 000?

6. An arrow is fired into the air so that its height varies with time according to the following formula.

$$h = 75t - 4.9t^2$$

   a. What is the maximum height of the arrow?
   b. How many seconds does it take for the arrow to reach this height?

7. A computer is equipped with an emergency battery in case of power failure. The computer can drain the battery in 7 min. The printer alone can drain the battery in 3 min. If the battery is used to operate the computer and the printer at the same time, how long will it take to drain the battery?

8. In a swimming race, a contestant swims the first half of the distance in 5 h, and swims the second half 0.36 km/h slower, in 6.25 h. At what rate does the swimmer swim both legs of this long-distance event?

7 Geometry and the Circle

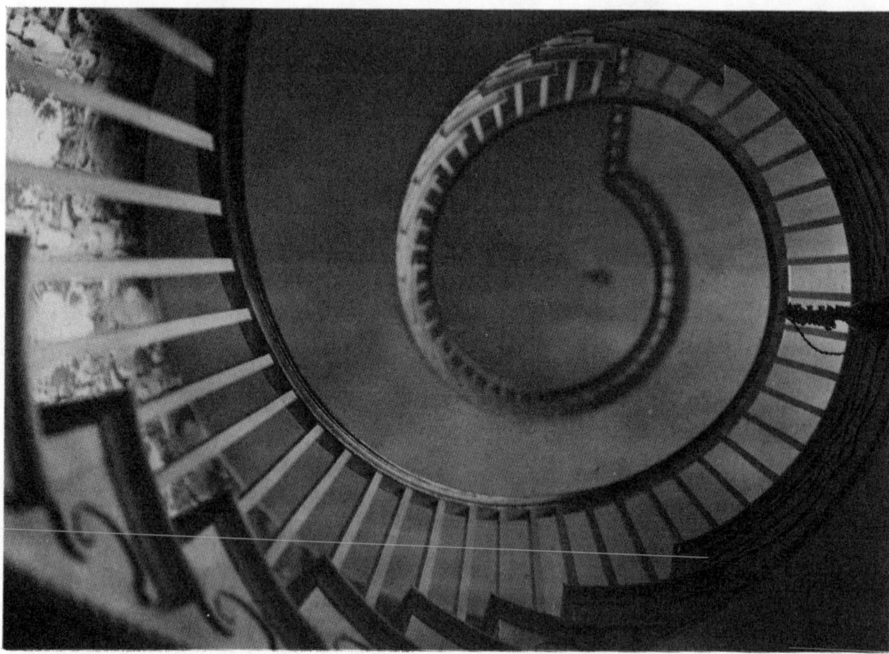

Circles play an important role in a wide variety of fields, including architecture. The spiral staircase is an ingenious application of the circle.

7-1 Equation of a Circle with Centre (0, 0) and Radius *r*

Some basic terms related to circles are reviewed below and shown in the diagram at the right.

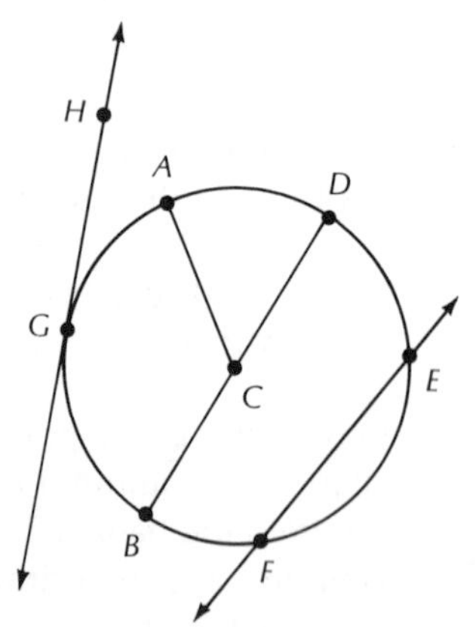

A **circle** is a set of points equidistant from a fixed point. The fixed point is the **centre**. (The centre will always be labelled **C** in this text.)

The distance from the centre to any point on the circle is the **radius**. Segment *CA* is also called a radius of the circle.

A line segment joining any two points on the circle is a **chord**. $\overline{BD}$ and $\overline{FE}$ are both chords.

A chord, such as $\overline{BD}$, that passes through the centre is a **diameter**.

A **tangent** line intersects a circle in only one point, the **point of contact**. For the tangent line $\overleftrightarrow{GH}$ in the diagram, *G* is the point of contact.

A line $\overleftrightarrow{FE}$ that passes through two points on a circle is a **secant line**.

The equation of any circle having centre at the origin and radius r can be found by using the distance formula,

$$P_1P_2 = \sqrt{(x_2 - x_1)^2 + (y_2 - y_1)^2}.$$

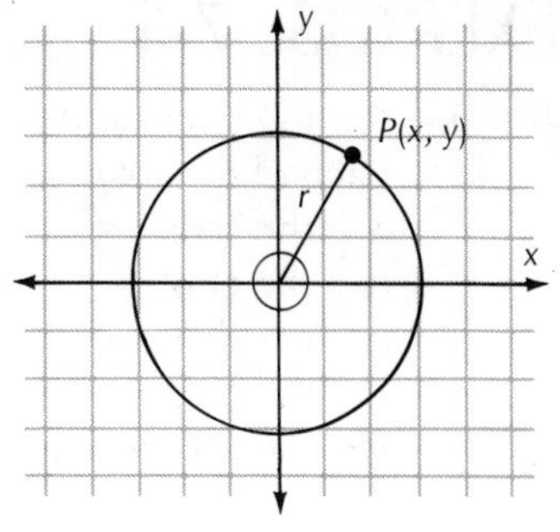

The distance r between the origin and any point $P\ (x, y)$ on a circle with centre $C(0, 0)$ is given below.

$$\sqrt{(x - 0)^2 + (y - 0)^2} = r$$

$$\sqrt{x^2 + y^2} = r \qquad \text{Square both sides.}$$

$$x^2 + y^2 = r^2$$

In general, $x^2 + y^2 = r^2$ represents the equation of a circle with centre $C(0, 0)$ and radius r.

EXAMPLE 1: Write an equation of a circle with centre $C(0, 0)$ and radius $2\sqrt{3}$.

$$x^2 + y^2 = (2\sqrt{3})^2$$

$$\therefore x^2 + y^2 = 12$$

The general equation of a circle with centre $C(0, 0)$ can be used to graph circles on the coordinate plane.

EXAMPLE 2: Graph the circle defined by each equation.

a. $x^2 + y^2 = 49$

$r^2 = 49$

$r = 7$

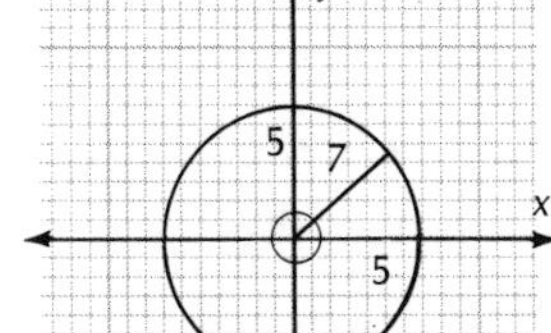

b. $3x^2 + 3y^2 = 16$

$r^2 = \frac{16}{3}$

$r = \frac{4}{\sqrt{3}}$

$\doteq 2.3$

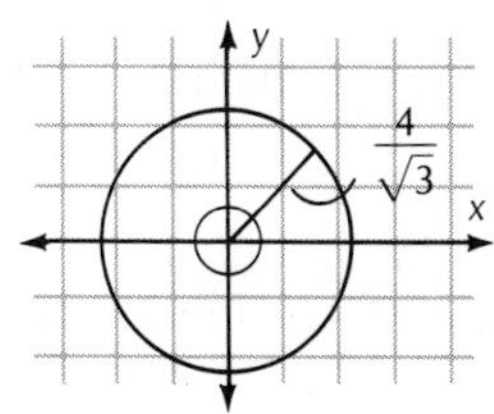

EXAMPLE 3: A circle has a diameter with endpoints $(4, 4)$ and $(-4, -4)$. Write an equation of the circle.

The centre is the midpoint of the diameter. Use the midpoint formula to find the coordinates of the centre.

$$M = \left(\frac{4 + (-4)}{2}, \frac{4 + (-4)}{2}\right)$$

$$= (0, 0)$$

Since the centre is the origin, the radius is the distance from $(0, 0)$ to $(4, 4)$.

$$r = \sqrt{(4 - 0)^2 + (4 - 0)^2}$$

$$= \sqrt{32}$$

Therefore, an equation of the circle is $x^2 + y^2 = 32$.

EXERCISE 7-1

A

1. For the circle at the right with centre C, identify each of the following.
   a. the radii
   b. the chords
   c. the diameter
   d. the tangent line
   e. the secant line

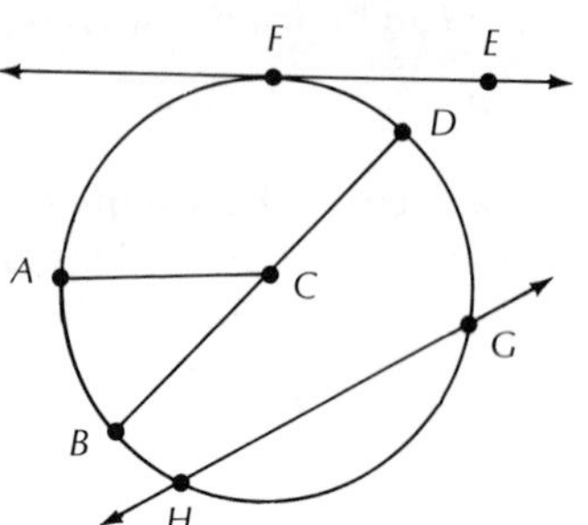

2. Find the distance between each given pair of points.
   a. $P(2, 4)$, $Q(5, 7)$
   b. $A(-2, 5)$, $B(1, 1)$
   c. $C(-4, -1)$, $D(0, 7)$
   d. $O(0, 0)$, $E(-3, 4)$
   e. $F(2, 0)$, $G(-2, -2)$
   f. $H(9, 0)$, $I(0, -9)$

3. Write an equation of the circle with centre at the origin and the given radius.
   a. $r = 8$
   b. $r = 4$
   c. $r = \frac{4}{3}$
   d. $r = 0.5$
   e. $r = q$
   f. $r = 2a$
   g. $r = \sqrt{3}$
   h. $r = 2\sqrt{5}$

4. Find the centre and radius of the circle defined by each equation.
   a. $x^2 + y^2 = 16$
   b. $x^2 + y^2 = 100$
   c. $x^2 + y^2 = 5$
   d. $x^2 + y^2 = 7$
   e. $2x^2 + 2y^2 = 5$
   f. $x^2 + y^2 = \frac{16}{25}$

5. Graph each circle in exercise 4.

B

6. Which points lie on the circle defined by $x^2 + y^2 = 25$?
   a. $(4, -3)$
   b. $(\sqrt{21}, 2)$
   c. $(2\sqrt{2}, 3\sqrt{2})$
   d. $(\sqrt{3}, \sqrt{22})$

7. Write an equation of the circle having centre at the origin and passing through the given point.
   a. $A(3, 4)$
   b. $P(-5, 12)$
   c. $K(-6, 8)$
   d. $H(2, \sqrt{3})$
   e. $F(7, 24)$
   f. $B(-4, -3)$
   g. $R(-3, -7)$
   h. $S(\sqrt{2}, 2\sqrt{3})$

8. Find an equation of the circle whose diameter has the given endpoints.
   a. $(5, 12)$, $(-5, -12)$
   b. $(8, -6)$, $(-8, 6)$
   c. $(-4, -3)$, $(4, 3)$
   d. $(6, 4)$, $(-6,$ -

9. A circle with centre $C(0, 0)$ is tangent to the line defined by $y = 2$.
   a. Graph the circle.
   b. State the x and y-intercepts.

10. Find an equation of the circle with centre at the origin and tangent to the given line.
    a. $x = 6$
    b. $x = -4$
    c. $x + 9 = 0$
    d. $2y - 5 = 0$

11. Graph the circle defined by each equation and state its x and y-intercepts.
    a. $x^2 + y^2 = 36$
    b. $x^2 + y^2 = 48$
    c. $4x^2 + 4y^2 = 49$
    d. $x^2 + y^2 = 90$

12. Write an equation of the circle having the given intercept and centre at the origin.

a. x-intercept 8
b. y-intercept -4
c. x-intercept $\frac{2}{3}$
d. y-intercept 0.2

13. Describe the graph of each equation.

a. $x^2 + y^2 = 0$
b. $x^2 + y^2 = 9$
c. $x^2 + y^2 - 16 = 0$
d. $x^2 - 25 = -9 - y^2$

14. A point A is in the **interior** of a circle if the distance CA between the point and the centre C is less than the radius. A point B is in the **exterior** of a circle if the distance CB between the point and the centre C is greater than the radius. For the circle defined by $x^2 + y^2 = 25$, where does each point lie in relation to the circle?

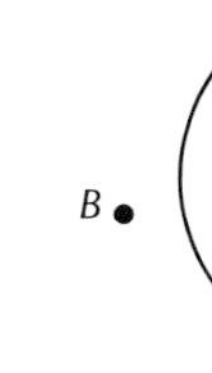

a. $(2, 3)$
b. $(6, 5)$
c. $(-3, 1)$
d. $(-8, 0)$
e. $(3, -4)$
f. $(-4, -4)$

15. Graph the region defined by each inequality.

a. $x^2 + y^2 \geq 36$
b. $x^2 + y^2 \leq 16$
c. $x^2 + y^2 \geq 9$
d. $x^2 + y^2 \geq 12$

C 16. Describe the graph of $y = \sqrt{100 - x^2}$.

17. A diameter divides a circle into two **semicircles** or **half-circles**, as shown in the diagram at the right.

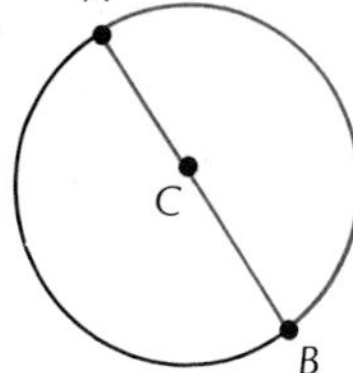

a. Graph $x = -\sqrt{64 - y^2}$ to show that it defines a semicircle.
b. Find the equation of the other half of the circle.

18. Write an equation to define each of the following.

a. the top half of the circle defined by $x^2 + y^2 = 25$
b. the left half of the circle defined by $x^2 + y^2 = 16$
c. the bottom half of the circle defined by $x^2 + y^2 = 4$
d. the right half of the circle defined by $x^2 + y^2 = 12$

19. For points $A(6, -8)$ and $B(8, 6)$, answer the following.

a. Find an equation of the perpendicular bisector of $\overline{AB}$.
b. Show that the centre of the circle defined by $x^2 + y^2 = 100$ lies on the perpendicular bisector of $\overline{AB}$.

EXTRA

Arcs Abound

The shaded region at the right is bounded by an arc of the circle defined by $x^2 + y^2 = 1$ and a segment of the line defined by $x + y = 1$. Find the area of the shaded region.

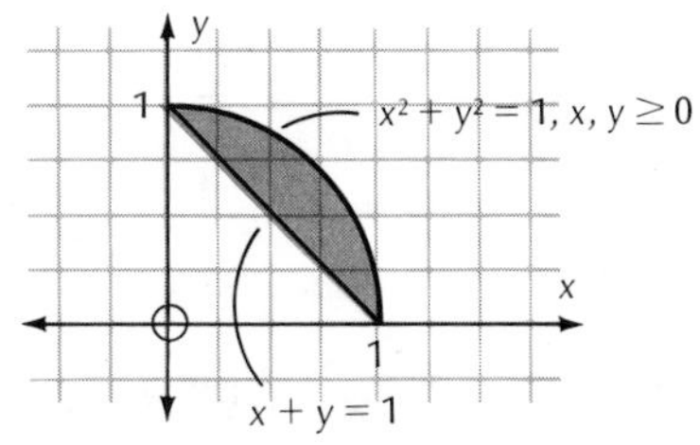

7-2 Arcs, Angles and Regions of Circles

Being familiar with the terminology related to circles can assist you in further study of circles. Lines, points, and angles determine various parts and regions of a circle.

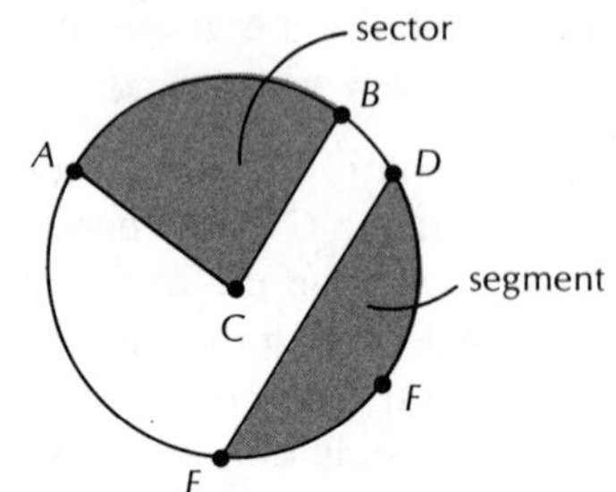

An **arc** AB consists of the points A and B and all the points on the circle between A and B.

A chord $\overline{ED}$ that is not a diameter determines a **major arc** EAD and a **minor arc** EFD.

As shown in the first diagram at the right, a **sector** of a circle is a region of the circle bounded by two radii and an arc. A **segment** is a region bounded by a chord and an arc.

$\angle FCI$ is a **central** or **sector angle**, as it is formed by two radii.
$\angle FCI$ is **subtended** by minor arc FI.

$\angle FGI$ is an **inscribed angle**, as it is formed by two chords having a common endpoint on the circle. $\angle FGI$ is also subtended by minor arc FI.

EXAMPLE:

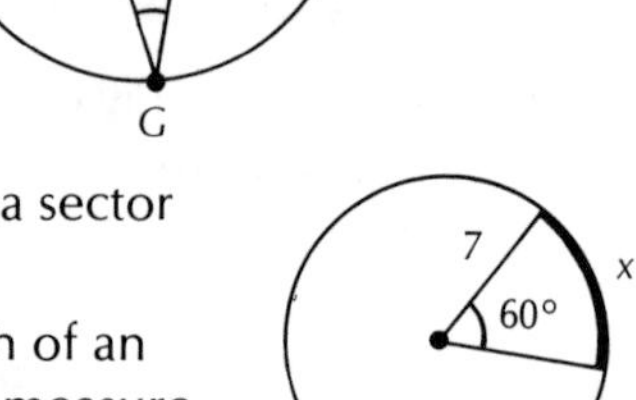

a. Find the length of the arc of a circle having a sector angle 60° and radius 7 cm.

Let x cm be the length of the arc. The length of an arc of a circle is directly proportional to the measure of its sector angle.

$$\frac{60}{360} = \frac{x}{2\pi r}$$
$$360x = 120\pi(7)$$
$$x = \frac{7\pi}{3}$$

Recall that $C = 2\pi r$, where C is the circumference and r is the radius of a circle.

Therefore, the length of the arc is $\frac{7\pi}{3}$ cm.

b. Find the area of the sector formed by the arc in part **a.**

Let a cm^2 be the area of the sector.
The area of a sector of a circle is proportional to the measure of its sector angle.

$$\frac{60}{360} = \frac{a}{\pi r^2}$$
$$6a = 49\pi$$
$$a = \frac{49\pi}{6} \text{ cm}^2.$$

Recall that $A = \pi r^2$, where A is the area and r is the radius of a circle.

Therefore, the area of the sector is $\frac{49\pi}{6}$ cm^2.

EXERCISE 7-2

A **1.** From the circle at the right with centre C, identify each of the following.

a. the sector angles
b. the inscribed angles
c. three minor arcs
d. three major arcs

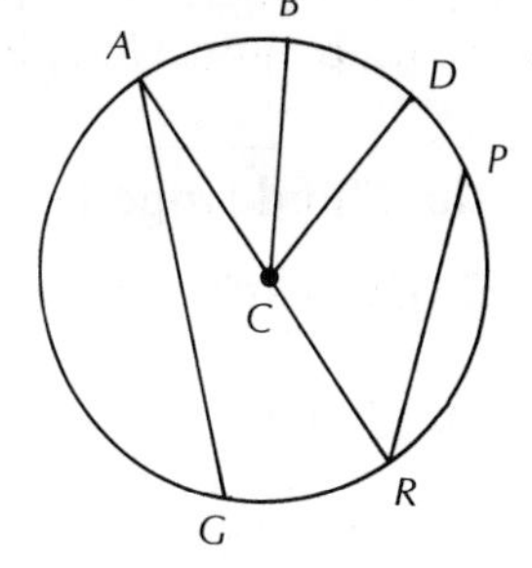

2. Answer the following, using the diagram for exercise 1.

a. Name a chord that bounds a segment.
b. Name a pair of radii that bound a sector.
c. Name the angle subtended by minor arc AP.

B **3.** Determine whether each statement is true or false. Modify each false statement to make it true.

a. An inscribed angle of a circle is subtended by an arc and two radii of the circle.
b. Every chord divides a circle into two arcs.
c. The area bounded by a semicircle and a diameter of a circle is given by $A = \pi r^2$.
d. The intersection of a secant to a circle and a diameter of the circle is called the point of contact.
e. Every major segment of a circle is bounded by a major arc and two radii.

4. Find the length of the arc that bounds each shaded sector. Leave your answers in terms of π.

a.

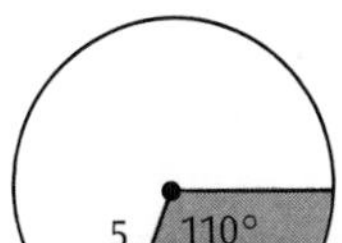

b.

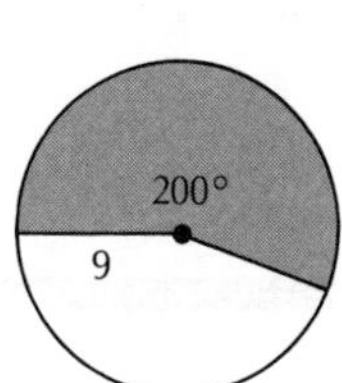

c.

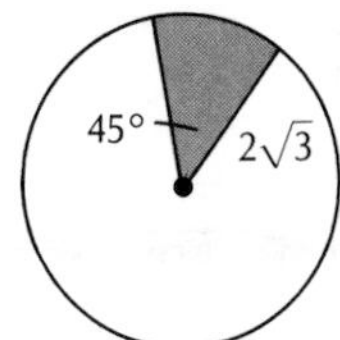

5. Find the area of each shaded sector given in exercise 4.

6. A circle defined by $x^2 + y^2 = 36$ contains chord $\overline{AB}$ that is 6 units long.

a. Find the area of the sector bounded by minor arc AB.
b. Find the length of minor arc AB.
c. Find the area of the segment bounded by minor arc AB and chord $\overline{AB}$.

C **7.** **a.** Find the area of the circle defined by $x^2 + y^2 = 16$.
b. Using the circle given in part **a**, find the area of the minor segment that is bounded by the chord with endpoints $A(0, 4)$ and $B(4, 0)$.

7-3 Chord Properties

Three key properties of chords of a circle are given below. The properties can be used in many applications involving chords of circles.

The Chord Properties

Given a circle with centre C and chord $\overline{AB}$, the following properties apply.

1. The perpendicular bisector $\overline{PQ}$ of a chord $\overline{AB}$ contains the centre of the circle.

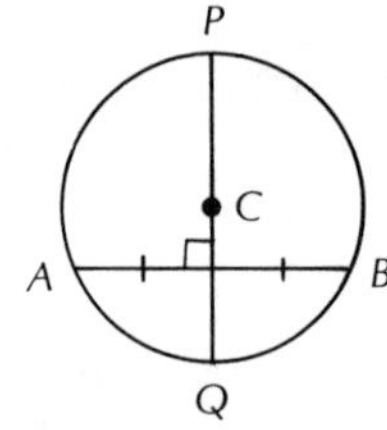

2. A line $\overleftrightarrow{PM}$ that passes through the centre of a circle and the midpoint of a chord $\overline{AB}$, is perpendicular to the chord.

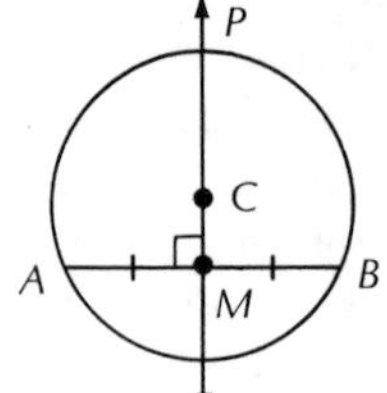

3. A line $\overleftrightarrow{PQ}$ that passes through the centre of a circle and is perpendicular to a chord $\overline{AB}$, bisects the chord.

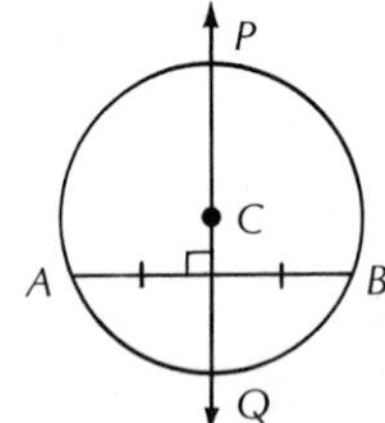

A proof of the first property is given below. The other two proofs are left to the exercises.

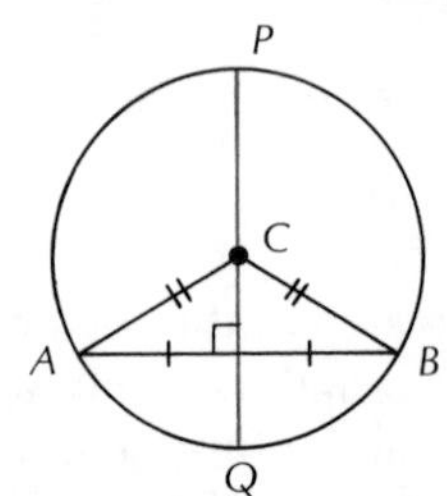

Given: Circle with centre C, chord $\overline{AB}$, and the perpendicular bisector $\overline{PQ}$ *of* $\overline{AB}$.

Prove: $\overline{PQ}$ contains the centre C.

Proof: $\overline{CA}$ and $\overline{CB}$ are radii of the circle — Definition

$\therefore CA = CB$ — Radii have equal measures.

$\therefore$ C is equidistant from A and B.

$\therefore$ the centre C lies on the perpendicular bisector $\overline{PQ}$ of $\overline{AB}$. — Perpendicular Bisector Theorem

EXAMPLE 1: For each circle with the given dimensions, calculate the value of x correct to two decimal places.

a.

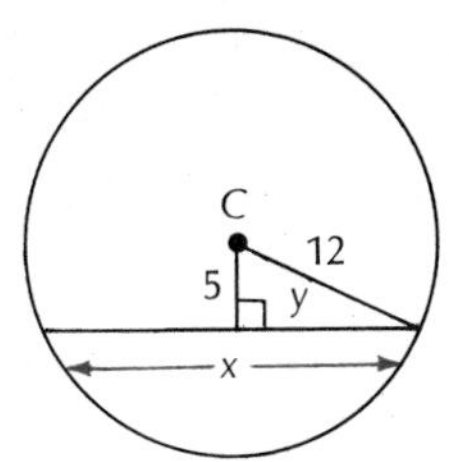

From the third chord property, the perpendicular from the centre of a circle to a chord bisects the chord.

$\therefore x = 2y$

Use the Pythagorean Theorem to calculate y.

$12^2 = 5^2 + y^2$

$y^2 = 144 - 25$

$y^2 = 119$

$y \doteq 10.91$

$\therefore x \doteq 21.82$

b.

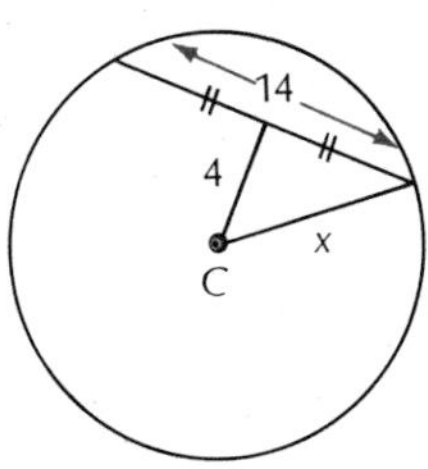

From the second chord property, a line through the centre of a circle and the midpoint of a chord is perpendicular to the chord. The length of half the chord is 7.

Use the Pythagorean Theorem to calculate x.

$x^2 = 7^2 + 4^2$

$x^2 = 49 + 16$

$x^2 = 65$

$\therefore x \doteq 8.06$

EXAMPLE 2: The equation of a circle with centre $C(0, 0)$ is $x^2 + y^2 = 100$. Two points on the circle are $A(8, 6)$ and $B(-6, 8)$. Show that a line passing through the centre of the circle and the midpoint M of $\overline{AB}$ is perpendicular to $\overline{AB}$.

Use the midpoint formula to find the coordinates of M.

$$M = \left(\frac{8-6}{2}, \frac{6+8}{2}\right)$$
$$= (1, 7)$$

The slope of $\overline{AB}$ is $\dfrac{8-6}{-6-8}$, or $-\dfrac{1}{7}$.

The slope of $\overline{CM}$ is $\dfrac{7-0}{1-0}$, or 7.

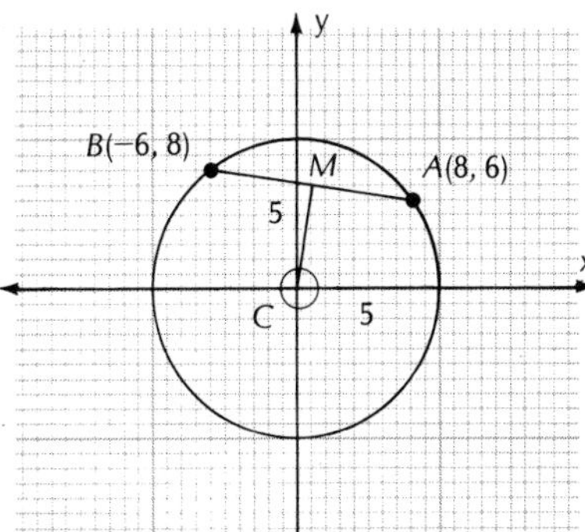

Since the slopes are negative reciprocals, the segments are perpendicular.

EXERCISE 7-3

A 1. For each circle with centre C and the given dimensions, find the length of each indicated segment.

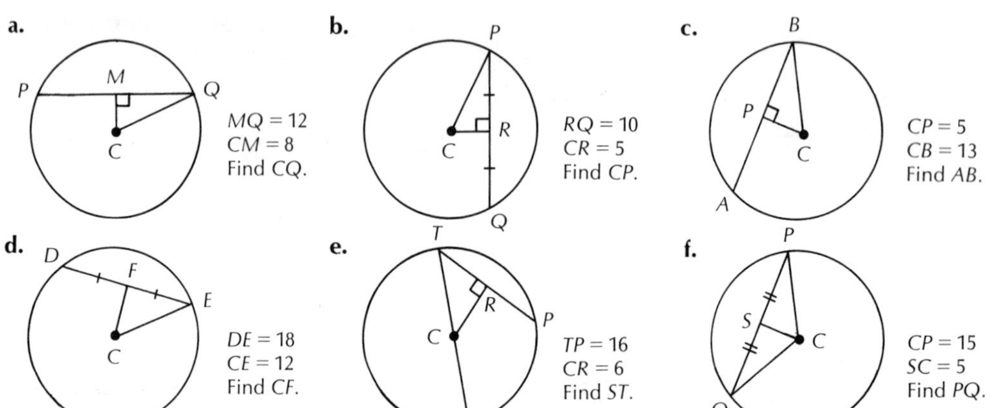

B 2. A circle has a radius 10 cm.

a. Find the length of a chord that is 8 cm from the centre of the circle.

b. How long is a chord in the same circle if it is 6 cm from the centre?

3. A circle has a diameter 50 cm. A chord $\overline{AB}$ is 48 cm long and a chord $\overline{PQ}$ is 14 cm long.

a. Which chord is closer to the centre of the circle?

b. How much closer to the centre is the chord you identified in part **a**?

4. *R*, *S*, and *T* are three non-collinear points. Describe a method for constructing a circle which passes through *R*, *S*, and *T*. Justify your construction.

5. Copy the arc at the right and locate the centre of the circle from which it was drawn. (Hint: Let *P* be any other point on arc *AB*. Draw chords $\overline{AP}$ and $\overline{BP}$.)

6. $\overline{PS}$ and $\overline{QR}$ are chords of two concentric circles with centre C. If *P*, *Q*, *R*, and *S* are collinear, prove that *PQ* = *RS*.

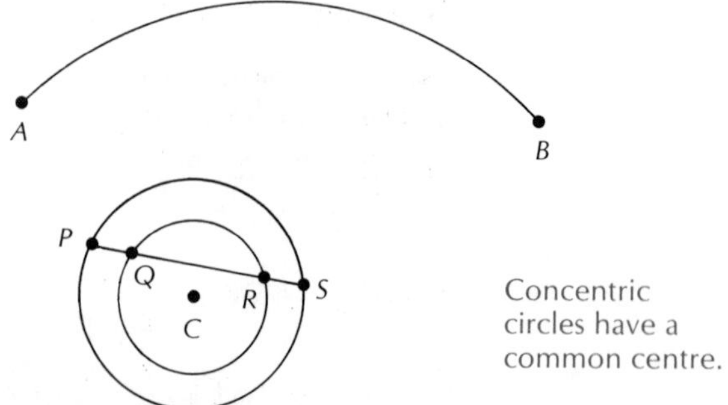

Concentric circles have a common centre.

7. **a.** Prove that if two chords are equidistant from the centre of a circle, then they are equal in length.

b. Prove that if two chords of a circle are equal in length, then they are equidistant from the centre of the circle.

8. The arch shown is an arc of a circle with radius 3 m. If the arch is 3 m wide, calculate the value of h, the highest part of the arch, correct to the nearest centimetre.

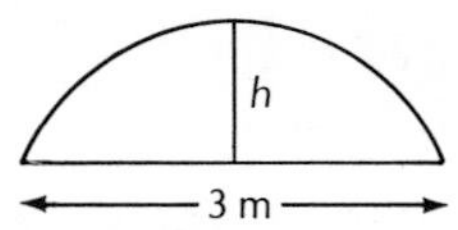

9. An arch is built in the form of a circular arc with its highest point 3 m above the horizontal chord connecting its two ends. If the length of this chord is 10 m, what is the radius of the arc, correct to the nearest centimetre?

10. A circle is defined by $x^2 + y^2 = 61$.

a. Verify algebraically that $P(5, 6)$ and $Q(6, -5)$ are on the circle.

b. Determine the equation of the perpendicular from the centre of the circle to $\overline{PQ}$.

c. Find the midpoint M of $\overline{PQ}$.

d. Show that M lies on the perpendicular from the centre of the circle to the chord $\overline{PQ}$.

11. A circle is defined by $x^2 + y^2 = 74$.

a. Show that $P(5, 7)$ is a point on the circle.

b. Find the coordinates of the endpoints of diameter $\overline{AB}$ on the x-axis.

c. Prove that $\angle APB$ is a right angle.

C 12. A cylindrical culvert 12.5 m long and 4.2 m in diameter is filled with water to a depth of 1.8 m.

a. Calculate the surface area of the water exposed to the air inside the culvert.

b. Calculate the volume of water in the culvert.

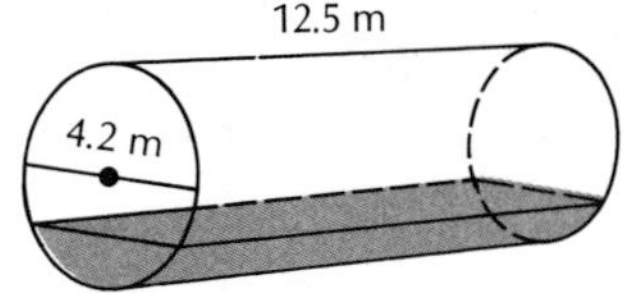

13. The first chord property given on page 218 of this lesson was proven using *deductive* geometry. The same property can be proven using coordinate geometry by writing an *analytical* proof. Follow the outline below to write an analytical proof of the first chord property for a circle with centre at the origin.

Given: A circle defined by $x^2 + y^2 = r^2$, chord $\overline{PQ}$ with endpoints $P(a, b)$ and $Q(c, d)$

Prove: The perpendicular bisector of $\overline{PQ}$ contains the centre of the circle.

To do the proof: Find the coordinates of the midpoint of $\overline{PQ}$.
Find the slope of $\overline{PQ}$.
Find the slope of the perpendicular bisector of $\overline{PQ}$.
Write an equation of the perpendicular bisector of $\overline{PQ}$ using point-slope form. Simplify the equation by first multiplying through by the LCD. Notice that $a^2 + b^2 = r^2$ and $c^2 + d^2 = r^2$, since points P and Q lie on the circle.
Verify that $C(0, 0)$ lies on the perpendicular bisector of $\overline{PQ}$.

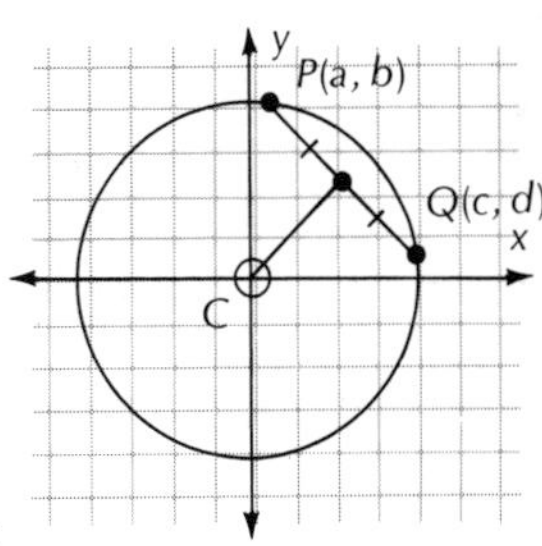

Write analytical proofs of the second and third chord properties given on page 218 of this lesson.

7-4 Angles in a Circle

The design at the right shows some inscribed angles and sector angles subtended by the same arc. Many relationships between inscribed angles and sectors exist. One such relationship is established below.

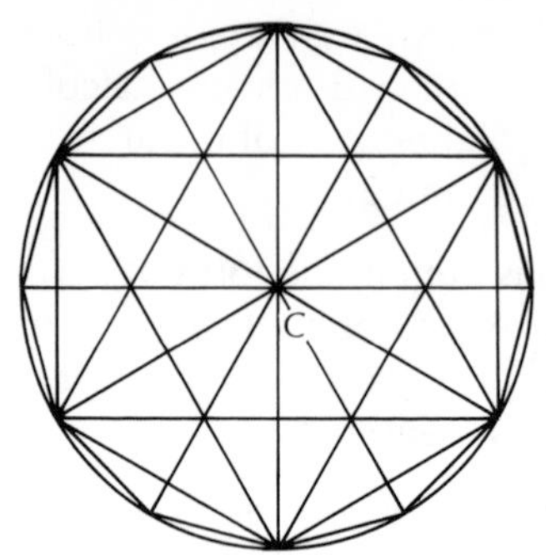

Inscribed Angle Theorem

An angle inscribed in a circle is one-half the central angle subtended by the same arc.

Given: $\angle ABD$ inscribed in a circle with centre C, sector $\angle ACD$

Prove: $\angle ABD = \frac{1}{2}\angle ACD$ (or $\angle ACD = 2\angle ABD$)

Proof: Draw diameter $\overline{BE}$.

$AC = CB$	Equal radii
$\angle CBA = \angle CAB$	Isosceles Triangle Theorem
$\angle ACE = \angle CBA + \angle CAB$	Exterior Angle Theorem
$\angle ACE = \angle CBA + \angle CBA$	Substitution
$\angle ACE = 2\angle CBA$	
Also $CB = CD$	Equal radii
$\angle CBD = \angle CDB$	ITT
$\angle ECD = \angle CDB + \angle CBD$	EAT
$\angle ECD = \angle CBD + \angle CBD$	Substitution
$\angle ECD = 2\angle CBD$	
Now $\angle ACD = \angle ACE + \angle ECD$	
$\angle ACD = 2\angle CBA + 2\angle CBD$	Substitution
$\angle ACD = 2(\angle CBA + \angle CBD)$	Distributive property
$\angle ABD = \angle CBA + \angle CBD$	
$\angle ACD = 2(\angle ABD)$	Substitution
$\angle ABD = \frac{1}{2}\angle ACD$	

Several corollaries result from the Inscribed Angle Theorem.

Corollaries

1. Inscribed angles subtended by the same arc are equal.
2. Inscribed angles subtended by a diameter are right angles.
3. Opposite angles of a cyclic quadrilateral are supplementary.
4. An exterior angle of a cyclic quadrilateral is equal to the interior angle at the opposite vertex.

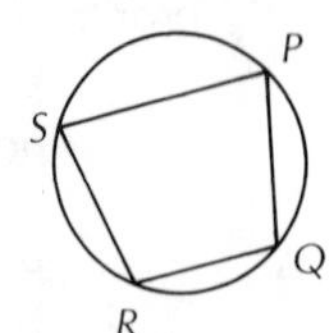

A cyclic quadrilateral is a quadrilateral having all four vertices on a circle.

EXAMPLE 1: Find the size of each indicated angle.

a.

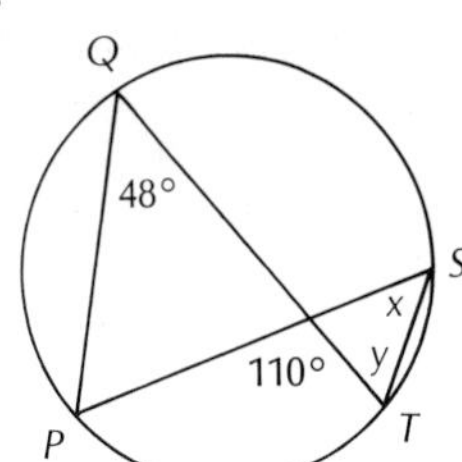

b.

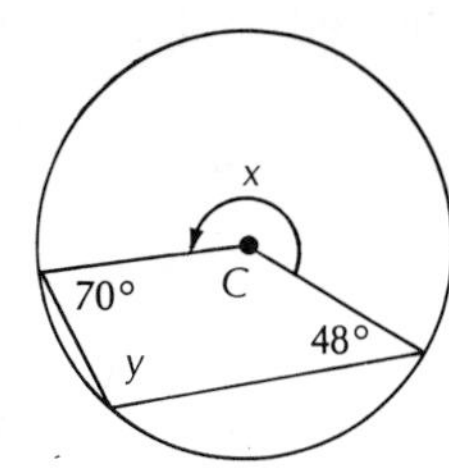

c.

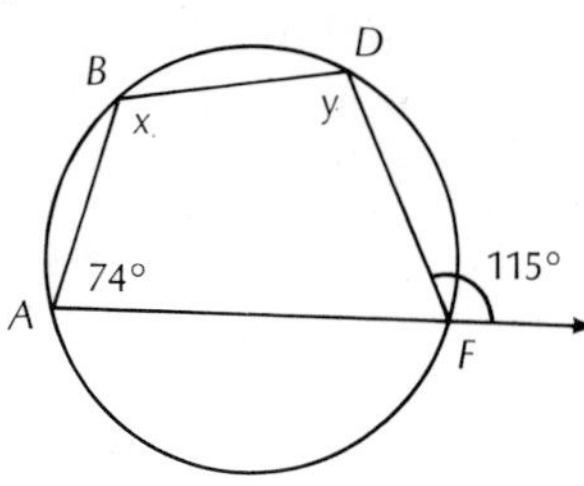

a. $x = 48°$ Inscribed angles subtended by *PT*
$x + y = 110°$ Exterior Angle Theorem
$y = 62°$ Subtraction

b. $x = 2y$ Sector angle is twice inscribed angle subtended by major arc *AD*.
$\angle ACD = 360 - 2y$ Angle sum of a complete revolution is 360°.
$70 + 360 - 2y + 48 + y = 360$ Angle sum of a quadrilateral is 360°.
$y = 118°$ Subtraction
$x = 264°$

c. $x = 115°$ Exterior angle is equal to interior angle at opposite vertex.
$y = 106°$ *y* is the supplement of 74°.

EXAMPLE 2: *PQRS* is a cyclic quadrilateral. $\overline{QP}$ and $\overline{RS}$ are extended to meet at point *T* outside the circle. Prove that the angles of $\triangle TQS$ are equal to the corresponding angles of $\triangle TRP$.

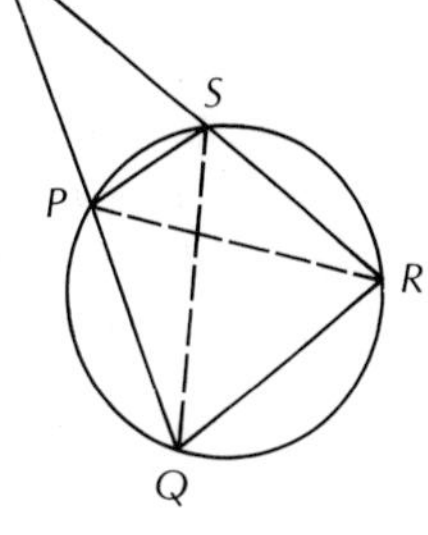

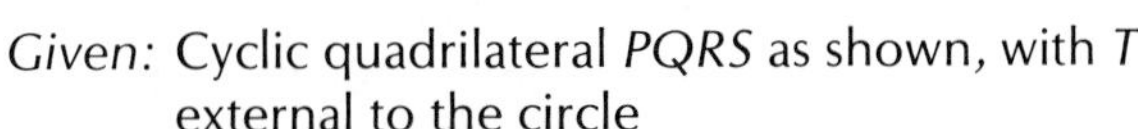

Given: Cyclic quadrilateral *PQRS* as shown, with *T* external to the circle

Prove: $\angle RPT = \angle QST$
$\angle QTS = \angle RTP$, or $\angle T = \angle T$
$\angle TQS = \angle TRP$, or $\angle PQS = \angle SRP$
That is, the angles of $\triangle TQS$ are equal to the corresponding angles of $\triangle TRP$.

Proof:

Statement	Reason
$\angle QPR + \angle RPT = 180°$	Straight angles
$\angle RSQ + \angle QST = 180°$	Straight angles
$\therefore \angle QPR + \angle RPT = \angle RSQ + \angle QST$	Substitution
$\angle QPR = \angle RSQ$	Inscribed angles subtended by arc *QR*
$\therefore \angle QPR + \angle RPT = \angle QPR + \angle QST$	Substitution
$\therefore \angle RPT = \angle QST$	Subtraction
$\angle T = \angle T$	Reflexive property
$\angle PQS = \angle SRP$	Inscribed angles subtended by arc *PS*

Therefore, the angles of $\triangle TQS$ are equal to the corresponding angles of $\triangle TRP$.

EXERCISE 7-4

A **1.** Find the size of each indicated angle. C is the centre of each circle, as indicated.

a.

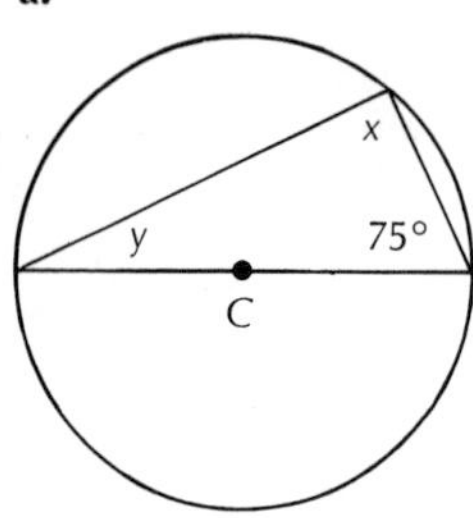

b.

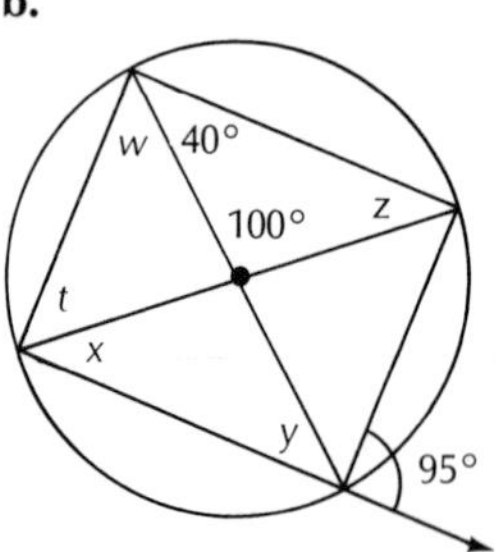

c.

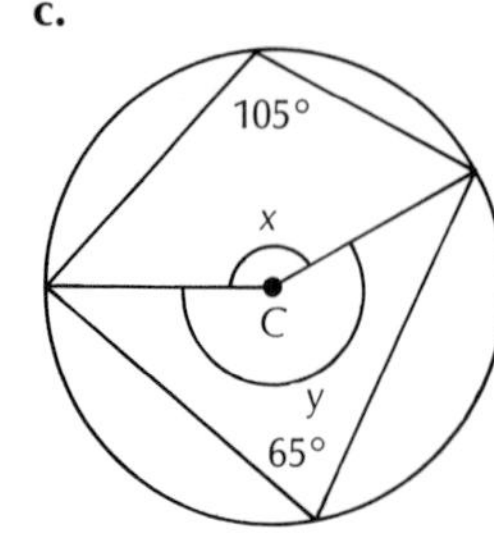

d.

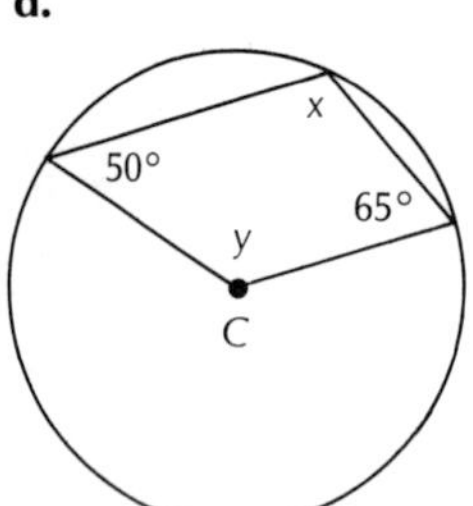

e.

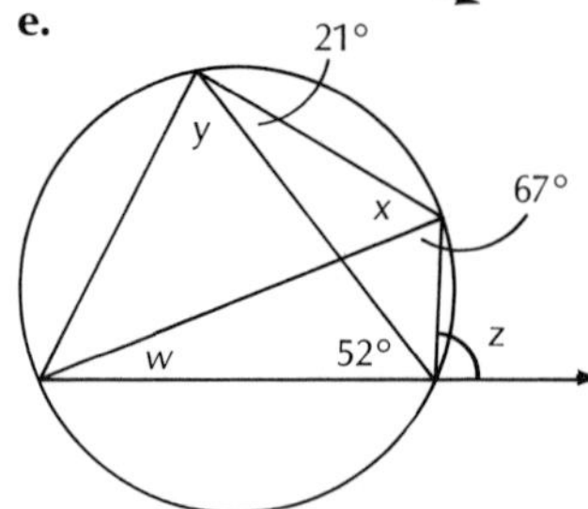

f.

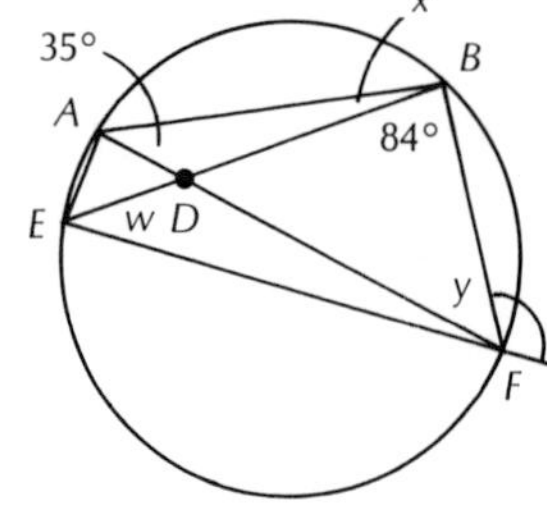

B **2.** Prove that $\triangle DEF$ and $\triangle ABD$ in exercise **1f** are isosceles triangles.

3. Prove each of the following corollaries of the Inscribed Angle Theorem.

- **a.** The inscribed angles subtended by the same arc are equal.
- **b.** An angle subtended by a diameter is a right angle.
- **c.** Opposite angles of a cyclic quadrilateral are supplementary.
- **d.** An exterior angle of a cyclic quadrilateral is equal to the interior angle at the opposite vertex.

4. Prove that equal chords of a circle with centre C subtend equal central angles.
(This result may be used in subsequent questions.)

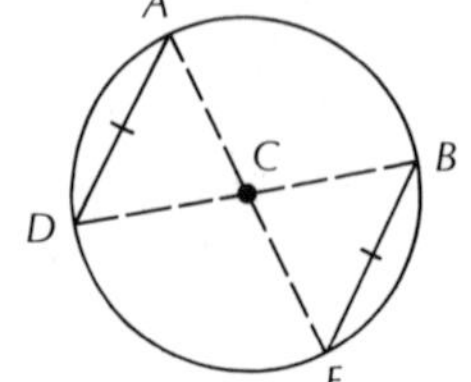

5. *PQRS* is a cyclic quadrilateral in which $PQ = RS$. Prove that $PR = QS$.

6. $\triangle PQR$ is an equilateral triangle inscribed in a circle. *S* and *T* are on minor arcs *PQ* and *PR* respectively such that $QS = RT$. Prove that $\triangle SQP$ is congruent to $\triangle TRP$.

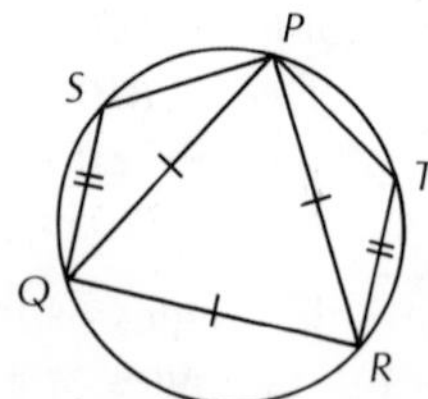

7. **a.** Prove that equal inscribed angles of a circle subtend equal chords.

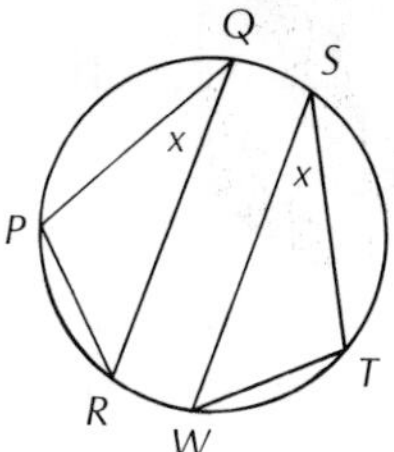

b. Prove that a trapezoid inscribed in a circle is isosceles, that is, in the diagram, $PR = QS$.

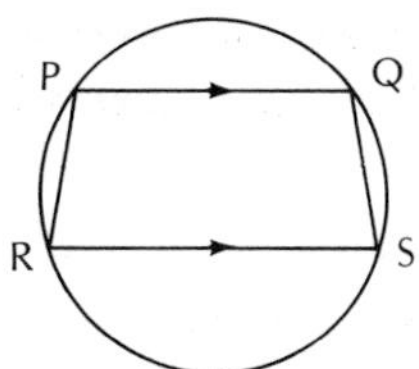

8. $\overline{AB}$ is a diameter of a circle with centre C. P is any point on the circle and E is in the interior of $\triangle PAB$ such that $\overline{AE}$ bisects $\angle PAB$, and $\overline{BE}$ bisects $\angle PBA$. Find the size of $\angle BEA$.

9. $PQRS$ is a quadrilateral inscribed in a circle with centre C, such that $\overline{SR}$ is a diameter of the circle. If the size of $\angle PCS$ is 80°, find the size of $\angle PQR$.

C 10. Two circles with different radii intersect at points X and Y. P and Q are points on one circle and B and D are points on the other circle such that $\overline{PB}$ and $\overline{QD}$ intersect at X. Prove that $\angle QYP = \angle BYD$.

11. Two circles with different radii intersect at X and Y. Points A and B are on one circle. $\overline{AX}$ intersects the other circle at Q and $\overline{BY}$ intersects it at P such that $\overline{AQ} \parallel \overline{BP}$. Prove that $\overline{AB} \parallel \overline{QP}$.

EXTRA

The Converse of the Inscribed Angle Theorem

If a line segment subtends two equal angles at points on the same side of it, then the vertices of the angles and the endpoints of the line segment are concyclic points.

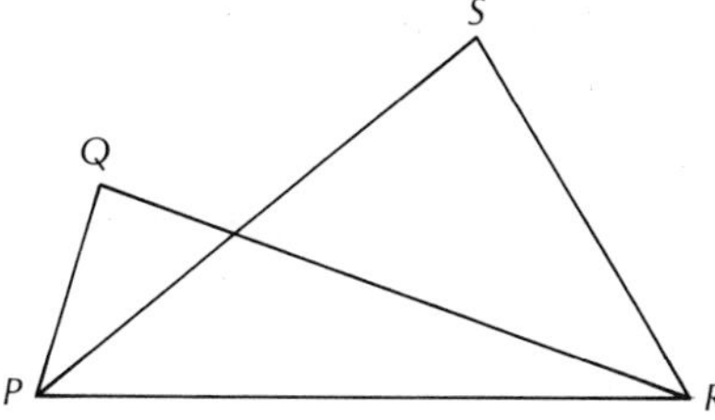

Concyclic points are points that lie on the same circle.

The proof will not be shown here.

1. Use the converse of the Inscribed Angle Theorem to prove each given deduction.
   a. The midpoint of the hypotenuse of a right-angled triangle is equidistant from the three vertices.
   b. The vertices of a rectangle are concyclic.

2. The altitudes $\overline{PL}$, $\overline{QM}$ and $\overline{RV}$ of $\triangle PQR$ meet at a point C. Prove each of the following.
   a. $\angle MQR = \angle RPL$ **b.** N, Q, L, and C are concyclic points.

7-5 Tangent Properties

A clock encased in a square frame has quarter-hour markings that are perpendicular to each side of the case. The construction is based on the following theorem.

> **Tangent Theorem for Circles**
>
> A line $\overleftrightarrow{AB}$ is a tangent to a circle with centre C if and only if $\overleftrightarrow{AB} \perp \overline{CA}$ and the line intersects the circle in only one point.

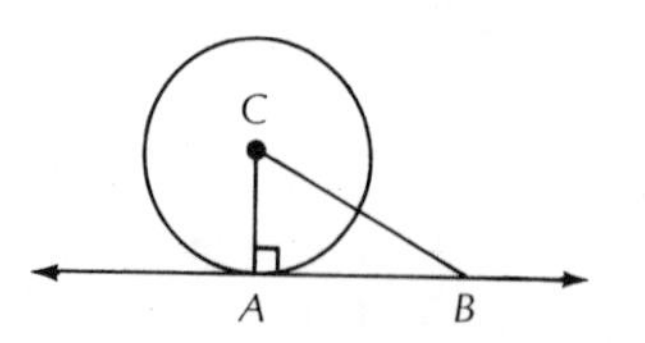

The proof of this theorem is done by methods not covered in this text.

EXAMPLE 1: A circle with centre C has radius 7 units. Find the length of the tangent segment *AB* where *A* is 25 units from the centre of the circle.

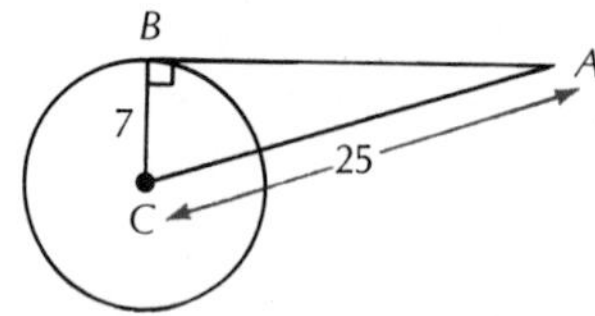

$\overline{CB} \perp \overline{AB}$	Tangent Theorem for Circles
$CB^2 + AB^2 = CA^2$	Pythagorean Theorem
$49 + AB^2 = 625$	
$AB^2 = 576$	
$AB = 24$	

Therefore, the tangent segment $\overline{AB}$ is 24 units long.

EXAMPLE 2: Prove that tangent segments from a point outside a circle are equal in length.

Given: A circle with centre C, point *P* external to the circle, and tangent segments $\overline{PA}$ and $\overline{PB}$, as shown.

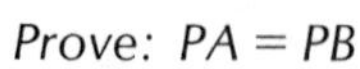

Prove: $PA = PB$

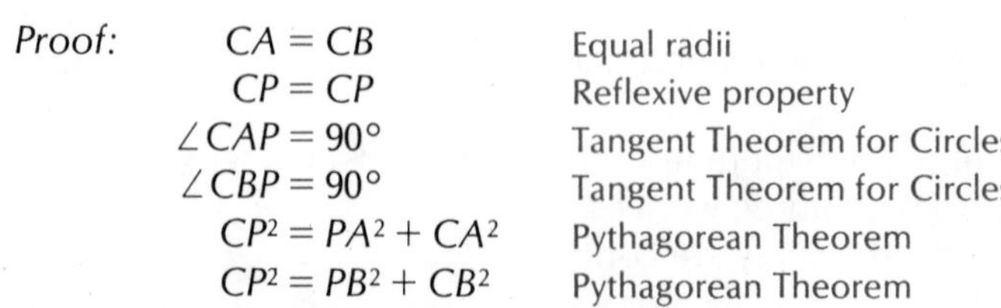

Proof:

$CA = CB$	Equal radii
$CP = CP$	Reflexive property
$\angle CAP = 90°$	Tangent Theorem for Circles
$\angle CBP = 90°$	Tangent Theorem for Circles
$CP^2 = PA^2 + CA^2$	Pythagorean Theorem
$CP^2 = PB^2 + CB^2$	Pythagorean Theorem
$PA^2 + CA^2 = PB^2 + CB^2$	Substitution
$PA^2 = PB^2$	Subtraction
$\therefore PA = PB$	Square root

Tangent Chord Theorem
The angle between a tangent and a chord of a circle is equal to the inscribed angle on the opposite side of the chord.

Given: QPR is tangent to a circle with centre C.
PB is a chord of the circle.
$\angle PAB$ is inscribed in the circle.

Prove: $\angle PAB = \angle BPR$

Proof: Let $\angle BPR = x$.

$CP \perp PR$	Tangent Theorem for Circles
$\angle CPB = 90 - x$	
But $CP = CB$	Equal radii
$\angle CBP = 90 - x$	ITT
$\angle PCB = 180 - 2(90 - x)$	Angle sum of a triangle is 180°.
$\angle PCB = 2x$	
$\angle PAB = x \quad \therefore \angle PAB = \angle BPR$	Inscribed Angle Theorem

EXAMPLE 3: Find the size of each indicated angle.

a.

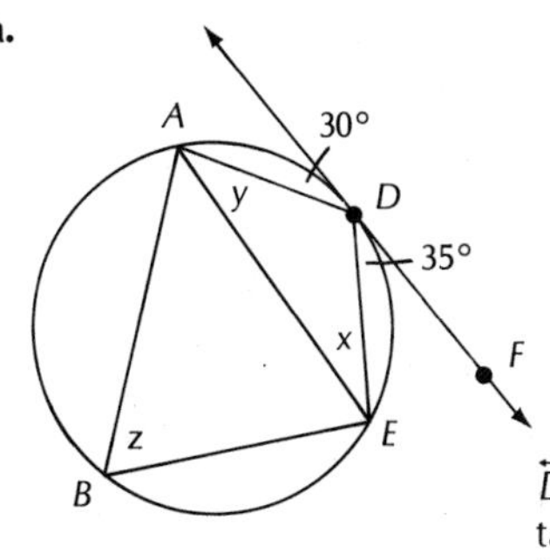

$\overleftrightarrow{DF}$ is a tangent line.

$x = 30°$ ✓	Tangent Chord Theorem
$y = 35°$ ✓	Tangent Chord Theorem
$\angle ADE = 180 - (30 + 35)$	Straight angle
$\therefore \angle ADE = 115°$	
$z = 180 - 115$	Inscribed Angle Theorem
$\therefore z = 65°$ ✓	

b.

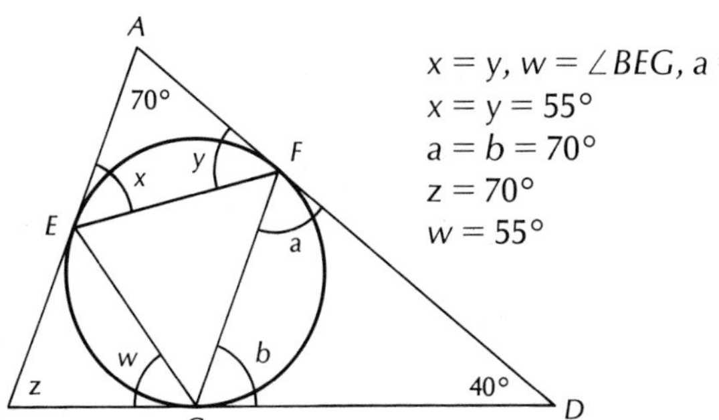

$AE = AF,\ BG = BE,\ DF = DG$ — Tangent segments from a point outside a circle are

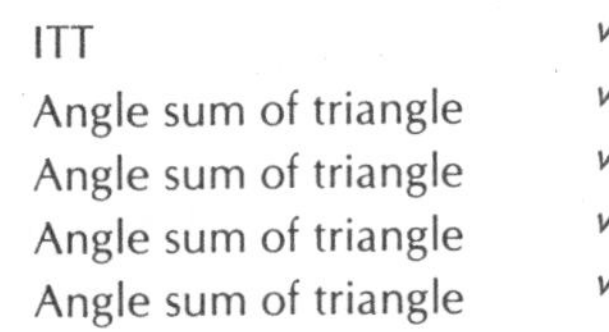

$x = y,\ w = \angle BEG,\ a = b$	ITT ✓
$x = y = 55°$	Angle sum of triangle ✓
$a = b = 70°$	Angle sum of triangle ✓
$z = 70°$	Angle sum of triangle ✓
$w = 55°$	Angle sum of triangle ✓

EXERCISE 7-5

A 1. Find the measure of each indicated segment. C is the centre of each circle.

a.

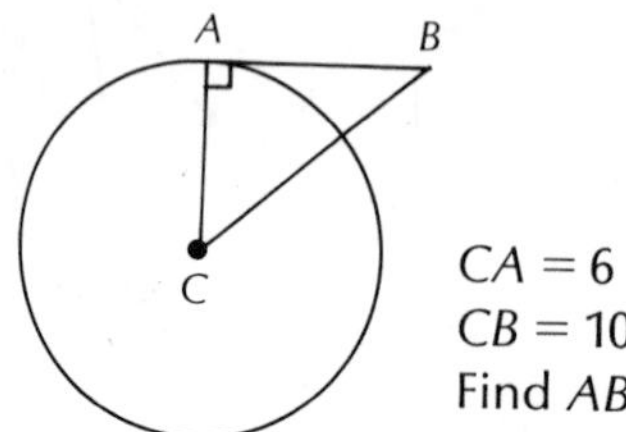

$CA = 6$
$CB = 10$
Find AB.

b.

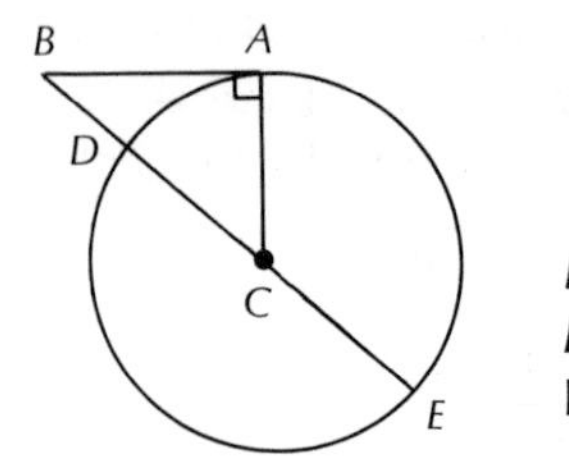

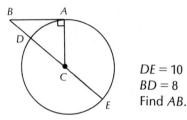

$DE = 10$
$BD = 8$
Find AB.

c.

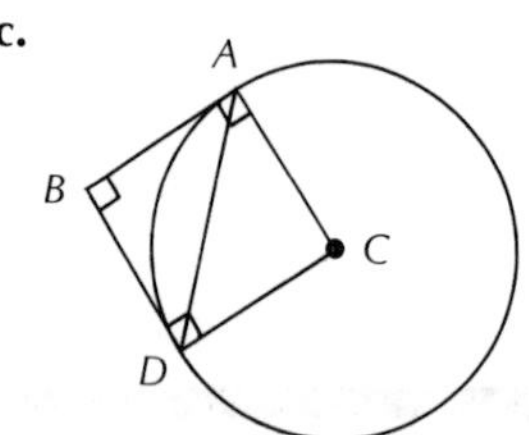

$AC = 6$
Find BA.
Find AD.

d.

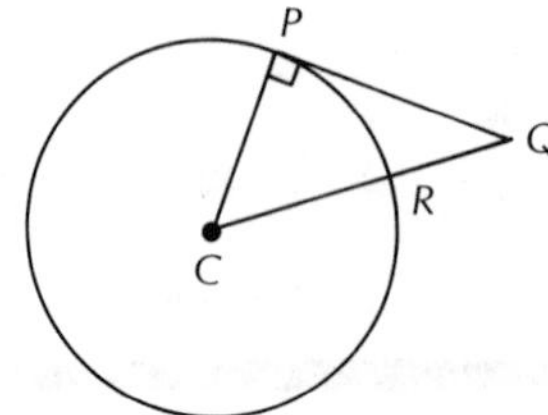

$PQ = 24$
$CP = 18$
Find RQ.

2. Find the size of each indicated angle.

a.

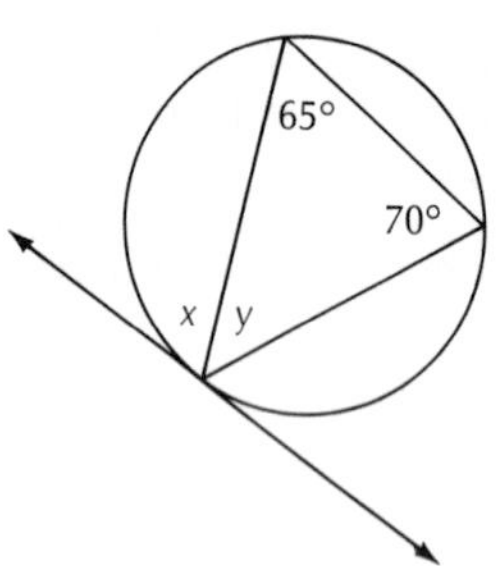

b.

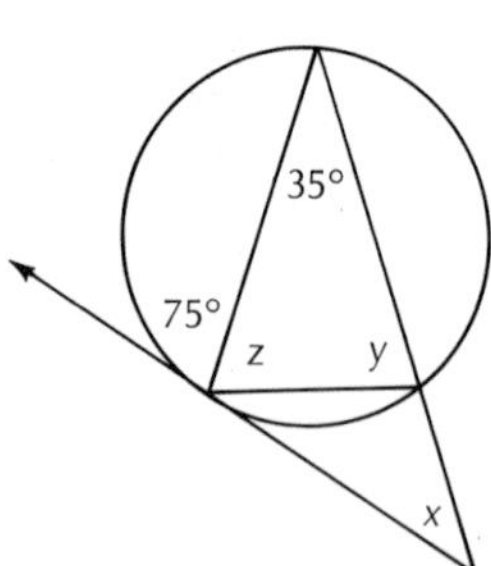

c.

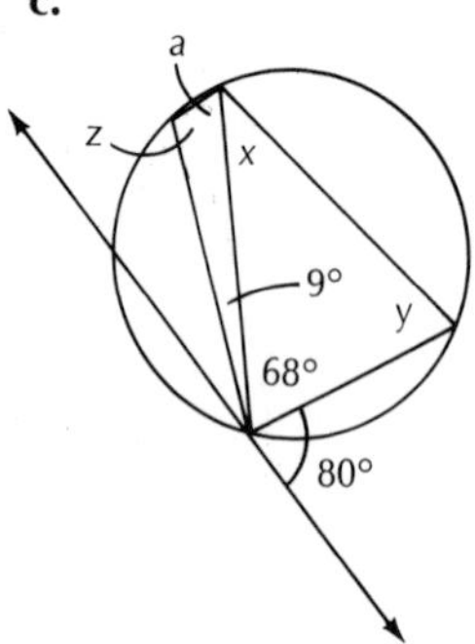

B 3. $\overline{PA}$ and $\overline{PB}$ are tangent segments drawn to a circle with centre C from point P lying outside the circle. Prove that $\angle ACP = \angle BCP$ and $\angle APC = \angle BPC$.

4. $\triangle XYZ$ is inscribed in a circle. If $XZ = YZ$, prove that $\overline{ZY}$ bisects the angle between the tangent to the circle at Y and $\overline{XY}$.

5. $PQRS$ is a cyclic quadrilateral in which $\overline{PQ} \parallel \overline{RS}$. A tangent is drawn as S so that the smaller angle between $\overline{RS}$ and the tangent is 55°. If $\angle QPR = 38°$, find the size of each given angle.

a. $\angle PRS$ **b.** $\angle SPR$ **c.** $\angle PQR$ **d.** $\angle QSR$

6. $\triangle PQR$ is inscribed in a circle. A tangent to the circle at P is drawn parallel to $\overline{QR}$. Prove that $\triangle PQR$ is isosceles.

7. Quadrilateral $QABD$ is inscribed in a circle with centre C as shown. Diagonal $\overline{AD}$ is parallel to $\overline{PQR}$. $\overline{PR}$ is tangent to the circle at Q. Prove that $\angle ABD = 2\angle PQA$.

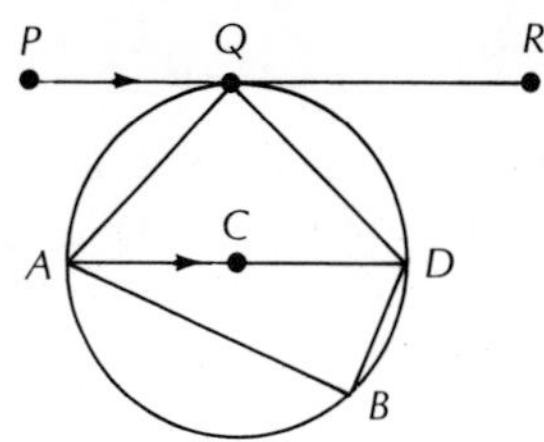

8. Two circles intersect at points D and F as shown. $\overline{AB}$ is tangent to the smaller circle at B. $\overline{BD}$ and $\overline{BF}$ are extended to meet the larger circle at E and G, respectively. Prove that $\overline{AB} \parallel \overline{EG}$.

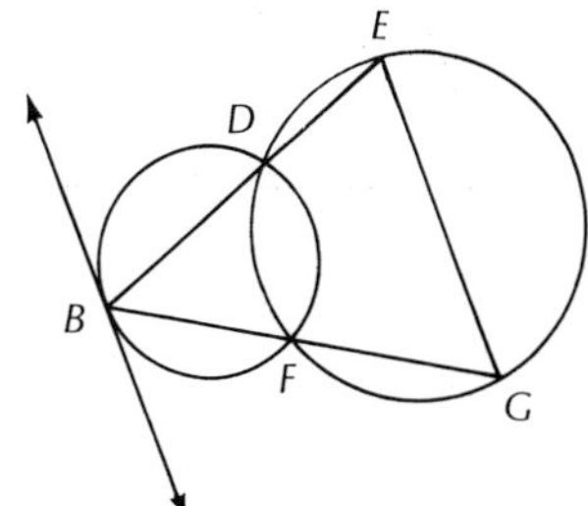

9. $\triangle ABD$ is a triangle inscribed in a circle. If $\angle A = 60°$ and $\angle B = 75°$, find the size of the three angles of the triangle formed by drawing tangents to the circle at A, B, and D.

C 10. $\triangle ABD$ is formed by the intersection of three tangents to a circle with centre C, as shown in the diagram at the right. Two of the tangents, $\overline{AM}$ and $\overline{AN}$, are in a fixed position, while $\overline{BD}$ touches the circumference at a variable point P. Show that the perimeter of $\triangle ABD$ is constant and that it is equal to $2AN$.

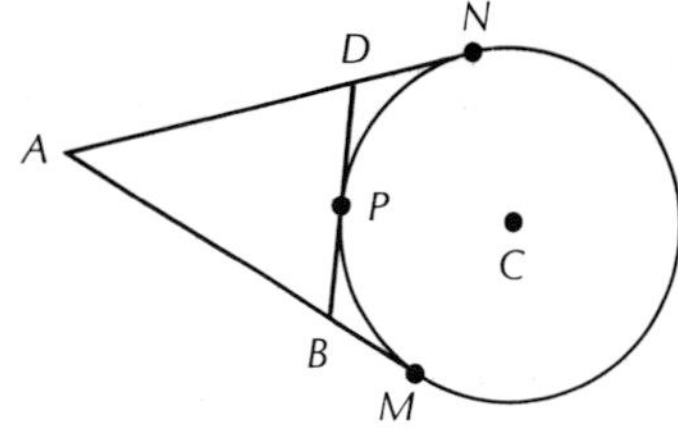

11. Prove that the diameter of a circle inscribed in a right triangle is equal to the sum of its legs minus the hypotenuse.

12. Two circles with centres C and T, are tangent externally at A. $\overline{PQ}$ is a common external tangent touching the circle with centre C at P and the circle with centre T at Q. A line through A intersects the circle with centre C again at R and the circle with centre T again at S. $\overline{RP}$ and $\overline{SQ}$, when produced, meet at X. Prove that $\angle RXS = 90°$.

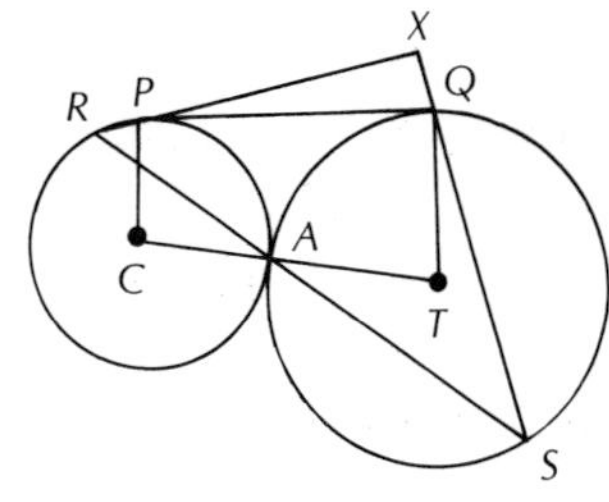

EXTRA

Spheres

A sphere has a radius of 26 units. How far from the centre of the sphere must a plane pass so that the circle formed has a radius of 24 units?

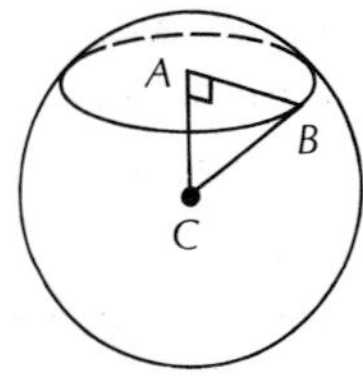

Grazing Goats

A goat is tied to a piece of rope 40 m long. The rope is fastened to a hook that is 10 m from the corner of the longest side of a rectangular barn. The dimensions of the barn are 50 m by 25 m. Over how much ground can the goat graze?

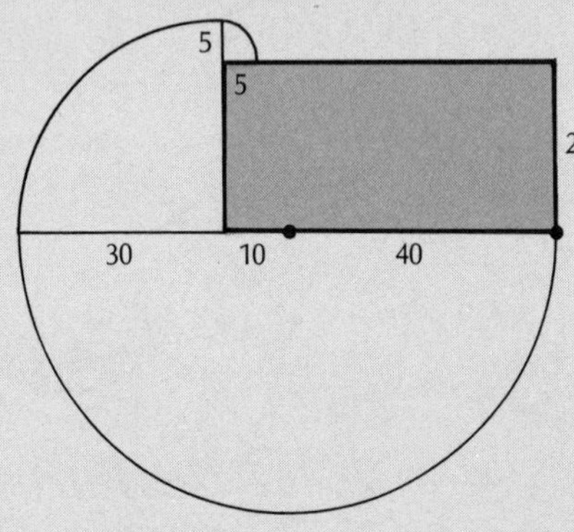

The goat can graze over three areas as described below.

a semi-circle with radius 40 m

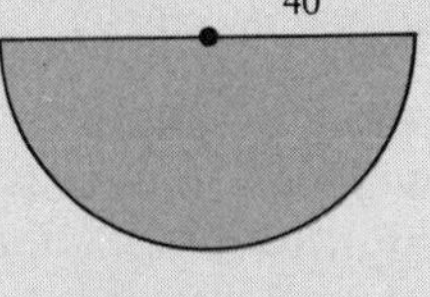

a quarter circle with radius 30 m

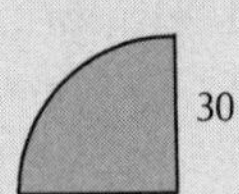

a quarter circle with radius 5 m

5

Sum the measures of the individual areas to determine the total grazing area.

$$\text{Total grazing area} = \frac{1}{2}\pi(40)^2 + \frac{1}{4}\pi(30)^2 + \frac{1}{4}\pi(5)^2$$
$$= 800\pi + 225\pi + \frac{25}{4}\pi$$
$$= 1031.25\pi$$

Therefore, the goat can graze over 1031.25π m^2.

---

1. Suppose that a goat is tied 10 m from the corner of the shorter side of the barn as described above. Does the goat have more or less grazing area than given above? By what amount do the areas differ?
2. If the hook is attached to one of the corners of the barn, would the amount of grazing area change? Describe.

Review

1. Write an equation of the circle with centre at the origin, having the given radius.
   a. 6
   b. $2\sqrt{3}$
   c. $\frac{1}{2}$

2. Find an equation of the circle with centre at the origin, having the given property.
   a. the circle passes through the point $P(7, -3)$.
   b. the circle is tangent to the line defined by $y = -8$.

3. A circle has radius 5. Find the length of the arc that subtends a sector angle of 80°.

4. Find the area of the sector bounded by the arc in question 3.

5. A circle with radius 10 has a chord 16 units long. How far is the chord from the centre of the circle?

6. A circle has a radius of 25 cm. A chord $\overline{AB}$ is 48 cm long and a chord $\overline{EF}$ is 14 cm long.
   a. Which chord is closer to the centre of the circle?
   b. How much closer is the chord identified in part **a** to the centre?

7. The equation of a circle is $x^2 + y^2 = 25$.
   a. Show that $P(-3, 4)$ and $Q(-4, -3)$ are points on the circle.
   b. Prove that the line through the centre of the circle and the midpoint of $\overline{PQ}$ is perpendicular to $\overline{PQ}$.

8. Determine the size of each indicated angle.

a.

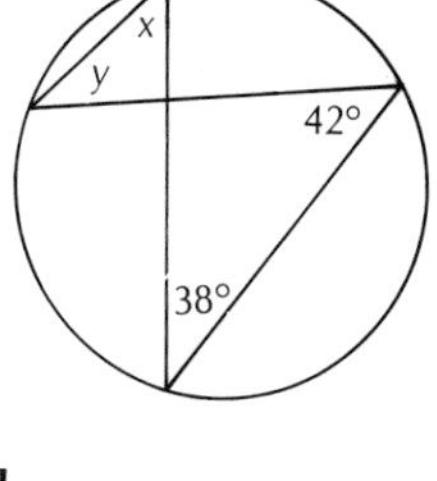

b.

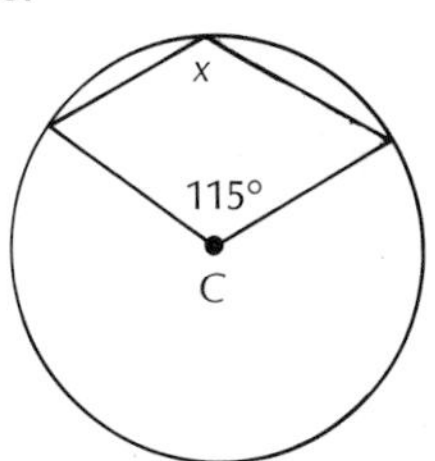

c.

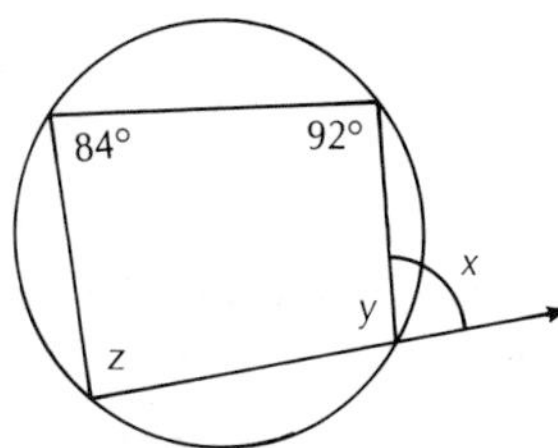

d.

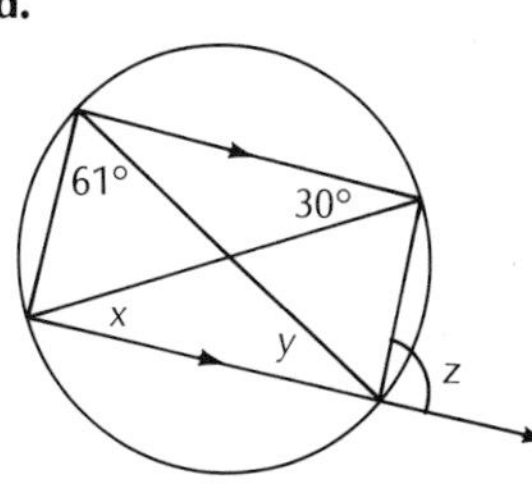

e.

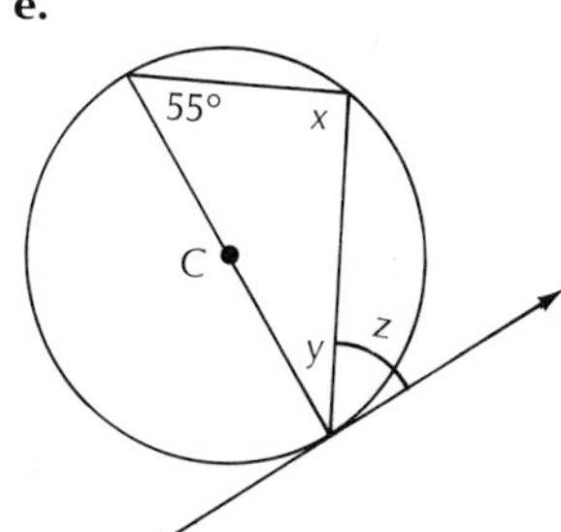

f.

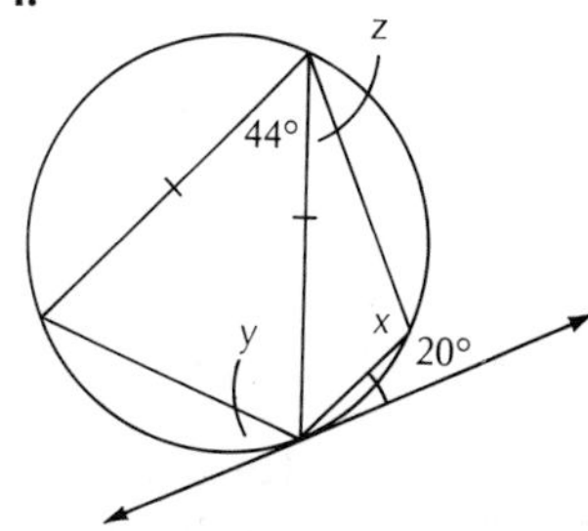

7-6 Equation of a Circle With Centre (h, k) and Radius r

In lesson 7.1, the equation of a circle with centre at the origin and radius r was developed using the distance formula. That is, $x^2 + y^2 = r^2$.
The equation of a circle with *any* point as the centre can be found using the distance formula.

EXAMPLE 1: Find an equation of the circle with centre $C(2, -3)$ and radius 5.

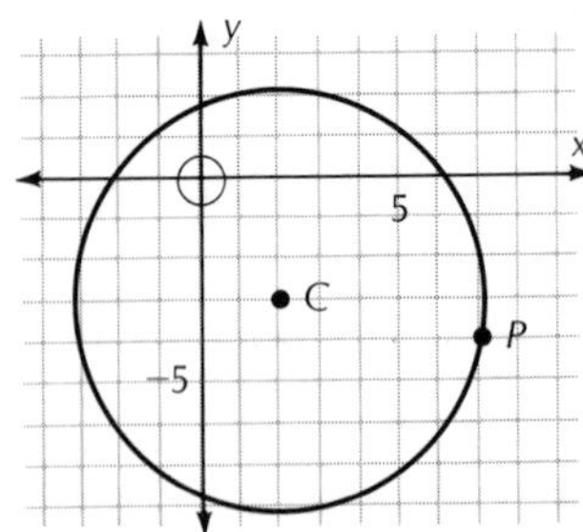

Let $P(x, y)$ be any point on the circle. The distance between $P(x, y)$ and $C(2, -3)$ is 5.
Apply the distance formula to the points $P(x, y)$ and $C(2, -3)$.

$$\sqrt{[x - 2]^2 + [y - (-3)]^2} = 5$$

$$x^2 - 4x + 4 + y^2 + 6y + 9 = 25 \qquad \text{Square both sides.}$$

$$x^2 + y^2 - 4x + 6y - 12 = 0$$

Therefore, the equation of the circle with centre $C(2, -3)$ and radius 5 is:

$$x^2 + y^2 - 4x + 6y - 12 = 0.$$

This equation is written in *expanded* form.

In general, let $C(h, k)$ be the centre of a circle with radius r and let $P(x, y)$ be any point on the circle. Applying the distance formula results in the following.

$$P_1P_2 = \sqrt{(x_2 - x_1)^2 + (y_2 - y_1)^2}$$

Substitute given values into the distance formula.

$$CP = \sqrt{(x - h)^2 + (y - k)^2}$$

$CP = r$

$$r = \sqrt{(x - h)^2 + (y - k)^2}$$

Square both sides.

$$.017r^2 = (x - h)^2 + (y - k)^2$$

> The **standard form** of the equation of a circle with centre $C(h, k)$ and radius r is $(x - h)^2 + (y - k)^2 = r^2$.

EXAMPLE 2: Write an equation of the circle with centre $C(6, 8)$ and radius 3.
Leave the equation in expanded form.

Substitute into the formula $(x - h)^2 + (y - k)^2 = r^2$.

$$(x - 6)^2 + (y - 8)^2 = 3^2$$

$$x^2 - 12x + 36 + y^2 - 16y + 64 = 9 \qquad \text{This is in standard form.}$$

Therefore, the expanded form of the equation of the circle with centre $C(6, 8)$ and radius 3 is: $x^2 + y^2 - 12x - 16y + 91 = 0$.

EXAMPLE 3: Find the centre and radius of the circle defined by $(x + 4)^2 + (y - 7)^2 = 100$.

Compare the given equation with the standard form of a circle, $(x - h)^2 + (y - k)^2 = r^2$.

$r^2 = 100$, so the radius r is 10.

The centre $C(h, k)$ is $C(-4, 7)$.

If the equation of a circle is given in exanded form, the method of completing the square can be used to find the centre and radius of the circle the equation defines.

EXAMPLE 4: Find the centre and radius of the circle defined by $x^2 + y^2 + 10x - 24y + 133 = 0$.

Rearrange the terms of the equation, grouping the x-terms together and the y-terms together. Then complete the square for each grouping.

$$(x^2 + 10x + \blacksquare) + (y^2 - 24y + \blacksquare) = -133$$
$$(x^2 + 10x + 25) + (y^2 - 24y + 144) = -133 + 25 + 144$$
$$(x + 5)^2 + (y - 12)^2 = 36$$

Compare the last equation with $(x - h)^2 + (y - k)^2 = r^2$. The centre of the circle is $C(-5, 12)$ and the radius is 6.

EXERCISE 7-6

A 1. For the circle defined by each given equation, state the centre and the radius.

a. $x^2 + (y - 3)^2 = 100$
b. $(x + 7)^2 + y^2 = 16$
c. $(x - 7)^2 + (y - 2)^2 = 25$
d. $(x + 1)^2 + (y - 1)^2 = 49$
e. $(x + 6)^2 + (y + 3)^2 = 64$
f. $(x - 9)^2 + (y + 4)^2 = 36$
g. $(x + 2)^2 + (y + 3)^2 = 8$
h. $(x - 5)^2 + (y + 7)^2 = 48$

2. Graph each circle defined in exercise 1.

3. State, in standard form, an equation of the circle having the given centre and radius.

a. $r = 5$, $C(5, 9)$
b. $r = 7$, $C(-3, 4)$
c. $r = 3$, $C(-4, -4)$
d. $r = 10$, $C(0, 6)$
e. $r = 2$, $C(-2, 0)$
f. $r = 13$, $C(6, -1)$
g. $r = \sqrt{7}$, $C(6, -7)$
h. $r = 3\sqrt{5}$, $C(2, -9)$
i. $r = 6\sqrt{3}$, $C(0, -4)$

B **4.** Write an equation of each circle in expanded form.

a. The circle has centre $(6, -4)$ and is tangent to $y = -2$.

b. The circle has centre $(-4, -6)$ and is tangent to $x = 2$.

c. The circle is tangent to $x = 3$ and $x = -5$ and has centre on $y = 2$.

d. The circle has centre on $x = 3$ and is tangent to both $y = 7$ and $y = -3$.

e. The circle is tangent to both axes and to $y = 10$. (There are two answers.)

f. The circle is tangent to both axes and to $x = 18$. (There are two answers.)

5. **a.** Two points on the circle defined by $(x - 3)^2 + (y + 4)^2 = 25$ have x-coordinate 7. Write the coordinates of both points.

b. Two points on the circle given in part (a) have y-coordinate -8. Find the x-coordinates of the points.

6. Find an equation of the circle having the given points as the endpoints of a diameter.

a. $A(6, -7), B(8, -5)$ **b.** $P(-11, 7), Q(-3, 5)$ **c.** $R(6, -9), S(0, 0)$

d. $H(-4, 9), M(8, 6)$ **e.** $J(-7, 8), L(-4, 11)$ **f.** $D(2, 0), E(-5, 3)$

7. A circle is defined by $x^2 + y^2 - 12x + ky - 55 = 0$. If $P(14, 3)$ is a point on the circle, find the value of k.

8. For the circle defined by each given equation, find the x- and y- intercepts.

a. $(x - 6)^2 + (y + 3)^2 = 25$ **b.** $(x + 4)^2 + (y + 3)^2 = 81$

c. $(x - 5)^2 + (y - 6)^2 = 36$ **d.** $4(x + 3)^2 + 4(y - 6)^2 = 9$

9. Write an equation of each circle described below.

a. centre $C(8, -9)$ and passing through $P(7, -2)$

b. centre $C(-4, -5)$ and passing through $P(8, 3)$

c. centre $C(-2, 6)$ and passing through $P(5, -8)$

10. The centre of a circle lies on the x-axis and is 5 units from the origin. If the circle passes through the point $P(2, 3)$, find an equation of the circle. (There are two solutions.)

11. Write an equation of the circle with centre $(3, 3)$ passing through the intersection of the lines defined by $2x + 3y = -1$ and $3x - 4y = 24$.

12. The centre of a circle is the intersection of the lines defined by $7x + y = 41$ and $3x - 2y = 3$. The circle passes through $P(-9, -2)$. Write an equation of the circle.

13. The centre of a circle lies on both the y-axis and on the line defined by $x - 6y = 18$. The circle passes through the origin. Determine an equation of the circle.

14. Find the centre and radius of the circle defined by each equation.
 a. $x^2 + y^2 - 2x + 4y - 11 = 0$ b. $x^2 + y^2 + 8x + 6y = 0$
 c. $x^2 + y^2 - 14x + 6y + 49 = 0$ d. $x^2 + y^2 - 14x - 51 = 0$
 e. $x^2 + y^2 + 24y + 80 = 0$ f. $4x^2 + 4y^2 + 4x - 32y + 49 = 0$

15. Find an equation of the circle with centre on the y-axis and passing through the points $A(3, 7)$ and $B(-4, 6)$.

16. A circle with radius $2\sqrt{10}$ passes through $E(-6, 2)$. Find an equation of the circle, given that its centre lies on the y-axis.

C 17. a. Graph the four circles defined by $(x \pm 4)^2 + (y \pm 4)^2 = 16$.
 b. Determine an equation of the circle that contains all four circles in part (a) and is tangent to each of them.

18. Write an equation of a circle with centre on the line defined by $2x - y = 10$ and passing through the points $A(1, 3)$ and $B(5, -3)$.

19. Three points on a circle are $D(4, 8)$, $E(12, -6)$, and $F(-2, -4)$.
 a. Determine the equation of the perpendicular bisector of $\overline{DE}$.
 b. Find the equation of the perpendicular bisector of $\overline{DF}$.
 c. Find the coordinates of the centre of the circle by finding the intersection of the two lines in parts (a) and (b).
 d. Find the radius of the circle.
 e. Write an equation of the circle.

20. Follow the procedure given in exercise 19 to determine an equation of the circle that passes through $P(3, 8)$, $Q(-5, 6)$, and $R(11, -4)$.

EXTRA

Transforming Circles

What mapping translates $x^2 + y^2 = 36$ onto $(x - 2)^2 + (y - 3)^2 = 36$?

$x^2 + y^2 = 36$ has centre (0, 0) and radius 6.
$(x - 2)^2 + (y - 3)^2 = 36$ has centre (2, 3) and radius 6.
So (0, 0) maps onto (2, 3).
The mapping is the translation $(x, y) \longrightarrow (x + 2, y + 3)$.
(Note that the signs in the mapping are opposite to those in the equation.)

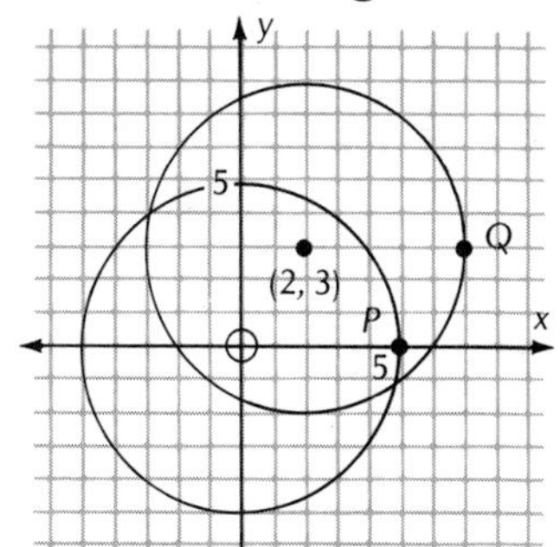

1. Point $P(6, 0)$ is mapped onto point Q. What are the coordinates of Q?
2. State the mapping that translates $x^2 + y^2 = 25$ onto $(x + 3)^2 + y^2 = 25$.
3. State the mapping that translates $x^2 + y^2 = 49$ onto $(x - 5)^2 + (y - 6)^2 = 49$.
4. Find an equation of the image of $x^2 + y^2 = 16$ under the given translation.
 a. $(x, y) \longrightarrow (x - 5, y)$ b. $(x, y) \longrightarrow (x, y + 7)$ c. $(x, y) \longrightarrow (x - 8, y + 6)$
5. Graph each pair of circles given in question 3.

7-7 Points of Intersection of Lines and Circles

The intersection of a line and a circle can result in three different situations.

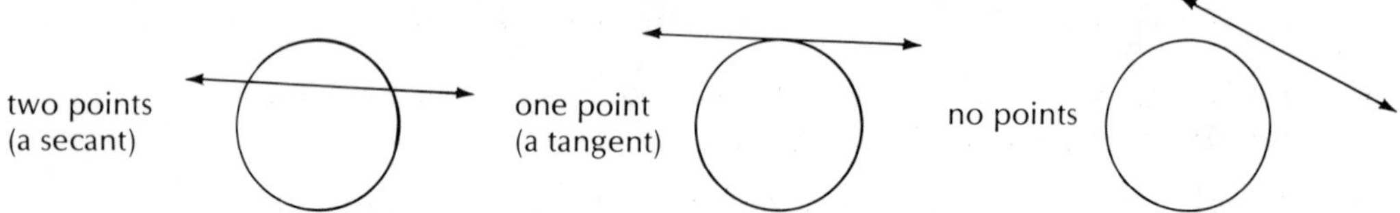

Given the equation of a line and a circle, such a system of two equations can be solved to determine whether the given line is a secant of the circle, tangent to the circle, or neither. If the system of equations has two solutions, the line is a secant. If the system has one solution, the line is a tangent. A system with no solutions implies that the line and circle do not intersect.

EXAMPLE 1: Determine the relationship between the line defined by $2x - y = 5$ and the circle defined by $x^2 + y^2 = 5$.

Find the intersection of $2x - y = 5$ and $x^2 + y^2 = 5$.

$$y = 2x - 5$$ Solve for y in $2x - y = 5$.

$$x^2 + (2x - 5)^2 = 5$$ Substitute y into $x^2 + y^2 = 5$.

$$x^2 + 4x^2 - 20x + 25 = 5$$ Simplify the equation.

$$5x^2 - 20x + 20 = 0$$

$$x^2 - 4x + 4 = 0$$

$$(x - 2)^2 = 0$$

$$x = 2$$

Substitute into $2x - y = 5$ to solve for y.
$\therefore y = -1$

Therefore, the one point of intersection $(2, -1)$ indicates that $2x - y = 5$ is tangent to $x^2 + y^2 = 5$.

EXAMPLE 2: Find the intersection of $x^2 + y^2 - 2x - 8y - 8 = 0$ and $2x + y - 16 = 0$.

$$y = -2x + 16$$ Solve for y in $2x + y - 16 = 0$

$$x^2 + (-2x + 16)^2 - 2x - 8(-2x + 16) - 8 = 0$$ Substitute y into the equation of the circle and simplify.

$$x^2 + 4x^2 - 64x + 256 - 2x + 16x - 128 - 8 = 0$$

$$5x^2 - 50x + 120 = 0$$

$$x^2 - 10x + 24 = 0$$

$$(x - 6)(x - 4) = 0$$

$\therefore x = 6$ or $x = 4$ Substitute into the linear equation.

If $x = 6$, then $y = 4$. If $x = 4$, then $y = 8$.
Therefore, the line is a secant of the circle and there are two intersection points: $(6, 4)$ and $(4, 8)$.

EXAMPLE 3: Determine the number of intersection points of $x + 2y = 20$ with $x^2 + y^2 = 45$.

$$x = 20 - 2y \quad \text{Solve for } x \text{ in } x + 2y = 20.$$
$$(20 - 2y)^2 + y^2 = 45 \quad \text{Substitute for } x \text{ in } x^2 + y^2 = 45.$$
$$400 - 80y + 4y^2 + y^2 = 45$$
$$5y^2 - 80y + 355 = 0$$
$$y^2 - 16y + 71 = 0$$

The discriminant $b^2 - 4ac$ is $256 - 4(1)(71)$ or -28. Since the discriminant is negative, there are no real solutions. Therefore, the circle and the line do not intersect.

In determining the number of intersection points of a given line with a given circle, the value of the discriminant should be calculated.

EXERCISE 7-7

B **1.** Find the number of intersection points of the given line with the given circle.

a. $2x + 3y = 13$, $x^2 + y^2 = 13$ **b.** $5x + y = 20$, $x^2 + y^2 = 26$
c. $7x - 6y = 85$, $x^2 + y^2 = 85$ **d.** $2x - y = 5$, $x^2 + y^2 = 5$
e. $3x - y = 5$, $x^2 + y^2 = 10$ **f.** $4x + y = 20$, $x^2 + y^2 = 68$

2. **a.** Determine whether the line $x + 2y + 5 = 0$ is a secant, or a tangent to the circle $x^2 + y^2 = 25$. Find the intersection point(s).
b. Graph the equations in part **a**.

3. **a.** Show algebraically that $3x + 5y = 40$ does not intersect $x^2 + y^2 = 34$.
b. Verify, by graphing, that the line and circle given in part **a** do not intersect.

4. The equation $3x + y + 10 = 0$ defines a secant to the circle $x^2 + y^2 = 20$ and, hence, defines a chord $\overline{AB}$. Find the coordinates of A and B and the length of $\overline{AB}$.

5. Show that the y-axis is tangent to the circle defined by $x^2 + y^2 - 8x = 0$.

6. Prove that $3x - 4y = 67$ is tangent to the circle defined by $x^2 + y^2 - 6x + 4y - 87 = 0$. Find the coordinates of the point of contact.

7. $A(7, 1)$ is one endpoint of chord $\overline{AB}$ in the circle defined by $x^2 + y^2 - 8x + 6y = 0$. If the chord has a slope of -1, find the coordinates of B.

8. Find the intersection points of the line defined by $7x + 3y = 53$ with the circle defined by $x^2 + y^2 - 6x - 2y - 19 = 0$.

7-8 Equation of a Tangent to a Circle

Given a point on a circle, the Tangent Theorem for Circles can be used to find an equation of a tangent to a circle.

EXAMPLE 1: $P(-4, 2)$ is a point on the circle defined by $x^2 + y^2 = 20$. Find an equation of the line tangent to the circle at P.

The centre of the circle defined by $x^2 + y^2 = 20$ is $C(0, 0)$.
The tangent is perpendicular to the radius $\overline{CP}$ at $P(-4, 2)$.

The slope of $\overline{CP}$ is $\frac{2-0}{-4-0}$ or $-\frac{1}{2}$.

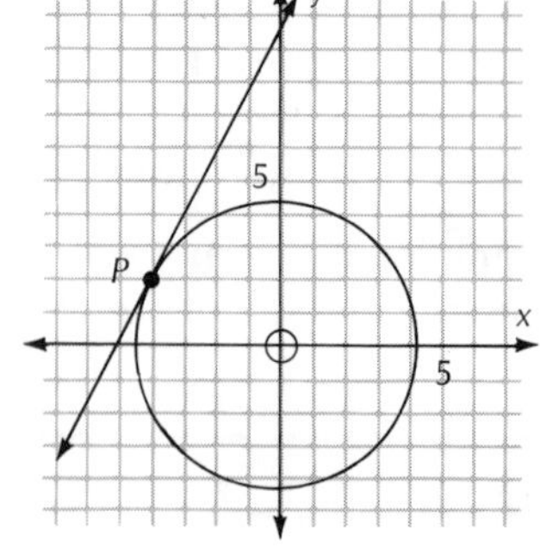

Therefore, the slope of the tangent is 2.
Use the point-slope form of a linear equation to find an equation of the tangent.

$$y - y_1 = m(x - x_1)$$
$$y - 2 = 2[x - (-4)]$$
$$y - 2 = 2x + 8$$
$$2x - y + 10 = 0$$

Write the equation in standard form, $Ax + By + C = 0$.

Therefore, $2x - y + 10 = 0$ is an equation of the tangent to $x^2 + y^2 = 20$ at $P(-4, 2)$.

EXAMPLE 2: Find equations of the tangents from $P(0, 4)$ to the circle defined by $x^2 + y^2 = 8$.

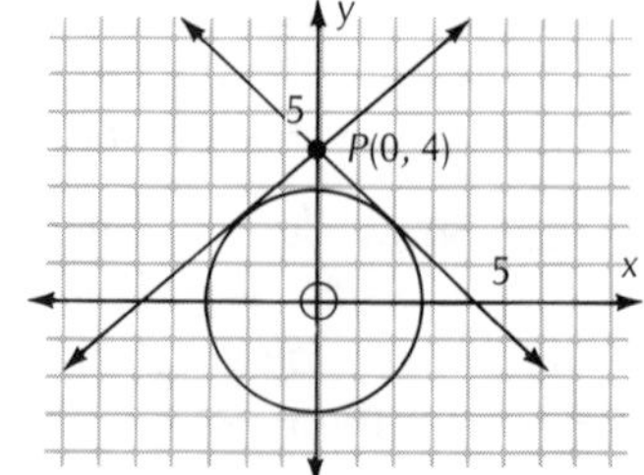

Since $P(0, 4)$ lies outside the circle, a method other than the one used in Example 1 is needed.

Use the point-slope form to write an equation of the tangent.

$$y - 4 = m(x - 0)$$
$$y = mx + 4$$

Now substitute the value of y into $x^2 + y^2 = 8$ and simplify.

Write the equation in standard form. In order for the equation to define a tangent, the discriminant must be zero.

$$x^2 + (mx + 4)^2 = 8$$
$$x^2 + m^2x^2 + 8mx + 8 = 0$$
$$(1 + m^2)x^2 + 8mx + 8 = 0$$

Solve for m.

$$(8m)^2 - 4(1 + m^2)(8) = 0$$

Set the discriminant equal to zero.

$$64m^2 - 32m^2 - 32 = 0$$
$$m^2 - 1 = 0$$
$$m = \pm 1$$

Therefore, when $m = 1$, an equation of the tangent is $y = x + 4$.
When $m = -1$, an equation of the tangent is $y = -x + 4$.

EXERCISE 7-8

A **1.** Write an equation of the tangent to the given circle at the given point on the circle.

a. $x^2 + y^2 = 25$, $P(-3, 4)$
b. $x^2 + y^2 = 34$, $P(5, 3)$
c. $x^2 + y^2 = 37$, $P(6, -1)$
d. $x^2 + y^2 = 29$, $P(-5, -2)$
e. $x^2 + y^2 = 100$, $P(-8, 6)$
f. $x^2 + y^2 = 52$, $P(6, 4)$

B **2.** Find equations of the tangents from each given point to the circle defined by $x^2 + y^2 = 14$.

a. $P(0, 4)$ **b.** $A(0, 7)$ **c.** $Q(-5, 0)$

3. **a.** Determine an equation of the tangent to the circle defined by $x^2 + y^2 - 6x - 2y + 5 = 0$ at the point $Q(5, 2)$.
b. Graph the circle and the tangent.

4. Find an equation of the tangent to the circle defined by $x^2 + y^2 - 2x + 16y + 40 = 0$ at the point $R(4, -12)$.

5. Write an equation of the tangent to the circle defined by $x^2 + y^2 = 26$, given that the slope of the tangent is 5.

6. **a.** Write the general equation of the set of lines having y-intercept 26.
b. Find an equation of the tangent to $x^2 + y^2 = 26$ having y-intercept 26. (There are two solutions.)
c. Graph the circle and the tangents.

7. Find an equation of the tangent to the circle with the given y-intercept.

a. $x^2 + y^2 = 8$, y-intercept 4
b. $x^2 + y^2 = 45$, y-intercept 15
c. $x^2 + y^2 = 17$, y-intercept 17
d. $x^2 + y^2 = 20$, y-intercept 10

8. Determine an equation of the tangent from the given point to the given circle. (Each part has two answers.)

a. $x^2 + y^2 = 25$, $P(7, 5)$
b. $x^2 + y^2 = 5$, $P(-1, 7)$
c. $x^2 + y^2 = 20$, $P(-4, -3)$
d. $x^2 + y^2 = 5$, $P(-3, 1)$
e. $x^2 + y^2 = 8$, $P(3, 7)$
f. $x^2 + y^2 = 10$, $P(2, -4)$

C **9.** **a.** Find equations of the tangents from $P(-5, 4)$ to the circle given by $x^2 + y^2 - 6x + 4y - 7 = 0$.
b. Graph the circle and the tangents.

10. **a.** Find equations of the lines with slope 4 that are tangent to the circle defined by $x^2 + y^2 - 12x + 8y + 35 = 0$.
b. Graph the circle and tangents.

11. Find an equation of the line with y-intercept 15 that is tangent to the circle defined by $x^2 + y^2 - 2x - 6y - 10 = 0$.

7-9 Constructing Tangents to Circles

Properties of circles can be used to determine the methods for constructing tangents to a circle. For example, to construct a tangent to a circle at a given point on the circle, apply the Tangent Theorem for Circles.

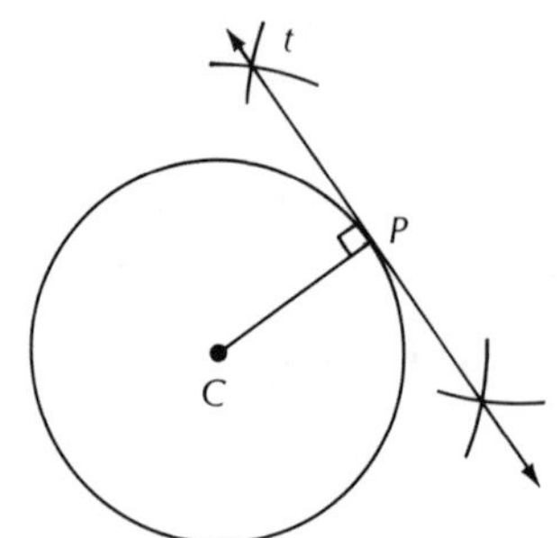

Given: A circle with centre *C* and point *P* on the circle.

Construct: A tangent *t* to the circle at *P*.

Method: Draw radius $\overline{CP}$.
Construct line *t* perpendicular to $\overline{CP}$ at *P*.

Since a tangent is perpendicular to a radius at the point of contact, *t* is the desired tangent.

To construct a tangent to a circle from a point outside the circle, apply the Inscribed Angle Theorem.

Given: A circle with centre *C* and point *P* outside the circle.

Construct: A tangent to the circle through point *P*.

Method: First notice that if a point *A* could be located on the circle so that $\angle CAP = 90°$, then $\overleftrightarrow{AP}$ would be the desired tangent.

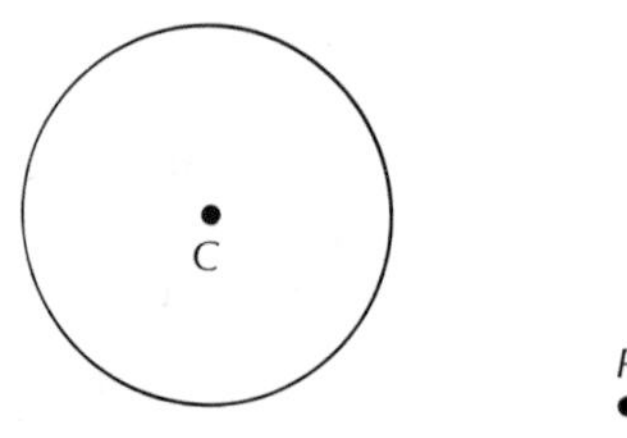

Draw $\overline{CP}$.

Construct the perpendicular bisector of $\overline{CP}$.

Label *M* the midpoint of $\overline{CP}$.

Using $\overline{CP}$ as a diameter, draw the circle having centre *M*.

Label the points of intersection of the two circles *A* and *B*.

Draw $\overline{CA}$ and $\overline{CB}$.

Draw $\overleftrightarrow{PA}$ and $\overleftrightarrow{PB}$.

Notice that $\angle CAP = 90°$ and $\angle CBP = 90°$, because they are inscribed angles subtended by diameter $\overline{CP}$.

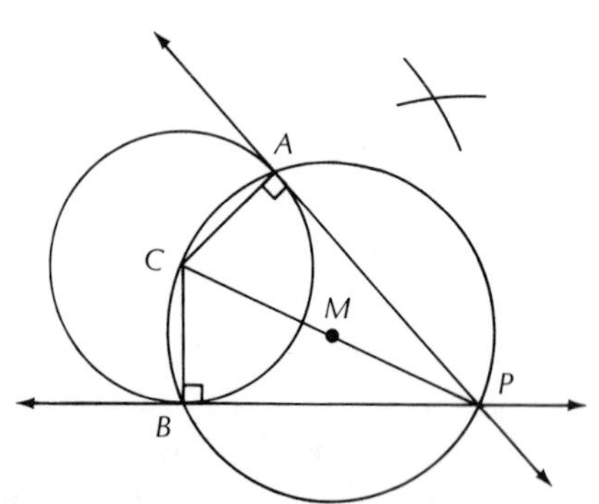

Since $\overleftrightarrow{PA}$ and $\overleftrightarrow{PB}$ are each perpendicular to a radius at the respective points of contact, both lines are tangent to the circle with centre *C*.

EXERCISE 7-9

A **1.** Copy each diagram. Construct a tangent to each circle with centre C, at the given point P.

a.

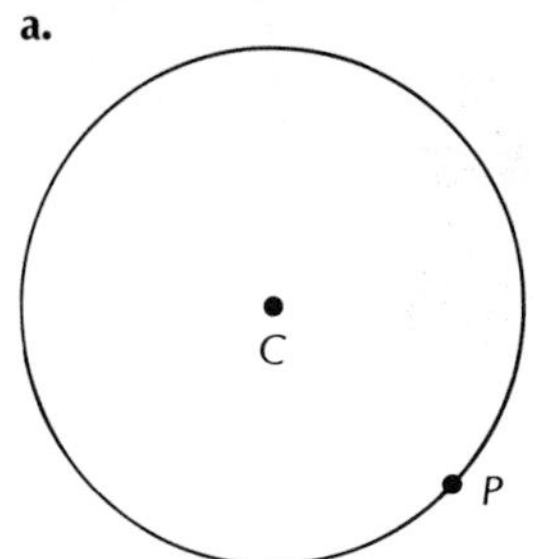

b.

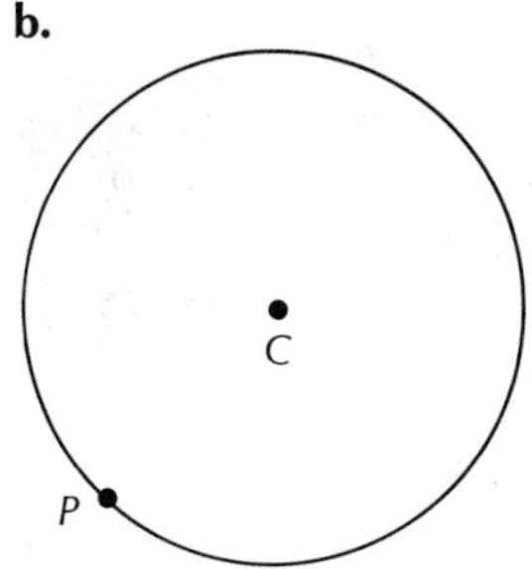

c.

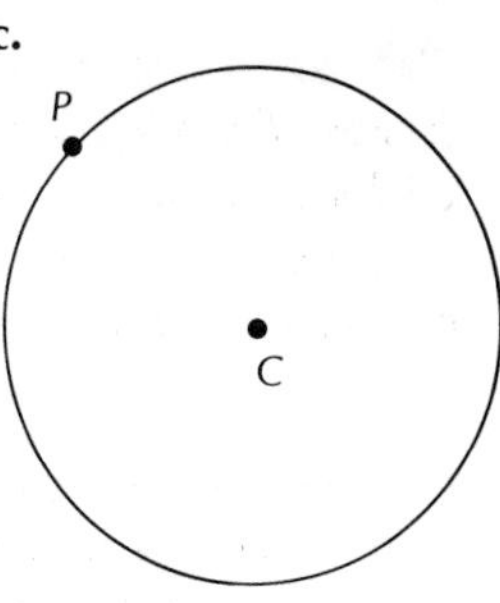

2. Copy each diagram. Construct tangents to each circle with centre C, from the given point P outside the circle.

a.

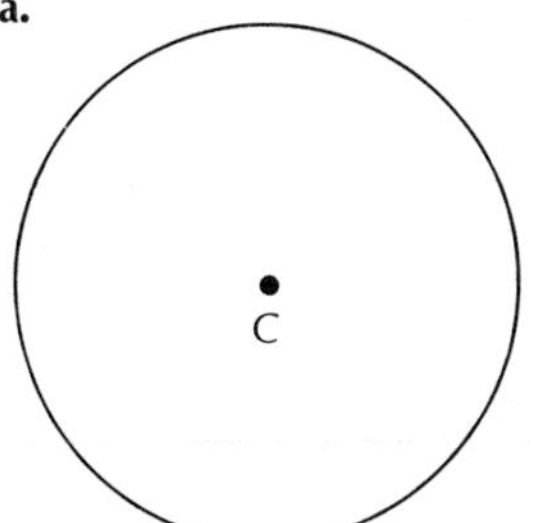

P

b.

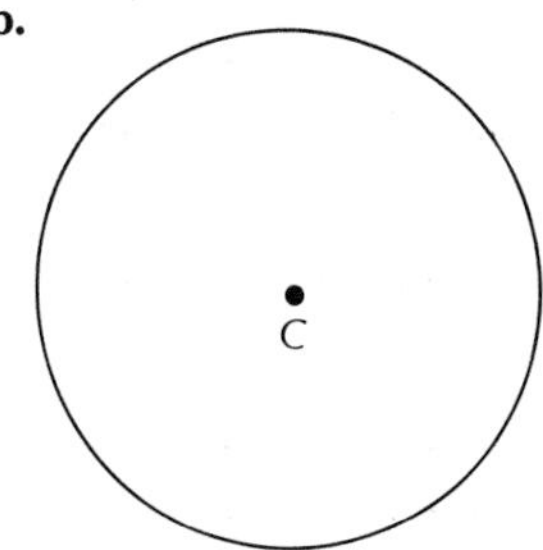

P

B **3.** **a.** Draw a circle with centre C(0, 0) and radius 5.
b. Verify that $P(3, -4)$ is a point on the circle.
c. Construct a tangent to the circle at $P(3, -4)$.

4. **a.** Draw a circle with centre C(0, 0) and radius 4.
b. Construct a tangent segment PA from $P(7, 8)$ to the circle.
c. Measure the tangent segment.
d. Determine the lengths of $\overline{PC}$ and $\overline{CA}$.
e. Use the Pythagorean Theorem to verify that the radius of the circle is, indeed, 4.

5. Repeat the instructions given in exercise 4 for a circle with centre C(3, −2) and radius 5. The tangent passes through point $Q(10, 7)$.

6. Copy each diagram. Use the Tangent Chord Theorem to construct a tangent to each given circle at the given point A.

a.

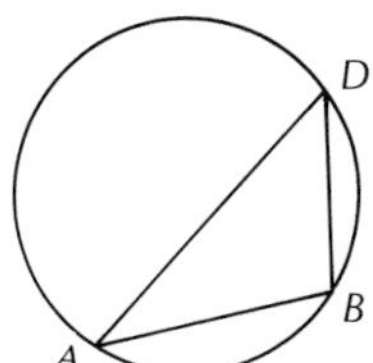

b.

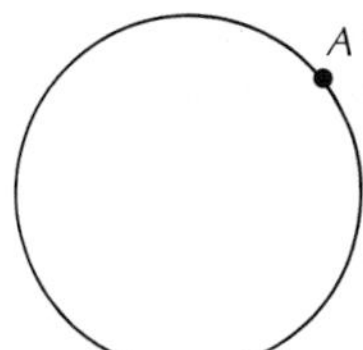

Application

Circular arches are incorporated in the design of many common objects, such as bridges, doorways, and windows. Properties of circles can be applied to calculate measurements of such arches.

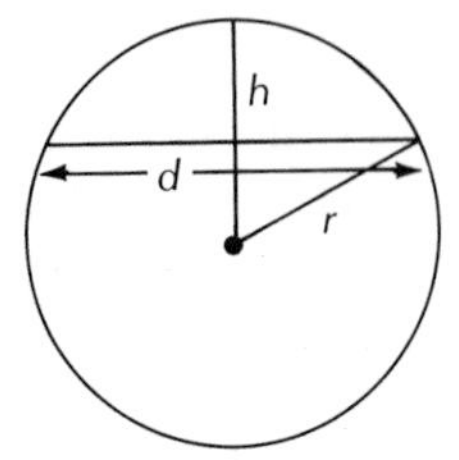

For example, a general formula can be developed to calculate the radius of a circle, given only the height and length of an arch of the circle.

Given a circular arch with height h and width d as shown in the diagram at the right, determine the length of the radius of the circle.

Use the Pythagorean Theorem to develop a general equation.

$$c^2 = a^2 + b^2$$
$$r^2 = \left(\frac{d}{2}\right)^2 + (r - h)^2$$

---

1. **a.** Simplify the above equation and solve for r.
   b. A circular arch of a bridge has width 15 m and height 2.9 m. How long is the radius of the circle?
   c. Calculate the radius of a circular arch of a bridge 20 m long if the height of the arch is 3.5 m.

2. The arch between a foyer and a livingroom has dimensions as shown. The radius used to construct the circular part was 4 m. Calculate the height of the arch.

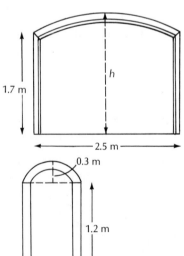

3. A window is to be designed with a circular part above a rectangular section as shown. Calculate the radius that must be used to design the circular part of the window.

Review

1. State the centre, the radius, and the x- and y-intercepts of each given circle.
   a. $x^2 + y^2 = 81$ **b.** $4x^2 + 4y^2 = 9$
   c. $x^2 + (y - 2)^2 = 4$ **d.** $(x - 4)^2 + (y + 3)^2 = 16$

2. Find an equation of the circle that is tangent to the y-axis and the line $x = 4$, given that the centre of the circle lies on the line $y = 5$.

3. Write an equation of the circle having $A(4, -7)$ and $B(-8, 13)$ as endpoints of a diameter.

4. A sector angle of a circle is 70°. Find the area of the sector and the length of the arc bounding it if the radius of the circle is 8 cm.

5. Prove that the perpendicular from the centre of a circle to a chord bisects the chord.

6. Find the measure of each indicated segment. C is the centre of each circle, as indicated.

a.

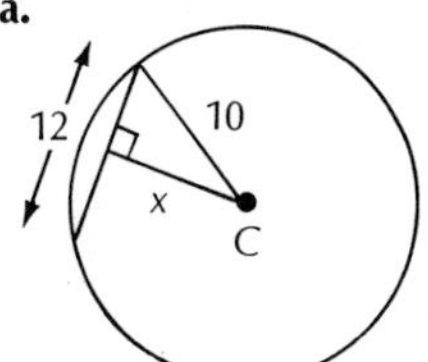

b.

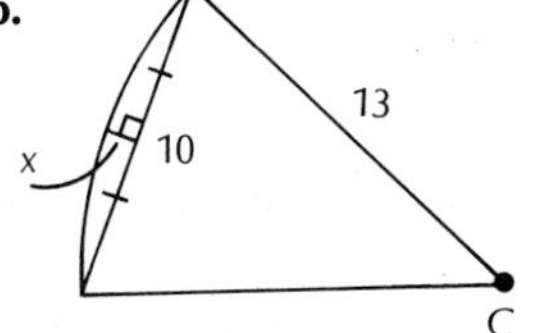

c.

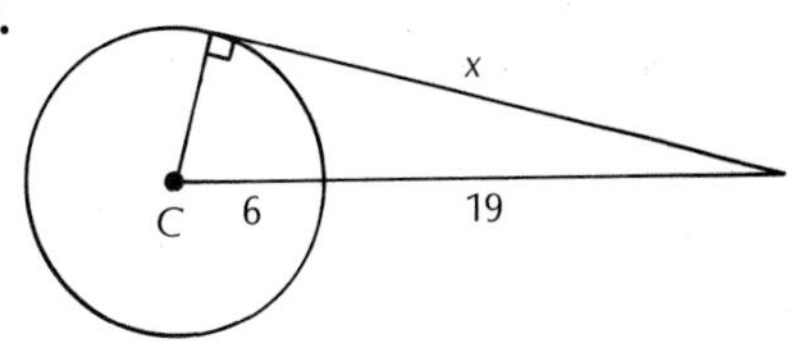

7. Find the size of each indicated angle. C is the centre of each circle, as indicated.

a.

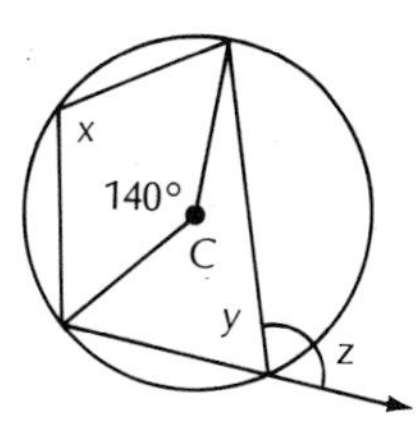

b.

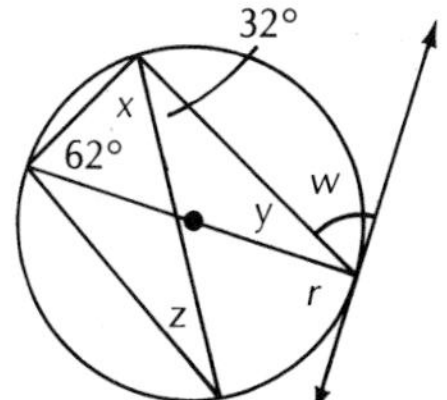

c.

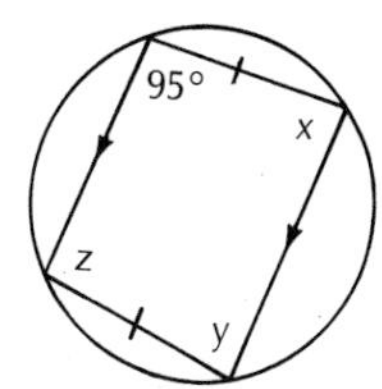

8. **a.** Prove that $2x + y + 10 = 0$ defines a line that is tangent to the circle $x^2 + y^2 = 20$.
   b. Find the point of contact of the tangent in part **a**.

9. **a.** Show that $x - 7y = 15$ defines a secant of the circle $x^2 + y^2 + 6x - 2y - 15 = 0$.
   b. Find the intersection points of the secant with the circle in part **a**.

10. Find an equation of the tangent to the circle $x^2 + y^2 = 13$ at the point $P(3, -2)$.

11. Write an equation of the tangent to the circle $x^2 + y^2 = 40$ from the point $Q(10, 10)$.

1. Copy the diagram and construct a tangent from point P to the circle with centre C.

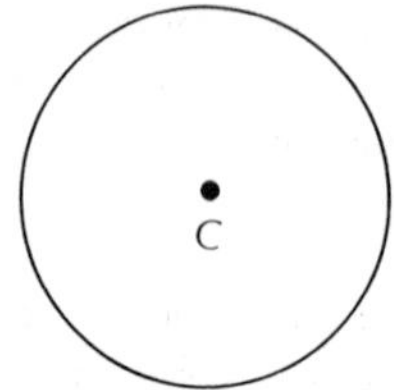

2. Find an equation of the circle with the given properties.
   - **a.** radius 7, centre origin.
   - **b.** centre $(5, -2)$, radius 8.
   - **c.** tangent to $y = 12$, $y = 8$ and $x = 3$.

3. The area of a sector having radius 6 cm is $8\pi(\text{units})^2$. Find the length of the arc bounding the sector.

4. If a tangent from $P(5, -4)$ to the circle defined by $x^2 + y^2 = r^2$ is $\sqrt{37}$ units long, find the value of r.

5. **a.** Show that the points $A(-3, 6)$ and $B(-6, -3)$ are on the circle defined by $x^2 + y^2 = 45$.
   b. Prove that the line joining the midpoint M of $\overline{AB}$ to the centre of the circle is perpendicular to $\overline{AB}$.

6. Find an equation of the circle having $P(-8, 5)$ and $Q(12, -7)$ as the endpoints of a diameter.

7. Find the value of each indicated segment or angle. C is the centre of each circle.

a.

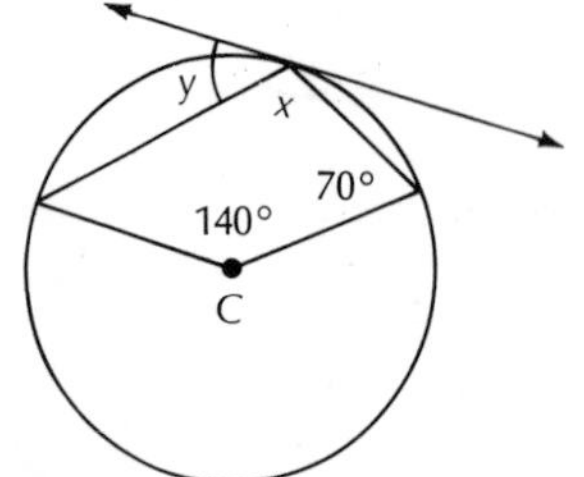

b.

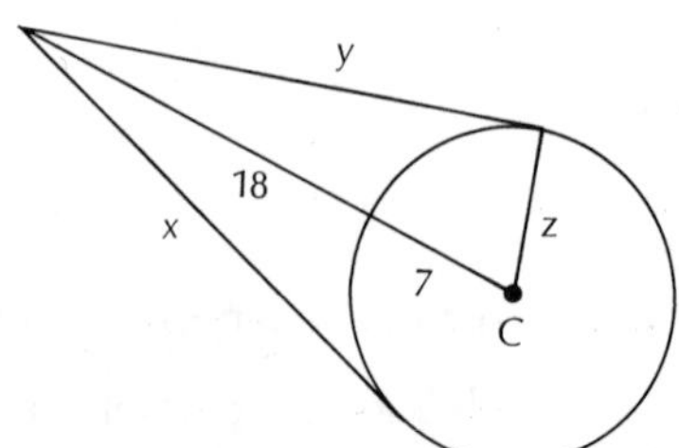

8. A highway overpass is supported by an arch which is an arc of a circle. If the arch is 7.5 m high and 30 m wide, find the radius of the circle.

9. Find an equation of the tangent to the circle $x^2 + y^2 = 40$ at the point $S(-6, -2)$.

Cumulative Review

1. Evaluate.
   a. $5^{-2} + 2^{-3}$ b. $(1.3)^{-1} - (2.5)^{-2}$ c. $\left(-\frac{2}{7}\right)^{-3}$ d. $27^{\frac{1}{3}}$
   e. $1000^{-\frac{1}{3}}$ f. $32^{-\frac{2}{3}}$ g. $(2^{-2} + 2^{-3})^{-1}$ h. $[4^3(8^{-2})]^{-2}$

2. Factor.
   a. $6xy + 15xz + 12x$ b. $x^3yz + xy^2z + xy$ c. $x^2 + 2x + 1$
   d. $144x^2 - 17x - 35$ e. $216y^6 - x^9$ f. $48x^2 - 27$
   g. $xy + 3x - y^2 - 3y$ h. $x^2y - 4y + 2x^2 - 8$ i. $4z + 16y + 3xz + 12xy$

3. Simplify.
   a. $\dfrac{y}{y+3} + \dfrac{3}{3-y}$ b. $\dfrac{2}{5a} - \dfrac{3}{5a-6}$ c. $\dfrac{8}{2x-6} - \dfrac{4}{2x-12}$
   d. $\dfrac{3x}{1-x} + \dfrac{2}{4x-6}$ e. $\dfrac{2m+3}{m-4} + \dfrac{m+3}{m-1}$ f. $\dfrac{6t+1}{1+2t} - \dfrac{2-3t}{5t+3}$

4. Find the distance between each pair of points. Leave each answer in simplest radical form.
   a. $(1, -1)\ (3, 2)$ b. $(2, 3)\ (6, -7)$ c. $(-1, -2)\ (-10, 6)$ d. $(-4, -2)\ (-3, 9)$
   e. $(3, -8)\ (8, 2)$ f. $(0, 4)\ (-5, 0)$ g. $(9, -4)\ (1, -3)$ h. $(9, 5)\ (-9, -7)$

5. Solve.
   a. $2x - 3 = x + 2$ b. $\dfrac{x+3}{2x-1} = 4$ c. $x^2 - 5x - 6 = 0$
   d. $\sqrt{3x+1} = 2\sqrt{5}$ e. $3x^2 + 5x + 2 = 0$ f. $6x^2 + 3x - 2 = 0$

6. On the same set of axes, graph the regions defined by each pair of inequalities.
   a. $x + 3y < 6$, $2y - x > 7$ b. $3x + y - 3 < 0$, $x - y + 1 > 0$ c. $y \geq x^2 - 3$, $y > 4$
   d. $2x - y - 5 \leq 0$, $x - 2y - 5 \geq 0$ e. $2x + y - 10 \leq 10$, $x + 3y - 5 \geq 10$ f. $y \geq 2x^2 - 4x - 2$, $2x - 6y + 3 > 0$

7. Simplify.
   a. $\sqrt{126}$ b. $\sqrt{147}$ c. $\sqrt{119}$ d. $\sqrt{63}$
   e. $\sqrt{x^3y^2}$ f. $\sqrt[3]{513}$ g. $\sqrt{x^2y^3z}$ h. $\sqrt{5148}$

8. The strength of a magnetic field is directly proportional to the square of the distance from the magnet. A magnet can pick up a 10 kg mass from 1 cm away. How far away could it pick up a 5 kg mass?

9. A boat company manufactures pleasure yachts that are shipped out at the end of every month. It can produce a maximum of 10 yachts per month of two sizes, 15 m and 21 m. No more than 5 large yachts can be stored in the warehouse at a time, and demand for small yachts never exceeds 8 per month. $5000 profit is made on each small yacht, and $6000 on each large yacht. Graph the constraints of the above system, and determine how many of each type of yacht should be built every month to maximize profits.

8 Relations and Functions

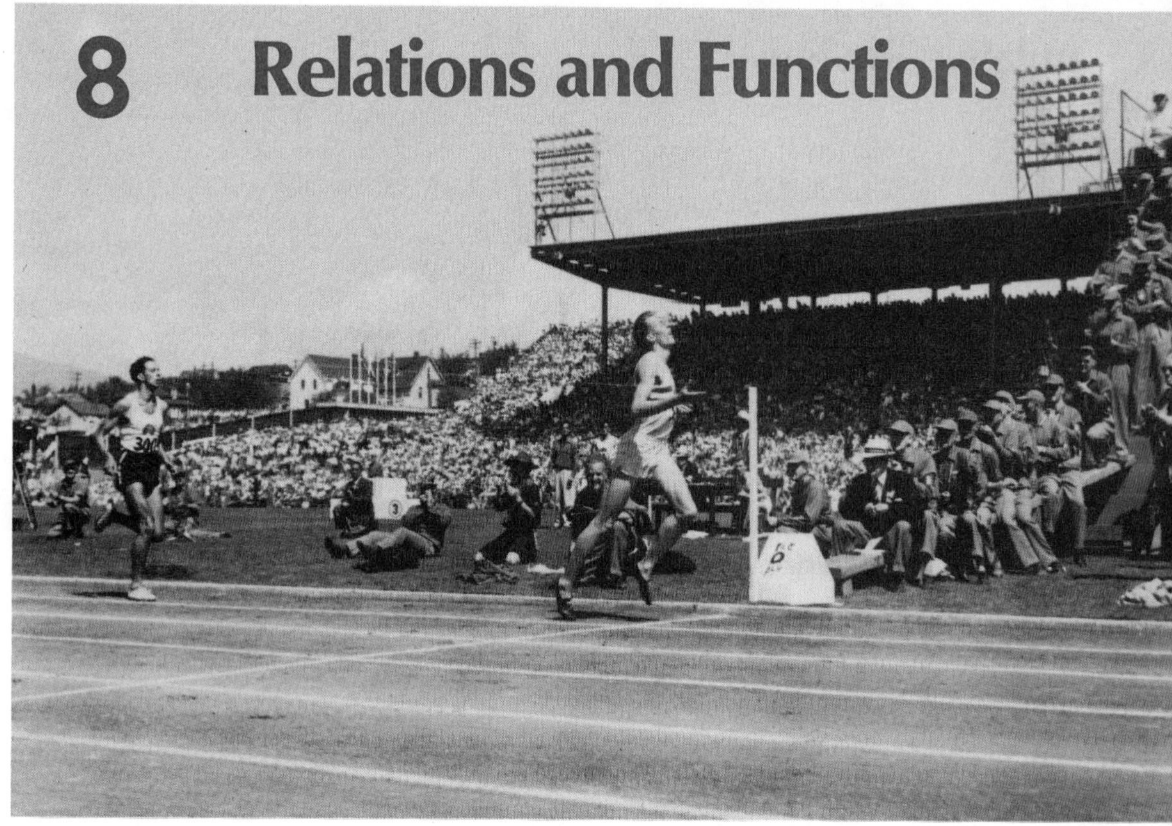

8-1 Relations and Functions

At the 1954 Commonwealth Games in Vancouver, Roger Bannister set a record by running a mile in less than four minutes. His actual running time was 3:59.4. Later that year, John Landy set a new record of 3:58. In track-record books, each year from 1895–1975 is matched with the fastest time run that year. These records can be listed as *ordered pairs* in the form (year, time). John Landy's track record can be represented as (1954, 3:58).

A set of ordered pairs is a **relation**. The pairs may be given in a table, on a graph, in a diagram, as a set of ordered pairs, or defined by an equation.

The set of all *first components* of the ordered pairs in a relation is the **domain** of the relation.
The set of all *second components* of the ordered pairs in a relation is the **range** of the relation.

EXAMPLE 1: Determine the domain and range of the relation
$T = \{(1, 3), (2, -1), (5, 8), (-1, 2), (8, 18)\}$

The domain of T is $\{1, 2, 5, -1, 8\}$.
The range of T is $\{3, -1, 8, 2, 18\}$.

An **arrow diagram** can be used to represent a relation. For the relation $S = \{(0, 4), (-1, 5), (-2, 6), (3, 7)\}$, the domain of S is $\{0, -1, -2, 3\}$, and the range of S is $\{4, 5, 6, 7\}$. In the diagram at the right, the arrows pair each member of the domain with the member it corresponds to in the range.

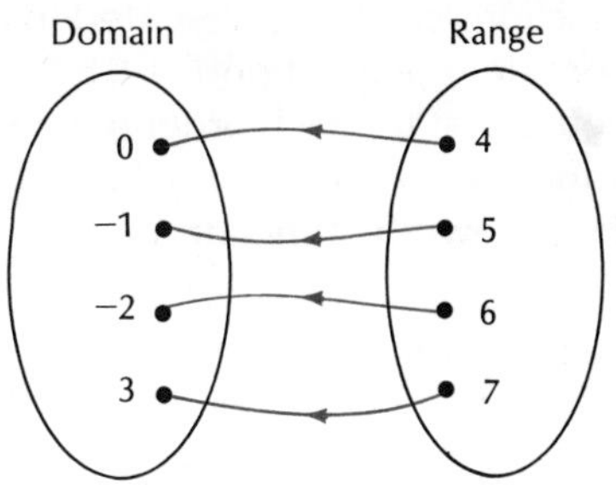

The domain and range of a relation can be identified from the graph of the relation.

EXAMPLE 2: Determine the domain and range of the relation defined by each graph.

a.

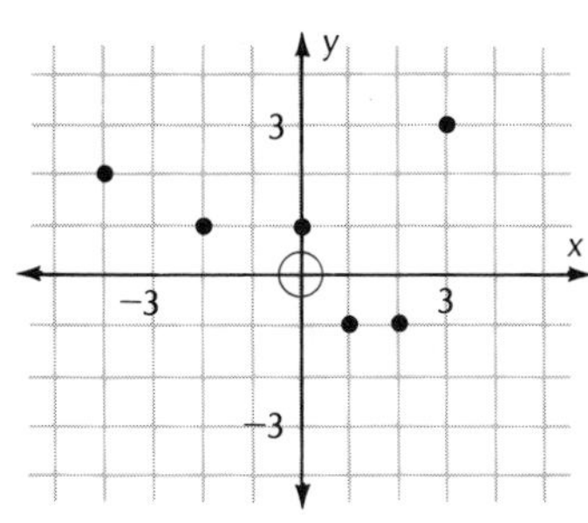

Domain = $\{-4, -2, 0, 1, 2, 3\}$
Range = $\{2, 1, -1, 3\}$

b.

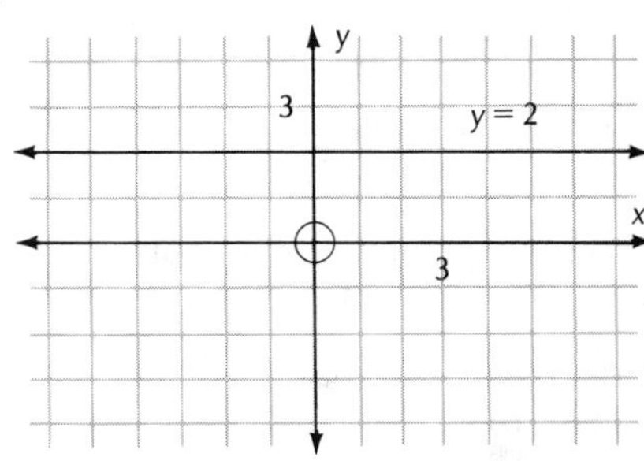

Domain = $\{x \mid x \in \mathbf{R}\}$
Range = $\{y \in \mathbf{R} \mid y = 2\}$ or $\{2\}$

$x \in \mathbf{R}$ means that x is a member of the real numbers.

A **function** is a special type of relation in which each element of the domain is paired with exactly one element of the range.

For a given function f, each element x in the domain has an **image**, ***f(x)***, in the range.

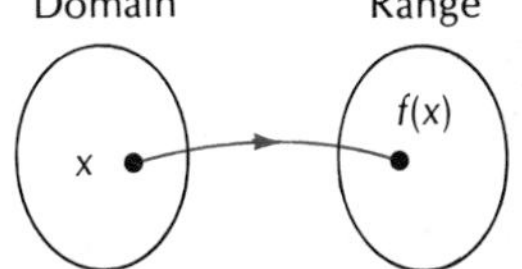

$f(x)$ is the image of x.

EXAMPLE 3: Which of the given arrow diagrams represent functions?

a.

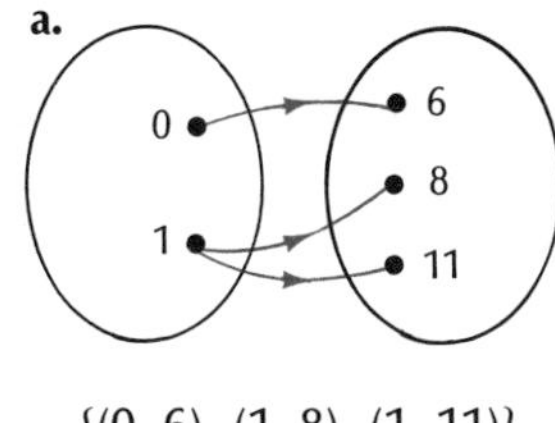

$\{(0, 6), (1, 8), (1, 11)\}$

b.

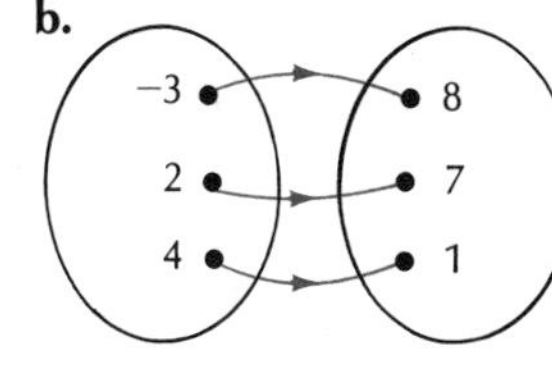

$\{(-3, 8), (2, 7), (4, 1)\}$

c.

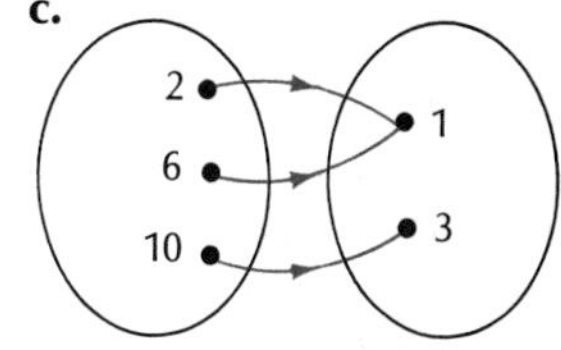

$\{(2, 1), (6, 1), (10, 3)\}$

Part **a.** does not represent a function since 1 is paired with both 8 and 11. Parts **b.** and **c.** both represent functions since each element of the domain has exactly one image in the range.

Functions can be represented in a variety of ways. Consider the function $T = \{(1, 2), (3, 6), (5, 10), (7, 14)\}$. Notice that for each ordered pair, the second component is double the first. The arrow diagram at the right shows the function T.

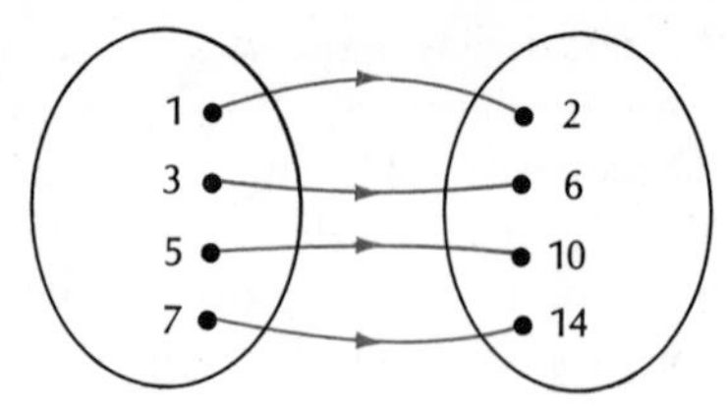

An equation can also be used to describe T.

$T = \{(x, y) | y = 2x, x \in \{1, 3, 5, 7\}\}$

Read: The set of all (x, y), such that $y = 2x$, and x is a member of $\{1, 3, 5, 7\}$.

In fact, each of the following notations represents the same function T.

$T = \{(x, y) | y = 2x, x \in \{1, 3, 5, 7\}\}$
$T: x \rightarrow 2x, x \in \{1, 3, 5, 7\}$
$T: x \rightarrow y = 2x, x \in \{1, 3, 5, 7\}$
$T(x) = 2x, x \in \{1, 3, 5, 7\}$

$2x$, y, and $T(x)$ all denote the image of x.

Functions are often called **mappings**. For the function $T = \{(x, y) | y = 2x, x \in \{1, 3, 5, 7\}\}$, the following notation applies.

1 maps to 2 *or* $1 \rightarrow 2$ *or* 2 is the image of 1
3 maps to 6 *or* $3 \rightarrow 6$ *or* 6 is the image of 3

Using the notation developed thus far, a general definition of a function can be given.

A **function** f is a relation whereby each element x in the domain corresponds to a unique element y in the range, such that $(x, y) \in f$. If $f(x) = y$, and $f(x) = z$, then $y = z$.

This definition ensures that, in an arrow diagram for a function, exactly one arrow leaves each element of the domain.

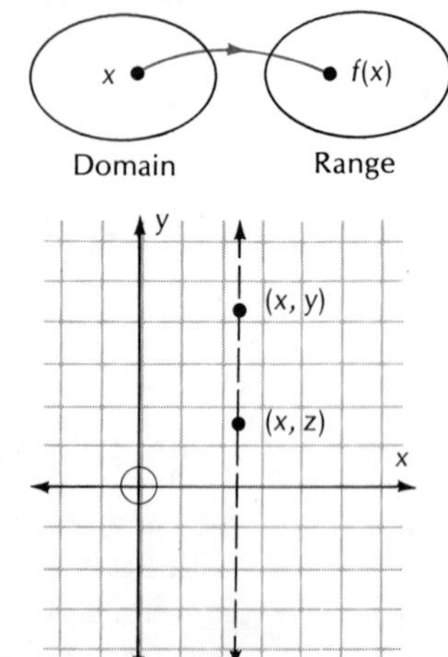

The property of ordered pairs that belong to a function, namely that (x, y) and (x, z) both belong to the same function only if $y = z$, can be used to illustrate a simple test to determine if a graph represents a function. The test is called the **vertical line test**.

If a vertical line cuts a graph in two distinct points (x, y) and (x, z), then the graph does *not* represent a function. If a vertical line through a point in the domain of a relation intersects the graph of the relation in at most one point, then the relation *is* a function.

EXAMPLE 4: Given $f = \{(x, y) | y = x^2 - 4\}$.

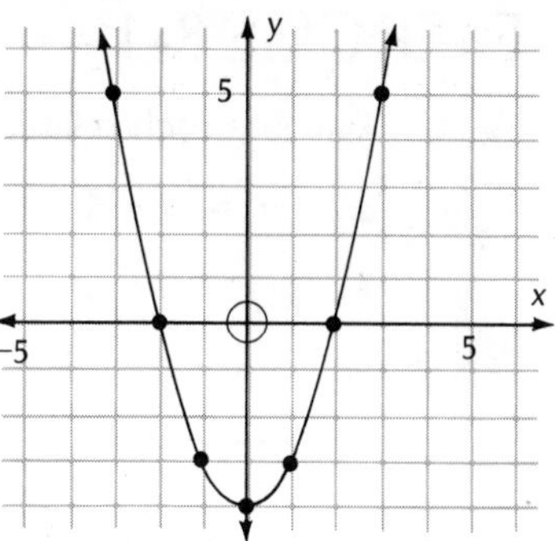

a. Determine if f is a function by graphing.

Use a table of values to graph f.

x	y
0	−4
±1	−3
±2	0
±3	5

The vertical line test shows that f is a function.

b. Draw an arrow diagram to represent f.

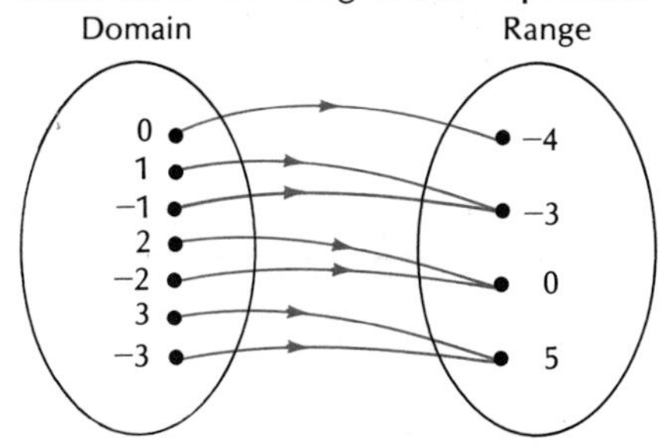

c. Find $f(x)$ for $x = -3$ and $x = 12$.

Note that $f(x)$ is the image of x.
Therefore, $f(-3)$ is the image of -3, that is,
$f(-3) = (-3)^2 - 4$, or $f(-3) = 5$.
Similarly, $f(12) = 12^2 - 4$, or $f(12) = 140$.

Evaluating functions can sometimes involve algebraic expressions or other functions.

EXAMPLE 5: a. Given that $f(x) = 3x^2 + 2x - 1$, find an expression for $f(2a)$.

Substitute $2a$ for x in $f(x) = 3x^2 + 2x - 1$.

$$f(x) = 3x^2 + 2x - 1$$
$$f(2a) = 3(2a)^2 + 2(2a) - 1$$
$$= 3(4a^2) + 4a - 1$$
$$= 12a^2 + 4a - 1$$

b. Given that $f(x) = x^2 + 3$ and $g(x) = 2x + 1$, find an expression for $f(g(x))$.

$$f(x) = x^2 + 3$$
$$f(g(x)) = [g(x)]^2 + 3$$
$$= (2x + 1)^2 + 3 \quad \text{Substitute } g(x) \text{ for } x.$$
$$= 4x^2 + 4x + 4 \quad \text{Substitute } (2x + 1) \text{ for } g(x).$$

EXERCISE 8-1

A **1.** Evaluate each relation for the given values.

a. $f(x) = 3x - 5$; $f(4)$, $f(-3)$, $f(0)$, and $f(6)$

b. $g(x) = x^2 - x$; $g(3)$, $g(-1)$, $g(4)$, and $g(-3)$

c. $h\colon x \to 2x^2 - 5$; $h(4)$, $h(-4)$, $h(0)$, and $h(7)$

d. $m(x) = \dfrac{7}{x^2 - 9}$; $m(3)$, $m(-1)$, $m(4)$, and $m(6)$

2. Determine whether or not each graph represents a function. Give the domain and range of each relation.

a.

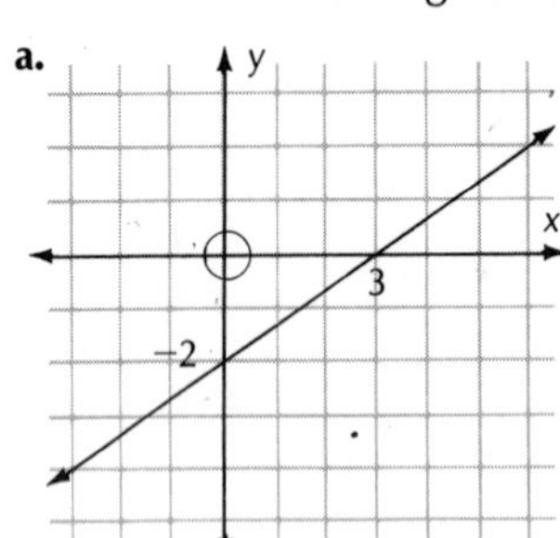

b.

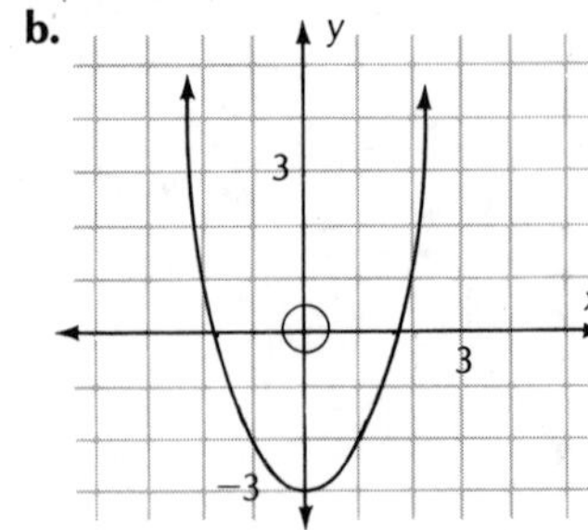

c.

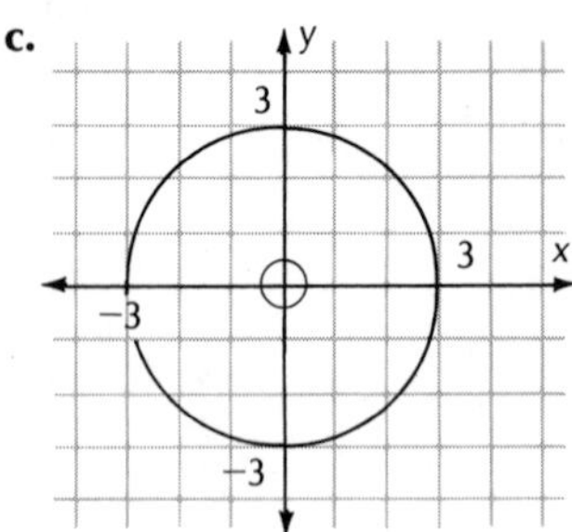

d.

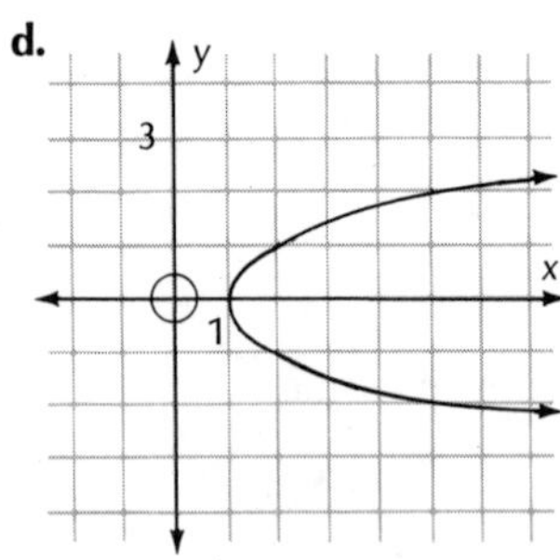

e.

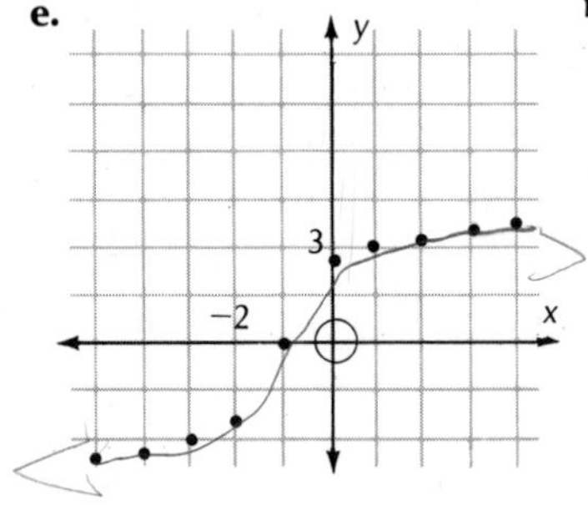

f.

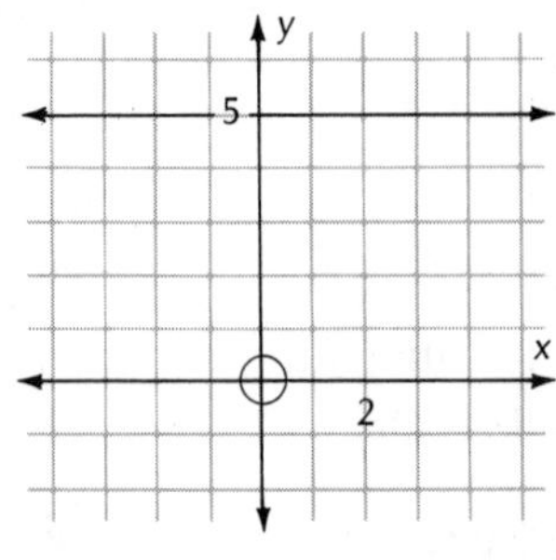

B **3.** Given that the domain of each function is $\{-3, -2, -1, 0, 1, 2, 3\}$, find the range of each function.

a. $f = \{(x, y) \mid y = 7 - x\}$

b. $g = \{(x, y) \mid y = x^2 - 5\}$

c. $h\colon x \to 3 - |x|$

d. $k\colon x \to \dfrac{1}{x + 4}$

e. $s\colon x \to y = x^3 - x^2$

f. $p\colon x \to y = \dfrac{1}{1 - x^2}$

4. Graph each relation using the given domain. State the range of each relation.

a. $f(x) = \dfrac{x - 1}{2}$; domain of f is $\{x\colon x \in R, -3 \leq x \leq 5\}$

b. $g(x) = \frac{1}{2}x^2$; domain of g is $\{x\colon 0 < x \leq 4\}$

5. Given that $f(x) = x + 3$, $g(x) = 3 - x^2$, and $h(x) = \frac{2}{x} - 1$, find the following.

a. $f(7) + g(2)$

b. $h(2) - g(1)$

c. $g(5) + f(6)$

d. $3f(2) + g(1)$

e. $2h(0) - 3g(2)$

f. $\frac{f(7)}{g(3)}$

g. $\frac{g(5)}{h\left(\frac{1}{2}\right)}$

h. $\frac{f(4) + g(1)}{h(2)}$

i. $\frac{h(3)}{f(0) + g(0)}$

j. $\frac{2f(2)}{3h(4)}$

6. Given $f(x) = 3x - 1$, $g(x) = x^2$, and $h(x) = \sqrt{x}$, find an expression for each of the following.

a. $f(g(x))$

b. $g(f(x))$

c. $f(h(x))$

d. $h(f(x))$

e. $g(h(x))$

f. $h(g(x))$

C 7. Solve for each unknown.

a. $f(x) = 4x + 3$; $f(a) = 23$, $a = ?$ ← $4(a) + 3 = 23$

b. $g(x) = x^2 - 2$; $g(b) = 23$, $b = ?$

c. $h(x) = x^2 - 3$; $h(c) = 0$, $c = ?$

d. $k(x) = \frac{12}{x^2 - 1}$; $k(d) = 4$, $d = ?$

e. $s(x) = \frac{x^2 - 9}{x - 1}$; $s(e) = 4$, $e = ?$

8. Each given graph represents a function. Write an equation for each function.

a.

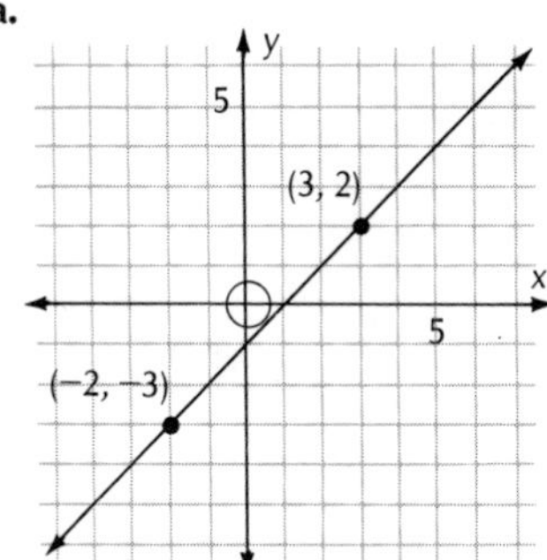

b.

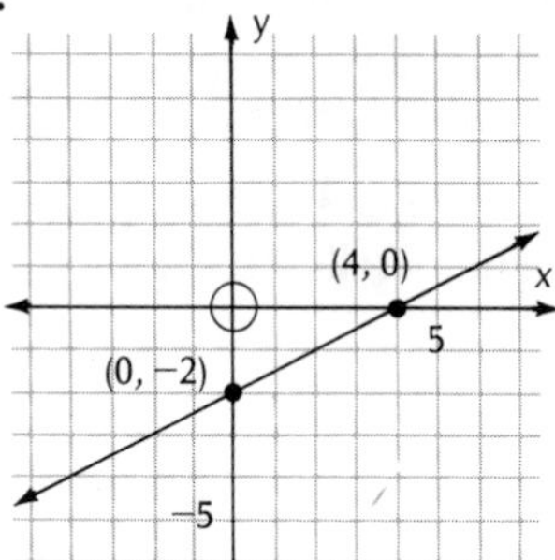

c.

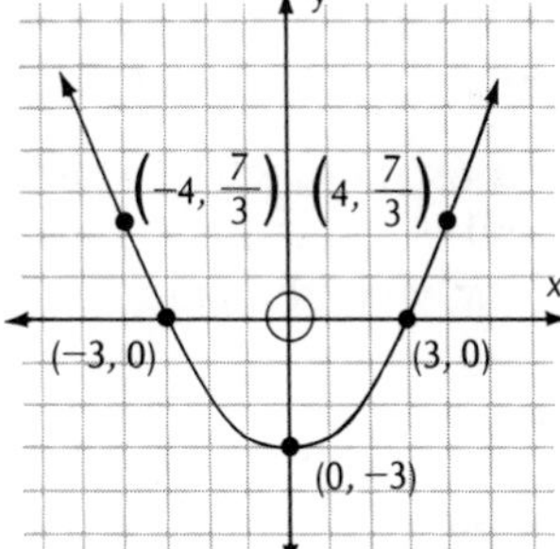

9. Given that $f(x) = 3x - 2$ and $g(x) = x^2$, find each of the following.

a. $f(x) + g(x)$

b. $g(x) - f(x)$

c. Graph $f(x)$, $g(x)$, $f(x) + g(x)$, and $g(x) - f(x)$.

8-2 Special Types of Functions

When one end of a coiled spring is attached to a ceiling, a mass attached to the other end will stretch the spring. The length l of a particular spring is increased by 2 cm for each 1 kg increase in the mass. That is, x kg will stretch the spring $2x$ cm. When a mass of x kg is attached to a spring 12 cm long, the spring will stretch to a length of $(2x + 12)$ cm.

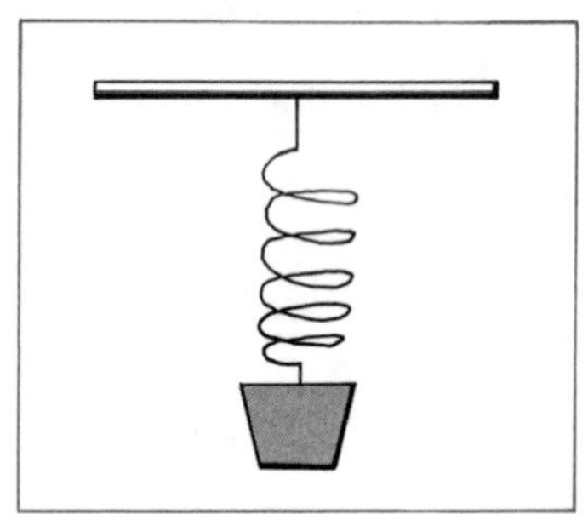

Each mass of x kg on the end of the spring can be associated with a length l. In particular, $x \rightarrow 2x + 12$, which represents a function f whose graph is a straight line. The function can be written as $f{:}x \rightarrow 2x + 12$ or $f = \{(x, l) \mid l = 2x + 12\}$, where the domain is $\{x \mid x \geq 0\}$ and the range is $\{l \mid l \geq 12\}$. ***f*** is a **linear** function. A function f is linear if there are numbers a and b, such that $f{:}x \rightarrow ax + b$. The graph of a linear function is a straight line.

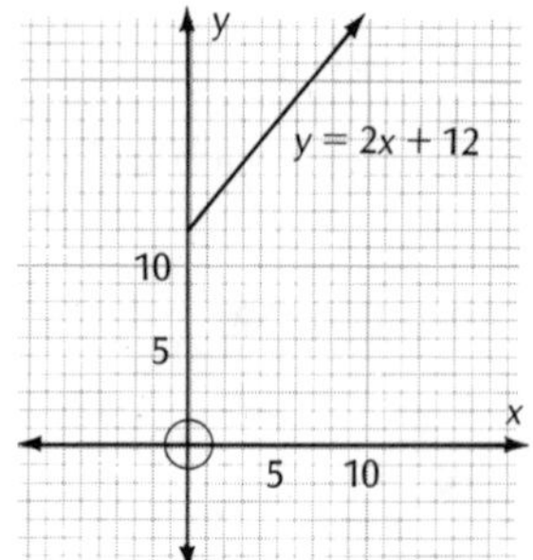

The **identity** function, denoted by ***I***, maps each number to itself. The identity function can be represented as $I = \{(x, y) \mid y = x\}$. The graph of the identity function is a straight line as shown in the diagram at the right. The domain and range of I is the set of real numbers.

A **constant** function is defined by $f(x) = k$, where k is any number. Its graph is a straight line parallel to the x-axis, as shown in the graph at the right.

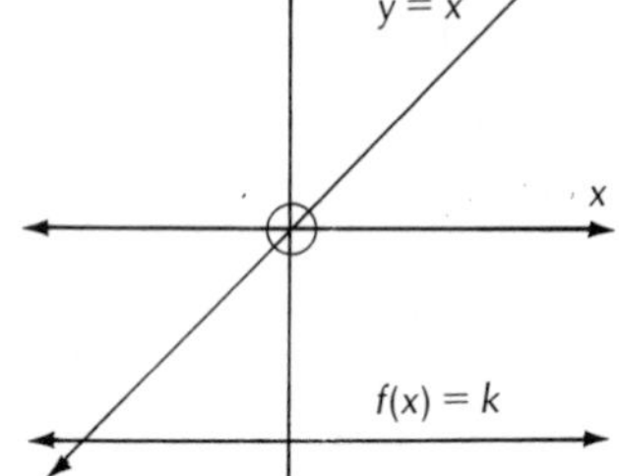

Suppose a stone is hurled at an angle of 30° to the horizontal from a cliff that is 30 m above water level. If the stone's initial speed is 40 m/s, it can be verified experimentally that the height of the stone above the water, t seconds after it is thrown, is $h(t) = 30 + 20t - 5t^2$. h is a **quadratic** function (recall quadratics from chapter 5). A function f is quadratic if $f(x) = ax^2 + bx + c$, where $a, b, c \in \mathbf{R}, a \neq 0$.

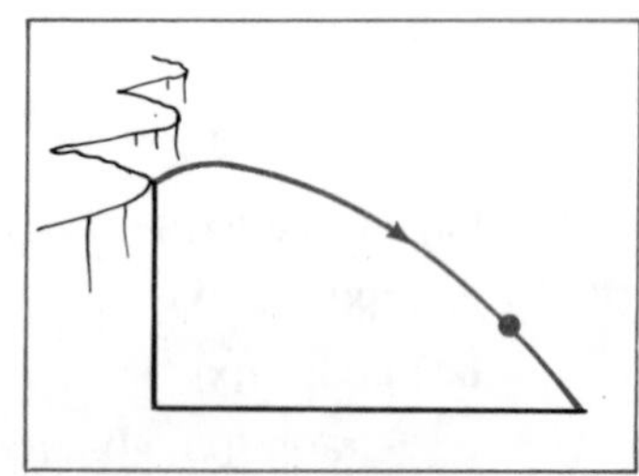

EXAMPLE 1: Determine the minimum value of the quadratic function $f: x \rightarrow y = x^2 - 4$.

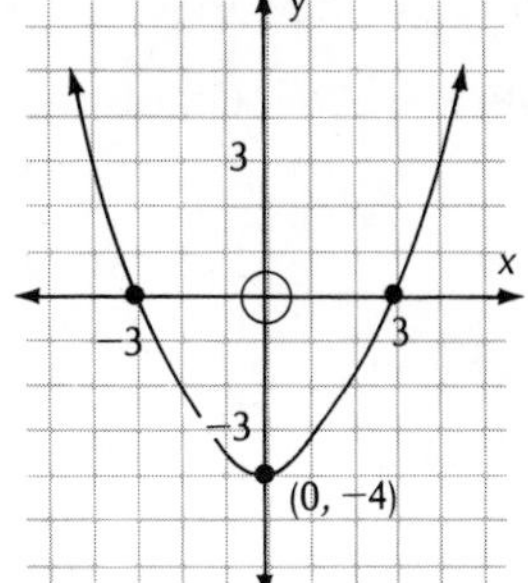

The graph of the function is a parabola, as shown. Each x-value yields one y-value. The domain of the function is $\{x \mid x \in \boldsymbol{R}\}$. The minimum y-value can be found algebraically.

$y = x^2 - 4$
$x^2 = y + 4$
$x = \sqrt{y+4}$, or $x = -\sqrt{y+4}$

In either case, for x to be a real number, $y + 4 \geq 0$, or $y \geq -4$.

The least value that y can have is -4.

Therefore, the minimum value of the function is -4.

A courier service charges a delivery fee based on the distance a package is sent.

Distance (km)	0–5	5^+–15	15^+–30	30^+–40
Rate	\$10	\$15	\$22	\$30

The fees for given distances are shown in the graph.

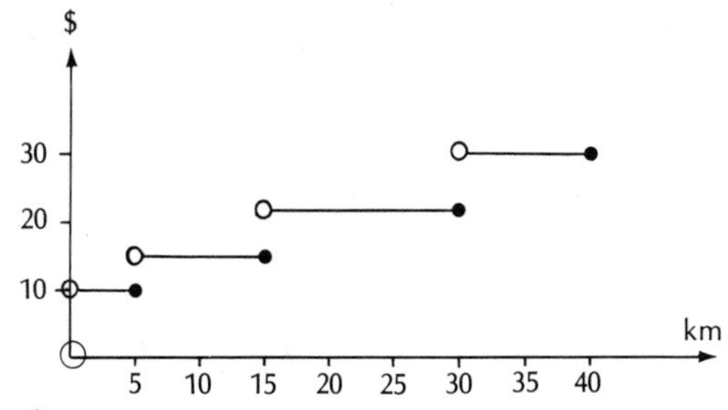

o depicts a point not included in the graph.

• depicts a point that is included in the graph.

The vertical line test shows that this graph is a function. This type of function is sometimes called a **postal** or **step** function. Functions whose graphs consist of a line and line segments are called **piecewise linear**.

EXAMPLE 2: Graph the function defined as follows.

$$f: \begin{array}{l} x \rightarrow 2x + 1, \text{ if } x < 0 \\ x \rightarrow 1 - x, \text{ if } 0 \leq x \leq 2 \\ x \rightarrow x - 3, \text{ if } x > 2 \end{array}$$

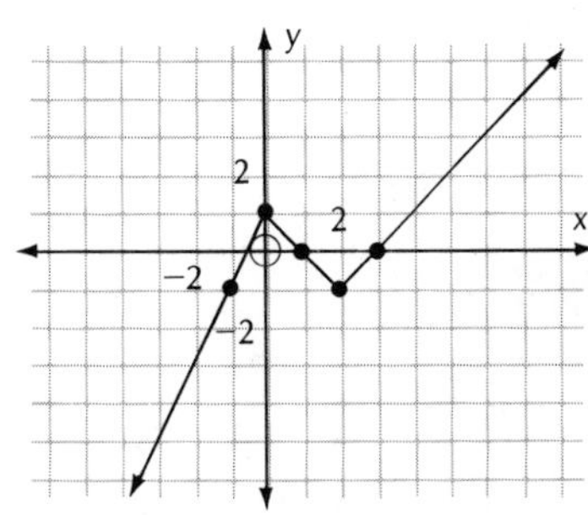

Each part of the function represents a linear equation with given restrictions. Notice that both the domain and the range are the set of real numbers. This function is piecewise linear.

The domain and range of functions can consist of sets of distinct elements.

EXAMPLE 3: Graph the function defined by $g(x) = |x| - 3$, $x \in \{-2, -1, 0, 1, 2\}$. Determine its range.

Evaluate $g(x)$ for each number in the domain.

$g(-2) = |-2| - 3 = -1$
$g(-1) = |-1| - 3 = -2$
$g(0) = |0| - 3 = -3$
$g(1) = |1| - 3 = -2$
$g(2) = |2| - 3 = -1$

The range is $\{-2, -1, 0\}$.

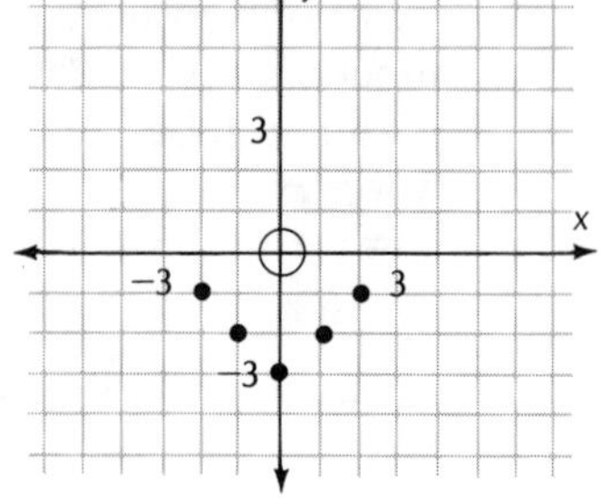

EXAMPLE 4: The graph of $h(x) = \dfrac{1}{x^2 - 4}$ is given below.

Find the domain and range of the function.

Note that $x^2 - 4 = (x - 2)(x + 2)$ and $x^2 - 4 = 0$ for $x = \pm 2$.

Therefore, $h(x)$ is not defined for $x = \pm 2$, but is defined for all other values of x.

So, the domain is $\{y|\ y \in \mathbf{R};\ y \neq 2, -2\}$. From the graph it appears that the range is $\{y|\ y \in \mathbf{R};\ y > 0, y < -\frac{1}{4}\}$.

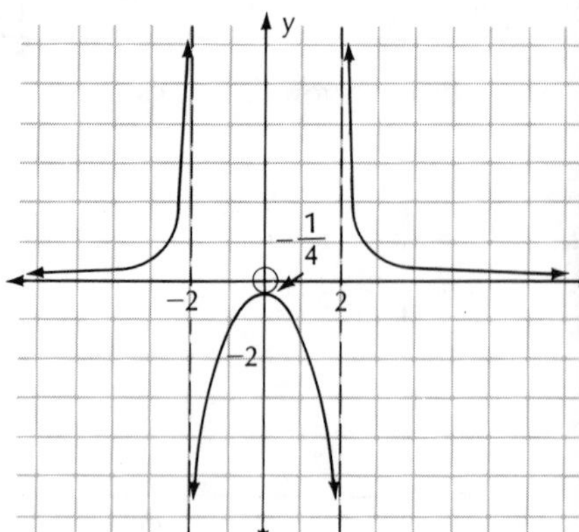

EXERCISE 8-2

A **1.** State whether or not each given function is linear.

a. $f{:}x \rightarrow 2x + 5$ **b.** $f{:}x \rightarrow x^2 + 2$

c. $f{:}x \rightarrow \dfrac{(x - 7)}{5}$ **d.** $f = \{(x, y)|\ y = 3x^2\}$

e. $f = \{(x, y)|\ y = 5 - 2x\}$ **f.** $f = \{(x, y)|\ x + 3y = 12\}$

2. Find the range of each given function.

a. $f{:}x \rightarrow 2x$ **b.** $f{:}x \rightarrow |x|$

c. $f{:}x \rightarrow \sqrt{5 - x}$ **d.** $f{:}x \rightarrow \sqrt{x + 3}$

e. $f{:}x \rightarrow \sqrt{4 - x^2}$ **f.** $f{:}x \rightarrow \sqrt{25 - x^2}$

3. Graph each given piecewise linear function.

a. $f(x) = 1$, if $x \geq 0$
$= -2$, if $x < 0$

b. $g(x) = x$, if $x \geq 0$
$= -2$, if $x < 0$

c. $h(x) = x$, if $x \geq 0$
$= -x$, if $x < 0$

d. $k(x) = -1$, if $x < -1$
$= x$, if $-1 < x < 1$
$= 1$, if $x > 1$

e. $h(x) = 2x$, if $-3 \leq x \leq 2$
$= x + 2$, if $2 \leq x \leq 4$

f. $k(x) = 6$, if $0 \leq x \leq 5$
$= -1$, if $-3 \leq x \leq 0$

g. $s(x) = \dfrac{6}{x - 2}$ $D(s) = \{x \mid x \in \boldsymbol{R}, \text{ if } 2 < x < 6\}$
$= x \in \boldsymbol{Z}$, if $0 \leq x < 2$
$= x + 2$, if $2 \leq x \leq 4$

4. Define the function associated with each graph, and identify each function as linear, piecewise linear, step, or quadratic.

a.

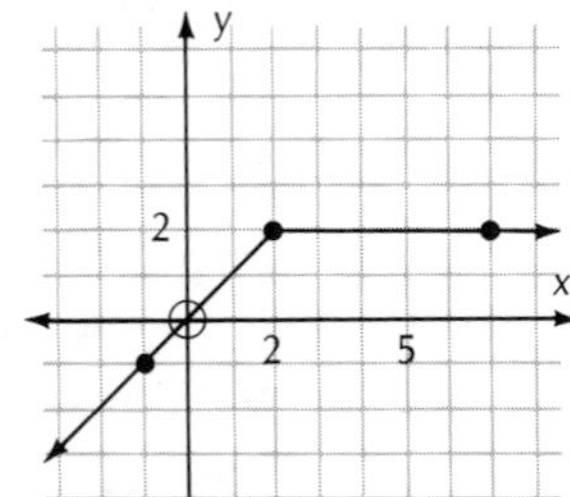

b.

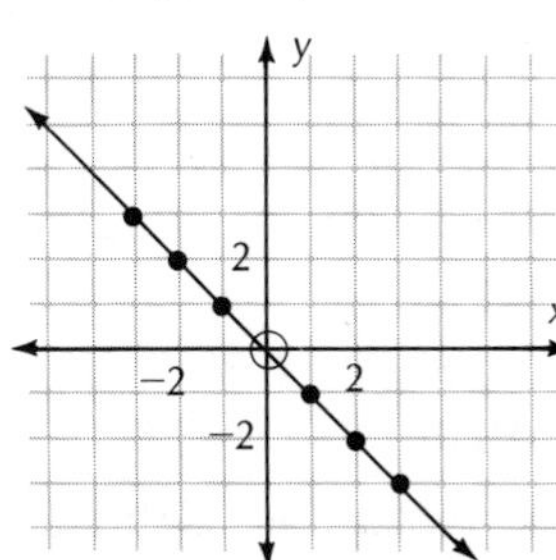

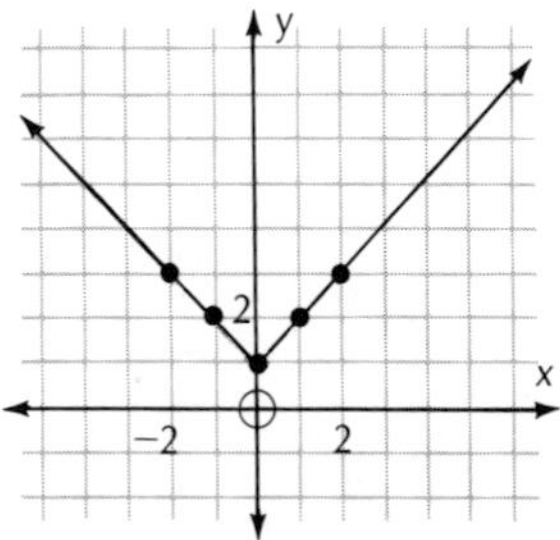

d.

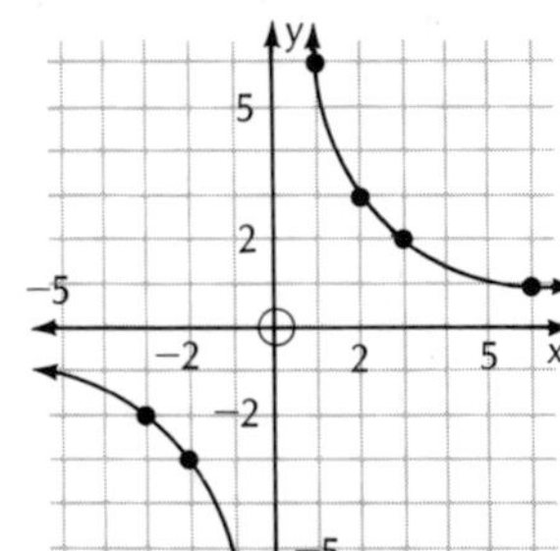

e.

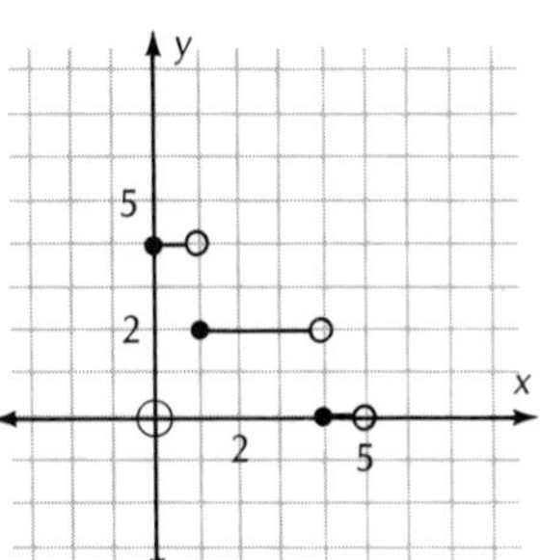

f.

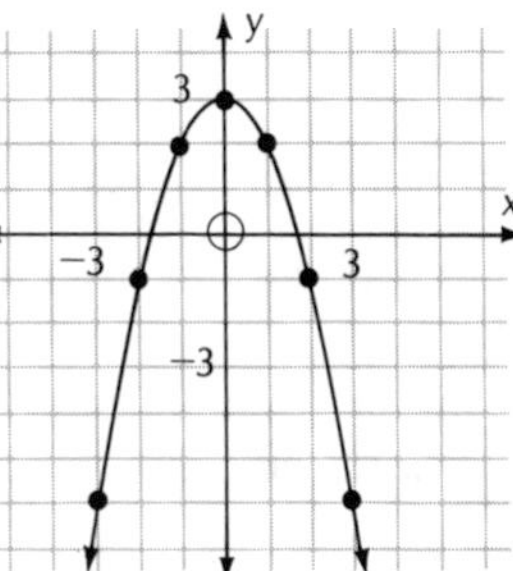

5. In the example of the stone hurled from a cliff, the height function was defined by $h(t) = 30 + 20t - 5t^2$.

a. Show that $30 + 20t - 5t^2 = 5[6 + 4t - t^2]$
$= 5[6 - (t^2 - 4t + 4) + 4]$
$= 5[10 - (t - 2)^2]$

b. Find the value of t that will maximize $h(t)$.

c. Find the greatest height above the water that the stone will reach.

6. Determine whether each of the following has a maximum or minimum value and then find the corresponding value of x.

a. $x^2 + 5$

b. $5 - x^2$

c. $(x - 2)^2 + 3$

d. $7 - (x + 5)^2$

e. $x^2 + 6x + 7$

f. $12 + 2x - x^2$

8-3 Inverses

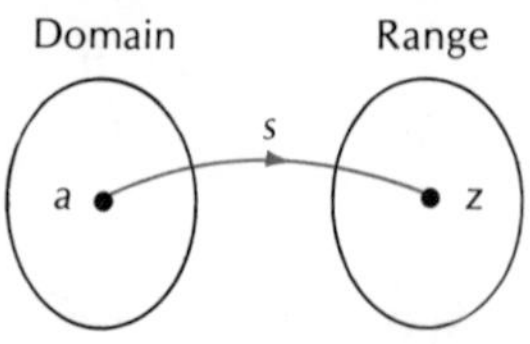

London Bridge was dismantled in England and then reassembled in a park in the state of Arizona. The acts of dismantling and reassembling represent inverse operations, since the bridge was put together in the inverse order in which it was taken down.

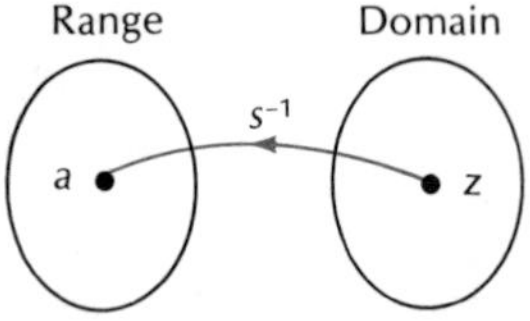

Inverses are operations that "undo" one another. Therefore, if a relation s maps domain element a onto range element z, then the **inverse** of s maps z onto a. The inverse of s is denoted by $\mathbf{s^{-1}}$. Therefore, if $s: a \rightarrow z$, then $s^{-1}: z \rightarrow a$.

EXAMPLE 1: Given the relation s:{(3, 1), (−2, 5), (4, 3), (2, 8), (1, −1)}, find s^{-1}.

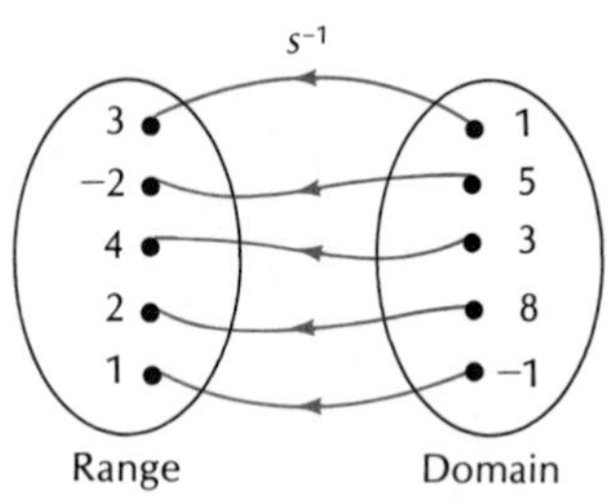

To find s^{-1}, reverse the order of the domain and range elements for each ordered pair.

Since s is {(3, 1), (−2, 5), (4, 3), (2, 8), (1, −1)}, then s^{-1} is {(1, 3), (5, −2), (3, 4), (8, 2), (−1, 1)}.

Notice that the domain of s is the range of s^{-1}, and that the range of s is the domain of s^{-1}.

For the relation s given in Example 1, $A(3, 1)$ is in s and $B(1, 3)$ is in s^{-1}.
The coordinates of the midpoint of $\overline{AB}$ are $\left(\frac{3+1}{2}, \frac{1+3}{2}\right)$, or (2, 2).

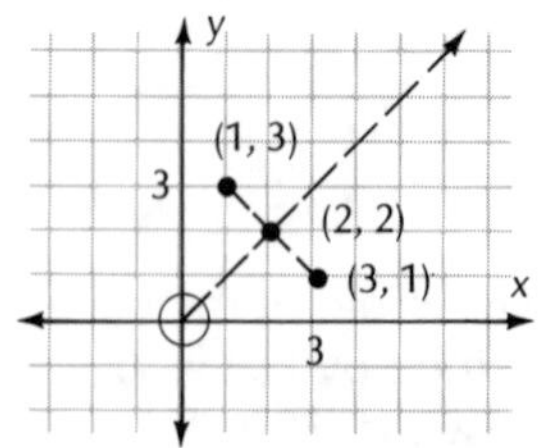

In general, for any point $P(a, b)$ in a relation s, the corresponding point in s^{-1} is $Q(b, a)$. The midpoint of $\overline{PQ}$ is $\left(\frac{a+b}{2}, \frac{a+b}{2}\right)$, which lies on the line $y = x$.
It appears that each point in s^{-1} is the mirror image of a point in s in the line $y = x$.
Therefore, the graphs of a relation and its inverse are reflections of one another through the line $y = x$.

EXAMPLE 2: Graph the inverse of $f(x) = \frac{2}{3}x - 2$.

First, graph $y = \frac{2}{3}x - 2$.
Then reflect the graph in the line $y = x$.

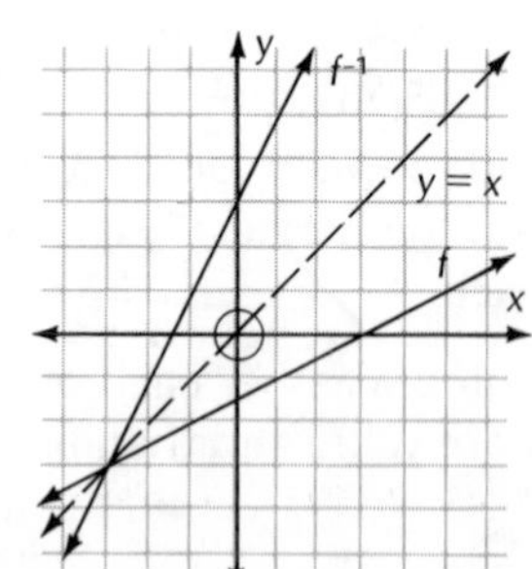

EXERCISE 8-3

A 1. Find the inverse relation of each given relation.

a. $s:\{(3, 6), (2, 4), (1, 2), (0, 0)\}$

b. $f:\{(-3, 5), (2, 7), (6, -1), (4, 3)\}$

c. $T:\{(9, 3), (4, -2), (4, 2), (1, -1)\}$

d. $G:\{(1, 1), (2, 6), (-3, 12), (4, 20), (-5, 30)\}$

2. a. Given that $S:\{(2, 5), (3, 1), (0, 6)\}$, find the domain of S^{-1}.

b. Given that $Q:\{(-3, 1), (-2, 2), (5, 4)\}$, find the range of Q^{-1}.

3. Copy the graph of each function. Sketch the inverse of each function by reflecting each graph in the line $y = x$.

a.

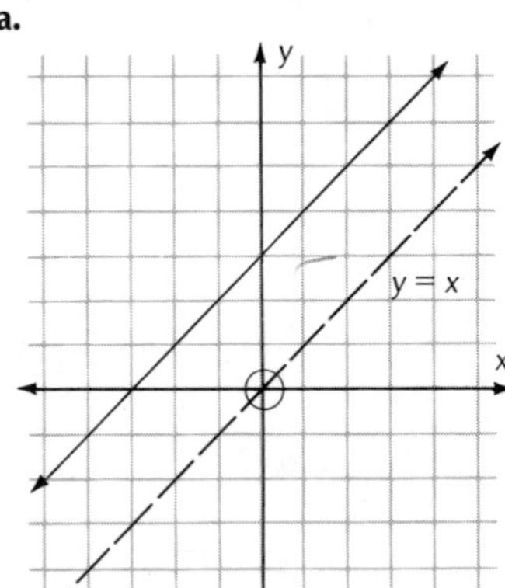

b.

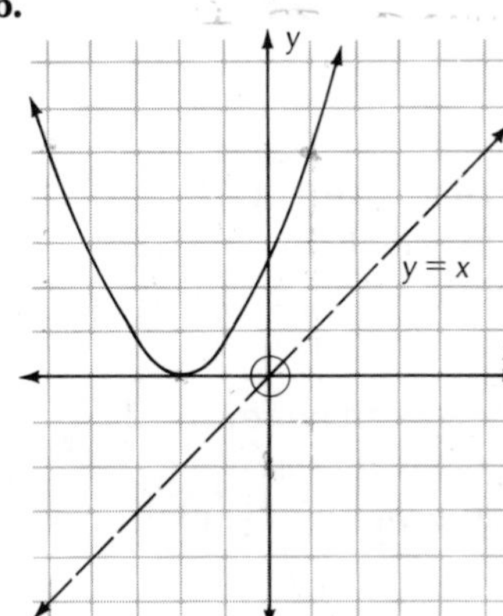

c.

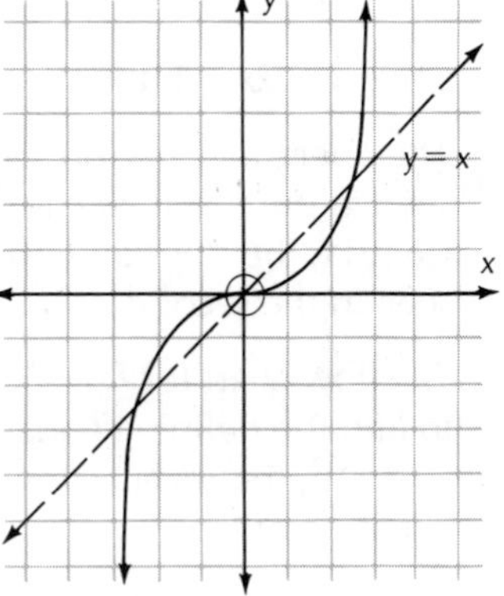

B 4. Graph the inverse of each given relation.

a. $s:\{(5, 2), (3, 1), (-1, -1), (-3, -2)\}$

b. $f(x) = x - 3$

c. $g(x) = \frac{3}{2}x + 3$

d. $h(x) = x^2$

e. $f(x) = (x - 2)^2 - 1$

f. $k(x) = x^2 + x - 1$

5. a. The relation S contains (3, 7) as an element. Name at least one element of S^{-1}.

b. The function S contains (3, 7). The function Q contains (5, 3). Could S and Q be inverses?

c. $S(x): y = 3x - 2$ and the domain of S is $\{0, 3, 4, -1\}$. What is the range of S^{-1}?

d. $Q(x) = x^2$ and the domain of Q is $\{-2, -1, 0, 1, 2\}$. List the domain and range of Q^{-1}. Is Q^{-1} a function?

C 6. The constant function has the form $y = k$. What is the equation of the inverse of this function? Is the inverse a function?

7. Find an equation of the inverse of each given function by graphing.

a. $x + 2y = 5$

b. $3x - y = 5$

c. $2x + 3y = 12$

just write the inverse

8-4 Inverse of a Function

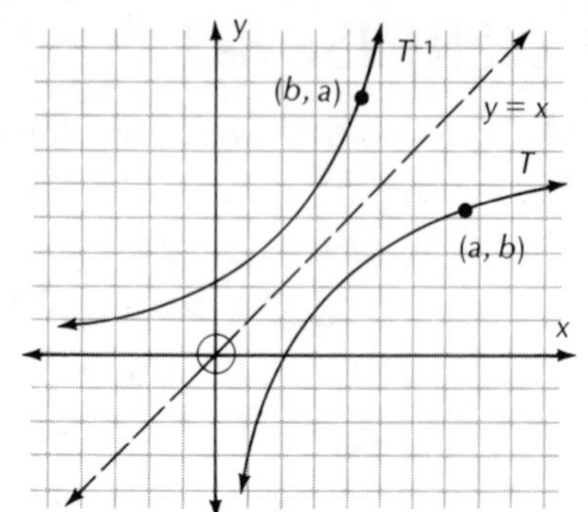

When the graph of a relation T is reflected in the line $y = x$, the resulting graph is the graph of T^{-1}, the inverse of T.

Each point $A(a, b)$ in T has a reflection image $B(b, a)$ in T^{-1}. To find the coordinates of B, the image of A, interchange the coordinates of A.

Use the idea that an inverse is an undoing operation, and the defining equation of f^{-1} can be derived from the defining equation of f.

To illustrate this, consider the function

$$f(x): x \rightarrow y = 2x - 1.$$

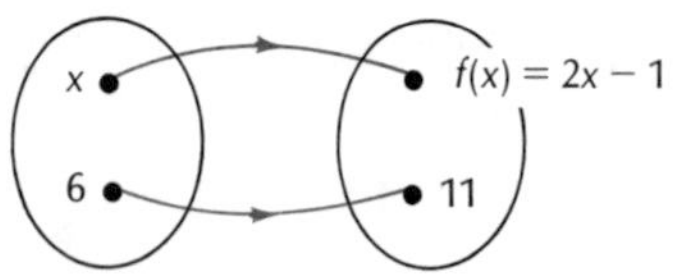

Since $x \rightarrow 2x - 1$, then $6 \rightarrow 11$.

The operations performed on 6 to give 11 can be seen in the first flow chart at the right. To obtain 6 from 11, the steps and operations are reversed, as seen in the second flow chart.

$\boxed{6} \rightarrow \boxed{\times 2} \rightarrow \boxed{-1} \rightarrow \boxed{11}$

$\boxed{6} \leftarrow \boxed{\div 2} \leftarrow \boxed{+1} \leftarrow \boxed{11}$

The flow chart for $f: x \rightarrow y = 2x - 1$ can be reversed to find the defining equation of f^{-1}. If f^{-1} is a function, the reverse flow chart gives the defining equation of f^{-1}.

$\boxed{x} \rightarrow \boxed{\times 2} \rightarrow \boxed{-1} \rightarrow \boxed{y} = 2x - 1$

$\dfrac{x+1}{2} = \boxed{y} \leftarrow \boxed{\div 2} \leftarrow \boxed{+1} \leftarrow \boxed{x}$

$$\therefore f^{-1}: x \rightarrow y = \frac{x+1}{2}.$$

By comparing the defining equations of f and f^{-1}, a relationship between the two equations can be found.

This defines f. $\boxed{y = 2x - 1}$

Solve for x in f^{-1}.

This defines f^{-1}.

$$y = \frac{x+1}{2}$$

$$2y = x + 1$$

$$\boxed{x = 2y - 1}$$

Notice that one equation can be obtained from the other by interchanging x and y in the equations. The equations that define inverse functions should "undo" one another. That is, if one function maps a onto b, then the inverse function should map b back onto a.

EXAMPLE 1: **a.** Given that $f(x) = 3x + 2$, find $f(2)$ and $f^{-1}(8)$.

Since $f(x) = 3x + 2$, then $f(2) = 3(2) + 2$, or 8.

Since $f(x) = 3x + 2$, then $f^{-1}(x) = \frac{x - 2}{3}$.

So, $f^{-1}(8) = \frac{8 - 2}{3}$, or 2.

Therefore, $f(2) = 8$ and $f^{-1}(8) = 2$.

b. Given that $f(x) = 3x + 2$, find $f^{-1}(f(2))$.

First, notice that $f(2) = 8$, from part **a**.
So, $f^{-1}(f(2)) = f^{-1}(8)$.
Use the defining equation of $f^{-1}(x)$, and $f^{-1}(8) = \frac{8 - 2}{3}$, or 2.
$\therefore f^{-1}(f(2)) = 2$.

In Example 1, you could use a similar process to show that $f(f^{-1}(8)) = 8$.

The preceding results can be summarized as: $f(f^{-1}(n)) = n$ and $f^{-1}(f(n)) = n$. The result of applying f and f^{-1}, one after the other, is the identity function $I: x \rightarrow x$.

> In general, f and g are inverses if and only if $f(g(n)) = n$ for n in the domain of g, or $g(f(n)) = n$ for n in the domain of f. Then $g = f^{-1}$ and $f = g^{-1}$. The graph of f^{-1} is the reflection image of the graph of f in the line $y = x$.

EXAMPLE 2: **a.** Find the inverse of $f: x \rightarrow y = \frac{1}{x + 1}$.

Since $f: y = \frac{1}{x + 1}$, then $f^{-1}: x = \frac{1}{y + 1}$. Interchange x and y.

$(y + 1)(x) = (y + 1)\left(\frac{1}{y + 1}\right)$ Substitute for x.

$(y + 1)(x) = 1$

$y + 1 = \frac{1}{x}$

$y = \frac{1}{x} - 1$

b. Prove that f and f^{-1} are indeed inverses for f in part **a**.

Since f^{-1} is the inverse, then $f^{-1}(f(n)) = n$.

So, $f^{-1}(f(n)) = f^{-1}\left(\frac{1}{n + 1}\right)$

$= \frac{1}{\left(\frac{1}{n + 1}\right)} - 1$

$= (n + 1) - 1$

$= n$

Therefore, f and f^{-1} are inverses.

EXAMPLE 3: Graph $h: x \rightarrow y = \frac{1}{2}x^2 - 1$ and its inverse h^{-1}.

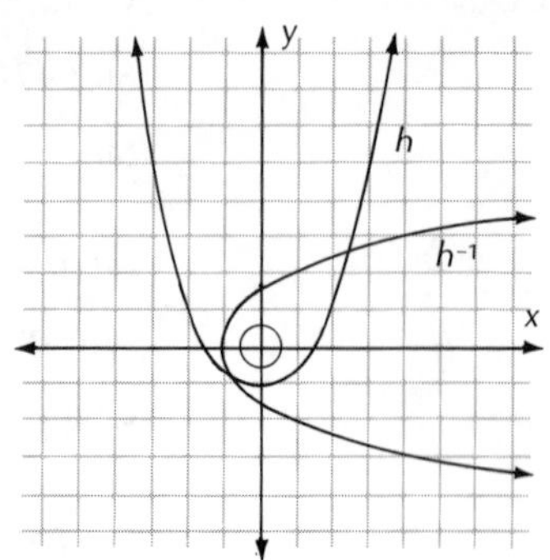

To find the defining equation of h^{-1}, interchange x and y, and then solve for y.

$$x = \frac{1}{2}y^2 - 1$$

$$x + 1 = \frac{1}{2}y^2$$

$$y^2 = 2x + 2$$

The defining equation of h^{-1} is $y^2 = 2x + 2$. The graphs of h and h^{-1} are parabolas as shown.

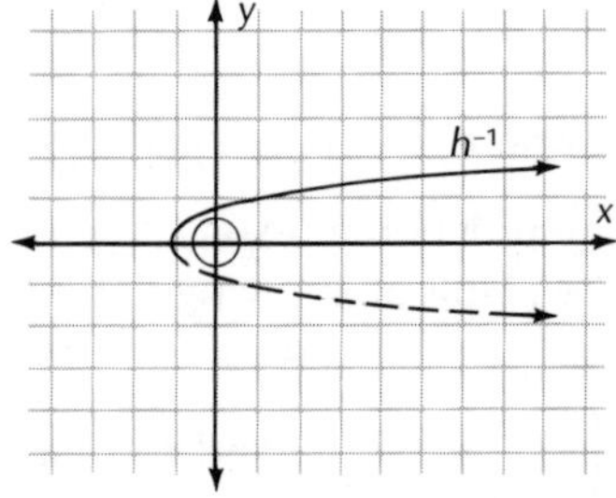

The equations $y^2 = 2x + 2$ and $y = \frac{1}{2}x^2 - 1$ define inverses, but note that $y^2 = 2x + 2$ does not define a function.

If the graph were considered in two parts—the "top" part and the "bottom" part, each part would represent a function. Since $y^2 = 2x + 2$, then $y = \sqrt{2x + 2}$ or $y = -\sqrt{2x + 2}$.

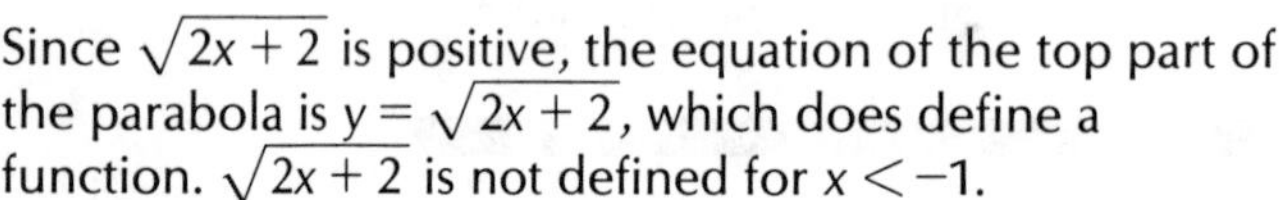

Since $\sqrt{2x + 2}$ is positive, the equation of the top part of the parabola is $y = \sqrt{2x + 2}$, which does define a function. $\sqrt{2x + 2}$ is not defined for $x < -1$.

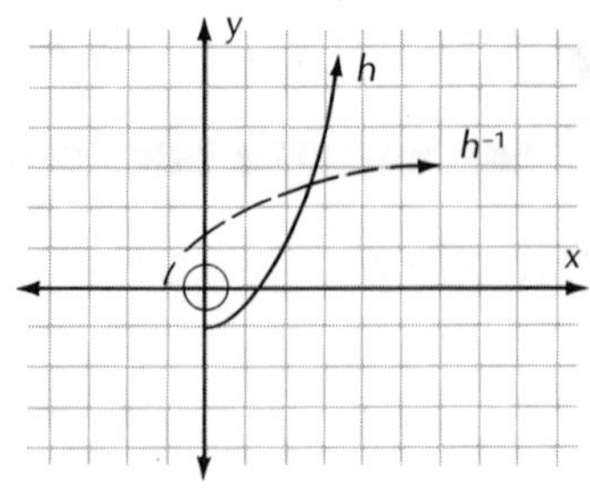

The graph of $y = \sqrt{2x + 2}$ is the reflection image of $y = \frac{1}{2}x^2 - 1$, where $x \geq 0$. Therefore, restricting the range of h^{-1} to $\{y \mid y \geq 0\}$ will ensure that h^{-1} is a function.

In general, to determine whether f and f^{-1} are functions, consider the case where f^{-1} is *not* a function. Here, a vertical line cuts the graph of f^{-1} in points (a, b) and (a, c). The corresponding points on the graph of f would be (b, a) and (c, a). These two points lie on a *horizontal line*.

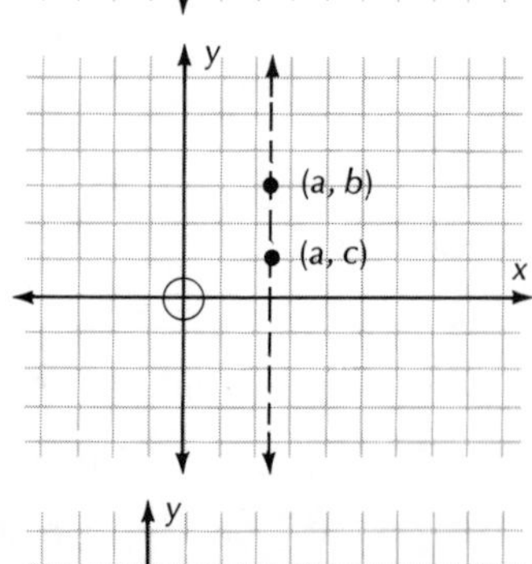

Thus, if f^{-1} is not a function, some horizontal line will cut the graph of f in at least 2 points. This is called the **horizontal line test**.

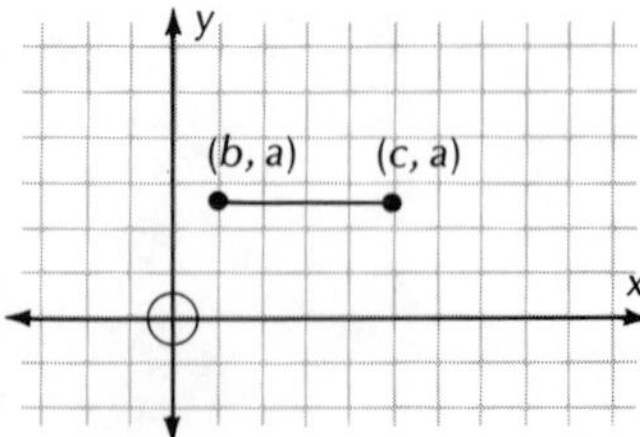

If a horizontal line cuts the graph of a function f in two or more points, then f^{-1} is not a function.

EXAMPLE 4: For the function represented by each graph, determine if the inverse is a function.

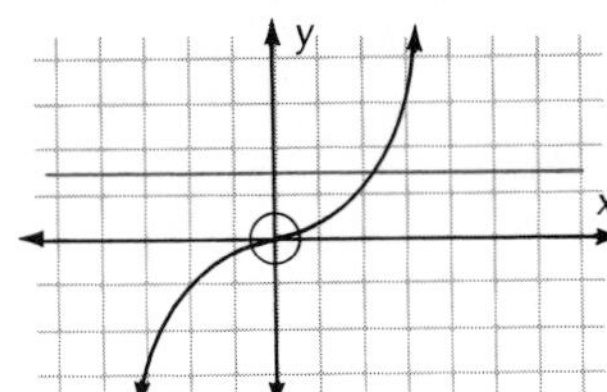

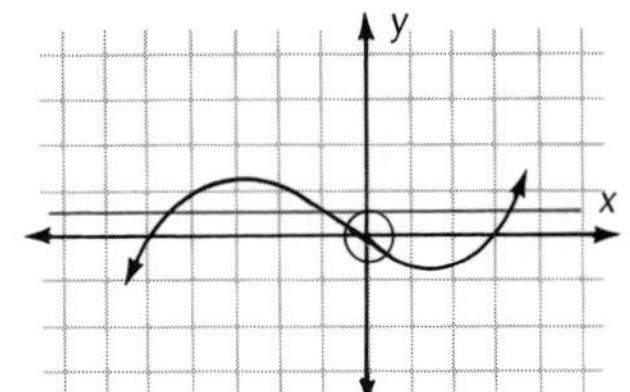

f passes the horizontal line test.
f^{-1} is a function.

g does not pass the horizontal line test.
g^{-1} is not a function.

EXAMPLE 5: Given the function h shown in the graph, how could h be restricted so that h^{-1} is a function?

Part of the graph of h must be removed so that the horizontal line test holds. Removing the points on the graph with coordinates (x, y) such that $x \leq -2$ ensures that h passes the horizontal line test. Therefore, restrict the domain of h to be $\{x|\ x \geq -2\}$.

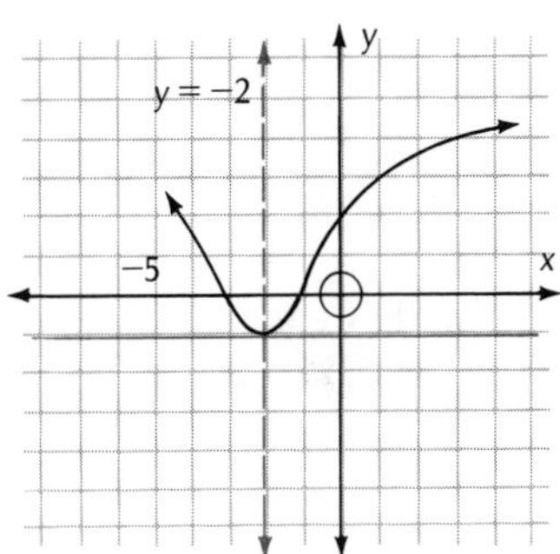

Of course, f^{-1} would also be a function if the domain were restricted to values greater than −2. For example, $\{x|\ x \geq -1\}$ would also ensure f^{-1} to be a function.

EXERCISE 8-4

A **1.** Each given equation defines a function. Find an equation of the inverse of each function.

a. $y = 3x$ **b.** $y = x - 1$ **c.** $y = 2x + 3$

d. $y = 3x + 5$ **e.** $y = \frac{3x + 2}{5}$ **f.** $y = \frac{2x + 1}{3}$

g. $y = -x$ **h.** $y = 3(x + 4)$ **i.** $y = -(2x - 5)$

2. For the function represented by each graph, which has an inverse that is also a function?

a.

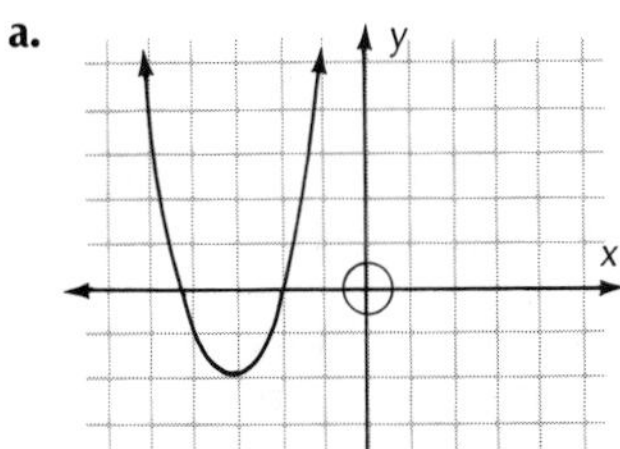

b.

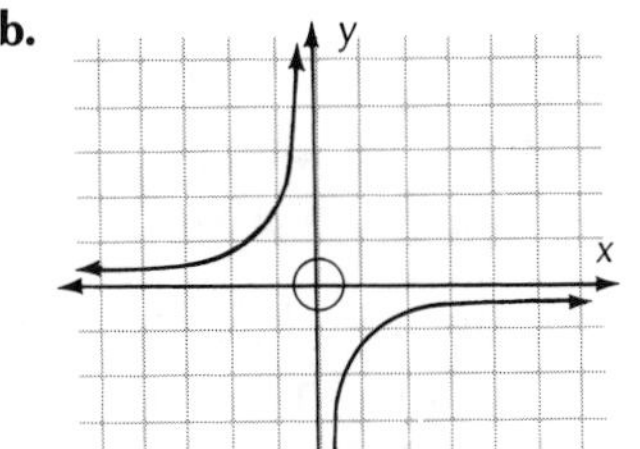

c.

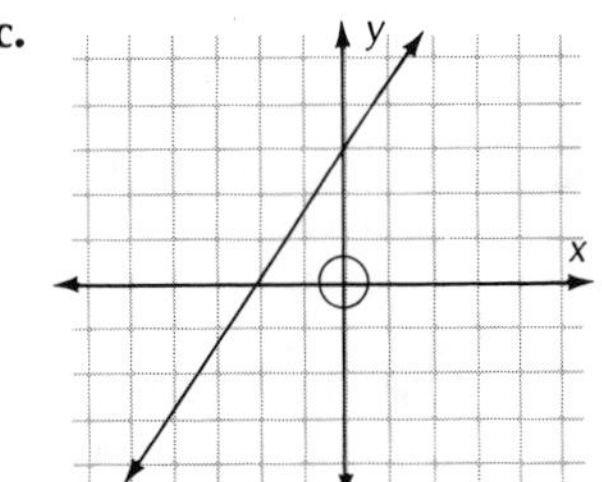

B 3. Find the inverse of the function defined by each given equation.

a. $y = \dfrac{1}{x}$ b. $y = x^2$ c. $y = x^3$

d. $y = \dfrac{1}{x - 1}$ e. $y = \dfrac{1}{x^2}$ f. $y = \sqrt[3]{3}$

g. $y = 3x^2 - 2$ h. $y = \dfrac{1}{2x + 3}$ i. $y = \dfrac{1}{x^2 - 3}$

4. How could the domain of each given function be restricted so that each inverse is also a function?

a.

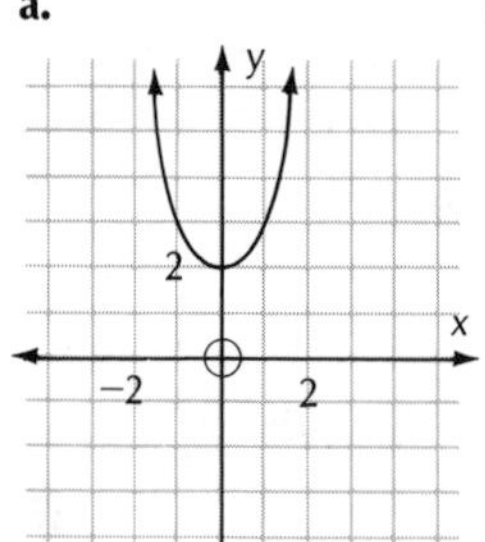

b.

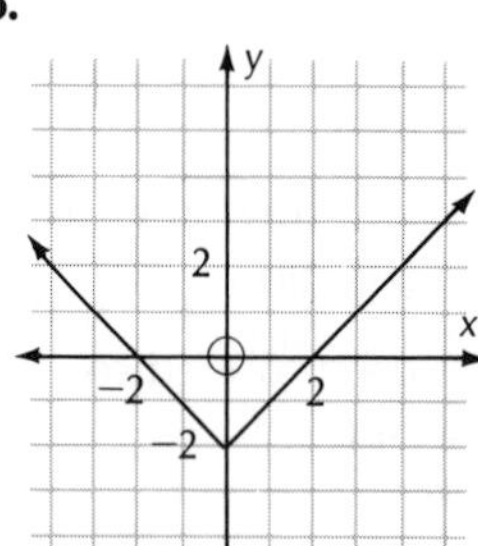

c.

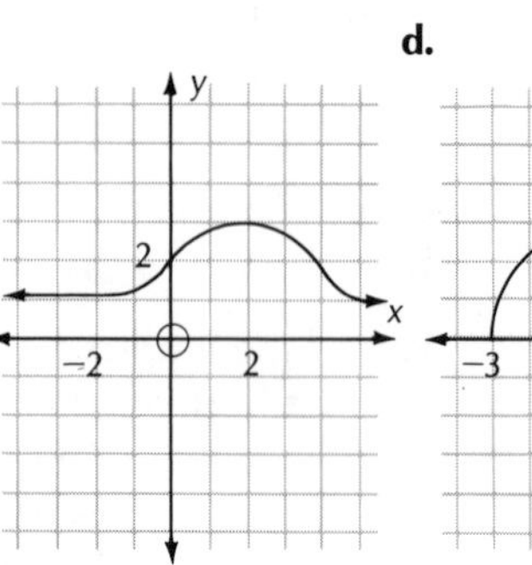

d.

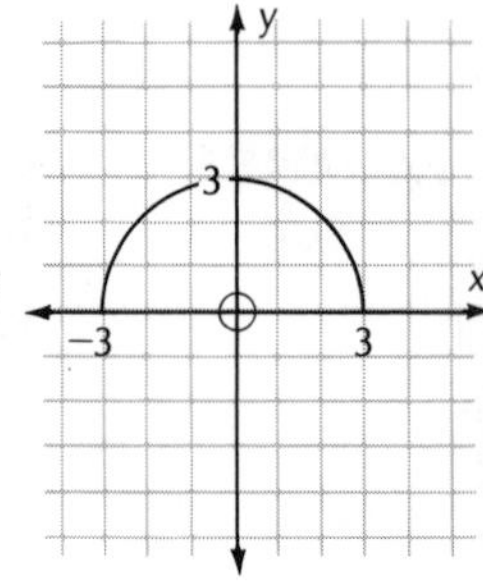

5. For each given pair of functions, determine whether or not f and g are inverses by finding $f(g(x))$.

a. $f(x) = 2x + 1$, $g(x) = \dfrac{x - 1}{2}$ b. $f(x) = \frac{1}{3}x - 1$, $g(x) = 3x + 3$ c. $f(x) = 3x + 2$, $g(x) = \dfrac{x - 3}{2}$

d. $f(x) = \dfrac{1}{x}$, $g(x) = x^2$ e. $f(x) = \sqrt{x - 1}$, $g(x) = x^2 + 1$ f. $f(x) = \sqrt{x + 1}$, $g(x) = (x + 1)^3$

g. $f(x) = \dfrac{1}{x + 1}$, $g(x) = \dfrac{1 - x}{x}$ h. $f(x) = \dfrac{1}{2x + 1}$, $g(x) = 2x + 1$ i. $f(x) = x^2 + 2$, $g(x) = \sqrt{x - 2}$

6. Graph each given function and its inverse on the same set of axes. If necessary, restrict the domain of f so that the inverse is also a function.

a. $f(x) = \dfrac{1}{x^2}$ b. $f(x) = \sqrt{x + 3}$ c. $f(x) = -\dfrac{\sqrt{x - 1}}{3}$

d. $f(x) = 4 - x^2$ e. $f(x) = \sqrt{x}$ f. $f(x) = x^3$

C 7. The quadratic function Q has a defining equation in the form $Q(x) = ax^2 + bx + c$, where $a, b, c \in \mathbf{R}$, and $a \neq 0$. Is Q^{-1} a function?

8. The function L is a linear function defined by $L(x) = ax + b$, where $a, b \in \mathbf{R}$, and $a \neq 0$. What restrictions could be placed on a, or b, or both to ensure that L^{-1} is also a function?

Review

1. Given that $f(x) = 3x^2 - 2$ and the domain of f is $\{-1, 0, 1, 2\}$, find the range of f.

2. Determine the domain and range of the function defined by each given equation.

   a. $y = 2x + 5$ b. $y = \dfrac{1}{x+2}$ c. $y = \dfrac{1}{x^2}$

   d. $y = 2x^2 + 3$ e. $y = \sqrt{x-4}$ f. $y = \sqrt{x^2 - 4}$

3. State whether or not each given relation is also a function.

   a. $\{(0, 3), (2, 3), (5, 1), (-1, 1)\}$

   b. 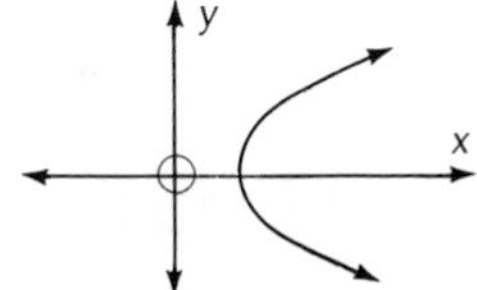

   c. 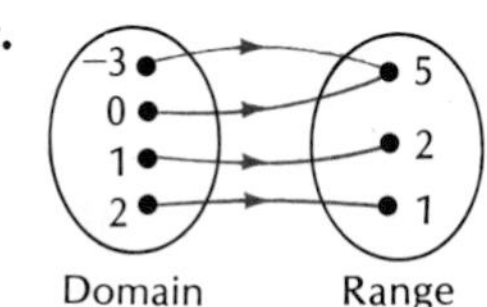

4. Evaluate each of the following, given that $f(x) = 2x + 5$, $g(x) = x^2 - 1$, and $h(x) = \dfrac{6}{x-2}$.

   a. $f(3)$ b. $g(-3)$ c. $h(4)$ d. $g(5) - h(1)$ e. $\dfrac{3f(2)}{h(0)}$ f. $\dfrac{f(7) - g(8)}{h(-1)}$

5. Find the inverse of each given relation.

   a. $s = \{(3, 7), (2, 5), (1, 3), (0, 1), (-1, 2), (-2, 3)\}$ b. $f(x) = \dfrac{x+3}{2}$

   c. $g(x) = 2x + 5$ d. $h{:}y = \dfrac{1}{x+3}$ e. $k{:}y = \sqrt{x-2}$ f. $m{:}y = x^{\frac{1}{3}} - 7$

6. For each function graphed below, determine whether the inverse is also a function.

   a. 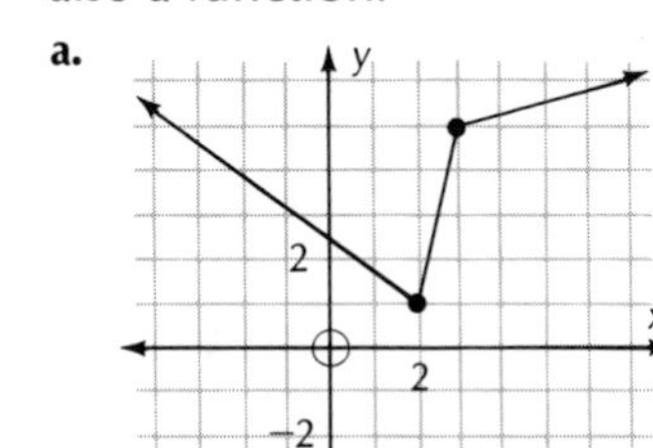

   b. 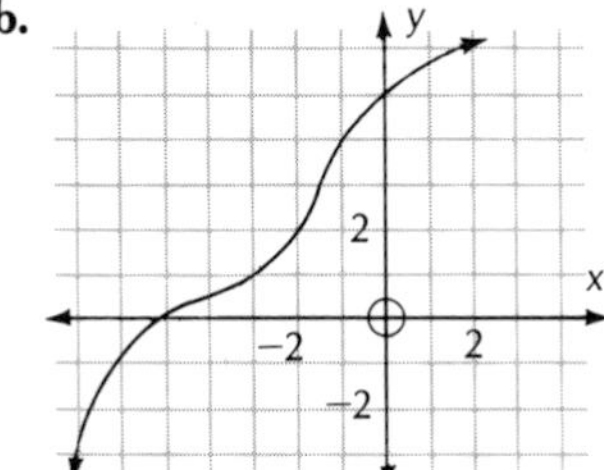

   c. 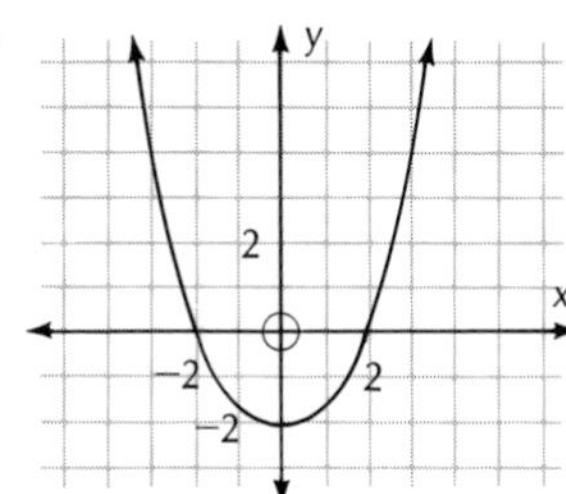

7. a. For each inverse in question 6 that is not a function, identify restrictions on the domain that would ensure the inverse is a function. Sketch the graph of each inverse.

   b. Classify each function in question 6 as linear, quadratic, or piecewise linear.

8. Determine whether or not f and g are inverses by finding $f(g(x))$.

   a. $f{:}y = 4x + 1$, $g{:}y = \dfrac{x-1}{4}$

   b. $f{:}y = x^2 - 1$, $g{:}y = \sqrt{x+1}$

   c. $f{:}y = \sqrt{x+2}$, $g{:}y = x^2 - 2$

8-5 Reflections and Translations

When a reflection or a translation is performed on the graph of an equation, the equation changes in a predictable manner.

EXAMPLE 1: Compare the graphs of $y = f(x)$ and $y = -f(x)$, for $f(x) = 2x + 3$.

$y = f(x)$ is the same as $y = 2x + 3$.
$y = -f(x)$ is the same as $y = -(2x + 3)$.
Graph both functions on the same axes.

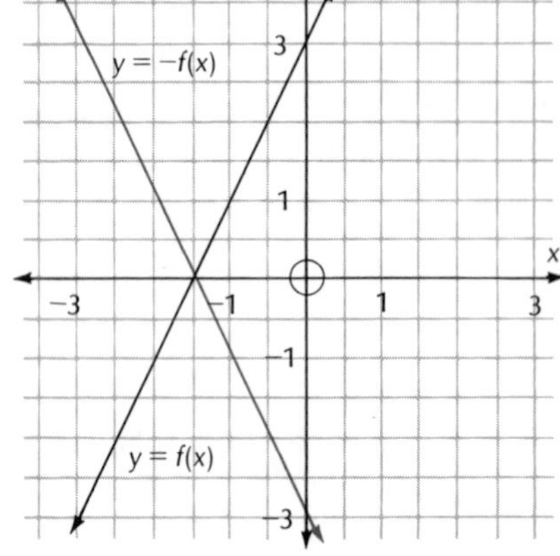

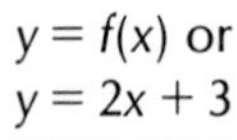

$y = f(x)$ or
$y = 2x + 3$

x	y
0	3
$-\frac{3}{2}$	0

$y = -f(x)$ or
$y = -(2x + 3)$

x	y
0	-3
$-\frac{3}{2}$	0

The graph of $y = -(2x + 3)$ is the image of $y = 2x + 3$ under reflection in the x-axis. Notice that (x, y) in $f(x)$ maps onto $(x, -y)$ in $-f(x)$.

EXAMPLE 2: Compare the graphs of $y = f(x)$ and $y = f(-x)$, for $f(x) = 2x + 3$.

$y = 2x + 3$

x	y
0	3
$-\frac{3}{2}$	0

$y = 2(-x) + 3$
$= -2x + 3$

x	y
0	-3
$\frac{3}{2}$	0

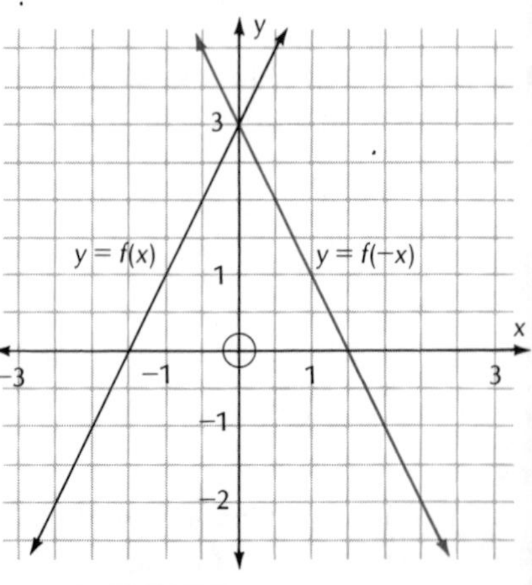

The graph of $y = -2x + 3$ is the image of the graph of $y = 2x + 3$ under reflection in the y-axis. Each (x, y) in $f(x)$ maps onto $(-x, y)$ in $f(-x)$.

- The graph of $y = -f(x)$ is the image of the graph of $y = f(x)$ under reflection in the x-axis.
- The graph of $y = f(-x)$ is the image of the graph of $y = f(x)$ under reflection in the y-axis.

EXAMPLE 3: Compare the graphs of $y = f(x)$ and $y = f(x + 3)$, given that $f(x) = x^2 + 2$.

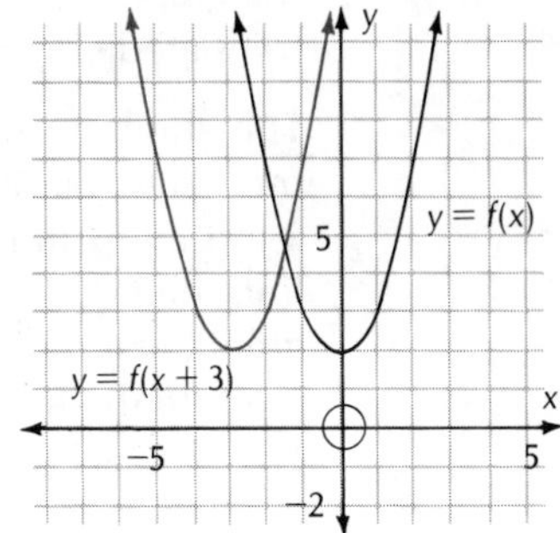

$y = x^2 + 2$

x	y
±3	11
±2	7
±1	3
0	2

$y = f(x + 3)$
$= (x + 3)^2 + 2$

x	y
−3	2
−2	3
−1	7
0	11

The graph of $y = f(x + 3)$ is the image of the graph of $y = f(x)$, shifted, or translated, 3 units *left*.

You can confirm, in a similar way, that the graph of $y = f(x - 3)$ is the image of the graph of $y = f(x)$, translated 3 units *right*.

- The graph of $y = f(x - a)$, $a > 0$, is the image of the graph of $y = f(x)$, translated a units *right*.
- The graph of $y = f(x + a)$, $a > 0$, is the image of the graph of $y = f(x)$, translated a units *left*.

EXAMPLE 4: Given that $f(x) = x^2 + 2$, compare the graphs of $y = f(x)$ and $y - 4 = f(x)$.

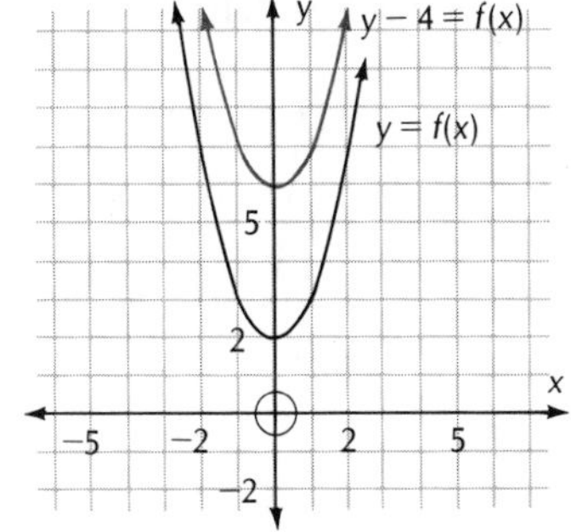

$y = x^2 + 2$

x	y
±3	11
±2	7
±1	3
0	2

$y - 4 = f(x)$
$y = x^2 + 6$

x	y
±3	15
±2	10
±1	7
0	6

The graph of $y - 4 = f(x)$ is the image of the graph of $y = x^2 + 2$ translated *up* 4 units.

You can show, in a similar way, that the graph of $y + 4 = f(x)$ is the image of the graph of $y = f(x)$ shifted *down* 4 units.

- The graph of $y - b = f(x)$, $b > 0$, is the image of the graph of $y = f(x)$, translated b units *up*.
- The graph of $y + b = f(x)$, $b > 0$, is the image of the graph of $y = f(x)$, translated b units *down*.

EXAMPLE 5: The graph of $x^2 + y^2 = 4$ is shown below. A translation of the graph is also shown. Find an equation of the translated graph.

The graph of $x^2 + y^2 = 4$ has been translated 5 units right along the x-axis and 2 units down the y-axis. To find the equation of the translated graph, first replace x with $(x - 5)$ to indicate the translation 5 units right. Then replace y with $(y + 2)$ to indicate the translation 2 units down.

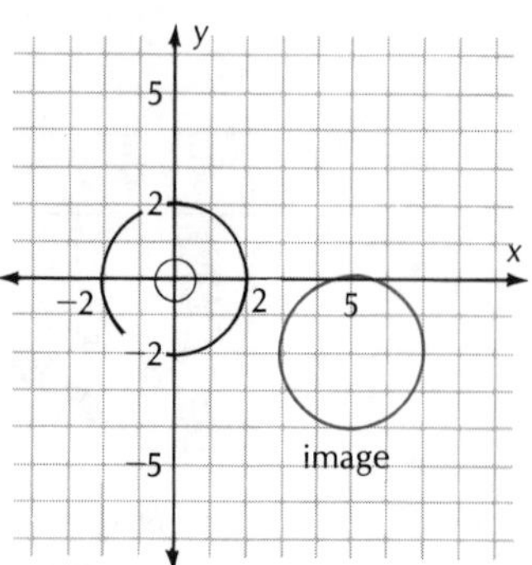

Thus, the equation of the translated graph is $(x - 5)^2 + (y + 2)^2 = 4$.

EXERCISE 8-5

A **1.** Describe the effect each transformation has on a given point (x, y).

a. $(x, y) \to (x - 3, y)$
b. $(x, y) \to (x, -y)$
c. $(x, y) \to (x, y - 2)$
d. $(x, y) \to (x + 1, y)$
e. $(x, y) \to (-x, y)$
f. $(x, y) \to (x, y + 5)$
g. $(x, y) \to (-x, -y)$
h. $(x, y) \to (-x, y - 2)$
i. $(x, y) \to (x + 2, -y)$
j. $(x, y) \to (x + 3, y - 1)$

2. A function and its transformation image are given below. Describe the transformation applied to each function.

a.

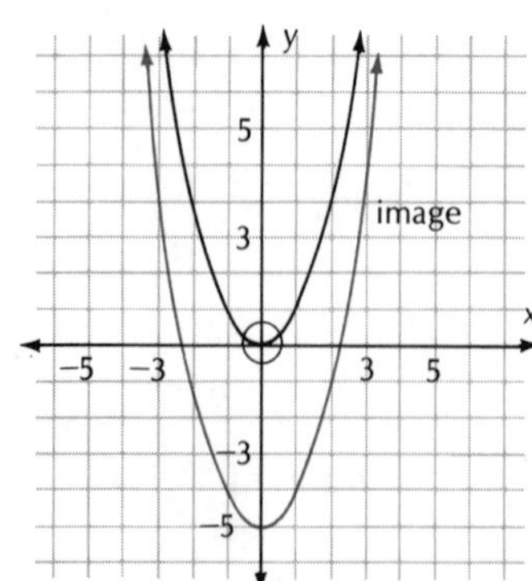

b.

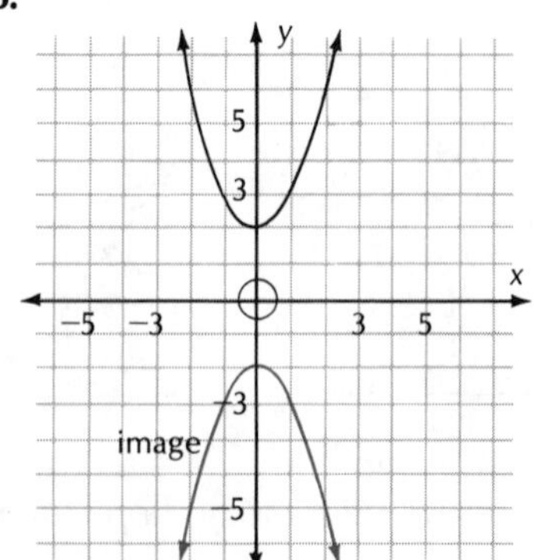

3. The equation of a curve and its transformation image are given. Describe the transformation applied in each case.

a. $y = 3x \to y - 2 = 3x$
b. $y = 3x \to y + 2 = 3x$
c. $y = 4x \to y = 4(x + 1)$
d. $y = 4x \to y = 4(x - 3)$
e. $y = 2x + 3 \to y = 2(-x) + 3$
f. $y = 2x + 3 \to y = -(2x+3)$
g. $y = x^2 \to y - 2 = (x + 1)^2$
h. $y = 3x^2 \to y = -3(x + 1)^2$
i. $y = 3x - 1 \to y + 2 = -3x - 1$
j. $y = x^2 \to y + 5 = (x - 4)^2$

B 4. The graph of each given function is transformed as indicated. Determine the equation of each transformed graph.

a. $y = x$; translated up 2 units
b. $y = x^2$; reflected in the x-axis
c. $y = 2x - 3$; translated left 5 units
d. $y = x^2 + 1$; translated right 7 units
e. $y = 3x + 5$; reflected in the y-axis
f. $y = 5x + 1$; translated down 10 units
g. $y = 2x^2$; translated up 1 unit and left 2 units
h. $y = 3x + 1$; reflected in the x-axis and then the y-axis
i. $y = 2x^2 - 1$; translated up 1 unit and reflected in the y-axis
j. $y = 3x^2$; reflected in the x-axis and translated 3 units right

5. The graph of $x^2 + y^2 = 9$ is given below. Using transformations, sketch the graph of each equation.

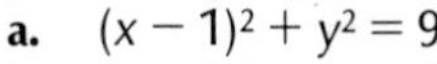

a. $(x - 1)^2 + y^2 = 9$
b. $(x - 3)^2 + (y + 2)^2 = 9$
c. $x^2 + (y + 5)^2 = 9$
d. $(x + 5)^2 + (y - 2)^2 = 9$
e. $x^2 + (y - 4)^2 = 9$

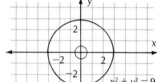

6. A graph and its image are given below. Find an equation of the image.

a.

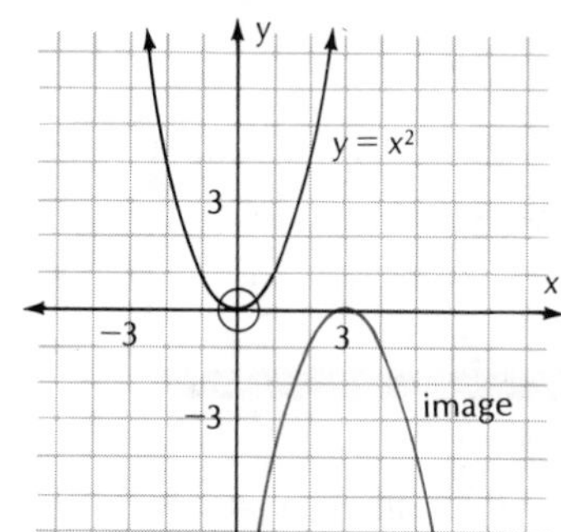

b.

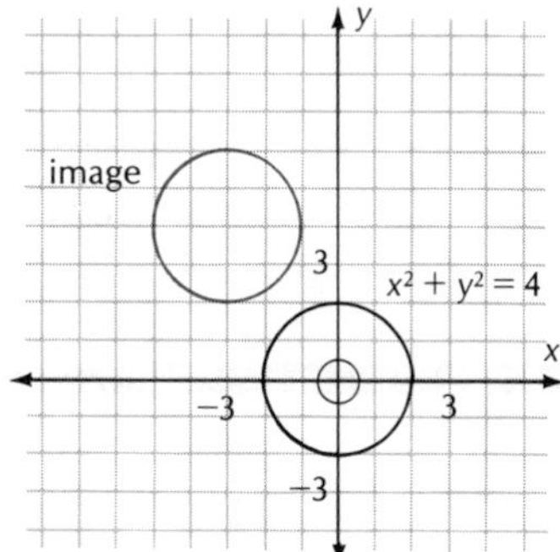

C 7. The *commutative* property does not always apply to transformations. That is, when two transformations are applied to a graph, the order in which the transformations are applied may affect the image. Apply each pair of transformations to several graphs in the order that the transformations are stated. Then apply the transformations in reverse order to determine if the order of application makes a difference in the result.

a. Translate 1 unit to the right; translate 2 units down.
b. Reflect in the x-axis; reflect in the y-axis.
c. Translate 1 unit to the right; reflect in the y-axis.
d. Translate 2 units up; reflect in the x-axis.

8-6 Horizontal and Vertical Stretches

In addition to being reflected and translated, graphs can also be "stretched" along the axes by a given factor. An equation of the graph obtained by a **stretch** is predictable, much like those for reflections and translations.

EXAMPLE 1: Compare the graphs of $y = f(x)$ and $4y = f(x)$, given that $f(x) = x^2$.

$y = x^2$

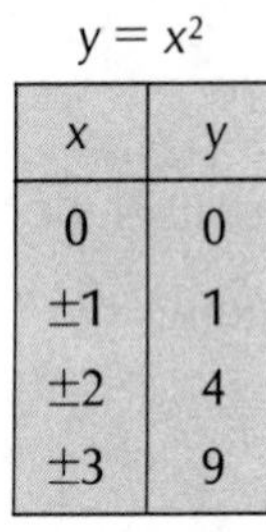

x	y
0	0
±1	1
±2	4
±3	9

$4y = x^2$

x	y
0	0
±1	$\frac{1}{4}$
±2	1
±3	$\frac{9}{4}$

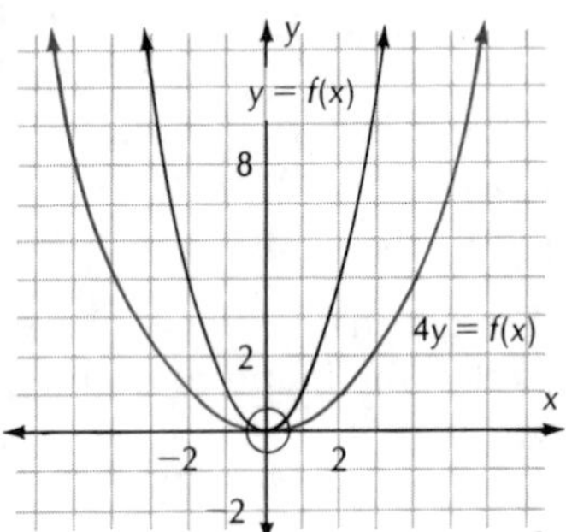

The graph of $4y = x^2$ is the image of the graph of $y = x^2$ under a **vertical stretch** of factor $\frac{1}{4}$.

Similarly, the graph of $\frac{y}{4} = x^2$ is the image of the graph of $y = x^2$ under a vertical stretch of factor 4.

- The graph of $ay = f(x)$, is the image of $y = f(x)$ under a vertical stretch of factor $\frac{1}{a}$.

EXAMPLE 2: Compare the graphs of $y = f(x)$ and $y = f(2x)$, given that $f(x) = x^2$.

$y = x^2$

x	y
0	0
±1	1
±2	4
±3	9

$y = (2x)^2$

x	y
0	0
$\pm\frac{1}{2}$	1
±1	4
$\pm\frac{3}{2}$	9

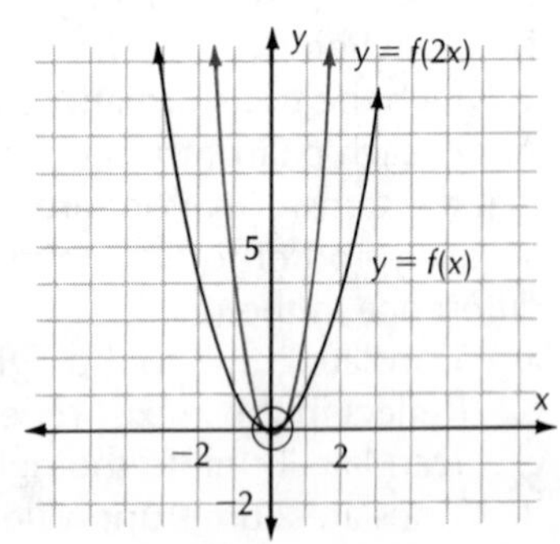

Notice that the values of x for $y = (2x)^2$ are half the values of x for $y = x^2$. The graph of $y = (2x)^2$ is the image of the graph of $y = x^2$ under a **horizontal stretch** of factor $\frac{1}{2}$.

Similarly, the graph of $y = \left(\frac{x}{2}\right)^2$ is the image of the graph of $y = x^2$ under a horizontal stretch of factor 2.

- The graph of $y = f(ax)$, $a > 0$, is the image of the graph of $y = f(x)$ under a horizontal strecth of factor $\frac{1}{a}$.

EXAMPLE 3: The graph of $x^2 + y^2 = 9$ is shown below, along with its image under a transformation. Find an equation of the transformation.

The graph shows two stretches.
One stretch is horizontal of factor 2.

So, x is replaced by $\frac{x}{2}$.

The other stretch is vertical of factor $\frac{1}{3}$. So, y is replaced by $3y$.

An equation of the image then is found by replacing these values of x and y in the original equation.

$$x^2 + y^2 = 9$$

$$\text{So, } \left(\frac{x}{2}\right)^2 + (3y)^2 = 9$$

$$\frac{x}{4} + 9y^2 = 9$$

$$x^2 + 36y^2 = 36$$

The new equation represents an **ellipse**.

Therefore, an equation of the image is $x^2 + 36y^2 = 36$.

When both stretch factors are equal, the transformation is called a **dilatation**. That is, if: $(x, y) \rightarrow (ax, ay)$ then, for example, the circle $x^2 + y^2 = 9$ becomes the circle $\left(\frac{x}{a}\right)^2 + \left(\frac{y}{a}\right)^2 = 9$ or $x^2 + y^2 = 9a^2$.

EXAMPLE 4: Given the graph of $y = x^2$, sketch the graph of $y - 2 = \left(\frac{x}{3}\right)^2$.

Since x is replaced with $\frac{x}{3}$, the graph shows a horizontal stretch of factor 3.

Since y is replaced with $y - 2$, the graph also shows a translation two units up from the y-axis.

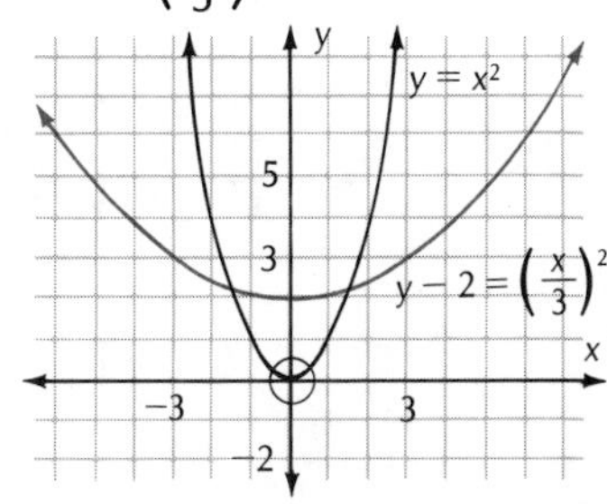

EXERCISE 8-6

A 1. Determine the transformations that have been applied to each graph to obtain its image.

a.

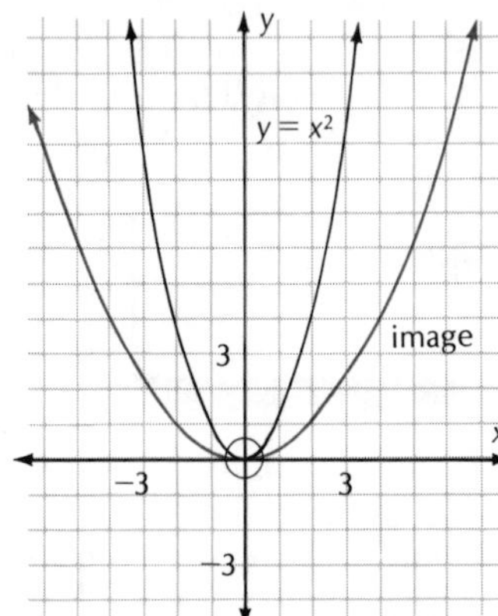

b.

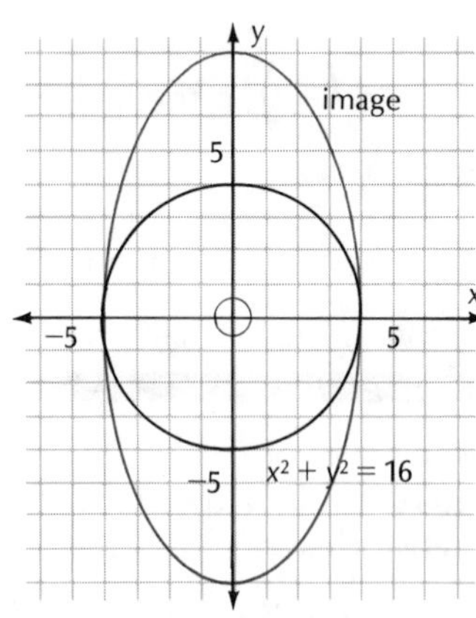

2. The equation of a graph and its transformation image are given. Describe the transformation(s) that have been applied to each equation to obtain the image.

a. $y = x^2 \rightarrow y = (5x)^2$

b. $y = 3x + 1 \rightarrow \frac{y}{2} = 3x + 1$

c. $y = 2x - 3 \rightarrow y = \frac{2}{3}x - 3$

d. $y = 3x^2 \rightarrow 5y = 3x^2$

e. $3y = x^2 \rightarrow y = x^2$

f. $2y = x^2 \rightarrow 4y + 1 = x^2$

3. A graph and its transformation image are shown. Given an equation of each graph, find an equation of its image.

a.

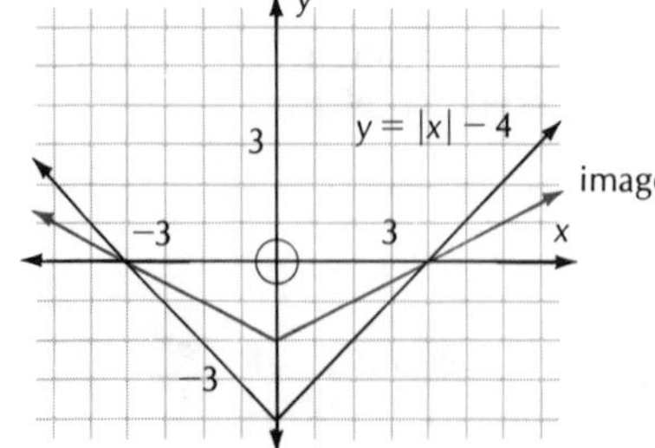

b.

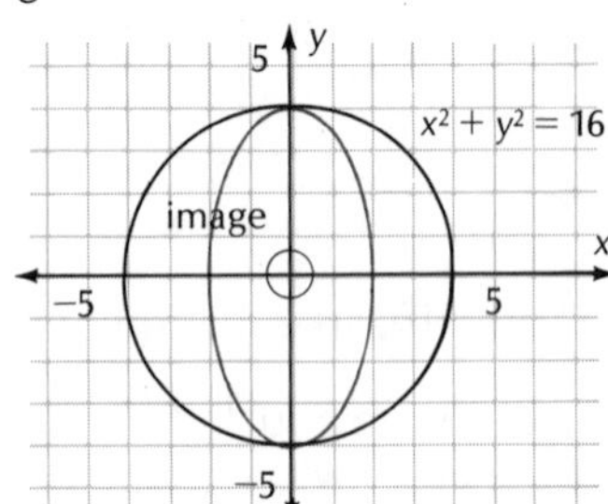

c.

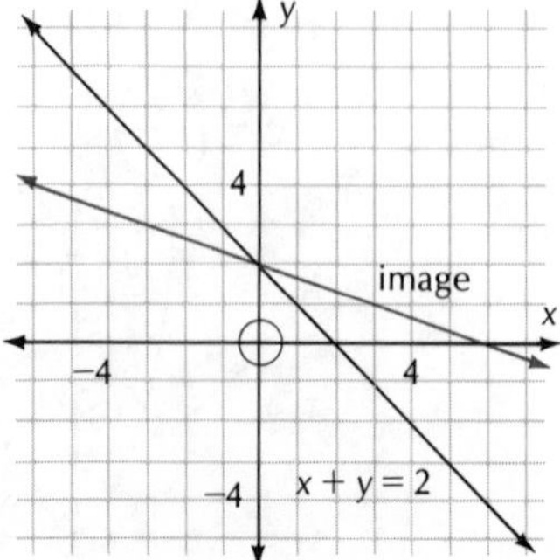

d.

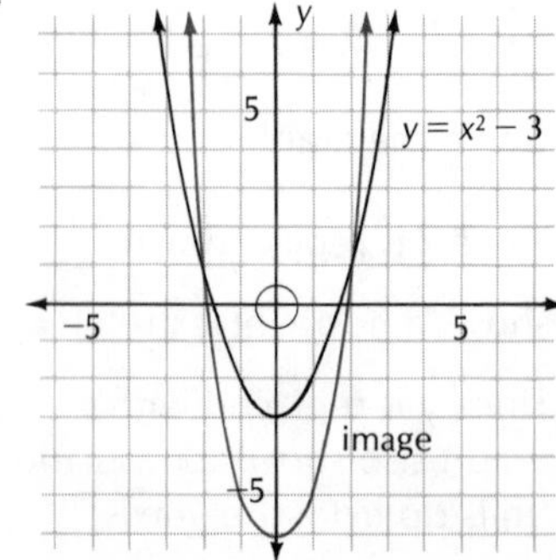

B 4. Given the graph of $y = f(x)$, sketch the graph of each given equation.

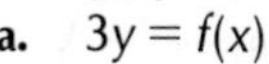

a. $3y = f(x)$

b. $y = f\left(\dfrac{x}{2}\right)$

c. $\dfrac{y}{2} = f(x)$

d. $\dfrac{y}{3} = f\left(\dfrac{x}{2}\right)$

e. $2y = f\left(\dfrac{x}{2}\right)$

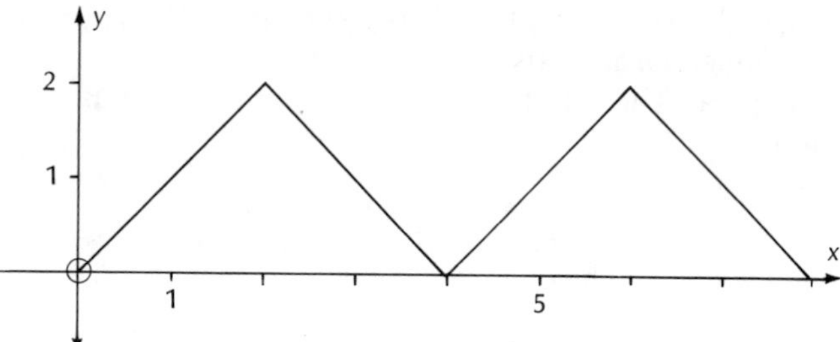

5. Determine what transformations have been applied to the graph of $x^2 + y^2 = 1$ to obtain the graph of each given equation. Graph each equation on a set of axes with the graph of $x^2 + y^2 = 1$.

a. $x^2 + y^2 = 25$ b. $\left(\dfrac{x}{2}\right)^2 + \left(\dfrac{y}{3}\right)^2 = 1$ c. $\left(\dfrac{x}{6}\right)^2 + \left(\dfrac{y}{6}\right)^2 = 1$

6. For each given pair of equations, describe the transformations that map the graph of the first equation onto the graph of the second equation.

a. $y = x \rightarrow y - 2 = 3x$ b. $y = x^2 \rightarrow \dfrac{y}{2} = (x + 1)^2$

c. $y = |x| \rightarrow y - 3 = |3x|$ d. $y = \dfrac{1}{x} \rightarrow -y = \dfrac{2}{x}$

e. $y = \sqrt{x} \rightarrow \dfrac{y}{3} = -\sqrt{x}$ f. $y = 2x^2 \rightarrow \dfrac{y}{2} = \sqrt{x}$

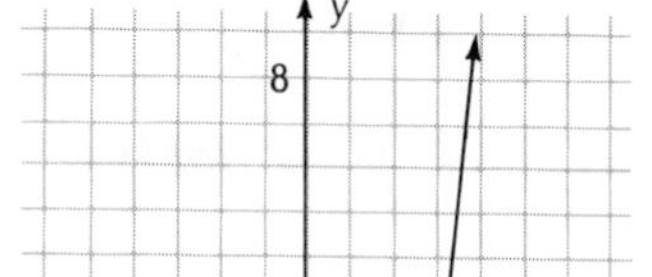

7. Given the graph of $y = f(x)$ at the right, sketch the graph of each equation.

a. $y + 3 = f(2x)$ b. $y = f(-3x)$

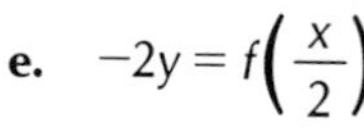

c. $\dfrac{y}{2} = f(x - 2)$ d. $y + 2 = f(x - 3)$

e. $-2y = f\left(\dfrac{x}{2}\right)$

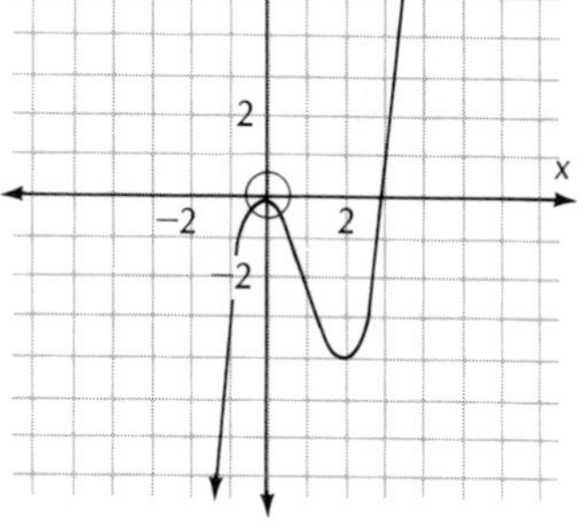

8. The graph of each given equation is transformed as described. Determine an equation of the graph of each transformation image.

a. $y = x$; a translation 3 units right along the x-axis and a vertical stretch of factor 4

b. $y = \dfrac{1}{x}$; a reflection in the y-axis and a horizontal stretch of factor $\frac{1}{2}$

c. $y = x^2$; a reflection in the x-axis and a vertical stretch of factor 3

d. $y = \frac{1}{2}x - 2$; a translation 4 units left along the x-axis and a vertical stretch of factor 2

8-7 Inverse Variation

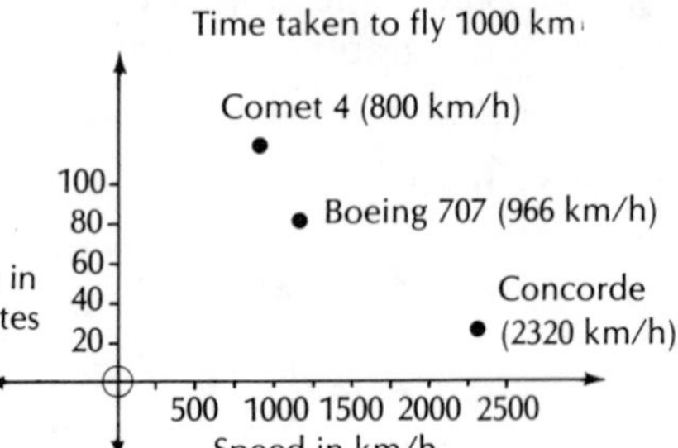

The graph shows the length of time taken by each of three commercial aircrafts to fly 1000 km at typical cruising speed. The set of ordered pairs (time, speed) is a function.

The Comet 4 cruises at 800 km/h.
The Boeing 707 cruises at 966 km/h.
The Concorde cruises at 2320 km/h.

As speed increases, time decreases. The relationship between speed, v, and time, t, is called an **inverse variation**. In this case, time **varies inversely** as speed. Notice that the product vt is a constant, 1000. This product is the **constant of variation**, k.

Since $vt = k$, then $t = \frac{k}{v}$. This can also be written as $t \propto \frac{1}{v}$.

> An inverse variation is a function defined by an equation in the form $xy = k$, $k \neq 0$. The relation between x and y is defined by $y = \frac{k}{x}$, $x \neq 0$, where k is the constant of proportionality.
> For (x_1, y_1) and (x_2, y_2) in the variation, $x_1y_1 = x_2y_2$ and $\frac{x_1}{x_2} = \frac{y_2}{y_1}$.

EXAMPLE: The wavelength of a radio wave is inversely proportional to its frequency, measured in kiloHertz (1 kHz = 1000 cycles per second). A wave with frequency 2500 kHz has a wavelength of 120 m. What is the length or a radio wave with frequency 1500 kHz?

Let l be the wavelength in metres. Let f be the frequency in kiloHertz.

$$l \propto \frac{1}{f} \text{ or } l = \frac{k}{f} \text{ or } lf = k$$

Given that $f_1 = 2500$ and $l_1 = 120$, find l_2 when $f_2 = 1500$.

$$l_1f_1 = k$$
$$= 2500 \times 120$$
$$l_2f_2 = k$$
$$\therefore l_2(1500) = 2500 \times 120$$
$$l_2 = 200$$

A radio wave with frequency 1500 kHz has wavelength 200 m.

EXERCISE 8-7

A **1.** For each given ordered pair, x varies inversely as y. Find each constant of variation.

a. (3, 8) **b.** (2, 5) **c.** (8, 5) **d.** (0.6, 1.5)

2. For each of the following, an ordered pair from an inverse relation and the constant of variation is given. Find each missing coordinate.

a. $(3, y)$; $k = 18$ **b.** $(x, 5)$; $k = 35$ **c.** $(x, 4)$; $k = 14$

3. Write a general equation describing the relationship between the given variables.

a. $l \propto \frac{1}{m}$ **b.** Current varies inversely as resistance.

c. $a \propto \frac{1}{t^2}$ **d.** Intensity varies inversely as the square of the distance.

4. **a.** If y varies inversely as x, and $y = 5$ when $x = 9$, find y when $x = 6$.

b. If I varies inversely as R, and $I = 0.03$ when $R = 15\ 000$, find I when $R = 25\ 000$.

c. If r varies inversely as t, and $r = 17.5$ when $t = 2.5$, find r when $t = 1$.

B **5.** **a.** Given that y varies inversely as the square of x, and $y = 5$ when $x = 3$, find y when $x = 6$.

b. Given that y varies inversely as $x + 3$, and that $y = 8$ when $x = 2$, find y when $x = 5$.

c. Given that y varies inversely as x^2, and that $y = 3.2$ when $x = 0.6$, find x when $y = 7.2$.

6. Graph each relation described in exercise 5.

7. The time needed to landscape a yard is inversely proportional to the number of people working on the job. If 3 people take 12 h to complete the job, could 5 people complete the job in a 7.5 h day, so that the job is completed in a single day without overtime having to be paid?

8. The force of attraction between two charged particles varies inversely as the square of the distance between them. Two charged spheres exert a force of 0.08 N on each other, at a distance of 3 cm. What will be the attractive force if they are separated by 2 cm?

C **9.** The pressure of a fixed amount of gas in a spherical container is inversely proportional to the cube of the radius of the container. For a container with radius 25 cm, the pressure of the gas in the container is 80 kPa. What would be the pressure of the same amount of gas in a container with radius 15 cm?

8-8 Joint and Combined Variation

In most practical situations involving variation, there are more than two variables involved. For instance, suppose a solar panel were installed in a home to generate power. The power generated, P, depends on both the strength of the sunshine (the intensity of solar radiation), S and the area of the panel, A.
The variables P, S, and A exhibit **joint variation**. P varies directly as S and, simultaneously, P varies directly as A. That is, $P \alpha S$ and $P \alpha A$. Combining the two relationships gives $P \alpha SA$, or $P = kSA$, where k is a constant.

EXAMPLE 1: Given that $x \alpha yz$, and that $x = 24$ when $y = 5$ and $z = 6$, what is x when $y = 10$ and $z = 2$?

$x = kyz$	Since $x \alpha yz$, then $x = kyz$, where k is a constant.
$24 = k(5)(6)$	Substitute known values of x, y, and z to find k.
$24 = 30k$	
$k = 0.8$	Since $k = 0.8$, then $x = 0.8yz$.
$x = 0.8yz$	Substitute y and z into $x = 0.8yz$ to find x.
$x = 0.8(10)(2)$	
$= 16$	

The method illustrated in example 1 can be used to solve practical applications.

EXAMPLE 2: A solar panel with an area of 5 m^2 generates 360 W of power under solar intensity of 600 W/m^2. How much power would be generated by a panel with an area of 12 m^2 if the solar intensity were 400 W/m^2?

Let P watts be the power generated; let S watts per square metre be the intensity of solar radiation; let A square metres be the area of the solar panel.

$P = kSA$	
$360 = k(600)(5)$	Substitute.
$360 = k(3000)$	Solve for k.
$k = 0.12$	Since $k = 0.12$, then $P = 0.12\,SA$.
$P = 0.12SA$	
$P = 0.12(400)(12)$	Substitute.
$= 576$	Solve for P.

The solar panel generates 576 W of power under the given conditions.

In some situations, a variable may vary directly as one quantity, and inversely as another. For instance, if x varies directly as y but inversely as z, then both of the following are true simultaneously.

$x \propto y$ and $x \propto \frac{1}{z}$. If we combine the two statements: $x \propto y\left(\frac{1}{z}\right)$, or $x \propto \frac{y}{z}$.

This is called **combined** variation.

EXAMPLE 3: L varies directly as p but inversely as the square of d. If L is 36 when p is 9 and d is 12, what is L when p is 3 and d is 6?

$L \propto \frac{p}{d^2}$, so $L = \frac{kp}{d^2}$

$$36 = \frac{k(9)}{(12)^2}$$
$$9k = 36(144)$$
$$k = 576$$

Since $k = 576$, then $L = \frac{576p}{d^2}$.

$$L = \frac{576p}{d^2}$$

Substitute for $p = 3$ and $d = 6$.

$$L = \frac{576(3)}{36}$$

The value of L is 48.

$$= 48$$

A practical example combining direct and inverse variation is that of using a lever to move an object. The arms of the lever can be identified as the **effort arm** and the **resistance arm**. The load is on the resistance arm. The maximum mass that can be moved with a given lever varies directly as the length of the effort arm and inversely as the length of the resistance arm.

EXAMPLE 4: A worker can just move a mass of 300 kg using a lever with an effort arm 4 m long and a resistance arm 1.5 m long. What mass could the same worker move, using a lever with an effort arm 2 m long and a resistance arm 1 m long?

Let E metres be the length of the effort arm, R metres be the length of the resistance arm; let m be the maximum mass.

Then $m = \frac{kE}{R}$.

$$300 = \frac{k(4)}{1.5}$$

Substitute for known values of m, E, and R.

$$4k = 450$$
$$k = 112.5$$

Since $k = 112.5$, then $m = \frac{112.5E}{R}$.

$$m = \frac{112.5(2)}{(1)}$$
$$m = 225$$

Using the new lever, the same worker would just be able to lift a mass of 225 kg.

EXERCISE 8-8

A **1.** Determine the missing value so that both ordered pairs illustrate the type of variation described.

a. $y \alpha x$; (3, 5), (a, 10) **b.** $y \alpha \frac{1}{x}$; (7, 2), (14, b) **c.** $y \alpha \frac{1}{x}$; (16, 9), (8, c)

d. $y \alpha x$; (d, 12), (15, 18) **e.** $y \alpha \frac{1}{x}$; (6, e), (12, 9) **f.** $y \alpha \frac{1}{x}$; (9, 8), (f, 6)

2. Write a general equation to represent the given relationship among the variables.

a. y varies jointly as v and t.
b. m varies directly as g and inversely as l.
c. d varies jointly as a and the square of t.
d. A varies directly as r^2 and inversely as u.
e. f varies directly as c and inversely as n.
f. F varies jointly as m and a.
g. F varies jointly as r and inversely as the square of d.
h. x varies directly as l^2 and inversely as the cube of r.

B **3.** Find the constant of variation, given that the ordered pair belongs to the variation.

a. $y \alpha x^2$; (3, 18) **b.** $y \alpha \frac{1}{x^2}$; (3, 4) **c.** $y \alpha \frac{1}{x^2}$; (5, 4)

d. $y \alpha x$; (25, 1) **e.** $y \alpha \frac{1}{x}$; (2, 4) **f.** $y \alpha x^2$; (6, 12)

g. $y \alpha x$; (4, 6) **h.** $y \alpha \frac{1}{x^2}$; (3, 2) **i.** $y \alpha x^2$; (5, 5)

4. The value of x varies jointly as y and z. When y is 3 and z is 12, the value of x is 15.

a. Write a general equation relating x, y, and z.
b. What is the constant of variation?
c. What is the value of x when y is 6 and z is 4?

5. A varies jointly as l and w. A is 35 when l is 16 and w is 10.

a. Write a general equation relating A, l, and w.
b. Find the constant of variation.
c. What is A when w is 2 and l is 32?

6. The value of r varies directly as d and inversely as t. The value of r is 21 when d is 105 and t is 45.

a. Write a general equation relating r, d, and t.
b. Find the constant of variation and write an equation that can be used to solve for r, d, or t.
c. What is r when d is 15 and t is 15?

7. Given that a varies directly as d and inversely as the square of t, and that a is 75 when d is 15 and t is 6, find the constant of variation. Find the value of a when d is 3 and t is 3.

8. Given that p varies directly as m and inversely as t^2, and given also that the value of p is 42 when m is 15 and t is 7, what is the value of p when m is 30 and t is 14?

C 9. As well as generating power for a home, solar panels can be used to heat water for general use in the home. A desired water temperature can be achieved by controlling the rate of flow of water through the panel. The rate of flow must vary jointly as the area of the panel and the intensity of solar radiation. A particular panel with an area of 5 m^2 can heat 20 L of water every hour when the solar intensity is 800 W/m^2. What should be the rate of flow in a solar panel with area 10 m^2 if the solar intensity is 500 W/m^2 and the same water temperature is desired?

10. To achieve the desired cutspeed for a metal being machined, a machinist must compute the appropriate rate of rotation of a lathe. The rate of rotation varies directly as the cutspeed and inversely as the diameter of the metal stock. Mild steel has a cutspeed of 6.5 m/s and 4 cm stock requires a lathe speed of 250 revolutions per minute. What should be the lathe speed for 5 cm of brass stock, which has a cutspeed of 0.75 m/s?

11. Part of an engineer's task is to cost the materials and parts that are used in making the item designed. Cylindrical cement columns, used in making bridges, for instance, can be allotted approximate costs by first assessing their mass. The mass of a cement column varies jointly as its length and the square of its diameter. A column 6 m tall and 0.5 m in diameter has a mass of 13 500 kg. What would be the mass of a column 4 m tall and 0.8 m in diameter?

12. The resistance of an electrical wire, measured in ohms (Ω) varies directly as the length of the wire and inversely as the square of its diameter. If 100 m of wire with a diameter of 1 mm has a resistance of 150 Ω, what is the resistance of 50 m of wire with a diameter of 5 mm?

Historical Note

Archimedes' Boast

Archimedes was once supposed to have boasted, "Give me a place to stand and I can move the earth," presumably using simple machines like the lever. If Archimedes could move 0.5t using a lever with resistance arm 1 m long and effort arm 5 m long, how long an effort arm would he have needed to move Earth, with a mass of $6 \times 10^{21}t$, using a lever with resistance arm 2 m long?

Applications Involving Variation

A 1. Under a given set of crop conditions, the amount of grain produced on a field is directly proportional to the area of the field. One year, a 2500 ha field produced 525 000 kL of grain. How much grain would you expect to have been produced on a neighbouring 1500 ha field, assuming grain variety, fertilizers used, planting time, and other conditions were the same on the two fields?

2. To cut down on drag and improve general performance, a bicycle racer typically crouches into the handlebars, thus reducing the "effective frontal area" of both rider and bicycle. Effective frontal area varies directly as the drag coefficient. A fully crouched bicycle racer has a drag coefficient of 0.9 and an effective frontal area of about 0.35 m^2. What would be the drag coefficient of the same cyclist if the bicycle is modified to result in an effective frontal area of 0.28 m^2?

3. Under stable conditions, the power that a cyclist must expend to achieve a desired speed varies as the cube of the speed. It takes a cyclist 300 W to pedal at 40 km/h. How fast will the same cyclist travel with a power output of 600 W?

4. For a computer to operate at maximum speed, its circuit elements should be close together, because the time taken for an electrical impulse to travel from one place to another varies directly as the distance between them. The time delay for an impulse to travel 8 cm across a circuit board is 0.7 nanoseconds. How far apart should circuit elements be if the maximum time delay is to be one nanosecond?

B 5. The pressure of a gas in a fixed volume varies jointly as the amount of gas and the temperature of the gas, measured in kelvins (K). Three moles of a gas produce a pressure of 750 kPa at a temperature of 200 K. What will be the pressure of four moles of gas at a temperature of 250 K?

6. When meteorologists launch weather balloons to monitor weather data, they must account for the fact that the volume of the gas in the balloon will change as temperature and air pressure change. The volume occupied by a fixed amount of gas varies directly as the temperature in kelvins and inversely as the pressure, measured in kilopascals. A weather balloon containing 5 m^3 of helium gas is launched from sea-level at a pressure of 100 kPa and temperature of 290 K. By the time the balloon has risen to 30 000 m, the pressure has dropped to 20 kPa and the temperature is 220 K. What volume does the gas now occupy?

7. If you use an electric burner and start from room temperature, the time it takes to bring water to a boil varies directly as the mass of water and inversely as the square of the current drawn by the burner, measured in amperes (A). A burner that draws 1.5 A will heat 500 g of water in 140 s. How long would it take to boil 1 kg of water using a burner that draws 1.0 A?

8. The distance travelled by a free-falling object varies jointly as acceleration due to gravity and the square of the time it takes for the object to fall. On Earth's surface, acceleration due to gravity is the gravitational constant, g, which is 9.8 m/s. An object falling for 2 s travels 19.6 m before hitting Earth's surface.
   a. Acceleration due to gravity on the surface of the moon is one-sixth that on Earth. How far will an object have travelled if it falls for 5 s before hitting the surface of the moon?
   b. Use the constant of variation (the gravitational constant) to write an equation to represent the distance travelled by a free-falling object to Earth's surface.

C 9. The illumination provided by a light source is measured in luxes (lx), which indicates the amount of light energy per second that falls on a unit area. The sun's illumination of Earth is approximately 10^5 lx. The illumination of any other planet in our solar system varies directly as the square of its mean radius (relative to Earth's radius) and inversely as the square of its mean distance from the sun (in terms of Earth's distance). Find the illumination the sun provides for each of Venus, Mars, and Jupiter.

Planet	Mean Distance from Sun	Mean Diameter
Earth	1.00	1.00
Venus	0.72	0.96
Mars	1.52	0.53
Jupiter	5.20	11.0

10. For planets orbiting the sun, the square of the orbital period varies directly as the cube of the mean distance from the sun. Earth's orbital period is one year.
   a. Using the table of values given in question 9, find the orbital period of Venus, Jupiter, and Mars.
   b. The mean distance from Earth to the sun is 1.5×10^8 km. The mean distance from Mercury to the sun is 5.8×10^7 km. What is the length of Mercury's "year"?
   c. Saturn's orbital period is 29.5 years. What is Saturn's mean distance to the sun?

Review

1. Which of the following are not functions?
   a. $\{(2, 7), (5, 0), (3, -1), (4, -1), (2, 0)\}$
   b. $\{(0, 4), (3, 1), (2, 0), (7, 1), (-3, 5)\}$
   c. $f(x) = \pm\sqrt{x}, x \geq 0$
   d. $h: x \rightarrow 2x - 5, x \in \mathbf{R}$

2. Given that $f(x) = 3x - 2$, $g(x) = x^2 - x - 2$, and $h(x) = \dfrac{1}{x-2}$, find each of the following.
   a. $f(3)$
   b. $g(-2)$
   c. $h(4)$
   d. $3f(-1)$
   e. $f(5) - g(3)$
   f. $2g(4) + 5f(2)$
   g. $6h(-4) - f(2)$
   h. $f(g(3))$
   i. $g(h(1))$

3. Determine the domain and range of each given function.
   a. $f = \{(3, 1), (2, -4), (5, 6), (-3, 2)\}$
   b. $\{(0, 4), (3, 1), (2, 0), (7, 1), (-3, 5)\}$
   c.

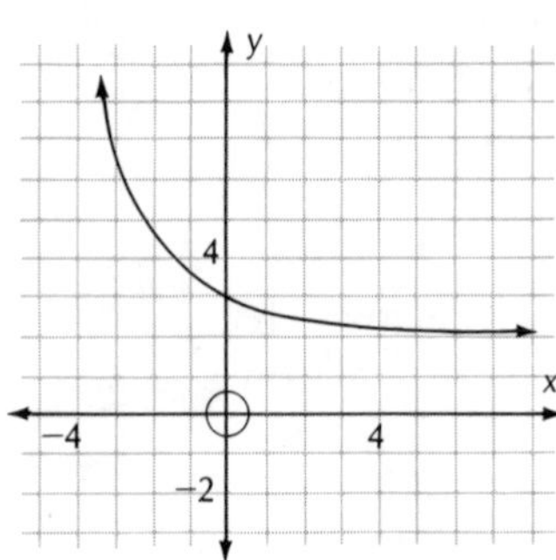

   d.

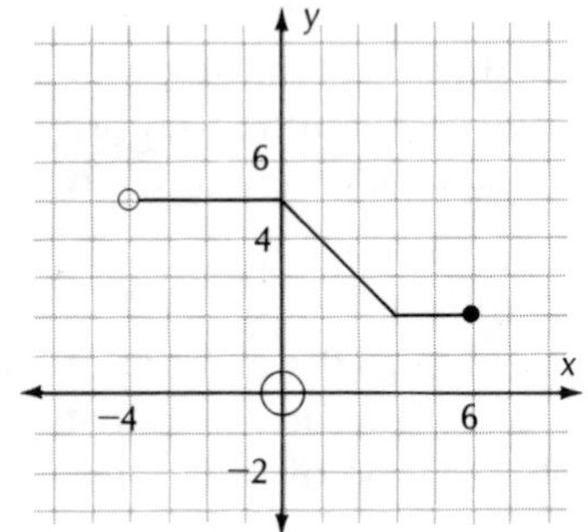

4. Classify each function as linear, quadratic, step, constant, or piecewise linear.
   a. $y = 3x + 1$
   b. $y = x^2 - 2$
   c. $\{(x, y) \mid y = 5, x \in \mathbf{R}\}$
   d. $f: y = 2$, if $2 \geq x > -3$
      $y = 4$, if $3 \geq x > 0$
      $y = 6$, if $6 \geq x > 4$
   e. $g: y = x$, if $x \leq 3$
      $y = 3$, if $x > 3$

5. For each given function, determine if its inverse is also a function.
   a.

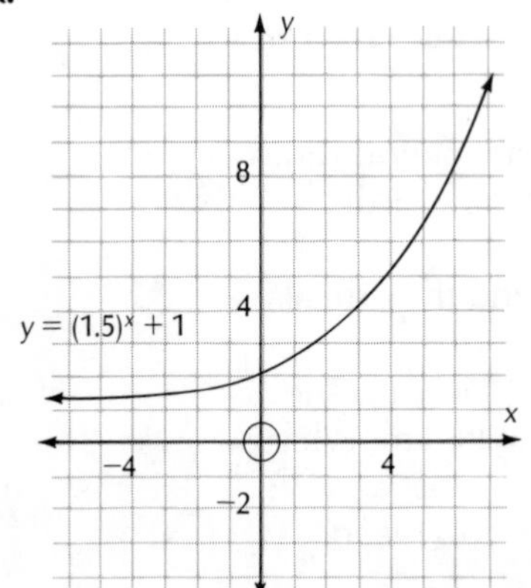

   b.

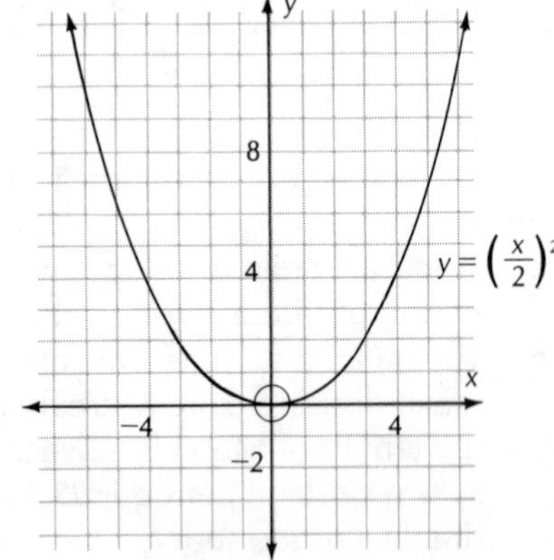

6. Find an equation of the inverse of each given function.

a. $x - y = 5$ b. $y = x^2 + 2$ c. $y = \dfrac{1}{2x - 1}$

7. For each given pair of functions, show that f and g are inverses.

a. $f(x) = 3x - 5$

$g(x) = \dfrac{x + 5}{3}$

b. $f(x) = \dfrac{1}{x + 1}$

$g(x) = \dfrac{1}{x} - 1$

8. The equation of a graph and its transformation image are given. Describe the transformations applied to each graph that result in the image.

a. $y = x^2 + 2 \rightarrow -y = x^2 + 2$

b. $y = 2x \rightarrow y - 3 = 2(x + 2)$

c. $y = x^3 \rightarrow y + 1 = (3x)^3$

d. $y = x \rightarrow y + 2 = -\dfrac{x}{3}$

9. For each given equation, a description of its transformation image follows. Find an equation of each image.

a. $y = \frac{1}{2}x - 1$; translated 4 units up along the y-axis

b. $y = \frac{1}{2}x - 2$; reflected in the x-axis

c. $y = |x|$; translated 2 units up along the y-axis and 3 units to the right along the x-axis

d. $y = x^2$; reflected in the x-axis

10. Given the graph of f below, sketch the graph of each function.

a. 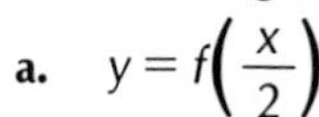 $y = f\left(\dfrac{x}{2}\right)$

b. $y + 2 = f(x)$

c. $2y = f\left(\dfrac{x}{3}\right)$

d. $y - 3 = -f(x)$

e. $\dfrac{y}{2} = f(x - 3)$

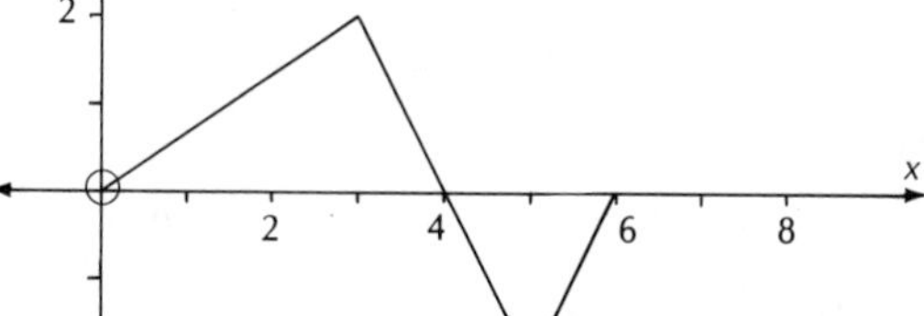

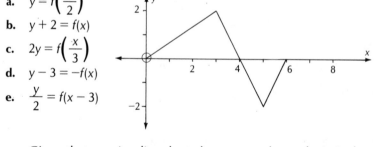

11. a. Given that y varies directly as the square of x, and y is 6 when x is 8, find y when x is 12.

b. F varies inversely as the square of d and directly as M. If F is 20 when d is 5 and M is 8, find F when d is 10 and M is 20.

c. y varies inversely as $x + 3$. If y is 12 when x is 5, find y when x is 9.

d. L varies jointly as t and r. If L is 36 when t is 6 and r is 15, find L when t is 9 and r is 5.

12. The time it takes to boil water in an electric kettle varies inversely with the power rating (W) of the kettle and directly with the mass of water (g) in the kettle. If a 300 W kettle will boil 500 g of water in 4 min, how long will it take a 500 W kettle to boil 700 g of water?

Test

1. Graph each given function. Classify each as linear, quadratic, step, constant, or piecewise linear.

   a. $y = 2x + 3$

   b. $f = \{(x, y) \mid y = x^2 - 2, x \in \mathbf{R}\}$

   c. $f: y = 3$ if $-4 \leq x < -1$
      $y = 0$ if $-1 \leq x < 2$
      $y = -2$ if $2 \leq x \leq 5$

   d. $f: y = x + 2$ if $-4 \leq x < 0$
      $y = -\frac{1}{2}x + 2$ if $0 \leq x < 4$
      $y = x - 4$ if $4 \leq x < 8$

   e. $f = \{(x, y) \mid y = 3\}$

   f. $f: x \rightarrow 3x - 5, x \in \mathbf{R}$

2. Determine the domain and range of each function in question 1.

3. Sketch the graph of each given function. Then sketch the inverse and determine if each inverse is also a function.

   a. $y = 3x - 6$ b. $y = \frac{1}{4}x^2 - 4$ c. $xy = -4$

4. The graph of each given equation is transformed as described. Determine an equation of the transformation image of each graph.

   a. $y = \frac{1}{x^2}$; a translation 3 units to the right along the x-axis

   b. $y = 3x - 2$; a reflection in the y-axis and then a translation 5 units up along the y-axis

   c. $y = x - \frac{1}{2}$; a horizontal stretch of factor 3.

   d. $x^2 + y^2 = 9$; a vertical stretch of factor $\frac{1}{3}$ and a translation 4 units to the left along the x-axis

   e. $y = x$; a reflection in the y-axis and then a vertical stretch of factor 4

5. The value of s varies inversely as the square of L and directly as f. The value of s is 2.4 when L is 5 and f is 4.

   a. Write a general equation relating s, L, and f.

   b. Find the constant of variation.

   c. Determine the value of s if both f and L are doubled.

6. The mass of pancake batter varies jointly as the square of the diameter of the pancake and the thickness of the pancake. It takes 60 g of batter to produce a pancake 10 cm in diameter and 15 mm thick. How much batter does it take to produce a pancake 12 cm in diameter and 10 mm thick?

Cumulative Review

1. a. Find the slope of a line parallel to the line defined by $5x - 6y = 14$.

   b. Find the slope of a line perpendicular to the line defined by $3x + 7y - 11 = 0$.

2. Solve each system of equations.

   a. $2x - 5y = 11$
   $4x - y = 12$

   b. $2x - 3y = -2$
   $3x - 2y = 5$

   c. $\frac{3}{x} - \frac{1}{y} = 15$
   $x + 3y = 4$

   d. $x^2 + y^2 = 36$
   $4x - 3y = 8$

   e. $xy = 12$
   $2x - 5y = 9$

   f. $x^2 + y^2 = 8$
   $xy = -12$

3. For each given equation, describe the curve it defines and sketch the graph.

   a. $y = 3x^2 - 2x + 5$ b. $y = -2x^2 + 5x - 8$ c. $y = -\frac{1}{2}x^2 + 6x$

4. Find the x-intercepts of the parabola defined by each equation.

   a. $y = x^2 + 3x - 4$ b. $y = 3x^2 - 5x - 10$ c. $y = -5x^2 + 2x - 1$

5. Find the value of each indicated angle.

   a.

   b.

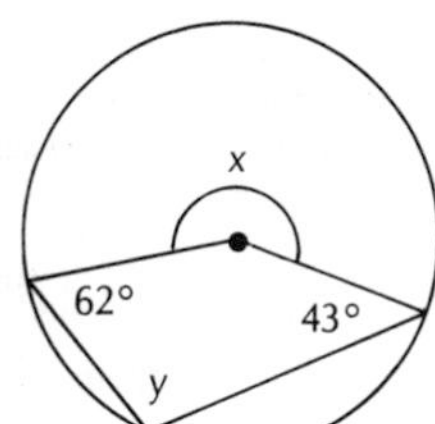

6. Determine the centre and radius of the circle defined by $x^2 + y^2 + 8x - 12y = 48$.

7. a. Find the values of k so that $y = 2x + k$ is tangent to $x^2 + y^2 = 36$.

   b. Find the values of k so that $y = 2x + k$ is a secant to $x^2 + y^2 = 36$.

   c. Find the values of k so that $y = 2x + k$ does not intersect $x^2 + y^2 = 36$.

8. Draw a circle with centre C.

   a. Construct a tangent to the circle from a point P on the circle.

   b. Construct a tangent to the circle from a point P outside the circle.

9. State the range of each given function.

   a. $f(x) = x^2 - 1, x = \{-4, -2, 0, 3\}$

   b. $r: x \rightarrow 5 - x, x = \{1, 2, 3, 4\}$

   c. $h(x) = |x| + 3, x = \{-4, -3, -2, 0\}$

   d. $m(x) = \sqrt{x^2 + 5}, x = \{-2, 2\}$

9 Sequences and Serie

9-1 Sequences

Leonardo Fibonacci, sometimes known as Leonardo of Pisa, was a great mathematician who lived during the Middle Ages. In 1202, he posed a problem like the one below.

When they are one month old, a pair of rabbits cannot breed new rabbits. However, suppose that at two months old and every month that follows, they breed a new pair of rabbits. Further, every new pair does the same. How many pairs of rabbits will there be at the start of each month? (Assume no rabbits die.)

Let f_n represent the number of pairs of rabbits at the start of the nth month.
At the start of the first month, there is only one pair of rabbits. $f_1 = 1$
At the start of the second month, there is still one pair of rabbits. $f_2 = 1$
In the second month, a pair of rabbits is born. Therefore, at the start of the third month there are two pairs of rabbits. $f_3 = 2$
In the third month, the original pair produces another pair, but the second pair is too young to have offspring. So there are three pairs of rabbits at the start of the fourth month. $f_4 = 3$

On your own, verify that $f_5 = 5$, $f_6 = 8$, and $f_7 = 13$.

The number of pairs of rabbits at the start of each month is 1, 1, 2, 3, 5, 8, 13, … . This is a famous sequence, called the Fibonacci sequence, and it occurs in many places in the biological and physical worlds.

A **sequence** is a function in which the domain is the set of natural numbers. A member of the range of a sequence is called a **term** of the sequence. The terms of a sequence are denoted $t_1, t_2, t_3, \ldots$. The third term in the Fibonacci sequence, for example, is t_3 or 2.

A sequence can often be defined by its **general term, t_n**.

The sequence 2, 4, 6, 8, 10, … can be defined by its general term, $t_n = 2n$.

The domain of a sequence is always **N**.

EXAMPLE 1: Find the first 3 terms of the sequence defined by each general term.

a. $t_n = 2n - 1.$

$t_1 = 2(1) - 1 = 1$
$t_2 = 2(2) - 1 = 3$
$t_3 = 2(3) - 1 = 5$

The terms are 1, 3, 5.

b. $t_n = 3^n$

$t_1 = 3^1 = 3$
$t_2 = 3^2 = 9$
$t_3 = 3^3 = 27$

The terms are 3, 9, 27.

Some sequences can be found when only a few terms are given. A pattern or rule can sometimes be found that indicates how successive terms are obtained.

EXAMPLE 2: **a.** Find a possible general term for the sequence $\frac{1}{2}, \frac{2}{3}, \frac{3}{4}, \frac{4}{5}, \frac{5}{6}, \ldots$.

The numerators are 1, 2, 3, 4, 5, ... These are the natural numbers.
The denominators are 2, 3, 4, 5, 6, ...
For each term, the denominator is one more than the numerator.
The general term would then be $t_n = \frac{n}{n+1}$.

b. For the sequence given in part **a.** and the general term $t_n = \frac{n}{n+1}$, determine t_6, t_7, and t_{11}.

$t_6 = \frac{6}{6+1} = \frac{6}{7}$ $\quad t_7 = \frac{7}{7+1} = \frac{7}{8}$ $\quad t_{11} = \frac{11}{11+1} = \frac{11}{12}$

The terms of some sequences can be defined by relating them to previous terms.

EXAMPLE 3: Given that $t_1 = 1$ and $t_n = 3t_{n-1}$ for $n > 1$, find t_2 and t_3.

According to the general term, $t_n = 3t_{n-1}$, each term is obtained by multiplying the previous term by 3.

$t_1 = 1$ This was given.
$t_2 = 3t_1 = 3(1) = 3$ Multiply t_1 by 3 to get t_2.
$t_3 = 3t_2 = 3(3) = 9.$ Multiply t_2 by 3 to get t_3.

In Example 3, the first term is given and each subsequent term is obtained by relating it to the *previous* term. A sequence having terms defined in relation to preceding terms is said to have a **recursive definition**.

EXAMPLE 4: Given that $t_1 = -2$ and $t_n = 2t_{n-1} + 3$ for $n > 1$, determine the first four terms of the sequence.

According to the general term, each term is obtained by multiplying the previous term by 2, and then adding 3. The procedure applies to all terms greater than t_1.

$t_1 = -2$

$$\begin{aligned} t_2 &= 2t_1 + 3 \\ &= 2(-2) + 3 \\ &= -1 \end{aligned} \qquad \begin{aligned} t_3 &= 2t_2 + 3 \\ &= 2(-1) + 3 \\ &= 1 \end{aligned} \qquad \begin{aligned} t_4 &= 2t_3 + 3 \\ &= 2(1) + 3 \\ &= 5 \end{aligned}$$

The terms are $-2, -1, 1, 5$.

EXERCISE 9-1

A **1.** Write the next four terms that seem appropriate for each sequence.

a. 2, 4, 6, 8, ...
b. 1, 4, 9, 16, 25, ...
c. 1, 3, 5, 7, 9, ...
d. 1, 8, 27, 64, ...
e. 1, 1, 1, 2, 1, 3, 1, 4, 1, 5, ...
f. 2, 1, 2, 4, 2, 9, 2, 16, ...
g. 1, 5, 2, 10, 3, 15, 4, 20, ...
h. $3, 3\sqrt{5}, 15, 15\sqrt{5}, 75, \ldots$

B **2.** Write the first five terms of each sequence. The general term is given.

a. $t_n = 4n - 2$
b. $t_n = n^2$
c. $t_n = 5^n$
d. $t_n = \dfrac{2n-1}{n+1}$
e. $t_n = 3 - (2n + 1)$
f. $t_n = \dfrac{n^2}{n+2}$
g. $t_n = 2^{n-1}$
h. $t_n = 3(2^n)$
i. $t_n = 3n^2 + 1$

3. Determine the general term of each sequence.

a. 3, 6, 9, 12, 15, ...
b. −1, 1, 3, 5, 7, 9, ...
c. 1, 4, 9, 16, 25, ...
d. 3, 6, 12, 24, 48, ...
e. $\frac{2}{3}, \frac{3}{4}, \frac{4}{5}, \frac{5}{6}, \ldots$
f. $\frac{2}{3}, \frac{3}{8}, \frac{4}{15}, \frac{5}{24}, \frac{6}{35}, \ldots$

4. **a.** For the sequence defined by $t_n = 5n - 3$, find t_7 and t_{25}.
b. For the sequence defined by $t_n = 2^{n-1} + 1$, find t_4 and t_8.

5. The first term and general term of each sequence are given. Find the next four terms of each sequence.

a. $t_1 = 3, t_n = t_{n-1} + 4, n > 1$
b. $t_1 = -2, t_n = 4t_{n-1}, n > 1$
c. $t_1 = 5, t_n = t_{n-1} + (n - 1), n > 1$
d. $t_1 = -1, t_n = 2t_{n-1} - 3n, n > 1$
e. $t_1 = 2, t_n = 5t_{n-1} + (2n + 1), n > 1$
f. $t_1 = -4, t_n = t_{n-1} + n^2, n > 1$

6. Sherry has \$215 in her bank account. She deposits \$25 per week each week for the next 7 weeks. Write a sequence that represents the weekly amounts, excluding interest, in Sherry's account.

7. City High School has been experiencing a declining student enrolment for the past five years. The enrolment five years ago was 1450 and it has decreased by 110 students each year.
   a. Write a sequence that represents the enrolment for the five years.
   b. Determine the general term of the sequence.
   c. If the pattern continues, when will the enrolment drop below 500 students?

8. Write a recursive definition for the Fibonacci sequence: 1, 1, 2, 3, 5, 8, 13, ...

9. A bacterial culture starts with 5 bacteria and doubles every hour.
   a. Write the sequence for the first 6 hours.
   b. Write the general term of the sequence.
   c. Write a recursive definition for the sequence.
   d. In order to find t_{15}, which definition is easier to use? Explain.
   e. Find t_{15}.
   f. After how many hours will there be 20 480 bacteria?

10. The value of a certain car, bought at \$12 000, depreciates 20% the first year and 5% each year thereafter.
   a. Find the value of the car at the end of the first year.
   b. Write the general term of the sequence representing the value of the car after n years.
   c. What will the value of the car be after 5 years?

C 11. The population of the world was 4 842 042 000 in mid-1985, according to the estimate by the UN Population Division.
   a. If the annual growth rate is expected to be 1.5% until the year 2000, write the general term for the sequence representing the estimated population in the world after n years.
   b. Calculate the estimated population of the world in the year 2000.

EXTRA

Regions and Lines

Lines are drawn so that no two are parallel and no three lines are concurrent. A recursive definition determines the number of parts into which the plane is divided by n lines. Complete the pattern and find the general term.

1 line,
2 regions
$t_1 = 2$

2 lines,
4 regions
$t_2 = 4$

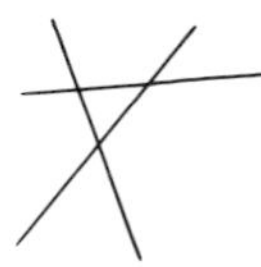

3 lines,
7 regions
$t_3 = 7$

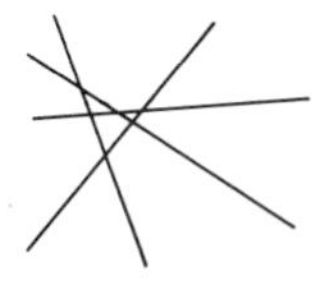

4 lines
11 regions
$t_4 = 11$

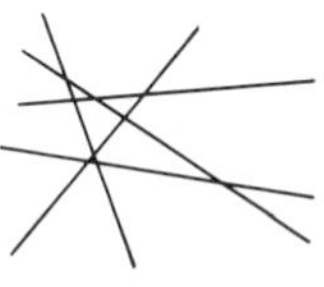

5 lines,
■ regions
$t_5 = t_4 + ■$

In general $t_n = t_{n-1} + ■$

9-2 Arithmetic Sequences

Kate has been swimming 11 lengths of a pool on a regular basis. She now intends to increase her endurance by swimming an additional 2 lengths every week. Her plans can be shown as a sequence.

11, 13, 15, 17, 19, 21, ...

Each term of the sequence differs from the previous term by 2.

A sequence that has terms that differ by a constant amount is called an **arithmetic sequence**. The difference between successive terms, or the constant value, is the **common difference, *d***. The **first term** of an arithmetic sequence is denoted by **a**.

Some other examples of arithmetic sequences are given below.

7, 10, 13, 16, 19, ...	$a = 7, d = 3$
5, 3, 1, −1, −3, −5, ...	$a = 5, d = -2$
2.75, 3, 3.25, 3.50, 3.75, ...	$a = 2.75, d = 0.25$

In general, an arithmetic sequence with first term a and common difference d can be written as $a, a + d, a + 2d, a + 3d, a + 4d, \ldots$ which corresponds to $t_1, t_2, t_3, t_4, t_5, \ldots$. That is, $t_1 = a$, $t_2 = a + d$, $t_3 = a + 2d$, $t_4 = a + 3d$, etc. The general term t_n will have d added to the first term $(n - 1)$ times.

> In an arithmetic sequence, $t_n - t_{n-1} = d$, where d is the common difference and n is the number of the term. The general term of an arithmetic sequence is $t_n = a + (n - 1)d$, where a is the first term.

The formula for the general term of an arithmetic sequence can be applied to many situations involving sequences.

EXAMPLE 1:

a. Write the first five terms of an arithmetic sequence having first term 6 and a common difference of −5.

The first five terms are 6, 1, −4, −9, −14.

b. For the sequence in part **a.**, find t_{60}.

Substitute known values into the formula for the general term.

$t_n = a + (n - 1)d$

$t_{60} = 6 + (60 - 1)(-5)$

$= -289$

Therefore, $t_{60} = -289$.

EXAMPLE 2: In the arithmetic sequence 8, 12, 16, 20, 24, ..., 144, which term is 144?

Substitute known values into the formula for the general term. Then solve for n.

$$t_n = a + (n - 1)d$$
$$144 = 8 + (n - 1)(4)$$
$$= 8 + 4n - 4$$
$$4n = 140$$
$$n = 35$$

Therefore, 144 is the 35th term or t_{35}.

EXAMPLE 3: In an arithmetic sequence, $t_{11} = 72$ and $t_{21} = 142$. Find the common difference, the first term, and the general term of the sequence.

Since $t_{11} = 72$ and $t_{21} = 142$, known values can be substituted into the formula for the general term, $t_n = a + (n - 1)d$, to obtain two equations.

$$t_n = a + (n - 1)d \qquad\qquad t_n = a + (n - 1)d$$
$$72 = a + (11 - 1)d \qquad\qquad 142 = a + (21 - 1)d$$
$$a + 10d = 72 \quad ① \qquad\qquad a + 20d = 142 \quad ②$$

Now solve the system of two linear equations.

$$a + 20d = 142 \quad ②$$
$$a + 10d = 72 \quad ①$$

Use subtraction to solve the system of equations.

$$10d = 70$$

Solve for d.

$$d = 7$$

Therefore, the common difference is 7.

Substitute $d = 7$ into one of the original equations to find the first term, a.

$$a + 10d = 72$$
$$a + 10(7) = 72$$
$$a = 2$$

Therefore, the first term of the sequence is 2.

Finally, substitute known values into $t_n = a + (n - 1)d$ to find the general term of the sequence.

$$t_n = a + (n - 1)d$$
$$t_n = 2 + (n - 1)(7)$$
$$= 7n - 5$$

Substitute $a = 2$ and $d = 7$.

The general term of the sequence is $t_n = 7n - 5$.

EXERCISE 9-2

A **1.** Which of the following sequences are arithmetic sequences?

a. $3, 6, 9, 12, 15, \ldots$ **b.** $2, 4, 8, 16, 32, \ldots$

c. $-3, -5, -7, -9, \ldots$ **d.** $9, 3, -3, -9, -15, \ldots$

e. $\frac{1}{3}, \frac{5}{6}, \frac{4}{3}, \frac{11}{6}, \frac{7}{3}, \ldots$ **f.** $1, \frac{1}{2}, \frac{1}{3}, \frac{1}{4}, \frac{1}{5}, \ldots$

g. $1, 11, 21, 31, 41, \ldots$ **h.** $p, p-q, p-2q, p-3q, \ldots$

i. $-t, -t+3a, -t+6a, -t+9a, \ldots$ **j.** $0.1, 0.01, 0.001, 0.0001, \ldots$

2. Find the common difference for each arithmetic sequence given in exercise 1.

3. Determine the common difference and give the next three terms of each arithmetic sequence.

a. $2, 7, 12, 17, \ldots$ **b.** $9, 5, 1, -3, \ldots$

c. $18, 15, 12, 9, \ldots$ **d.** $-12, -8, -4, 0, 4, \ldots$

4. Find the term indicated and the general term for each arithmetic sequence.

a. $4, 7, 10, 13, 16, \ldots; t_{15}$ **b.** $81, 74, 67, 60, 53, \ldots; t_{25}$

c. $\frac{5}{3}, \frac{7}{3}, 3, \frac{11}{3}, \ldots; t_9$ **d.** $4, -2, -8, -14, -20, \ldots; t_{100}$

B **5.** Give the general term of each sequence.

a. the set of even positive integers

b. the set of odd positive integers

c. the set of positive integers that are multiples of 5

d. the set of negative integers that are divisible by 7

6. How many terms are in each arithmetic sequence?

a. $3, 7, 11, 15, \ldots, 191$ **b.** $-6, 5, 16, 27, \ldots, 390$

c. $13, 5, -3, -11, \ldots, -179$ **d.** $-5, -7, -9, -11, \ldots, -201$

7. Each pair of terms belongs to an arithmetic sequence. Find the first term, the common difference, and t_{100} of the arithmetic sequence.

a. $t_8 = 33, t_{14} = 57$ **b.** $t_{10} = 50, t_{27} = 152$

c. $t_6 = -30, t_{17} = -107$ **d.** $t_8 = -25, t_{15} = -53$

e. $t_5 = -17, t_{20} = -77$ **f.** $t_7 = 23, t_{16} = 68$

8. A number x is the **arithmetic mean** between two numbers a and b if a, x, and b are in arithmetic sequence. For example, 6 is the arithmetic mean between 2 and 10 since 2, 6, 10 are in arithmetic sequence. Find the arithmetic mean between each pair of numbers.

a. 5, 19 **b.** 26, 10 **c.** $-5.25, -9.75$

9. The given expressions are consecutive terms of an arithmetic sequence. Find x for each group of terms.

a. $3x+2, 18, 9x-2$ **b.** $4x+10, -2x, 3x+1$

c. $4x-1, 2x+2, 2x-3$ **d.** $2x-3, x+2, 19-x$

10. The sum of the first two terms of an arithmetic sequence is 29. The sum of the second and third terms is 39. Find the three terms.

11. Show that the sum of the first and fourth terms of an arithmetic sequence is the same as the sum of the second and third terms.

C 12. Three numbers are in arithmetic sequence. Is it possible for their squares to be in arithmetic sequence? Explain.

13. A sequence has the following terms: $1 \times 2, 3 \times 5, 5 \times 8, 7 \times 11, 9 \times 14, \ldots$. Its general term has factors that are the terms of arithmetic sequences.
    a. Find the general term of the given sequence.
    b. Is the sequence arithmetic?

14. Find a general term of each arithmetic sequence.
    a. $\frac{1}{3}, \frac{3}{5}, \frac{5}{7}, \frac{7}{9}, \frac{9}{11}, \ldots$
    b. $\frac{2}{5}, \frac{4}{9}, \frac{6}{13}, \frac{8}{17}, \frac{10}{21}, \ldots$
    c. $2 \times 3, 4 \times 7, 6 \times 11, 8 \times 15, \ldots$
    d. $7 \times 12, 9 \times 9, 11 \times 6, 13 \times 3, \ldots$

15. The sum of the first three terms of an arithmetic sequence is 30. The sum of their squares is 318. Find the three terms.

16. Is it possible to have an arithmetic sequence consisting of three positive integers whose sum is a prime number? Explain.

EXTRA

Pascal's Triangle

Blaise Pascal, (1623–1662), was one of the founders of probability theory in mathematics. Pascal's triangle, shown at the right, has many applications in mathematics. The top row consists only of the number 1. Each outside number in the other rows is 1. The remaining numbers in each row are obtained by summing the two numbers directly above it to the left and right. For example, in the last row, $6 = 1 + 5$, $15 = 5 + 10$, $20 = 10 + 10$, etc.

```
            1
          1   1
        1   2   1
      1   3   3   1
    1   4   6   4   1
  1   5  10  10   5   1
1   6  15  20  15   6   1
. . . . . . . . . . . . .
```

1. How many terms will be in the 20th row? the 100th row?

2. The numbers in each diagonal form a sequence. What will the first two terms be in the 20th row? the 100th row?

3. Write a recursive definition for the third terms in each row. Is this sequence arithmetic?

9-3 Geometric Sequences

Notes in musical octaves on a piano are related mathematically. The frequency of a C note is double the frequency of the previous C note. There are 8 C notes on a grand piano: $C_1, C_2, C_3, \ldots, C_8$. The frequency of C_4 is 261.6 Hz. The frequency of the other C notes can be found using the equation $C_n = 2C_{n-1}$.
For example, $C_5 = 2C_4$ or 2(261.6). So, $C_5 = 523.2$ Hz.

This sequence of frequencies is a **geometric sequence**. In a geometric sequence, the quotient of any two successive terms is constant. The constant quotient is called the **common ratio, *r***. In the above example, the common ratio is $\frac{C_n}{C_{n-1}}$ or 2.

Other examples of geometric sequences are given below.

2, 4, 8, 16, 32, ...	$a = 2, r = 2$	*a* is the first term.
3, 15, 75, 375, 1875, ...	$a = 3, r = 5$	*r* is the common ratio.
$8, -2, \frac{1}{2}, \frac{-1}{8}, \frac{1}{32}, \ldots$	$a = 8, r = \frac{-1}{4}$	

In general, if the first term of a geometric sequence is *a* and the common ratio is *r*, where $r \neq 0$, then the terms $t_1, t_2, t_3, t_4, t_5, \ldots$ of the sequence are given by $a, ar, ar^2, ar^3, ar^4, ar^5, \ldots$.

That is, $t_1 = a, t_2 = ar, t_3 = ar^2, t_4 = ar^3$, etc.

> In a geometric sequence, $\frac{t_n}{t_{n-1}} = r$, where *r* is the common ratio and $r \neq 0$. The general term of a geometric sequence is $t_n = ar^{n-1}$, where *a* is the first term.

EXAMPLE 1: Write the first five terms of a geometric sequence having first term 5 and common ratio 3.

The first five terms of a geometric sequence are given as follows.
$t_1 = a, t_2 = ar, t_3 = ar^2, t_4 = ar^3, t_5 = ar^4$
Substitute known values into each expression to find the terms.
$t_1 = 5$
$t_2 = 5 \times 3$ or 15
$t_3 = 5(3)^2$ or 45
$t_4 = 5(3)^3$ or 135
$t_5 = 5(3)^4$ or 405
Therefore, the first five terms are 5, 15, 45, 135, 405.

EXAMPLE 2: How many terms are in the geometric sequence $256, 128, 64, \ldots, \frac{1}{16}$?

The common ratio is $\frac{128}{256}$ or $\frac{1}{2}$ and the first term is 256.

The nth term is $\frac{1}{16}$. Substitute known values into the formula for the general term of a geometric sequence and solve for n.

$t_n = ar^{n-1}$ — Recall that $n > 1$.

$\frac{1}{16} = 256\left(\frac{1}{2}\right)^{n-1}$

$\frac{1}{4096} = \frac{1}{2}^{n-1}$ — Simplify each side by eliminating fractions and writing each side as a power of 2.

$4096 = 2^{n-1}$

$2^{12} = 2^{n-1}$

$12 = n - 1$

$n = 13$

Therefore, there are 13 terms in the sequence.

EXAMPLE 3: In a geometric sequence, $t_3 = 20$ and $t_9 = 1280$. Determine the common ratio, the first term, and t_{12}.

Use the formula for the general term to obtain two equations.

$t_n = ar^{n-1}$

$20 = ar^2$ ① — Substitute $t_3 = 20$ into the formula.

$1280 = ar^8$ ② — Substitute $t_9 = 1280$ into the formula.

Solve for r by dividing ② by ①.

$\frac{1280}{20} = \frac{ar^8}{ar^2}$ $\frac{②}{①}$

$64 = r^6$

$r = \pm 2$

The common ratio is ± 2.

Substitute $r = \pm 2$ into one of the original equations to find a. Notice that there are two cases.

$20 = ar^2$	$20 = ar^2$
$20 = a(2)^2$	$20 = a(-2)^2$
$a = 5$	$a = 5$

The first term is 5.

Substitute known values into $t_n = ar^{n-1}$ to find t_{12}.

If $r = 2$, then $t_{12} = 5(2)^{11}$ or 10 240. — Use a calculator.

If $r = -2$, then, $t_{12} = 5(-2)^{11}$ or -10 240.

Thus, there are two sequences. One sequence has $a = 5$, $r = 2$, and $t_{12} = 10$ 240, and the other sequence has $a = 5$, $r = -2$, and $t_{12} = -10$ 240.

EXERCISE 9-3

A 1. Which of the following are geometric sequences?

a. 8, 24, 72, 216, 648, 1944, ...
b. 1, −1, 1, −1, 1, −1, 1, −1, ...
c. 0.1, 0.01, 0.001, 0.0001, 0.000 01, ...
d. 76, 74, 72, 70, 68, 66, ...
e. 5, 1, 7, 1, 9, 1, 11, 1, 13, 1, ...
f. 16, −8, 4, −2, 1, $\frac{-1}{2}$, ...
g. 0.4, 0.04, 0.004, 0.0004, 0.000 04, ...
h. 1, 1, 1, 1, 1, 1, 1, ...
i. 0.3, 0.33, 0.333, 0.3333, 0.333 33, ...
j. 12, 3, $\frac{3}{4}$, $\frac{3}{16}$, $\frac{3}{64}$, ...

2. Determine the common ratio for each geometric sequence in exercise 1.

3. Find the common ratio and the next three terms of each geometric sequence.

a. 6, 12, 24, 48, 96, ...
b. 8, −8, 8, −8, 8, −8, ...
c. $3^0, 3^{-1}, 3^{-2}, 3^{-3}, 3^{-4}, \ldots$
d. 18, −6, 2, $\frac{-2}{3}$, $\frac{2}{9}$, $\frac{-2}{27}$, ...
e. $\sqrt{2}, \sqrt{6}, 3\sqrt{2}, 3\sqrt{6}, \ldots$
f. $5\sqrt{5}, 25, 25\sqrt{5}, 125, \ldots$

4. For each geometric sequence, find t_7 and t_{12}.

a. 2, 4, 8, 16, 32, ...
b. 0.6, 0.06, 0.006, 0.0006, ...
c. 5, $\frac{-5}{3}$, $\frac{5}{9}$, $\frac{-5}{27}$, $\frac{5}{81}$, ...
d. $at, at^2, at^3, at^4, at^5, \ldots$

5. The general term of a geometric sequence is given. Find t_3 and t_{10}.

a. $t_n = 4(3)^{n-1}$
b. $t_n = 5(-2)^{n-1}$
c. $t_n = 9\left(\frac{1}{2}\right)^{n-1}$
d. $t_n = 6(-0.1)^{n-1}$
e. $t_n = 2(\sqrt{2})^{n-1}$
f. $t_n = 24(\sqrt{3})^{n-1}$

6. Solve for n.

a. $27 = (3)^{n-1}$
b. $125 = (5)^{n-5}$
c. $-32 = (-2)^{n-3}$

7. For each given geometric sequence, find x and y.

a. 3, x, 12, y, ...
b. −2, x, y, 1024, ...

B 8. Find the number of terms and the general term for each geometric sequence.

a. 25, 125, 625, ..., 9 765 625
b. 4, 12, 36, 108, ..., 26 244
c. 32, −8, 2, −0.5, 0.125, ..., -2^{-13}
d. 0.1, 100, 100 000, ..., 10^{16}
e. 36, 12, 4, $\frac{4}{3}$, ..., $\frac{4}{3^{10}}$
f. 80, −400, 2000, ..., −10 000

9. The expressions $(x + 2)$ and $(x^2 - 4)$ represent the first two terms in a geometric sequence. Find an expression for t_3.

10. The expressions $5x + 5$, $2x - 1$, and $x - 3$ represent consecutive terms in a geometric sequence. Find the value(s) of x and the terms of the sequence.

11. Find three terms between 8 and 648 so that the 5 terms are consecutive terms of a geometric sequence.

12. Determine the first term, the common ratio, and the general term of a geometric sequence having the given terms.

    a. $t_4 = 96$ and $t_8 = 1536$ **b.** $t_3 = \frac{5}{3}$ and $t_7 = \frac{5}{243}$

    c. $t_5 = \frac{-3}{2}$ and $t_{11} = \frac{-3}{128}$ **d.** $t_9 = 656.1$ and $t_{14} = 159\ 432.3$

13. The 10th term of a geometric sequence is 78 732 and the third term is 36. Find the 8th term of the sequence.

14. A sequence is defined recursively as follows: $t_1 = 3$, $t_n = 6t_{n-1}$, $n > 1$. Is the sequence geometric? Explain.

15. A number x is the **geometric mean** between two numbers a and b if a, x, b are in geometric sequence. For example, the geometric mean between 5 and 45 is 15, since 5, 15, 45 are in geometric sequence.

    a. Find the geometric mean between 3 and 12.

    b. Find the relationship between a, x, and b.

    c. 15 is the geometric mean between 25 and q. Find the value of q.

16. Find the geometric mean between each pair of numbers.

    a. 8, 128 **b.** 245, 5 **c.** $\frac{16}{27}, \frac{1}{3}$

17. **a.** Insert three geometric means between 3 and 48.

    b. Insert four terms between 96 and 3 to complete the geometric sequence.

18. The first three terms of the sequence 6, x, y, 27 are the terms of an arithmetic sequence, and the last three terms are the terms of a geometric sequence. Find the values of x and y.

C 19. In a geometric sequence, $t_1 + t_2 + t_3 = 21$ and $t_3 + t_4 + t_5 = 84$. Find the five terms of the sequence.

20. In a geometric sequence, $t_2 + t_3 = 48$ and $t_5 + t_6 = 1296$. Find the first six terms of the sequence.

21. The sum of the first two terms of a geometric sequence is 12. The sum of the reciprocals of the first two terms of the sequence is $\frac{3}{8}$. Find the two terms.

22. Calculate the frequencies of the eight C notes in the grand piano described in this lesson.

You will need to determine whether each problem involves an arithmetic or a geometric sequence. A calculator may be used for these questions.

1. Elias has a job with a starting salary of \$17 500. He receives an annual raise of \$750.
   a. What will his salary be at the end of 5 years?
   b. When will his salary exceed \$24 000?

2. As part of her exercise program, Megan does situps. She starts with ten situps per day and increases the number of situps by three each day to a maximum of 100 situps. When will she achieve her goal?

3. Ben can trace his ancestors though eight previous generations: his two parents, his four grandparents, his eight great-grandparents, and so on. How many ancestors were in the eighth generation?

4. A staircase is to be built between the first and second floors of a house. If the two floors are 3.36 m apart, how many steps with risers of 21 cm will be required?

5. The population of a town has increased 3% per year for the past 4 years. If there were 3500 people in the town four years ago, what is the present population?

6. The price of a ticket to a movie was \$3.50 five years ago. The price increased 10% per year. What is the current price of a movie? (Round your answer to the nearest 25¢.)

7. A discount store reduces its price on end-of-season clothing by 10% of the previous week's price each week until the prices are half of the original price. How long will it take for a dress originally priced at \$80 to be reduced to half-price?

8. The speed of sound in air is approximately 332.1 m/s at 1°C and increases about 0.6 m/s for each degree of increase in air temperature. Find the speed of sound in air when the temperature is 15°C.

9. Halley's comet has been sighted at intervals of approximately 76 years. Appearances of the comet have been recorded since 240 B.C.
   a. How many times had the sighting of the comet been recorded when it was seen in 1986?
   b. Some calculations speculate that Halley's comet was seen during the Norman conquest of England in 1066. Is this consistent with the information in part **a**?

Review

1. From the given information, determine the first four terms of each sequence.
   a. $t_n = 4n - 1$ b. $t_1 = -3, t_n = 2t_{n-1} + 1, n > 1$ c. $t_n = \frac{n^2}{n+3}$

2. Which of the following sequences are arithmetic sequences? Which are geometric sequences?
   a. 3, 6, 12, 24, ..., 768
   b. 18, 14, 10, 6, ..., −42
   c. 0.5, 0.05, 0.005, ..., 0.000 000 5
   d. 1, 4, 9, 16, 25, ..., 625

3. For each sequence given in question 2, determine the general term and the number of terms in the sequence.

4. Find the tenth term of an arithmetic sequence having $t_4 = 20$ and $t_{15} = 86$.

5. Find t_6 of a geometric sequence in which $t_4 = \frac{4}{3}$ and $t_9 = \frac{4}{729}$.

6. The Commonwealth Games were first held in Hamilton, Ontario, in 1930. The Games take place every four years, except 1942 and 1946 due to World War II. Canada has been a leading participant in the Games and hosted them in 1954 (Vancouver) and in 1978 (Edmonton).
   a. How many times have the Games been held?
   b. If the pattern continues, will the Games be held in 1992? in 2006?
   c. In the sequence of Games, which terms of the sequence did Canada host?
   d. If Canada hosts the Games in 1994, which term of the sequence will this represent?

7. Find the first three terms of each sequence.
   a. The sum of the first three terms of an arithmetic sequence is 2 and the sum of the fourth and fifth terms is 3.
   b. The sum of the first three terms of a geometric sequence is 13 and the sum of the third, fourth, and fifth terms is 117.

8. The first three terms of an arithmetic sequence are represented by $3x + 2, 2x + 4, 3x$. Find the value of the three terms.

9. The first three terms of a geometric sequence are represented by $x - 3, 2x + 1, 6x - 3$. Find the value of the three terms.

10. The first three terms of the sequence $-8, x, y, 72$ form an arithmetic sequence and the last three terms form a geometric sequence. Find the value of x and y.

11. The first month that a novel was for sale, 10 000 copies were sold. Subsequently sales dropped by 1250 copies per month for six months. How many were sold in the seventh month?

9-4 Series

The number of students per grade at Confederation High School are in arithmetic sequence. There are 270 students in grade 9 and 250 students in grade 10. How many students are in the school if the school has grades 9 to 12?

The sequence is 270, 25[illegible] $a = 270$ and $d = -20$.

Determining the total number of students involves finding the *sum* of the terms of an arithmetic sequence. Such a sum is called a **series**.

In the example above, the terms of the sequence are a, $a + d$, $a + 2d$, $a + 3d$, where $a = 270$ and $d = -20$.

The sum would be $270 + 250 + x + y$.

Sum the terms to find the total number of students.

$$\begin{aligned} a + (a + d) + (a + 2d) + (a + 3d) &= 4a + 6d \\ &= 4(270) + 6(-20) \\ &= 960 \end{aligned}$$

There are 960 students at Confederation High School.

You could also determine that the sequence is 270, 250, 230, 210. Therefore, the sum is $270 + 250 + 230 + 210$ or 960.

A **series** $S_n = t_1 + t_2 + t_3 + \ldots t_n$ is the sum of the terms of a sequence. S_n represents the sum of the first n terms of a sequence.

Some examples of sequences and their corresponding series are given below.

Sequence	Corresponding Series
$1, 2, 3, 4, 5, 6, \ldots, n$	$1 + 2 + 3 + 4 + 5 + 6 + \ldots + n$
$\frac{1}{2}, \frac{2}{3}, \frac{3}{4}, \ldots, \frac{n}{n+1}$	$\frac{1}{2} + \frac{2}{3} + \frac{3}{4} + \ldots + \frac{n}{n+1}$
$1, 1.08, 1.08^2, 1.08^3, \ldots, 1.08^{n-1}$	$1 + 1.08 + 1.08^2 + 1.08^3 + \ldots + 1.08^{n-1}$

EXAMPLE 1: For the sequence 1, 4, 9, 16, 25, 36, 49, 64, ..., 144, find S_3 and S_7.

S_3 represents the sum of the first 3 terms of the sequence. So, $S_3 = 1 + 4 + 9$ or 14.
S_7 represents the sum of the first 7 terms of the sequence. So, $S_7 = 1 + 4 + 9 + 16 + 25 + 36 + 49$ or 140.

Since S_n is the sum of the first n terms of a sequence, then S_n can be written as follows.

$$S_n = t_1 + t_2 + t_3 + \ldots + t_{n-1} + t_n. \quad ①$$

So, $S_{n-1} = t_1 + t_2 + t_3 + \ldots + t_{n-1}$ ②

Subtracting ② from ① gives $S_n - S_{n-1} = t_n$.

For any series, $S_n - S_{n-1} = t_n$, where $n > 1$, and $S_1 = t_1$.

EXAMPLE 2: For a particular series, $S_n = \frac{n(n+3)}{2}$. Find t_1, t_2, and t_3.

First find S_1, S_2, and S_3.

$S_1 = \frac{1(1+3)}{2} = 2$ $\quad S_2 = \frac{2(2+3)}{2} = 5$ $\quad S_3 = \frac{3(3+3)}{2} = 9$

Since $S_1 = t_1$, then $t_1 = 2$.

Use the formula $S_n - S_{n-1} = t_n$ to find t_2 and t_3.

$t_2 = S_2 - S_1 = 5 - 2 = 3$ $\quad t_3 = S_3 - S_2 = 9 - 5 = 4$

Therefore, $t_1 = 2$, $t_2 = 3$, and $t_3 = 4$.

Note that the *sequence* is 2, 3, 4 and the *series* is $2 + 3 + 4$.

EXERCISE 9-4

A

1. Write the series that corresponds to each sequence.
   - **a.** 1, 3, 5, 7, 9, ..., 41
   - **b.** 0.7, 0.77, 0.777, 0.7777, 0.777 77
   - **c.** 1, 4, 9, 16, 25, 36, ..., n^2
   - **d.** 18, 6, 2, $\frac{2}{3}$, $\frac{2}{9}$, ..., $\frac{3}{243}$
2. In a particular series, $S_6 = 45$ and $S_5 = 39$. Find t_6.
3. For each series, find the indicated sum.
   - **a.** $1 + 2 + 3 + 4 + 5 + \ldots + n$; S_{10}
   - **b.** $3 + (-3) + 3 + (-3) + 3 + (-3) + \ldots$; S_{80}
   - **c.** $1^3 + 2^3 + 3^3 + 4^3 + \ldots + n^3$; S_6
   - **d.** $1(2) + 2(3) + 3(4) + \ldots + n(n+1)$; S_7
4. For each series, find S_1, S_2, and S_{10}.
   - **a.** $S_n = n(n+1)$
   - **b.** $S_n = 7n - 3$
   - **c.** $S_n = n^2 - n$
   - **d.** $S_n = 12 - 2n^2$
   - **e.** $S_n = \frac{n^2(n+1)^2}{4}$
   - **f.** $S_n = 2n^2 + 3n$
5. Find the first three terms of the sequence corresponding to each series in exercise 4.

B

6. Determine an expression for the general term of each series in exercise 4.
7. The general term of a sequence is given. Find S_1, S_5 and S_{10}.
   - **a.** $t_n = 2n - 1$
   - **b.** $t_n = 2n^2 - 1$
   - **c.** $t_n = \frac{n}{n^2 + 1}$

C

8. Calculate S_1, S_2, S_3, S_4, ..., examine the pattern, and find a possible expression for S_n.
   - **a.** $1 + 3 + 5 + 7 + \ldots + (2n - 1)$
   - **b.** $1 + 3 + 9 + 27 + \ldots + 3^{n-1}$
   - **c.** $\frac{1}{1 \times 2} + \frac{1}{2 \times 3} + \ldots + \frac{1}{n(n+1)}$
   - **d.** $\frac{1}{1 \times 5} + \frac{1}{5 \times 9} + \frac{1}{9 \times 13} + \ldots + \frac{1}{(4n-3)(4n+1)}$

9-5 Sigma Notation (Σ)

A series can be written in abbreviated form using the symbol Σ, which is the Greek letter **sigma**. Σ, the Greek letter for S, is used to mean **"the sum of"**.

Consider the following series.

$$(1 \times 2) + (2 \times 3) + (3 \times 4) + (4 \times 5) + \ldots + (16 \times 17)$$

This is the *expanded* form of the series.

The general term is $n(n+1)$ and there are 16 terms.
Using sigma notation, the series can be written as follows.

$$\sum_{n=1}^{16} n(n+1)$$

Read this as "the sum of terms of the sequence defined by $t_n = n(n+1)$ from $n = 1$ to $n = 16$."

EXAMPLE 1: Express each series in expanded form and evaluate each sum.

a. $\sum_{n=1}^{7} n^3$ **b.** $\sum_{j=1}^{6} (3j-1)$ **c.** $\sum_{k=1}^{4} (2kn)$

a. $$\sum_{n=1}^{7} n^3 = 1^3 + 2^3 + 3^3 + 4^3 + 5^3 + 6^3 + 7^3$$
$$= 1 + 8 + 27 + 64 + 125 + 216 + 343$$
$$= 784$$

b. $$\sum_{j=1}^{6} (3j-1) = 2 + 5 + 8 + 11 + 14 + 17$$
$$= 57$$

c. $$\sum_{k=1}^{4} (2kn) = 2(1)n + 2(2)n + 2(3)n + 2(4)n$$
$$= 2n + 4n + 6n + 8n$$
$$= 20n$$

Substitute the values 1, 2, 3, 4 for k.

In an expression like $\sum_{k=1}^{4} (2kn)$, k is called a **dummy variable** and can be replaced by any other variable not already used in the equation.
For example:

$$\sum_{k=1}^{4} (2kn) = \sum_{r=1}^{4} (2rn) = \sum_{i=1}^{4} (2in)$$

EXAMPLE 2: Write each series in Σ notation.

a. $2 + 4 + 6 + 8 + \ldots + 50$

The general term is $2n$ and there are 25 terms.

$$S_{25} = \sum_{n=1}^{25} 2n$$

b. $1 + 4 + 9 + 16 + \ldots + n^2$

The general term is given: $t_n = n^2$.

$$S_n = \sum_{k=1}^{n} k^2$$

Use a variable other than n.

For some series, the general term of the corresponding sequence may not be obvious. You can use previously learned skills to determine the general term.

EXAMPLE 3: Write each series in Σ notation.

a. $18 + 15 + 12 + 9 + 6 + \ldots + (-42)$

The series is the sum of an arithmetic sequence with $a = 18$ and $d = -3$. Find the general term t_n.

$t_n = a + (n - 1)d$
$t_n = 18 + (n - 1)(-3)$
$t_n = 21 - 3n$

Substitute known values into the general term to find n.

$21 - 3n = -42$
$-3n = -63$
$n = 21$

Therefore, the series in sigma notation is $\sum_{n=1}^{21}(21 - 3n)$.

b. $3 + (-6) + 12 + (-24) + 48 + (-96) + \ldots + (-6144)$

The series is the sum of a geometric sequence with $a = 3$ and $r = -2$. Find the general term t_n.

$t_n = ar^{n-1}$
$t_n = 3(-2)^{n-1}$

Substitute known values into the general term to find n.

$-6144 = 3(-2)^{n-1}$ — Divide both sides by 3.
$(-2)^{n-1} = -2048$
$(-1)^{n-1}(2)^{n-1} = (-1)^{11}(2^{11})$ — Write each side using exponents.
$n - 1 = 11$ — Solve for n.
$n = 12$

Therefore, the series in sigma notation is $\sum_{n=1}^{12} 3(-2)^{n-1}$.

Many **summation properties** can be proved using previously learned skills.

EXAMPLE 4: Prove that $\sum_{k=1}^{n} ak = a\sum_{k=1}^{n} k$

$$\sum_{k=1}^{n} ak = a + 2a + 3a + 4a + \ldots + na$$
$$= a(1 + 2 + 3 + 4 + \ldots + n)$$
$$= a\sum_{k=1}^{n} k$$

Show that the left side and the right side of the equation are equal.

You can use algebra to simplify expressions that involve sigma notation.

EXAMPLE 5: Simplify $\sum_{x=1}^{n}(4x - 6)$.

$$\sum_{x=1}^{n}(4x - 6) = 2\sum_{x=1}^{n}(2x - 3)$$

EXERCISE 9-5

A **1.** Write each series in expanded form.

a. $\sum_{n=1}^{6} 2n$ **b.** $\sum_{n=1}^{9} 2k$ **c.** $\sum_{m=1}^{5} 2^m$

d. $\sum_{n=1}^{8} (n-3)$ **e.** $\sum_{k=1}^{7} (k^2+1)$ **f.** $\sum_{j=1}^{6} \frac{(-1)^j}{j+1}$

2. Write each series in sigma notation.

a. $1 + 8 + 27 + 64 + \ldots + 15^3$

b. $1 + 2 + 3 + 4 + \ldots + 90$

c. $(1 \times 4) + (2 \times 5) + (3 \times 6) + \ldots + n(n+3)$

d. $\frac{1}{2} + \frac{2}{3} + \frac{3}{4} + \frac{4}{5} + \ldots + \frac{k}{k+1}$

e. $20^2 + 21^2 + 22^2 + \ldots + 29^2$

f. $1 + (-2) + 3 + (-4) + 5 + (-6) + \ldots + (-50)$

g. $\frac{1}{1 \times 2} + \frac{1}{2 \times 3} + \frac{1}{3 \times 4} + \ldots + \frac{1}{19 \times 20}$

h. $\frac{1}{2 \times 5} + \frac{3}{4 \times 8} + \frac{5}{6 \times 11} + \ldots + \frac{2n-1}{2n(3n+2)}$

B **3.** For each of the following, find the general term and then write the series in sigma notation.

a. $4 + 9 + 16 + 25 + 36 + \ldots + 900$

b. $5 + 10 + 15 + 20 + \ldots + 200$

c. $80 + 75 + 70 + 65 + \ldots + 5$

d. $2 + 4 + 8 + 16 + \ldots + 1024$

e. $4 + 12 + 36 + 108 + \ldots + 26\,244$

f. $5 + (-10) + 20 + (-40) + 80 + \ldots + (-10\,240)$

g. $(1 \times 3) + (2 \times 5) + (3 \times 7) + (4 \times 9) + \ldots + (50 \times 101)$

h. $(1 \times 5) + (4 \times 9) + (9 \times 13) + (16 \times 17) + \ldots + (144 \times 49)$

i. $\frac{1}{2} + \frac{1}{3} + \frac{1}{4} + \frac{1}{5} + \ldots + \frac{1}{80}$

j. $\frac{1}{7} + \frac{1}{9} + \frac{1}{11} + \frac{1}{13} + \ldots + \frac{1}{99}$

4. Evaluate each series.

a. $\sum_{n=1}^{8} (2n-1)$ **b.** $\sum_{i=1}^{8} (i^2-1)$ **c.** $\sum_{k=1}^{7} (3^k-1)$

d. $\sum_{t=1}^{5} (-1)^t 3^t$ **e.** $\sum_{j=1}^{100} (-1)^j$ **f.** $\sum_{n=1}^{4} (5n-2)(n+1)$

5. Prove that $\sum_{k=1}^{n} a = na$, where a is a constant.

6. Prove each of the following.

a. $\sum_{k=3}^{8} k = \sum_{k=1}^{6} (k+2)$ b. $\sum_{n=5}^{10} 3n = \sum_{n=1}^{6} 3(n+4)$ c. $\sum_{n=1}^{7} n^2 = \sum_{n=5}^{11} (n-4)^2$

7. Describe a general method for obtaining equivalent equations such as those given in exercise 6.

8. Simplify.

a. $\sum_{k=1}^{n} (5k-15)$ b. $\sum_{j=1}^{n} [2(3j-6)]$ c. $3\sum_{x=1}^{n} [(-4x+10)(x+5)]$

C 9. Complete each of the following.

a. $\sum_{n=3}^{8} 2n = \sum_{n=1}^{6} \blacksquare$ b. $\sum_{k=6}^{15} (k-5) = \sum_{k=1}^{10} \blacksquare$

c. $\sum_{i=4}^{20} 2(i^2-1) = \sum_{i=1}^{17} \blacksquare$ d. $\sum_{t=3}^{11} \blacksquare = \sum_{t=1}^{9} (3t^2+5)$

10. For $\sum_{n=1}^{k} n^3$, evaluate $S_{12} - S_{11}$.

11. Solve for x: $\sum_{k=1}^{8} (kx-1) = 100$

12. Evaluate: $\sum_{k=1}^{6} (2k-6) + \sum_{n=-2}^{4} (n+3)^2$

13. Prove:

a. $\sum_{x=1}^{n} x = \frac{n(n+1)}{2}$ b. $\sum_{i=1}^{n} (2i-1) = n^2$ c. $\sum_{k=1}^{n} \frac{1}{(k+1)(k+2)} = \frac{n}{2(n+2)}$

EXTRA

A Series from the Fibonacci Sequence

Recall that the Fibonacci sequence is 1, 1, 2, 3, 5, 8, 13, ... There are many interesting properties associated with the Fibonacci numbers.

For each series at the right, find the missing numbers. Describe the pattern that seems to appear. Continue the process with more series of Fibonacci numbers.

$$1^2 = 1 \times 1$$
$$1^2 + 1^2 = 1 \times 2$$
$$1^2 + 1^2 + 2^2 = 2 \times 3$$
$$1^2 + 1^2 + 2^2 + 3^2 = 3 \times \blacksquare$$
$$1^2 + 1^2 + 2^2 + 3^2 + 5^2 = \blacksquare \times \blacksquare$$
$$1^2 + 1^2 + 2^2 + 3^2 + 5^2 + 8^2 = \blacksquare \times \blacksquare$$
$$1^2 + 1^2 + 2^2 + 3^2 + 5^2 + 8^2 + 13^2 = \blacksquare \times \blacksquare$$

....

9-6 Arithmetic Series

Carl Gauss 1777–1855

Carl Friedrich Gauss (1777–1855) was called the Prince of Mathematicians because of his many contributions to pure and applied mathematics. At the age of ten, in Brunswick, Germany, Gauss was asked by his teacher to find the sum of the whole numbers from 1 to 100. Gauss astonished the teacher by immediately writing the answer, 5050, on his slate. It is believed that Gauss performed the calculation as follows.

$S_{100} = 1 + 2 + 3 + \ldots + 100$	Write the series.
$S_{100} = 100 + 99 + 98 + \ldots + 1$	Write the series in reverse order.
$2S_{100} = 101 + 101 + 101 + \ldots + 101$	Add.
$2S_{100} = 101(100)$	There are 100 terms.
$S_{100} = \frac{101(100)}{2}$	
$S_{100} = 5050$	

Notice that the series $1 + 2 + 3 + \ldots + 100$ is the sum of the terms of the arithmetic sequence $1, 2, 3, \ldots, 100$.

> An **arithmetic series** is the sum of the terms of an arithmetic sequence.
> For an arithmetic series, $S_n = a + (a + d) + (a + 2d) + \ldots + [a + (n - 1)d]$.

The method used above to find S_{100} can be applied to find a formula for the sum of the n terms of an arithmetic series $S_n = a + (a + d) + (a + 2d) + \ldots + [a + (n - 1)d]$.

$S_n = a + a + d + a + 2d + \ldots + a + (n - 1)d$	Write the series.
$S_n = a + (n - 1)d + a + (n - 2)d + a + (n - 3)d + \ldots + a$	Reverse the order.
$2S_n = [2a + (n - 1)d] + [2a + (n - 1)d] + [2a + (n - 1)d] + \ldots + [2a + (n - 1)d]$	Add.
$2S_n = n[2a + (n - 1)d]$	There are n terms.
$S_n = \frac{n}{2}[2a + (n - 1)d]$	

> The sum of the first n terms of an arithmetic series is
> $S_n = a + (a + d) + (a + 2d) + \ldots + [a + (n - 1)d]$ or
> $S_n = \frac{n}{2}[2a + (n - 1)d]$.

EXAMPLE 1: **a.** Find the sum of the first 50 terms of the arithmetic series $4 + 7 + 10 + 13 + \ldots$.

Use the formula to evaluate the sum.

$$S_n = \frac{n}{2}[2a + (n-1)d]$$

$$S_{50} = \tfrac{50}{2}[2(4) + (50-1)3] \qquad a = 4, d = 3, n = 50$$
$$= 25[8 + 49(3)]$$
$$= 3875$$

The sum is 3875.

b. Evaluate $200 + 195 + 190 + \ldots + 20$.

This is also an arithmetic series with $a = 200$, $d = -5$, and the last term is 20. First find n using $t_n = a + (n-1)d$.

$$20 = 200 + (n-1)(-5)$$
$$20 = 200 - 5n + 5$$
$$5n = 185$$
$$n = 37$$

Now use the formula to find the sum.

$$S_n = \frac{n}{2}[2a + (n-1)d]$$

$$S_{37} = \tfrac{37}{2}[2(200) + (37-1)(-5)]$$
$$= \tfrac{37}{2}[400 - 180]$$
$$= 4070$$

The sum is 4070.

EXAMPLE 2: Evaluate $\sum_{k=1}^{30}(2k-5)$.

First, write the series in expanded form.

$$\sum_{k=1}^{30}(2k-5) = -3 + (-1) + 1 + 3 + \ldots + 55$$

Knowing that $a = -3$, $d = 2$, and $n = 30$, you can use the formula.

$$S_n = \frac{n}{2}[2a + (n-1)d]$$

$$S_{30} = \tfrac{30}{2}[2(-3) + (30-1)(2)]$$
$$= 15(-6 + 58)$$
$$= 780$$

The sum is 780.

EXERCISE 9-6

A 1. Determine the number of terms in each arithmetic series.

a. $3 + 5 + 7 + 9 + 11 + \ldots + 99$

b. $60 + 57 + 54 + 51 + 48 + \ldots + 12$

c. $1 + 7 + 13 + 19 + \ldots + 175$

d. $-14 + (-9) + (-4) + 1 + 6 + \ldots + 166$

e. $\sum_{n=0}^{100} (2n - 3)$

f. $\sum_{k=-4}^{40} (3k + 1)$

g. $\sum_{i=-3}^{21} 2i^3$

h. $\sum_{t=5}^{-18} (t^2 + 2t)$

2. Find the sum of the first eight terms of each arithmetic series.

a. $1 + 2 + 3 + 4 + 5 + 6 + \ldots$

b. $5 + 10 + 15 + 20 + 25 + \ldots$

c. $-7 + (-4) + (-1) + 2 + 5 + \ldots$

d. $70 + 62 + 54 + 46 + 38 + \ldots$

e. $\sum_{x=0}^{10} (6x + 1)$

f. $\sum_{k=-4}^{20} (3 - 4k)$

g. $\frac{1}{2} + 1 + \frac{3}{2} + 2 + \frac{5}{2} + \ldots$

h. $\frac{11}{5} + 2 + \frac{9}{5} + \frac{8}{5} + \frac{7}{5} + \ldots$

3. The series $2 + 6 + 10 + 14 + 18 + \ldots$ is arithmetic.

a. Find the 10th term.

b. Find the sum of the first 10 terms.

4. The series $-12 + (-10) + (-8) + (-6) + \ldots$ is arithmetic.

a. Find S_{10}.

b. Find S_{25}.

B 5. Evaluate each arithmetic series.

a. $2 + 4 + 6 + 8 + 10 + \ldots + 600$

b. $3 + 6 + 9 + 12 + 15 + \ldots + 348$

c. $4 + 8 + 12 + 16 + 20 + \ldots + 392$

d. $5 + 10 + 15 + 20 + 25 + 30 + \ldots + 400$

e. $\sum_{n=1}^{15} (n + 3)$

f. $\sum_{k=-5}^{8} (2k + 1)$

g. $\sum_{i=0}^{10} (5 - 3i)$

h. $\sum_{x=-3}^{15} (2x + 5)$

i. $\sqrt{2} + 3\sqrt{2} + 5\sqrt{2} + \ldots + 39\sqrt{2}$

j. $\frac{1}{8} + \frac{1}{4} + \frac{3}{8} + \frac{1}{2} + \ldots + 6$

6. Prove that the sum of the positive integers from 1 to n is $\frac{n(n+1)}{2}$.

That is, prove that $\sum_{i=1}^{n} i = \frac{n(n+1)}{2}$.

7. Simplify each arithmetic series.

a. $1 + 2 + 3 + 4 + \ldots + 100$

b. $1 + 2 + 3 + 4 + \ldots + 250$

c. $1 + 2 + 3 + 4 + \ldots + (k + 1)$

d. $12 + 13 + 14 + 15 + 16 + \ldots + 125$

e. $20 + 21 + 22 + 23 + 24 + \ldots + 72$

f. $k + (k + 1) + (k + 2) + (k + 3) + \ldots + 2k$

8. Find the sum of all the integers from 1 to 100 inclusive that are *not* multiples of 7.

9. Find the sum of all the integers from 1 to 100 inclusive that are multiples of *both* 2 and 3.

10. Find the sum of all the integers from 1 to 100 inclusive that are *not* multiples of *either* 2 or 3.

11. The sum of the first six terms of an arithmetic series is −6 and the sum of the first twenty terms is −300. Find the general term of the series.

12. The seventh term of an arithmetic series is 29 and the sum of the first seventeen terms is 629. Find the sum of the first 100 terms of the series.

13. Find the sum of all two-digit numbers that are less than 150.

14. The sum of n terms of an arithmetic series is given by $S_n = \dfrac{17n - 3n^2}{2}$.

a. Find S_{30}.

b. Find an expression for the general term.

15. Calculate $3 + (-5) + 7 + (-9) + 11 + (-13) + 15 + \ldots + 83 + (-85)$.

C 16. a. Complete the chart and find an expression for $\sum_{i=1}^{n} i^3$.

n	t_n	S_n	Notes/Conjectures
1	1	1	$S_1 = 1^2 \;= 1^2$
2	8	9	$S_2 = 3^2 \;= (1 + 2)^2$
3	27	36	$S_3 = 6^2 \;= (1 + 2 + 3)^2$
4	■	■	■
5	■	■	■

b. Verify the answer obtained in part **a.** by showing that $S_1 = t_1$ and that $S_n - S_{n-1} = t_n, n > 1$.

9-7 Geometric Series

As part of her fitness program, Val goes for a walk each day. At first she walks 1 km per day. Each week she increases the distance walked by 10%. What is the total distance Val will have walked at the end of 10 weeks?

The first week, Val walks 7 km.
The second week, she walks 7×1.10 km. (110% of 7 km)
The third week, she walks 7×1.10^2 km. (110% of the distance walked in week 2)
The fourth week, she walks 7×1.10^3 km. (110% of the distance walked in week 3)
. . .
The tenth week, she walks 7×1.10^9 km.
At the end of 10 weeks, Val will have walked
$[7 + 7(1.10) + 7(1.10)^2 + 7(1.10)^3 + \ldots + 7(1.10)^9]$ km,
or $7[1 + 1.10 + 1.10^2 + 1.10^3 + \ldots + 1.10^9]$ km.
Notice that the distance involves the sum of the terms of a geometric sequence.

> If a series is the sum of a geometric sequence, then the series is a **geometric series**.
> For a geometric series, $S_n = a + ar + ar^2 + ar^3 + ar^4 + \ldots + ar^{n-1}, r \neq 0$.

A geometric series can be evaluated by using a method similar to that used for evaluating an arithmetic series.

Write the series: $S_n = 1 + 1.10 + 1.10^2 + \ldots + 1.10^9$ ① The common ratio r is 1.10
Multiply S_n by 1.10: $1.10S_n = 1.10 + 1.10^2 + 1.10^3 + \ldots + 1.10^{10}$ ②

Subtract ① from ②: $(1.10 - 1)S_n = 1.10^{10} - 1$

$$0.1S_n = 2.594 - 1$$ Use a calculator.

$$S_n = \frac{1.594}{0.1}$$
$$= 15.94$$
$$7 \times 15.94 = 111.58$$

Val will have walked approximately 111.6 km by the end of ten weeks.

The method used above can be applied to find a formula for the sum of a geometric series.

Write the series: $S_n = a + ar + ar^2 + ar^3 + ar^4 + \ldots + ar^{n-1}, \quad r \neq 0.$ ①
Multiply by r: $rS_n = ar + ar^2 + ar^3 + ar^4 + \ldots + ar^{n-1} + ar^n$ ②

Subtract ① from ②: $(r - 1)S_n = ar^n - a$

$$S_n = \frac{a(r^n - 1)}{r - 1}, r \neq 1$$

When $r < 1$, it is more convenient to write the formula as $S_n = \dfrac{a(1 - r^n)}{1 - r}, r \neq 1$

The sum of the first n terms of a geometric series is:
$$S_n = \frac{a(r^n - 1)}{r - 1}, r > 1 \text{ or } S_n = \frac{a(1 - r^n)}{1 - r}, r < 1.$$

EXAMPLE 1: Find the sum of the first 20 terms of the geometric series $3 + 6 + 12 + 24 + 48 + \ldots$.

For the series, $a = 3$, $r = 2$, and $n = 20$. Notice that $r > 1$.

$$S_n = \frac{a(r^n - 1)}{r - 1}, r \neq 1$$

$$S_n = \frac{3(2^{20} - 1)}{2 - 1}$$ Use a calculator.

$$= \frac{3(1\ 048\ 575)}{1}$$

$$= 3\ 145\ 725$$

The sum of the first 20 terms is 3 145 725.

EXAMPLE 2: Calculate the sum of the first 8 terms of the geometric series $24 + 12 + 6 + 3 + \ldots$.

For the series, $a = 24$, $r = \frac{1}{2}$, and $n = 8$.
Notice that $r < 1$.

$$S_n = \frac{a(1 - r^n)}{1 - r}$$

$$S_n = \frac{24\left(1 - \left(\frac{1}{2}\right)^8\right)}{1 - \frac{1}{2}}$$

$$= \frac{24\left(1 - \frac{1}{2^8}\right)}{\frac{1}{2}}$$ Multiply by $\frac{2^8}{2^8}$.

$$= \frac{24(2)(2^8 - 1)}{2^8}$$

$$= \frac{3(2^4)(2^8 - 1)}{2^8}$$ $24(2) = 48 = 2(2^4)$

$$= \frac{3(255)}{2^4}$$

$$= \frac{765}{16}$$

The sum of the first 8 terms of the sequence is $\frac{765}{16}$ or 47.8125.

If the number of terms n is not given, you can use the formula for the general term of a geometric sequence to find n.

EXAMPLE 3: Evaluate $8 + 16 + 32 + \ldots + 2048$.

The series is geometric with $a = 8$ and $r = 2$. Find n.

$$t_n = ar^{n-1}$$
$$2048 = 8(2)^{n-1}$$
$$256 = 2^{n-1}$$
$$2^8 = 2^{n-1}$$
$$8 = n - 1$$
$$n = 9$$

Now find S_9. Notice that $r > 1$.

$$S_n = \frac{a(r^n - 1)}{r - 1}$$

$$S_9 = \frac{8(2^9 - 1)}{2 - 1}$$
$$= 8(511)$$
$$= 4088$$

Therefore, the sum is 4088.

EXERCISE 9-7

A **1.** For each geometric series, find S_5.

a. $3 + 6 + 12 + 24 + \ldots$

b. $6 + (-18) + 54 + (-162) + \ldots$

c. $5 + \frac{5}{2} + \frac{5}{4} + \frac{5}{8} + \ldots$

d. $36 + (-9) + \frac{9}{4} + \left(\frac{-9}{16}\right) + \ldots$

e. $0.4 + 0.04 + 0.004 + \ldots$

f. $\sqrt{3} + (-3) + 3\sqrt{3} + \ldots$

2. The series $4 + (-8) + 16 + (-32) + 64 + \ldots$ is geometric.

a. Find the eighth term.

b. Find the sum of the first eight terms.

3. The series $64 + 32 + 16 + 8 + 4 + \ldots$ is geometric.

a. Find the tenth term.

b. Find the sum of the first ten terms.

4. Determine S_n for each geometric series.

a. $36 + 12 + 4 + \frac{4}{3} + \ldots;\ n = 9$

b. $7 + 21 + 63 + 189 + \ldots;\ n = 8$

c. $6 + (-12) + 24 + (-48) + \ldots;\ n = 15$

d. $24 + (-16) + \frac{32}{3} + \left(-\frac{64}{9}\right) + \ldots;\ n = 6$

e. $\sqrt{2} + (-2) + 2\sqrt{2} + \ldots;\ n = 8$

f. $0.3 + 0.03 + 0.003 + \ldots;\ n = 12$

5. **a.** Find S_{10} if the series $18 + 12 + \ldots$ is arithmetic.

b. Find S_{10} if the series $18 + 12 + \ldots$ is geometric.

B 6. Michael is preparing a chart of his ancestors. How many ancestors does he have in ten previous generations?

7. Find S_n for each geometric series.
   a. $1200 + 120 + 12 + 1.2 + \ldots + 0.0012$
   b. $2 + (-8) + 32 + (-128) + \ldots + 8192$
   c. $81 + (-27) + 9 + (-3) + \ldots + \left(-\frac{1}{243}\right)$
   d. $0.3 + 0.03 + 0.003 + \ldots + (3 \times 10^{-12})$
   e. $\frac{1}{3} + \frac{2}{9} + \frac{4}{27} + \ldots + \frac{128}{6561}$

8. Evaluate each series.
   a. $\sum_{n=1}^{10} 2^n$
   b. $\sum_{n=1}^{6} \left(\frac{1}{3}\right)^n$
   c. $\sum_{n=1}^{12} -3(2)^{n-1}$
   d. $\sum_{n=0}^{18} 48\left(-\frac{1}{2}\right)^n$

9. The sum of the first eight terms of a geometric series is 765 and the common ratio is 2.
   a. Find the first term.
   b. Find the sum of the first 10 terms.

10. Find the sum of each geometric series. Simplify the expressions, where possible.
   a. $p + p^2 + p^3 + p^4 + \ldots + p^n$
   b. $1 + x + x^2 + x^3 + \ldots + x^k$
   c. $1 + (-y) + y^2 + (-y^3) + \ldots + y^{28}$
   d. $x^{10} + x^8 + x^6 + \ldots + x^n$

11. When a ball is dropped, it rebounds to a height that is 0.6 of the height from which it was dropped. A ball is dropped from a height of 20 metres. How far will it have travelled when it touches the ground on the fourth bounce?

12. Maria has just accepted a job that pays \$18 000 per year. She expects an annual raise of 5%. Calculate her anticipated total salary for a five year period.

C 13. The sum of the first eight terms of a geometric series is 19 680 and the sum of the first four terms of the series is 240.
   a. Find the first term.
   b. Find the common ratio.

14. Show that $1 + \frac{1}{2} + \frac{1}{4} + \frac{1}{8} + \ldots + \left(\frac{1}{2}\right)^{k-1}$ is always less than 2, regardless how large the value of k is.

Review

1. If the series $4 + 12 + \ldots$ is arithmetic, find the general term and the sum of the first n terms.

2. Repeat the instructions for question 1 if the given series is geometric.

3. Given the arithmetic sequence $5 + 7 + 9 + 11 + \ldots$, find each of the following.
   a. t_{16} b. the general term c. S_{10}

4. Given the geometric sequence $-2, 6, -18, 54, \ldots$, find each of the following.
   a. t_5 b. the general term c. S_{10}

5. Determine whether each sequence is arithmetic, geometric, or neither.
   a. $11, 7, 3, -1, \ldots, -85$
   b. $4, 9, 16, 25, \ldots, 729$
   c. $1, 3, 9, 27, 81, \ldots, 6561$
   d. $12, -6, 3, -\frac{3}{2}, \frac{3}{4}, \ldots, -\frac{3}{128}$

6. For each sequence in question 5, find the number of terms and the general term.

7. First determine if each series is arithmetic, geometric, or neither. Then find S_6 for each series.
   a. $t_1 = -2, t_n = 2t_{n-1} + 4$
   b. $t_1 = 4, t_n = t_{n-1} + 7$
   c. $t_1 = 18, t_n = \frac{1}{3}t_{n-1}$
   d. $\sum_{k=1}^{n}(-1)^k 2^k$
   e. $\sum_{n=1}^{k}(4n - 5)$
   f. $\sum_{n=0}^{k} n^3$

8. An expression for the sum of the first n terms of a series is given. Find the first four terms of each series and identify the series as arithmetic, geometric, or neither.
   a. $S_n = \frac{5}{3}(4^n - 1)$
   b. $S_n = 7n^2 - 2$
   c. $S_n = \dfrac{11n - 3n^2}{2}$
   d. $S_n = 3^n - 1$

9. Write the next three terms of each sequence and find the general term.
   a. $5, 7, 9, 11, 13, \ldots$
   b. $0, 1, 3, 7, 15, 31, 63, \ldots$
   c. $2, 5, 10, 17, 26, 37, \ldots$
   d. $5, -10, 20, -40, 80, \ldots$
   e. $2 \times 5, 4 \times 8, 6 \times 11, 8 \times 14, 10 \times 17, \ldots$
   f. $\frac{1}{7}, \frac{2}{11}, \frac{3}{15}, \frac{4}{19}, \frac{5}{23}, \ldots$

10. Determine if each series is arithmetic or geometric. Then evaluate each series.
    a. $2 + 6 + 10 + \ldots + 154$
    b. $5 + 2 + (-1) + \ldots; n = 36$
    c. $64 + (-32) + 16 + \ldots; n = 12$
    d. $6 + (-18) + 54 + \ldots + (-13\,122)$

11. Find S_{20} for each series.
  a. a geometric series, first term 3, common ratio 2
  b. an arithmetic series, first term 14, common difference −5
  c. a geometric series, first term 48, common ratio $-\frac{1}{2}$
  d. $8 + (-8) + 8 + (-8) + 8 + \ldots$
  e. $\sqrt{2} + 2 + 2\sqrt{2} + 4 + 4\sqrt{2} + 8 + \ldots$

12. The sum of the first five terms of an arithmetic series is 20 and the sum of the first eleven terms is −55. Find the first term, the common difference, and S_{10}.

13. The sum of the first four terms of a geometric series is 156 and the sum of the first two terms is 6. Find S_6.

14. The Francis family has been renting a house for the past four years. During the first year of rental, they paid $400 per month. Each year, the rent increased by 10%.
  a. How much rent do they pay now?
  b. How much have they paid in rent over the four-year period?

15. Every hour a clock strikes as many times as the hour. How many times does the clock strike from 1 A.M. until midnight, inclusive?

16. 120 students are graduating from Fielding Secondary School this year. It is expected that there will be a 5% increase in the number of graduates for each of the next four years. How many graduates are expected in the fourth year?

17. A ball, when dropped, rebounds to a height that is $\frac{3}{5}$ of the height from which it was dropped. If the ball is dropped from a height of 15 metres, how far will it bounce on the fifth bounce?

18. Kevin is considering two job offers. One has a starting salary of $17 000 per year with a raise of $500 at the end of every six months, for three years. The other has a starting salary of $17 000 with an annual raise of 5% at the end of each year, for three years.
  a. Consider his salary as a sequence. Which job offer illustrates an arithmetic sequence? Which job offer illustrates a geometric sequence?
  b. Determine his new salary at the end of the three years for each job offer.

19. Jason starts a chain letter sequence by sending letters to each of five friends. Each friend, in turn, sends letters to five other friends. If the process continues, how many letters will have been sent after five mailings?

20. The Ski Club at Jeri's school has 100 members. If the club's membership increases by 2%/year for five consecutive years, how many members will it have at the end of five years?

Chapter Test

1. Determine the general term, t_{10}, and S_{10} of the arithmetic series $6 + 9 + 12 + 15 + \ldots$.

2. Find the fifth term of the geometric sequence having first term 8 and tenth term $-\frac{1}{64}$.

3. A sequence is defined recursively as follows: $t_1 = 7$, $t_n = 2t_{n=1}$, $n > 1$. Find the first five terms and determine if the sequence is arithmetic, geometric, or neither.

4. Write a recursive definition for the sequence $16, 12, 8, 4, 0, -4, \ldots$.

5. In an arithmetic series, $t_{10} = 27$ and $S_5 = 65$. Find the first four terms.

6. In a geometric series, $S_n = 5(2^n - 1)$.
   a. Find the first four terms of the series.
   b. Find the twelfth term.

7. Write a formula for each of the following.
   a. the sum of the first n even positive integers
   b. the sum of the first n positive integers that are multiples of 3

8. Find the sum of the integers between 100 and 300 that are *not* multiples of either 2 or 5.

9. Evaluate $\sum_{k=1}^{8}(2k - 1)$. Verify your answer.

10. A display of canned goods is set up with 4 cans in the top row, 7 cans in the second row, 10 in the third row, and so on in arithmetic sequence. If there are 246 cans altogether, how many rows are in the display?

11. From two towns, 155 km apart, Chris and Pat set out to meet each other. Chris travelled 1 km the first day, 2 km the second day, 3 km the third day, and so on while Pat travelled 1 km the first day, 3 km the second day, 5 km the third day, and so on, until they met. If both sequences are arithmetic, when will they meet?

12. The Doherty's spend a few days vacation every year at a ski resort. Over the past four years, rates have increased 15% per year. If they paid $1200 for their vacation four years ago, how much must they pay this year? Calculate the total amount paid over the four year period.

Cumulative Review

1. Solve each equation.
   a. $2x - 5 = x + 9$
   b. $-12p^2 - 28p = -8$
   c. $\frac{t^2 - 9}{t + 3} = 2t + 11$
   d. $x + \sqrt{x + 4} = 4$
   e. $\sqrt{a^2 - 25} = 25$
   f. $\sqrt[3]{2m - 5} + 4 = 1$

2. Find the number of intersection points of the given line with the given circle.
   a. $2x + 3y = 7;\ x^2 + y^2 = 10$
   b. $6x + y = 18;\ x^2 + y^2 = 32$
   c. $5x - 8y = 70;\ x^2 + y^2 = 30$
   d. $3x - y = 7;\ x^2 + y^2 = 7$
   e. $x + 4y = 12;\ x^2 + y^2 = 24$
   f. $x + 3y = 36;\ x^2 + y^2 = 36$

3. Determine the number of x-intercepts of each parabola.
   a. $y = -x^2 - 6x - 2$
   b. $y = -15x^2 + 5x + 1$
   c. $y = 4x^2$

4. Graph the circle defined by each equation and state its x and y-intercepts.
   a. $x^2 + y^2 = 64$
   b. $x^2 + y^2 = 24$
   c. $4x^2 + 4y^2 = 49$
   d. $x^2 + y^2 = 75$
   e. $x^2 + y^2 = \frac{25}{9}$
   f. $x^2 + y^2 - 6x + 3y - 8 = 0$

5. For each pair of functions, determine whether or not f and g are inverses.
   a. $f(x) = 2x + 3$, $g(x) = \frac{x - 3}{2}$
   b. $f(x) = -x + 2$, $g(x) = -x - 2$
   c. $f(x) = \frac{1}{2}x - 3$, $g(x) = 2x + 9$
   d. $f(x) = \frac{1}{x + 2}$, $g(x) = \frac{1 - 2x}{x}$
   e. $f(x) = \sqrt{x - 1}$, $g(x) = x^2 + 1$
   f. $f(x) = 2x^2 + 3$, $g(x) = \frac{x - 3}{2}$

6. Given that the domain of each function is $\{-2, -1, 0, 1, 2, 3\}$, find the range of each function.
   a. $f(x) = \frac{x + 3}{5}$
   b. $g: x \rightarrow 2 - 3|x|$
   c. $t = \{(x, y) \mid y = 2x^2 + 1\}$
   d. $m: x \rightarrow 2^x + 3$
   e. $s(x) = |-x|$
   f. $h: x \rightarrow (x - 2)^2$

7. Write an equation of each circle in simplified form.
   a. The circle has centre on $(2, -3)$ and is tangent to $y = -4$.
   b. The circle has centre on $x = 2$ and is tangent to both $x = 0$ and $y = -2$.
   c. The circle is tangent to $x = -1$ and $y = 3$, and has its centre on $x = 3$.

8. A real estate agent makes a commission of \$6000 on a house that sells for \$142 000. At the same rate of commission, what would be the selling price of a house for which the agent makes a commission of \$7500?

9. a. If y varies inversely as x and the value of y is 2 when x is 5, find the value of y when x is 8.
   b. If R varies inversely as T and the value of R is 0.02 when T is 6000, find the value of R when T is 9000.
   c. If d varies inversely as f and the value of d is 12.4 when f is 8.2, find the value of d when f is 1.

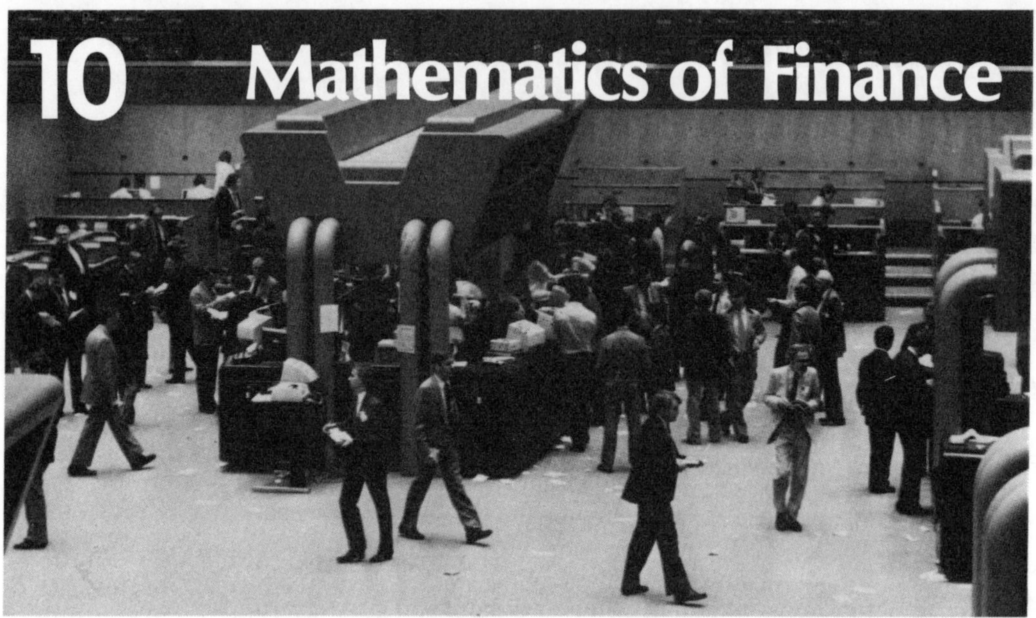

10-1 Borrowing at Simple Interest

Using credit to purchase items such as a car, a house, furniture, or a major appliance has become an important part of everyday life. A purchaser can borrow funds from a financial institution such as a chartered bank, trust company, or credit union.

Borrowing money from a lending institution actually entails paying for the use of the money for a set period of time. The amount borrowed is called the **principal**. The charge for using the principal is called the **interest**, which is added to the principal. Interest is usually specified by a percentage rate per year. When **simple interest** is charged, the interest payable on the loan is proportional to the length of time the loan is outstanding.

Simple Interest Formula

$I = Prt$ where P is the principal (total amount borrowed),
r is the annual interest rate in years, and
t is the period of time in years.

The **accumulated amount, A,** is equal to the principal, P, plus the interest I.

$$
\begin{aligned}
A &= P + I \\
&= P + Prt \qquad \text{Substitute for } I\text{, using } I = Prt. \\
&= P(1 + rt)
\end{aligned}
$$

Accumulated Amount Formula

$A = P(1 + rt)$, where A is the accumulated amount.

There are basically three different types of bank loans. When a bank issues a **promissory note**, the borrower agrees to pay the total amount of the loan plus interest on a specified date.

For a **demand loan**, there is no specific accumulated amount due nor is there a specified date of payment. The bank expects reasonable and regular payments, usually monthly, to keep up with interest charges. The interest on such loans is calculated according to the number of days between payments.

The terms of a **personal instalment loan** usually require the borrower to make a fixed payment including principal and interest at regular intervals for a specified time, at which point the loan is considered paid off.

EXAMPLE 1: On March 1, Sara borrowed \$1200 from her bank at $11\frac{1}{2}$%/a (per annum) interest on a three-month promissory note. What is the accumulated amount due after three months?

$A = P(1 + rt)$ Use the accumulated amount formula.

$= 1200\left[1 + \left(0.115 \times \frac{3}{12}\right)\right]$ Express the rate, 3 months, in years.

$= 1234.50$

The accumulated amount due is \$1234.50.

EXAMPLE 2: Brandon borrowed \$3500 on January 5 at 12%/a on a demand loan. On February 1 and March 1, he paid \$1300 on the principal. He made a final payment on April 1. Find the amount of the final payment and the total interest he paid on the principal.

Use a table to show the payments made and the accumulated amounts. Remember to express time t in years.

Date	Days Since Payment	Interest ($I = Prt$)	Payment	Principal plus Interest Owed
Jan. 5				\$3500.00
Feb. 1	27	$\$3500 \times 0.12 \times \frac{27}{365} \doteq \$31.07$	\$1300.00	\$2231.07
Mar. 1	28	$\$2231.07 \times 0.12 \times \frac{28}{365} \doteq \$20.54$	\$1300.00	\$951.61
Apr. 1	31	$\$951.61 \times 0.12 \times \frac{31}{365} \doteq \$9.70$	\$961.31	—

Brandon's final payment is \$951.61 + \$9.70, or \$961.31. The total interest he paid is \$31.07 + \$20.54 + \$9.70, or \$61.31.

EXERCISE 10-1

A **1.** What are some of the reasons that might be used to justify the extra cost of borrowing money to purchase an item?

2. Financial advisors usually recommend that money *not* be borrowed:

a. to finance small purchases;

b. when payments cannot be made with the present income level;

c. from an institution without a good reputation.

Justify each of the above recommendations.

3. Complete the simple interest table.

	Principal	Rate per Year	Time	Interest
a.	\$1000	8%	3 months	
b.	\$1500	11.5%	$2\frac{1}{2}$ years	
c.	\$25 000	$9\frac{1}{4}$%	18 months	
d.		12%	3 months	\$135.00
e.		10.5%	$2\frac{1}{2}$ years	\$551.25
f.		15.25%	7 months	\$24.90
g.	\$2200	12%		\$110.00
h.	\$7500	10.5%		\$1181.25
i.	\$10 000	$9\frac{3}{4}$%		\$1181.25
j.	\$5700		9 months	\$534.38
k.	\$9000		30 months	\$2981.25
l.	\$15 000		15 months	\$2765.63

B **4.** Determine the accumulated amount for each situation at the end of the given time period.

	Principal	Rate per Year	Time
a.	\$800	$\frac{1}{2}$%	6 months
b.	\$4000	10.125%	$2\frac{1}{3}$ years
c.	\$2500	$9\frac{1}{4}$%	9 months
d.	\$7500	$14\frac{1}{2}$%	$1\frac{1}{2}$ years
e.	\$12 000	$8\frac{3}{4}$%	40 months

5. Heather has agreed to lend her sister \$500 for two years at 12.5%/a simple interest. At the end of the two years, what amount should Heather collect?

6. Matthew deposited \$85 at $9\frac{1}{4}$%/a simple interest in his savings account. How many months will he have to wait before he can use the money to buy a \$100 skateboard?

7. In order to buy a new car, Darryl arranged a loan with a credit union. He signed a promissory note for $3500 at 14.25%/a for eight months. What accumulated amount did he pay at the end of the time period?

8. Mr. Palucci borrowed $15 000 on a demand loan at 12.125%/a to buy a new oven and other equipment for his bakery. He signed the note on March 1 and paid $4000 on April 1, May 1, and June 1. What should be the amount of the final payment on July 3?

C 9. A promissory note for $10 000 is arranged on January 15 with a due date of September 30. What is the accumulated amount due on September 30 if the interest rate is 13.5%/a?

10. Shira has $1000 in a term deposit at $8\frac{3}{4}$% per year. The term deposit has three months left in its term, but she finds that she needs the $1000 to pay a car repair bill of $780. If she takes the money out of the term deposit, the bank will pay her only $6\frac{1}{2}$% on the money for the three months. She could, however, borrow money on a 90 day demand loan at $9\frac{1}{2}$%. What should she do?

EXTRA

Personal Instalment Loan Rates

For a personal instalment loan, the bank specifies the number and amount of equal payments required to pay off the loan. For example, if a $5000 car loan is paid off in 36 monthly instalments of $165, the amount repaid is $5940. Therefore, the interest is $940, which is close to 20% of the principal. An exact formula for the *approximate* annual interest rate is difficult to obtain. However, a computer program can be used to approximate the rate by trial and error.

The actual annual interest rate on the $5000 loan can be expected to exceed 20% ÷ 3, or say 7%. So an initial estimate of 7% can be inputed in the program at the right to see what happens to the loan over the 36 month period. If the result is a negative balance, then the principal is being paid off too rapidly and the actual interest rate has been underestimated. If the result is a positive balance, then the rate has been overestimated. Thus, if 7% does not lead to a zero balance, you can decide whether the next approximation should be higher (for example, $7\frac{1}{2}$%) or lower (for example, $6\frac{1}{2}$%).

Approximate the actual interest rate for the $5000 car loan using the computer program to refine your guesses.

```
10  INPUT "ENTER PRINCIPAL     :";P
20  INPUT "ENTER ANNUAL RATE   :";R
30  INPUT "NUMBER OF PERIODS   :";N
40  INPUT "ENTER PAYMENT       :";PMT
50 R = R / 1200
60  PRINT : PRINT : PRINT "N","P"
70  PRINT 0,P
80  FOR I = 1 TO N
90 P = P * (1 + R)
100 P = P - PMT
110  PRINT I,P
120  NEXT I
130  END
```

10-2 Investing and Borrowing at Compound Interest

With many investments and loans, the interest over a period of time is added to the principal, or **compounded**, at the end of an interest period. A **compounding period** is the length of time between periods when interest is calculated. When interest is compounded semiannually, for example, the compounding period is 6 months.

Compound interest always involves a **periodic interest rate, *i*.**

$$i = \frac{\text{The actual interest rate}}{\text{number of compounding periods per year}}$$

For an interest rate of 8% compounded semiannually, $i = \frac{0.08}{2}$, or 4%.

That is, money invested at 8% interest compounded semiannually earns 4% interest every 6 months.

Earning compound interest is like earning "interest on the interest".

EXAMPLE 1: \$500 is invested for 3 years at 10% interest compounded annually. What is the amount of the investment after 3 years?

A chart can be used to show the calculations.

Compounding period (years)	Principal at start of compounding period (\$)	Accumulated amount at end of compounding period (\$)
1	500	$500 + 500(0.10) = 550$
2	550	$550 + 550(0.10) = 605$
3	605	$605 + 605(0.10) = 665.50$

The investment accumulated to \$665.50 after 3 years.

In Example 1, notice that the accumulated amounts could also have been calculated as follows.

Compounding period (years)	Principal at start of compounding period (\$)	Accumulated amount at end of compounding period (\$)
1	500	$500 + 500(0.10)$ $= 500(1 + 0.10)$ $= 500(1.10)$
2	$500(1.10)$	$500(1.10) + 500(1.10)(0.10)$ $= 500(1.10)(1 + 1.10)$ $= 500(1.10)^2$
3	$500(1.10)^2$	$500(1.10)^2 + 500(1.10)^2(0.10)$ $= 500(1.10)^2(1 + 0.10)$ $= 500(1.10)^3$

Use the distributive property.

Using a calculator, you can verify that $500(1.10)^3$ is equal to $665.50. The second chart shows the accumulated amounts as a geometric series, which leads to the following formula.

> The **accumulated amount *A* for compound interest** is $A = P(1 + i)^n$, where P is the original principal, i is the interest rate per compounding period, and n is the number of compounding periods.

EXAMPLE 2: Erin invests $1000 at 8% interest compounded semiannually. What amount will she have accumulated after two years?

The principal Erin starts with is $1000.
Since 8% interest is compounded twice a year, $i = \frac{0.08}{2}$, or 0.04.

There are 4 compounding periods during the two years. Substitute these values into the formula for accumulated interest.

$$\begin{aligned} A &= P(1 + i)^n \\ &= 1000(1 + 0.04)^4 \\ &= 1000(1.04)^4 \quad \text{Use a calculator.} \\ &\doteq 1169.86 \end{aligned}$$

The situation can be shown on a time-line diagram.

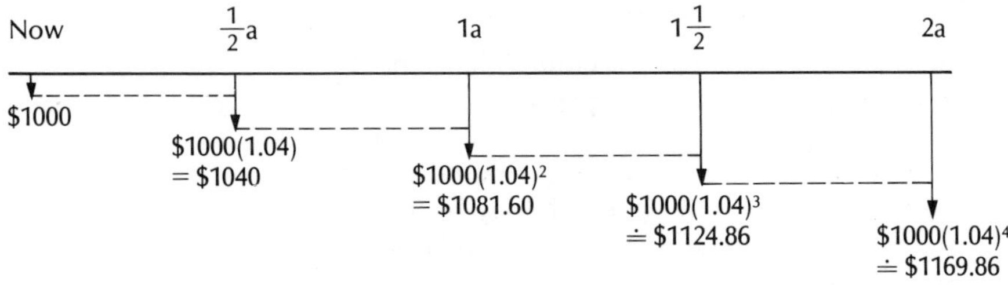

At the end of 2 years, or 4 compounding periods, Erin has accumulated $1000(1.04)^4, or $1169.86.

For 8%/a interest compounded semiannually, the 8% is called the **nominal annual interest rate**, or the **nominal rate**.
An **effective rate** is the annual rate of interest which, when compounded annually, is *equivalent* to the nominal rate compounded more than once per year.

> **Effective rate** $= (1 + i)^n - 1$, where i is the interest rate per compounding period, and n is the number of compounding periods per year.

The effective rate for the investment in Example 2 can be determined using the above formula. The interest rate per compounding period is 4% and there are two compounding periods per year.

$$\begin{aligned}\text{Effective rate} &= (1+i)^n - 1\\ &= (1+0.04)^2 - 1\\ &= 0.0816\end{aligned}$$

The effective rate is 8.16% per year.

This means that an effective rate of 8.16%, compounded annually, is equivalent to a nominal annual rate of 8% compounded semiannually. Thus, a $1000 investment at 8.16% compounded annually is equivalent to a $1000 investment at 8%/a compounded semiannually. Both investments yield $1169.86 at the end of two years.

EXAMPLE 3: $1500 is invested for 3 years at $9\frac{1}{2}$%/a compounded quarterly. What is the effective annual rate, correct to two decimal places?

There are four compounding periods per year. The interest rate per compounding period is $\frac{0.095}{4}$ or 0.023 75.

$$\begin{aligned}\text{Effective Rate} &= (1+i)^n - 1\\ &= (1+0.023\,75)^4 - 1\\ &\doteq 0.098\,438\end{aligned}$$

An effective rate of 9.84% is equivalent to the $9\frac{1}{2}$% nominal rate compounded quarterly.

EXAMPLE 4: What is the accumulated amount due on a $1500 promissory note issued on May 1, 1988 at 13.5%/a compounded semiannually and due on November 1, 1992?

Draw a time-line diagram to illustrate the situation. Then use the accumulated amount formula. The interest rate per compounding period is $\frac{0.135}{2}$ or 0.0675. There are nine 6-month compounding periods in the entire term.

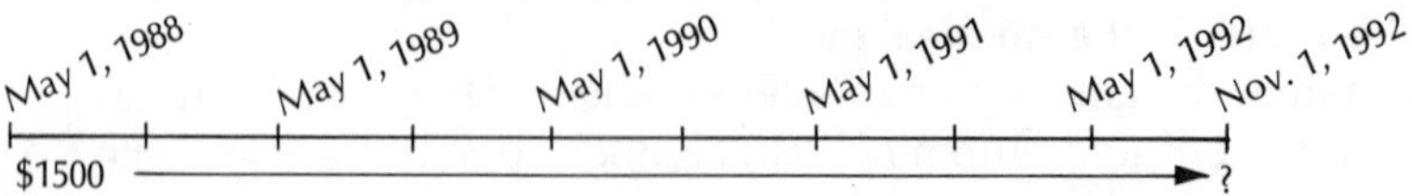

$$\begin{aligned}A &= P(1+i)^n\\ &= 1500(1+0.0675)^9\\ &\doteq 2700.239\end{aligned}$$

The accumulated amount due on the loan is $2700.24.

EXERCISE 10-2

A **1.** Use a calculator to simplify each expression. Round-off answers to the nearest hundredth.

a. 2^{12} **b.** 1.5^{9} **c.** 20^{11} **d.** $\frac{1}{18^{5}}$

e. $(3^{5})(4^{9})$ **f.** $(1.025)^{10}$ **g.** $(1.7)^{5}(205.6)^{3}$ **h.** $(110.26)^{6}(27.5)^{-3}$

2. Complete the compound interest table. Round-off interest rates to the nearest thousandth.

	Nominal Rate per Year	Compounding period	Time	Total number of compounding periods	Interest rate per period
a.	10%	six months	3 years	■	■
b.	$8\frac{1}{2}$%	quarterly	18 months	■	■
c.	15.25%	semiannually	7 years	■	■
d.	8%	monthly	$2\frac{1}{2}$ years	■	■
e.	10%	weekly	1 year	■	■
f.	12%	3 months	5 years	■	■
g.	■	semiannually	■	8	0.055
h.	■	■	18 months	12	0.013
i.	14%	■	■	9	0.035

B **3.** Calculate the accumulated amount of each given investment. Draw a time-line diagram for each investment.

	Principal	Rate per Year	Compounding Period	Term
a.	$1200	10%	semiannually	3 years
b.	$5000	11.5%	annually	7 years
c.	$2200	$8\frac{3}{4}$%	quarterly	$2\frac{1}{2}$ years
d.	$7500	6%	monthly	2 years
e.	$1400	10.5%	monthly	18 months
f.	$6300	7.8%	quarterly	$3\frac{1}{2}$ years
g.	$1900	9.8%	semiannually	5 years
h.	$4400	8.8%	weekly	2 years
i.	$3800	9.1%	monthly	4 years
j.	$8900	$12\frac{3}{4}$%	quarterly	21 months

4. Find the effective rate for each investment.

a. 12%/a compounded quarterly

b. 10.5%/a compounded semiannually

c. $8\frac{1}{2}$%/a compounded monthly

d. 11.75%/a compounded quarterly

e. 13%/a compounded weekly

5. An investment of $10 000 is made at 10%/a simple interest. How much more interest would be earned if the interest were compounded semiannually? quarterly? monthly?

6. Which loan terms are more appealing: a promissory note at 12%/a compounded semiannually or a promissory note at 11.75%/a compounded weekly?

7. Jacquie borrows $2800 from the bank on a promissory note for a term from May 20, 1988 until May 20, 1990 at $12\frac{1}{2}$%/a compounded quarterly. What is the accumulated amount on the promissory note?

8. Selwyn must decide on a loan. The bank offers him two options. One is a promissory note at 13.5% compounded annually and the other is at $12\frac{3}{4}$%/a compounded weekly. Which is the better loan?

9. In a science fiction short story called "John Jones' Dollar" by Harry Stephen Keller, John Jones makes a bank deposit of one dollar at 3% interest compounded annually and stipulates that the account is to be held for the oldest child of his fortieth descendant. If the length of each generation is 25 years (as is implied in the story), then what amount will be inherited by John Jones' descendant after 40 generations?

10. A hospital receives a gift of $1 500 000 from a donor to help finance a new wing. The hospital board decides to invest the gift at 10%/a compounded quarterly until they are ready to let the contract. If they keep the money for 20 months will they have enough to pay for a $1 750 000 contract without taking funds from elsewhere?

C 11. Jonas deposits $100 each January 1 into his savings account. If his account pays 8% interest compounded annually, how much money will there be in his account at the end of December in the fifth year?

EXTRA — Continuously Compounding Interest

Some institutions offer *continuously compounding interest*. They claim that the interest on your money is compounded each instant it is in your account.

1. To see the benefits of continuously compounding interest, find the *effective rate* for 10% for each compounding period below. Note how the rate changes as the compounding periods become shorter and more numerous.

   a. annually b. semiannually c. quarterly d. monthly
   e. weekly f. daily g. hourly h. by the minute

2. Does the effective rate increase without bound, or does it appear to approach a constant value?

EXTRA

The Consumer Price Index and Inflation

The Consumer Price Index measures the change in retail prices of goods and services. Each month in communities of 30 000 or more, Statistics Canada calculates the cost of a "shopping basket" of 375 different items. The index is weighted to emphasize the changes in food and housing prices and is published once a month for fifteen major cities and the country as a whole. The index figures published below use 1981 as the base year. That is, the 1981 index is adjusted so that for 1981 its value is 100.

The **rate of inflation** is the percentage change in the CPI. The purchasing power of the consumer's wages is diminished during periods of inflation increase unless the wages increase at a rate equal to or greater than the inflation rate.

Year	CPI (Canada)
1971	42.2
1972	44.2
1973	47.6
1974	52.8
1975	58.5
1976	62.9
1977	67.9
1978	73.9
1979	80.7
1980	88.9
1981	100.0
1982	110.8
1983	117.2
1984	122.3
1985	127.2
1986	132.4

1. Graph the Consumer Price Index for each year 1971 through 1986. Between which two years did the CPI jump the most?
2. Compute the percent change in the CPI between years from 1971 to 1986. Graph this inflation rate. Between which two years was it highest?
3. Sum the percent changes from 1971 to 1985. Does this sum equal the percent change between 1971 and 1986? Why or why not?
4. Inflation causes a drop in purchasing power, or real income. If you had money to invest and wished to earn a 10% rate of return in real income while the inflation rate stood at 7%, at what rate would you have to invest your money to realize that real rate of return?
5. Under what conditions would a person be better off to borrow money to finance a purchase than to save money in the bank until he or she had enough to buy the article outright?
6. Why are people on pensions likely to be hurt during periods of high inflation?

10-3 Present Value

Suppose you want to buy a $10 000 car three years from now. You could invest money now so that you would have $10 000 three years from now. The amount of money that needs to be invested *now* to accumulate to $10 000 in three years is called the **present value, $V_{present}$,** of the accumulated amount.

EXAMPLE: What is the present value of an accumulated amount of $10 000 at 8%/a compounded quarterly?

The time-line diagram illustrates the problem.

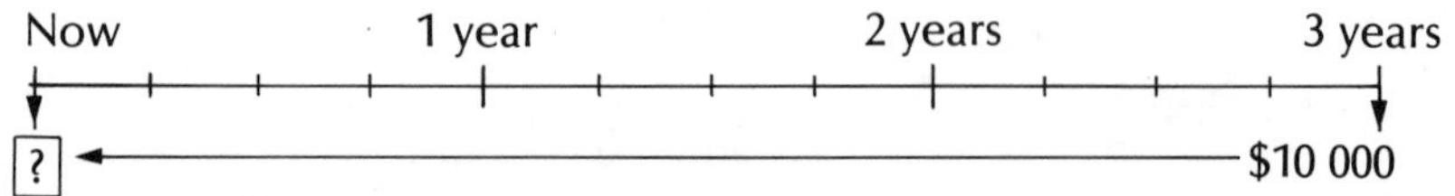

Substitute the present value $V_{present}$, for the principal, P, in the accumulated amount formula.

$$A = P(1 + i)^n$$

$$10\,000 = V_{present}(1 + 0.02)^{12}$$

$$V_{present} \doteq 7884.931$$

$i = \frac{0.08}{4}$, or 0.02

There are 12 compounding periods altogether.

The present value is $7884.93. This means that if $7884.93 were invested now at the given interest rate, a $10 000 car could be purchased in three years.

EXERCISE 10-3

A 1. Write a formula for present value using the accumulated amount formula.

2. Determine n, the number of compounding periods per year, and i, the interest rate per compounding period, for each investment.
   a. A future value of $1200 is accumulated on an investment after five years at $9\frac{1}{4}$% compounded annually.
   b. An account yields $2753 after four years at 10%/a compounded quarterly.
   c. $4398 is accumulated in a savings account after $2\frac{1}{2}$ years at 9%/a compounded semiannually.

3. Complete the given table.

	Nominal Rate per Year	Compounding period	Time	Total number of compounding periods	Interest rate per period
a.	10%	quarterly	5 years	■	■
b.	$8\frac{1}{2}$%	semiannually	$2\frac{1}{2}$ years	■	■
c.	9%	monthly	20 months	■	■
d.	■	semiannually	■	7	0.0475
e.	■	■	3 years	12	0.048

B 4. Draw a time-line diagram for each investment given in the table. Then calculate the present value of each investment.

	Accumulated Amount	Rate per Year	Compounding Period	Term
a.	$1000	10%	semiannually	4 years
b.	$1500	9%	quarterly	$1\frac{1}{2}$ years
c.	$2200	12%	monthly	$3\frac{1}{3}$ years
d.	$3500	$8\frac{1}{2}$%	annually	7 years
e.	$7500	9.6%	quarterly	27 months
f.	$10 000	7.5%	monthly	$2\frac{1}{2}$ years
g.	$3800	$11\frac{3}{4}$%	semiannually	5 years

5. Mr. Smith is investing money to pay for a new sailboat. He figures that in three years' time he can buy the boat he wants for $12 500. How much money should he invest at 10.4%/a compounded semiannually to accumulate such an amount?

6. Gina has borrowed enough money so that in two years she will have to repay $3850 in principal and interest. The terms of the loan were 12%/a compounded quarterly. What is the amount of the loan?

7. John needs to borrow a sum of money to buy a truck so that he can start his own landscape business. He feels that at the end of his second year in business he should be able to pay $3500 toward the loan and pay it off. If the terms of the loan are 14%/a compounded quarterly, how much can he borrow?

8. John and Marcia are getting married. For a wedding gift their parents want to give them enough money so that at the end of five years they will have $15 000 toward a down payment on a house. The money would be invested at $9\frac{3}{4}$%/a compounded semiannually. How much money should the parents give them?

9. Steven has two investment options. He wishes to invest enough so that in four years' time he will have \$400. He can either invest at 8%/a compounded monthly or $8\frac{3}{4}$% compounded annually. In each case, how much money would he have to invest? What is the better option?

C 10. A stereo store will offer to finance the purchase of new equipment. A stereo system is on sale for \$1800 cash or for \$700 down and \$600 in each of two instalments, one in six months, and the other in a year. If the money can be invested at 10.6%/a compounded semiannually, which offer is better?

Using the Calculator Logs and Compounding Periods

The **logarithm** of a number is the power to which 10 must be raised to obtain the number. For example, log(1000) is 3, since 10^3 is 1000. Every positive number can be expressed as 10 raised to some exponent.
In general, $y = 10^z$ is equivalent to $z = \log y$.

The [log] button on a calculator will tell you what the exponent is.

[100] [log] [=] [2]

It is often useful to know how long an investment must be made before it reaches a certain value. For example, how long must \$100 be invested at 10% interest compounded annually before it doubles to \$200?

Logarithms can be used to solve the problem.

First, substitute known values into $A = PV(1 + i)^n$.

$$
\begin{aligned}
200 &= 100(1 + 0.1)^n \\
&= 100(1.1)^n \\
(1.1)^n &= \frac{200}{100} \\
&= 2
\end{aligned}
$$

Now use logarithms to find n.

$$
\begin{aligned}
(1.1)^n &= 2 \\
n\log 1.1 &= \log 2 && \text{Find the log of each side of the equation.} \\
n &= \frac{\log 2}{\log 1.1} && \text{Use a calculator to find log 2 and log 1.1.} \\
&= \frac{0.30103}{0.04139} \\
&\doteq 7.27
\end{aligned}
$$

The money will double after the seventh year.

How long will it take for the \$100 investment to doubleif it is invested at 10%/a compounded semiannually; quarterly; monthly?

Review

1. Complete the given table.

	Principal	Rate per Year	Time	Interest
a.	$3500	7.5%	6 months	▬
b.	$2800	12.5%	18 months	▬
c.	$2200	8.5%	28 weeks	▬
d.	▬	11.5%	$1\frac{1}{2}$ years	$483

2. A deposit of $5000 is made on July 18 in an account which bears 9.5%/a daily interest. How much interest has accrued when the money is withdrawn on October 7?

3. Susan needs to borrow $1500 to finish furnishing her apartment. She signs a promissory note for that amount at 14.5% interest from April 17 to September 30. What is the total amount due?

4. Determine the accumulated amount of each investment at the end of the given term.

	Principal	Rate per Year	Compounding Period	Term
a.	$2000	8%	semiannually	2 years
b.	$1500	10%	monthly	$1\frac{1}{2}$ years
c.	$3750	11.5%	quarterly	3 years
d.	$6500	8%	monthly	15 months

5. **a.** Which is the best rate for a loan; 9.2%/a compounded monthly, 9.6%/a compounded quarterly, or 9.75%/a compounded semiannually?
   b. Using your answer from part **a**, calculate the effective rate and determine the best rate for an investment.

6. Charles negotiates a demand loan with the bank for $2200 at 12.5%/a compounded quarterly. He makes no payments for an entire year and then pays $1500.
   a. What is the balance of the loan after this first payment?
   b. If Charles then pays $300/month for the following three months, find the amount of the last payment at the end of the fourth month to cover the outstanding principal and interest.

7. What is the present value of a savings account that will accumulate to $1000 in 18 months at 8.5%/a compounded quarterly?

10-4 Annuities

Instead of investing a lump sum once and then waiting for the investment to accumulate to a certain value, many people make fixed deposits on a regular basis. An **annuity** is a series of equal deposits or payments made at regular intervals, such as annually, semiannually, quarterly, or monthly.

For an **ordinary annuity**, deposits or payments are made at the end of each designated time period. The accumulated amount of an ordinary annuity is the sum of the accumulated amounts of all deposits or payments made, from the time of investment until the last deposit or payment occurs.

EXAMPLE 1: Sally is saving for a car by depositing $500 semiannually in a savings account that bears 9.6%/a interest compounded semiannually. She makes the deposits at the end of each 6-month period. What amount will she have saved at the end of three years?

The investment is an ordinary annuity, since equal deposits are made at the end of each regular interval. Use the accumulated amount formula, $A = P(1 + i)^n$, to determine the accumulated amount of each 6-month deposit.

Notice that $i = \frac{0.096}{2}$ or 0.048, and so $(1 + i) = 1.048$.

The first deposit of $500 accumulates for 5 periods, and so $A = 500(1.048)^5$. Illustrate the situation with a time-line diagram.

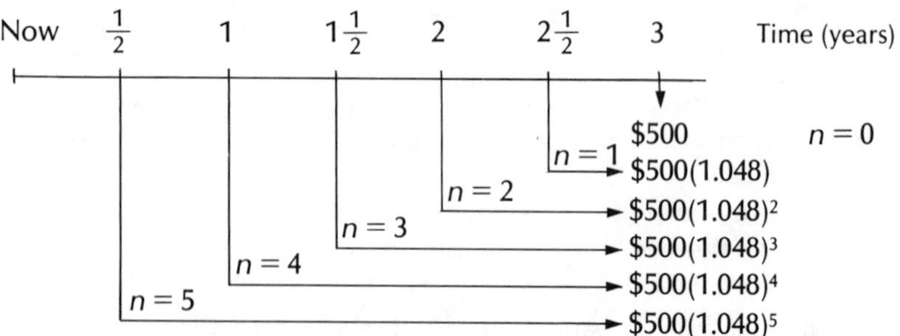

Sum the accumulated amounts of all the deposits to find the accumulated amount of the ordinary annuity.
$A = \$500 + \$500(1.048) + \$500(1.048)^2 + \ldots + \$500(1.048)^5$

Notice that the accumulated amount is a geometric series.

You can use the geometric series formula, $S_n = \dfrac{a(r^n - 1)}{r - 1}$, to find the accumulated amount of an ordinary annuity.

Substitute known values into the formula.

$$S_n = \frac{a(r^n - 1)}{r - 1}$$ a is the first term of the geometric series, so $a = 500$.

$$A = \frac{500(1.048^6 - 1)}{1.048 - 1}$$ $r = 1 + i$, or 1.08

The series has 6 terms, so $n = 6$.

$$\doteq \frac{500(0.324853)}{0.048}$$ Use a calculator for the calculations.

$$\doteq 3383.89$$

Sally will have $3383.89 saved at the end of three years.

Sometimes the compounding period is shorter than the deposit or payment period.

EXAMPLE 2: Ted is saving for a boat by depositing $500 semiannually in a savings account that bears 10%/a interest compounded quarterly. What amount will he have saved at the end of four years?

Notice that $i = \frac{0.10}{4}$, or 0.025. Thus, $(1 + i) = 1.025$. Draw a time-line diagram to illustrate the situation.

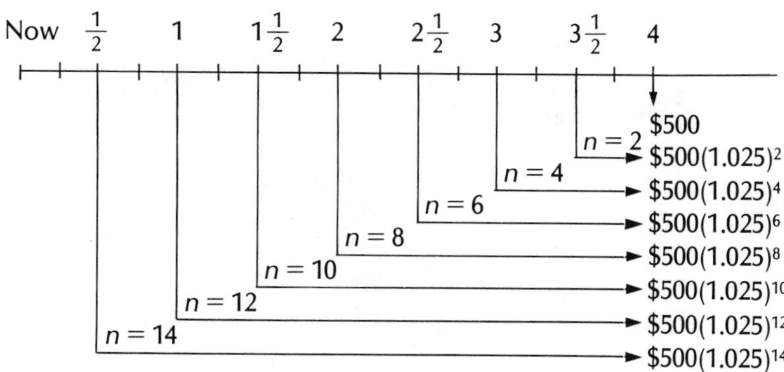

$A = \$500 + \$500(1.025)^2 + \$500(1.025)^4 + \$500(1.025)^6 + \ldots + \$500(1.025)^{14}$

Substitute known values into the geometric series formula. Notice that the common ratio r is $(1.025)^2$.

$$S_n = \frac{a(r^n - 1)}{r - 1}$$ $a = 500$, $r = (1.025)^2$, and $n = 8$

$$A = \frac{500[(1.025^2]^8 - 1}{(1.025)^2 - 1}$$

$$= \frac{500(1.025)^{16} - 1}{(1.025)^2 - 1}$$ Use a calculator.

$$\doteq 4785.24$$ Round-off to the nearest hundredth.

Ted will have saved $4875.24 at the end of four years.

EXERCISE 10-4

A **1.** Use the information in the diagram to calculate the accumulated amount of each ordinary annuity.

a. the annual interest rate is 10% compounded semiannually

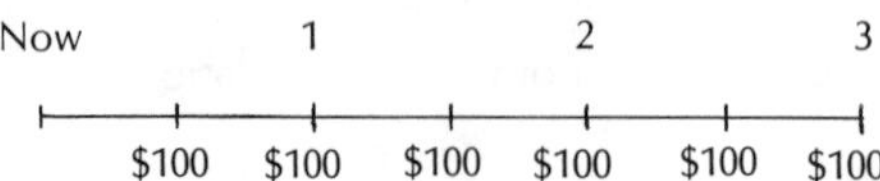

b. the annual interest rate is 6% compounded quarterly

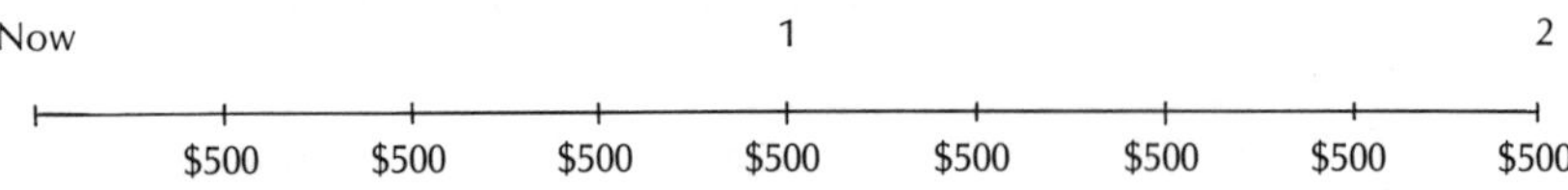

c. the annual interest rate is 9% compounded monthly

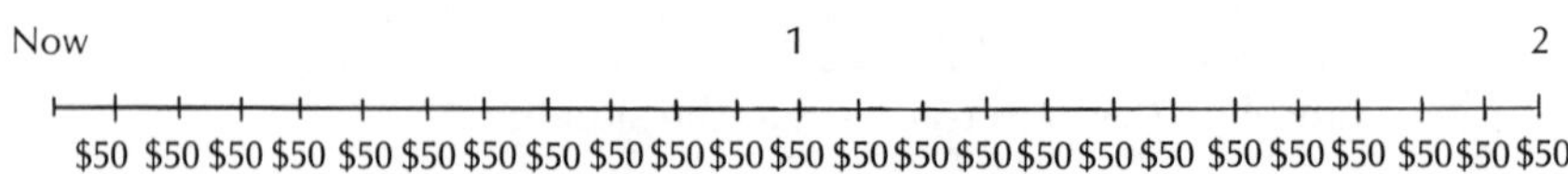

2. Calculate the accumulated amount of each ordinary annuity using the information given in the table.

	Deposit	Deposit Interval	Rate per Year	Compounding Period	Term
a.	$250	semiannually	8%	semiannually	2 years
b.	$100	monthly	12%	monthly	1 year
c.	$500	annually	$9\frac{1}{2}$%	annually	5 years
d.	$125	quarterly	12%	quarterly	2 years

	Payment	Payment Interval	Rate per Year	Compounding Period	Term
e.	$1000	annually	10%	semiannually	3.5 years
f.	$75	quarterly	8%	monthly	15 months
g.	$300	semiannually	12%	quarterly	18 months

	Payment	Payment Interval	Rate per Year	Compounding Period	Term
h.	$50	monthly	8%	semiannually	$2\frac{1}{2}$ years
i.	$200	semiannually	$8\frac{3}{4}$%	annually	3 years
j.	$65	semiannually	8%	monthly	$3\frac{1}{2}$ years

B **3.** Draw a time-line diagram for each annuity using the information given in the table.

	Payment	Payment Interval	Rate per Year	Compounding Period	Term
a.	$150	quarterly	10%	quarterly	18 months
b.	$80	semiannually	8%	semiannually	$2\frac{1}{2}$ years
c.	$300	annually	$9\frac{1}{2}$%	annually	5 years
d.	$100	semiannually	8%	monthly	3 years
e.	$200	annually	12%	semiannually	2 years

4. One hundred dollars is invested in a savings account twice a year, in June and December. The account bears interest of 8%/a compounded semiannually. What amount of money accumulated in the account at the end of the fifth year?

5. The Reids are saving for a vacation. They deposit $100 each month into a savings account that bears 9%/a interest compounded monthly. How much money will be in the account at the end of the third year?

6. Each year, Kathi invests $1000 in an investment fund that is guaranteed to earn 11%/a interest each year. How much money can Kathi expect to have accumulated at the end of the tenth year?

7. In order to encourage her friends to stop smoking, Gayle has calculated how much money could accumulate in five years if each friend deposited his or her cigarette money in a savings account that bore 8%/a compounded monthly. Assuming that her friends each spend $45 per month on cigarettes, how much would each friend accumulate if the cigarette money were invested instead?

8. The Plant family is saving for the down payment on a cottage at the lake. They deposit $1800 each year into an account that bears 10%/a interest compounded quarterly.

a. At the end of six years, how much money has accumulated in the account?

b. How much would have accumulated if they had deposited the money in an account that bears 9.5%/a compounded monthly?

C **9.** The Ames family has been investing $300 per year in accounts that bear 8%/a compounded semiannually to save for the college education of each of their children. An investment of $300 for each child is made at the *start* of each year. After 12 years, how much money will each child receive toward his or her education?

10-5 Present Value of an Annuity

If you had a lump sum of money to invest now, you could invest in an annuity to provide you with a regular and secure income.

EXAMPLE 1: What amount should be invested now to provide a regular income of \$2500 each year for the next four years if the money is invested at 8%/a compounded annually?

The first annuity payment occurs in one year. Determine what principal, P_1, will accumulate to \$2500 at the end of the first year.

$$A = P_1(1 + i)^n$$
$$2500 = P_1(1.08)$$
$$P_1 = 2500(1.08)^{-1}$$

Similarly, determine what principal, P_2, will accumulate to \$2500 at the end of the second year.

$$A = P_2(1 + i)^n$$
$$2500 = P_2(1.08)^2$$
$$P_2 = 2500(1.08)^{-2}$$

Draw a time-line diagram to illustrate the situation.

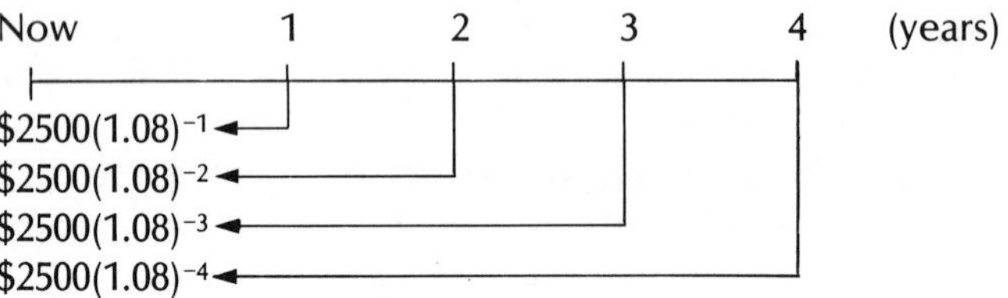

The present value of the annuity is the sum of the present value of each annual payment. Sum the terms starting with the last term to ensure that *r* will have a positive exponent.

$$\therefore V_{present} = 2500(1.08)^{-4} + 2500(1.08)^{-3} + 2500(1.08)^{-2} + 2500(1.08)^{-1}$$

Substitute into the geometric series formula.

$$S_n = \frac{a(r^n - 1)}{r - 1}$$

$$V_{present} = \frac{2500(1.08)^{-4}(1.08^4 - 1)}{1.08 - 1}$$

$a = 2500(1.08)^{-4}$, $r = 1 + i$ or 1.08, and $n = 4$

$$= \frac{2500(1.08^4 - 1)}{(1.08)^4(0.08)}$$

Use a calculator.

$$\doteq 8280.32$$

Round-off to the nearest hundredth.

The present value or the amount of money needed now to provide a regular income of \$2500 per year for the next four years is \$8280.32.

In the Example 1, the payment interval and the interest compounding period were the *same*. Sometimes, the compounding period is *shorter than* the payment interval.

EXAMPLE 2: What amount of money would you need to have now to invest in an ordinary annuity that would provide a $5000 per year income for the next three years if the money is invested at 10%/a compounded semiannually?

Since the money is invested annually, but the interest is compounded semiannually, determine the effective annual rate.
The effective annual rate is $(1.05)^2 - 1$, or 0.1025.

Now draw a time-line diagram.

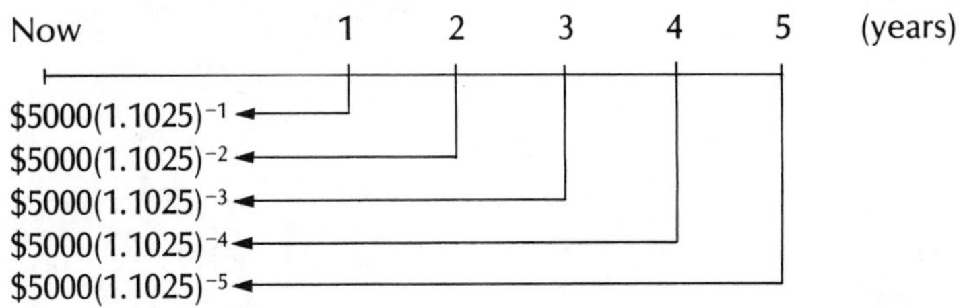

$V_{present} = \$5000(1.1025)^{-5} + \$5000(1.1025)^{-4} + \ldots + \$5000(1.1025)^{-1}$

Substitute into the geometric series formula. $a = \$5000(1.1025)^{-5}$, $r = 1 + i$, or 1.1025, and $n = 5$.

$$S_n = \frac{a(r^n - 1)}{r - 1}$$

$$A = \frac{5000(1.1025)^{-5}(1.1025^5 - 1)}{1.1025 - 1}$$

$$\doteq \frac{5000(0.613\,913)(0.628\,894)}{0.1025}$$

$\doteq$ \$18 833.50 (to the nearest cent)

You would have to invest $18 833.50 now.

EXERCISE 10-5

A **1.** Determine the present value of each ordinary annuity represented in each time-line diagram.

a. 10%/a interest compounded annually

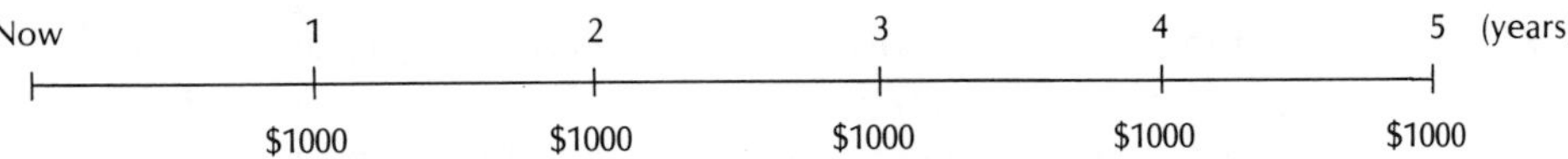

b. 8%/a interest compounded semiannually

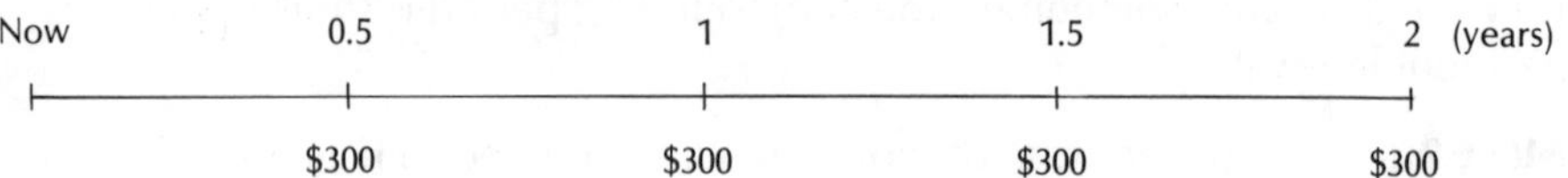

c. 6%/a interest compounded monthly

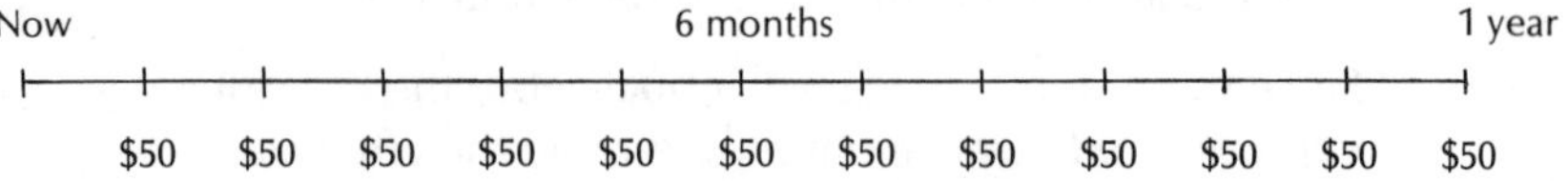

B **2.** Draw a time-line diagram for each ordinary annuity using the information in the given table. Then find the present value for each annuity.

	Rate per Year	Compounding Period	Term	Payment
a.	10%	annually	5 years	$1000 annually
b.	8%	semiannually	3 years	$250 semiannually
c.	12%	monthly	$1\frac{1}{2}$ years	$100 monthly
d.	7.6%	monthly	$4\frac{1}{2}$ years	$1500 quarterly
e.	8%	monthly	7 years	$500 semiannually

3. How much money must be invested now at 8%/a compounded monthly to provide a monthly income of $550 per month for ten years?

4. A scholarship is being endowed by a local service club for the high school. The club wishes to provide funds for one $1000 scholarship for each of the next ten years. The school board scholarship committee invest such endowments in a fund that earns 9.2%/a interest compounded semiannually. What amount should the club donate to the fund?

5. The Lee family has two options for receiving an inheritance. They can either take $42 000 in cash or receive annual payments of $6500 for ten years. Which option should they choose if they can invest the money at an effective rate of $9\frac{1}{2}$% annually?

6. There are two payment options on the purchase of a new stereo system. The marked price is $995 less 10% if paid in cash. The financed price is $350 down and the balance paid in equal monthly instalments of $53.75 for one year. If money is worth 9%/a compounded monthly, which is the better deal?

C **7.** A trust fund is set up to provide a yearly income of $30 000 for ten years. The value of money is compounded quarterly at a rate of 8.5%/a. How much must be invested *now* so that the payments may commence in five years' time?

Application

Mortgage Payments

A house mortgage is an example of an ordinary annuity. The interest rate and the term of the mortgage is usually known. The term is called the **amortization period**. The amount of the monthly payments on a mortgage can be determined by using the geometric series formula.

The Andersons have negotiated a $60 000 mortgage on their house for an amortization period of 25 years at 12%/a compounded monthly. What are the monthly payments?
Let M be the monthly mortgage payment. Notice that $V_{present}$ is $60 000.

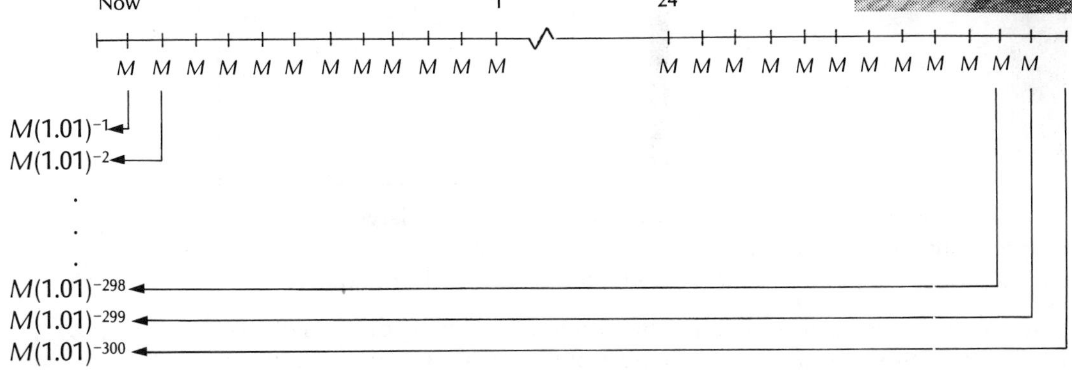

$$V_{present} = M(1.01)^{-300} + M(1.01)^{-299} + M(1.01)^{-298} + \ldots \text{ (to 300 terms)}$$

$$S_n = \frac{a(r^n - 1)}{r - 1} \qquad \therefore 60\ 000 = \frac{M(1.01)^{-300}(1.01^{300} - 1)}{1.01 - 1}$$

$$= \frac{M(1.01^{300} - 1)}{(1.01)^{300}(0.01)}$$

$$M = \frac{60\ 000(0.01)(1.01)^{300}}{(1.01^{300} - 1)}$$

$$\doteq 631.93$$

The monthly mortgage payments are $631.93.

1. Determine the monthly payment due on a mortgage of $58 000 amortized for 15 years at an interest rate of 15%/a compounded monthly.

2. What are the monthly payments on a mortgage of $135 000 at 10.5%/a interest compounded monthly and amortized over 30 years?

3. A large power company arranges a loan of 3.5 million dollars with the federal government. The loan is amortized over ten years at a rate of 9.8%/a compounded semiannually with payments to be made annually. What is the amount of each payment?

10-6 Bonds

Bonds are "instruments" by which governments and large corporations borrow money to finance their operations. When a purchaser buys a bond from a private corporation, he or she in effect is holding a mortgage on the corporation. This puts the bond owner in a more secure position than a company's shareholder because a bond debt takes precedence over any shareholder's claims.

Provincial, municipal, and federal governments, and some large public corporations, however, do not issue bonds in the form of a mortgage, but simply promise to pay the principal and interest due the bondholder.

Government, municipal, and corporate bonds carry varying degrees of risk, depending on the financial circumstances of the issuer. Issuers who are in a strong economic position, for example, have less risk associated with their bonds.

The **face value** of a bond is the amount of money that the bondissuer will pay to the bondholder on the **maturity date**.

The **term** of a bond is the time between the date of issue and the maturity date. Unlike stocks, bonds are issued for a fixed term.

An annual **interest rate** is paid to the bondholder, since money has been borrowed by a government or corporation from the holder. In Canada, traded bonds pay interest semiannually.

Bondholders do not always keep their bonds until their maturity dates. Bonds are sold at the **market value** of the bond. The market value is determined by a number of factors such as the face value of the bond, the term, the bond interest rate, the current interest rate, and the time since the last interest period.

If an investor can earn a better return on his or her investment than the bond interest rate, the value of the bond will decrease and it will sell at a **discount**. That is, the bond will sell for *less* than its face value.

If the bond has a higher rate of return than comparable investments, an investor would be willing to pay *more* than the face value for the bond. The bond is then said to sell at a **premium**.

For example, suppose that an investor could currently earn an 11% return on his or her money on other investments similar to bonds. If the interest rate on a particular bond with a face value of $100 is only 10%, the investor must be offered an incentive to buy that bond. Therefore, the price of the bond is *discounted*.

On the other hand, suppose an investor could currently earn only 9% interest on other investments. If the bond interest rate is 10%, the bond would be an attractive investment and would sell at a *premium*.

When a bond is redeemed, the issuer pays the owner the **redemption price**, which is the face value of the bond plus any interest earned on the bond. The market value of a bond is commonly stated as a **quote price**, or a price per $100.

EXAMPLE: A $500 corporate bond bearing 11.25%/a interest compounded semiannually was purchased on December 15. It was sold the following August 26 at a quote price of $106.50. The bond will pay interest on June 15 and December 15.

a. Find the redemption price.

To find the redemption price, first find the accrued interest. August 26 is 72 days after the last interest payment.

$$\begin{aligned}\text{Interest} &= Prt\\ &= 500 \times 0.1125 \times \frac{72}{365}\\ &= 11.10\end{aligned}$$

The interest earned after 72 days is $11.10.

$$\begin{aligned}\text{Redemption Price} &= \text{face value} + \text{accrued interest}\\ &= 500 + 11.10\\ &= 511.10\end{aligned}$$

The redemption price of the bond is $511.10.

b. Find the market value of the bond.

$$\begin{aligned}\text{Market Value} &= \frac{\text{quote price} \times \text{face value}}{100}\\ &= \frac{106.5 \times 500}{100}\\ &= 532.5\end{aligned}$$

The current market value of the bond is 532.50.

EXERCISE 10-6

A Complete each table.

1.

	Face Value	Quote Price	Market Value
a.	$1000	$101.375	■
b.	$5000	■	$4180
c.	$500	$93.625	■

2.

	Face Value	Market Value	Premium or Discount?	Amount of Premium or Discount
a.	$10 000	$9687.50	■	■
b.	$5000	$5487.50	■	■
c.	$500	$522.50	■	■

3. Find the accrued interest payable each interest period on each given bond.

a. a $1000 government bond at $10\frac{3}{4}$%/a semiannually

b. a $5000 Shell Oil bond at $11\frac{3}{4}$%/a semiannually

c. a $20 000 Quebec Hydro bond at $12\frac{1}{4}$%/a semiannually

4. Kerry wants to sell a $500 corporate bond with a current quote price of $101.375. What is the market value of the bond?

B **5.** A $10 000 bond sells at a discount of $1750. What is the quote price of the bond?

6. Lesley holds a $500 bond that is selling at a premium of $31.25. What is the quote price of the bond?

7. Find the market value and the redemption price for each bond.

a. a $50 000 corporate bond at 13.1%/a, quoted at $110 thirty-nine days after the last interest payment

b. a $15 000 municipal bond at $9\frac{5}{8}$%/a, quoted at $92.50 on September 7 if the interest is paid January 1 and July 1.

8. Max holds a $5000 bond that bears $9\frac{3}{4}$%/a interest from January 1 through June 30. The quote price on June 30 is $104.70. Is it more profitable for Max to redeem the bond or sell it at its market value on June 30?

Application

Stocks, like bonds, are a form of investment. Stock in a public company is sold as a means of raising money for the company to operate or expand. When a buyer purchases stock, he or she is actually purchasing part ownership or a share of the company.

Shareholders may be entitled to share in the profits of the company. These profits are distributed through the payment of **dividends**. When profits increase, the dividends generally do too. When profits decline, the dividends paid will generally also decline. Shares can be offered for sale either as **preferred shares** or as **common shares**. When a company cannot pay a regular dividend on all the shares it has issued, investors holding preferred shares will receive any dividends before those holding common stock. Stockholders may also participate in the management of the company by voting at stockholders meetings and by electing the board of directors, although not all shares may carry the right to vote.

The stock of stable, financially-sound companies that are willing to publicly report on their operations may also be listed on a stock exchange, such as the ones in Toronto, Montreal, and Vancouver. Once listed on an exchange, the shares can be bought and sold through a stockbroker who charges a commission to provide that service. The value of a share in a company depends on the status of the company, the number of shares that the company has issued, and its profits. Therefore, as a company makes more profit, the value of its shares increases. If the company's profits decline, then so does its stock prices. Stock prices are reported in the newspaper in the financial section.

The **high** is the highest price paid for a stock on a given trading day.
The **low** is the lowest price paid for a stock on a given trading day.
The **close** is the last price paid at the end of a trading day.
The **change** is the difference in the closing price between the last two trading days.
The **sales** is the number of shares traded on a given day.

Investors make money in the stockmarket by investing in companies whose share values increase. That way, the investor not only collects a dividend on his or her investment but will also realize a profit from the sale of the shares.

Choose a few companies from the financial section and chart their values for the next few weeks.

TORONTO QUOTATIONS

52 week High	52 week Low	Stock	Div	High	Low	Close	Ch'ge	Vol
20	10 1/8	A.G.F.M	.36	$18 1/8	17 3/4	18 1/8	+ 3/8	2430
9 1/8	5	AHA Auto o		$5 3/8	5 3/8	5 3/8		500
14 1/2	9	AMCA Int	a .25	$12 5/8	12 3/8	12 1/2	- 1/8	18762
25 5/8	22 3/4	AMCA p	2.21	$23 1/4	23 1/4	23 1/4		900
26	19	AMCA 2 p	2.37	$23 3/8	23 3/8	23 3/8		1796
25 1/2	22 3/4	AMCA 3 p	2.31	$23 1/4	23 1/4	23 1/4		104
8	425	ARC Int		$6 1/2	6 3/8	6 1/2		10500
55	52	Abbey E o		55	52	55	+ 5	2500
345	171	Abermin o		200	195	200	+ 5	5750
180	40	Abermin w		70	70	70	+15	5000
43	23	Abti Prce	.60	$32 3/8	31 3/4	32	+ 1/2	67593
15 1/2	375	Abitibi w		$9 3/4	9 3/8	9 3/4	+ 1/2	5200
26 1/8	24 1/2	Alexis N 1	1.85	$24 1/2	24 1/2	24 1/2		800
11 3/4	7 3/4	Algo Gr A f	.25	$10 3/8	10 3/8	10 3/8		1500
390	110	Algo Gr w		270	270	270	+ 5	1000
24	19	Algo Cent	.40	$21 3/4	21 1/4	21 3/4	+ 1/2	400
20 1/2	10	Algoma St		$19 3/4	19 5/8	19 5/8	- 1/8	4180
21 3/4	12 3/4	Algoma St p	2.00	$20 3/8	20 1/4	20 3/8	+ 1/8	2800
21 1/2	13 1/2	Algma St B	2.00	$21	20 3/4	20 3/4	- 1/4	5420
14 1/2	8	Algon Merc	.20	$11 1/2	11	11	- 1	10000
10	8 1/2	Alied Lyns		$9 3/8	9 1/4	9 3/8	+ 1/8	1250
6	480	Alied Lyns rsee below						
175	63	Altex		164	163	164	+ 9	4750
40 7/8	36 1/2	Amax Gld	a .02	$38	37 3/4	38	- 1/2	6200
40	30 1/2	A Barick		$38 1/4	37 7/8	38	+ 1/8	100000
14	200	A Barik w		$13 3/8	13 1/8	13 3/8	+ 3/8	8450
425	160	ABarik A w		305	300	300		3900

10-7 Buying Bonds for a Specific Yield

The bond market is different from the stock market. For instance, bond traders carry out all transactions over the phone, instead of on a trading floor, and they use price lists that each dealer maintains and makes known to clients.

If an investor can derive a rate of return, or **yield**, on his or her money that is higher than the interest rate of the bond, then the bond will not be worth its face value to investors and there will be a *discounted* quote price. If the bond's interest rate is greater than the desired yield rate, investors will be willing to pay a *premium* for the bond.

The principles of calculating present value can be applied to finding a quote price that will have a desired rate of return, or yield.

EXAMPLE: A \$1000 Ontario Hydro bond has an annual interest rate of $12\frac{1}{2}\%$ payable semiannually and there are six years remaining in the term of the bond. What quote price would yield an annual return of $9\frac{3}{4}\%$?

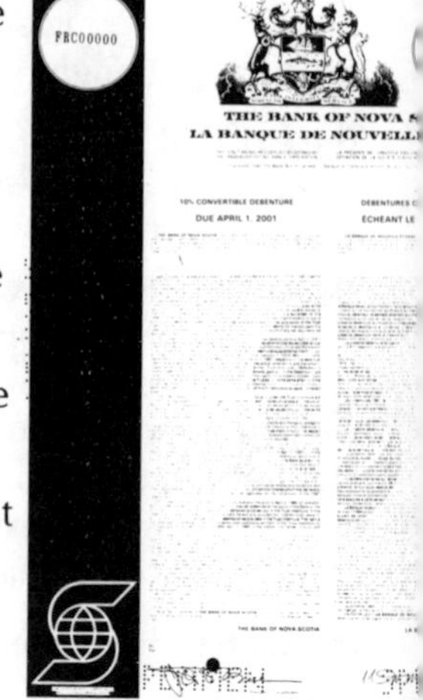

To determine the quote price of the bond, first find the present value of the face value at $9\frac{3}{4}\%$/a interest compounded semiannually over six years. Then find the present value of the interest payments at $9\frac{3}{4}\%$ compounded semiannually. Finally, add the two present values together.

1. Calculate the present value of the \$1000 face value six years from now at $9\frac{3}{4}\%$ interest compounded semiannually. Use $A = P(1 + i)^n$, or $P = A(1 + i)^{-n}$, where $P = V_{present}$.

Now	1	2	3	4	5	6 (years)
? ←						\$1000

$$
\begin{aligned}
V_{present} &= A(1 + i)^{-n} \\
&= 1000(1.048\ 75)^{-12} \\
&\doteq 1000(0.564\ 854) \\
&\doteq 564.85
\end{aligned}
$$

Since interest is compounded semiannually, $i = \frac{0.0975}{2}$ or 0.048 75. So, $1 + i = 1.048\ 75$.

The present value of the \$1000 face value in six years at $9\frac{3}{4}\%$/a interest compounded semiannually is \$564.85.

2. Calculate the semiannual interest payments made to the bondholder. Substituting into the formula, $I = Prt$, gives $I = 1000(0.125)\left(\frac{1}{2}\right)$, or 62.50. The semiannual interest payments are \$62.50.

3. Find the present value of the \$62.50 semiannual interest payments at $9\frac{3}{4}$%/a compounded semiannually.

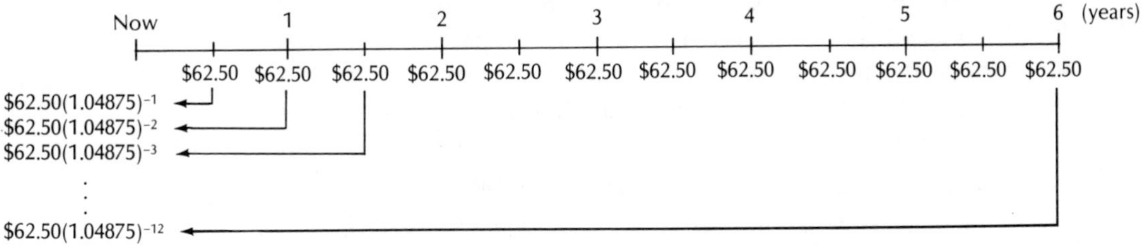

$$V_{present} = \$62.50(1.048\,75)^{-12} + \$62.50(1.048\,75)^{-11} + \ldots \$62.50(1.048\,75)^{-1}$$

$$V_{present} = \frac{a(r^n - 1)}{r - 1} \qquad \text{Use the geometric series formula.}$$

$$= \frac{62.5(1.048\,75)^{-12}[(1.048\,75)^{12} - 1]}{(1.048\,75 - 1)}$$

$$\doteq \frac{62.5[(1.048\,75)^{12} - 1]}{(1.048\,75)^{12}(0.048\,75)}$$

$$\doteq 557.88$$

The present value of the \$62.50 semiannual interest payments is \$557.88.

4. Find the *total* present value of the \$1000 bond to yield $9\frac{3}{4}$%. This figure will be the market value. Then find the quote price of the bond.

	Face value		Interest payments
Total present value (or market value)	$= [V_{present}$ of \$1000$] +$		$[V_{present}$ of \$62.50$]$
	$= \$564.85 + \$557.88$		
	$= \$1122.73$		

The total present value (or market value) of the bond is \$1122.73.

$$\text{quote price} = \frac{\text{market value}}{\text{face value}} \times 100$$

$$= \frac{1122.73}{1000} \times 100$$

$$= 112.27$$

A quote price of \$112.27 reflects an annual yield of $9\frac{3}{4}$%. Note that this is a *premium price*. This is what would be expected because the bond rate is greater than the desired yield, and therefore the bond would sell at a premium.

EXERCISE 10-7

A In each situation below, a bond is to be purchased before the end of its term with a desired yield in mind. Calculate the following for each situation.

1. the present value of the face value of each bond at the end of its term
2. the semiannual interest payments paid to the bondholder
3. the present value of the semiannual interest payments
4. the current quote price that would yield the desired rate
   a. a \$20 000 Government of Canada Bond at 11.25%/a interest payable semiannually with four years left in its term and a desired yield rate of $9\frac{1}{2}$%/a payable semiannually
   b. a \$1000 Saskatchewan provincial bond at 9.5%/a interest payable semiannually with seven years left in its term and a desired rate of return of 10.5%/a payable semiannually
   c. a \$25 000 Shell Oil bond at 10.5%/a interest payable semiannually with eight years left in its term and a desired yield of $11\frac{3}{4}$%/a payable semiannually

B

5. Complete the given table.

	Face Value	Interest Rate Per Year	Term Left	Desired Yield Per Year	Quote Price
a.	\$5000	$10\frac{1}{2}$%	8 years	9%	▬
b.	\$2000	$8\frac{3}{4}$%	3 years	$9\frac{1}{2}$%	▬
c.	\$10 000	11.25%	9 years	10.5%	▬

6. What price should be offered on a \$500 bond bearing 7.75%/a interest payable semiannually if there are six years left in the term and a yield of 9.25%/a payable semiannually is required?
7. The quote price on an $11\frac{3}{4}$%/a Manitoba provincial bond with interest payable semiannually is \$109.75. The bond has seven years to maturity. If the yield rate you desire is $9\frac{3}{4}$%/a payable semiannually, should you consider buying this bond?
8. Bell Canada issued bonds at 12.65%/a payable semiannually that mature in 11 years. If the desired yield on such a bond is to be 10.5%/a payable semiannually, what should the quote price be?
9. The asking price for a \$100 bond with an interest rate of $10\frac{3}{4}$%/a payable semiannually is \$105.65. If you need to have a yield of 10.1%/a interest payable semiannually on the bond over the five years left in its term, is the asking price fair?
10. A \$500 Nova Scotia provincial bond bears 10%/a interest compounded semiannually and has four years left in its term. What asking price for the bond yields a rate of 8%/a compounded semiannually?

Using the Computer

Approximating the Yield Rate

The exact yield rate is difficult to find by algebraic means because *i*, the interest rate per period cannot be accurately determined. One effective method for approximating the yield rate is to estimate the value of *i* and then refine the estimates to the desired degree of accuracy, using a calculator.

A computer program can also be used to approximate yield rate. For example, suppose a $10 000 Province of Alberta bond has a rate of 10% interest payable semiannually. The maturity date is December 1, 1995 and the bond is purchased on December 1, 1991. The computer program given below can be used to approximate the yield rate for a quote price of $106.00. The program used the annual bond rate and the annual yield, given that the interest is paid semiannually. The program does not use the face value of the bond because it gives the quote price based on $100.00.

```
100  INPUT "ENTER BOND RATE            : ";R
110 R = R / 2: REM  CONVERT TO SEMI-ANNUAL RATE
120  INPUT "ENTER NUMBER OF PERIODS : ";N
130  INPUT "ENTER ESTIMATED YIELD    : ";Y
140 Y = Y / 2: REM  CONVERT TO SEMI-ANNUAL RATE
150 PF = 100 * (1 + Y) ^ ( - N)
160 PI = ((100 * R) * (1 - (1 + Y) ^ ( - N))) / Y
170 QUOTE = PF + PI
180  PRINT "QUOTE PRICE = ";QUOTE
190  PRINT : INPUT "ANOTHER ESTIMATE? (Y/N)";R$
200  IF R$ = "Y" THEN  PRINT : GOTO 130
210  END
```

The output from the computer program shows that a quote of $106.00 for the bond described above gives a yield of *approximately* 8.21% annually.

```
ENTER BOND RATE            : .1
ENTER NUMBER OF PERIODS : 8
ENTER ESTIMATED YIELD    : .08
QUOTE PRICE = 106.732745

ANOTHER ESTIMATE? (Y/N)Y

ENTER ESTIMATED YIELD    : .082
QUOTE PRICE = 106.034527

ANOTHER ESTIMATE? (Y/N)Y
```

```
ENTER ESTIMATED YIELD    : .08208
QUOTE PRICE = 106.006717

ANOTHER ESTIMATE? (Y/N)Y

ENTER ESTIMATED YIELD    : .08209
QUOTE PRICE = 106.003242

ANOTHER ESTIMATE? (Y/N)N
```

A Government of Canada Bond has three years left in its term. The bond rate is 10% per year payable semiannually and the quote price is $95. Approximate the yield rate of the bond if it is bought at that price. (Round-off to the nearest tenth percent.)

Review

1. The Denton Credit Union issues a demand loan for \$1500 at $10\frac{3}{4}$%/a on March 8 and calls for repayment on July 25. What is the total amount that must be repaid?

2. The Telfer's borrow \$20 000 at 12%/a on March 1 to purchase a new car. They make payments of \$4500 on the first of each month from April to July 1. What is the balance that remains to be paid on the last payment date, August 1?

3. Two hundred dollars is invested in a savings account for two years at 8.6%/a compounded quarterly. What amount of money accumulates in the account after two years?

4. Delia is shopping for a term deposit. She has been quoted two rates, one at $11\frac{1}{2}$%/a compounded monthly and the other at $11\frac{3}{4}$%/a compounded quarterly. What are the effective rates of each? Which is the better investment?

5. Find the accumulated amount of the ordinary annuity shown in the diagram below. The annual interest rate is 8% compounded semiannually.

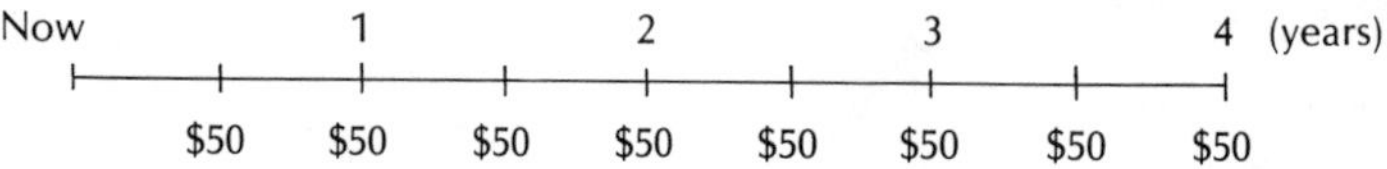

6. Calculate the present balue of the ordinary annuity represented in the diagram below. The annual rate is 10% compounded quarterly.

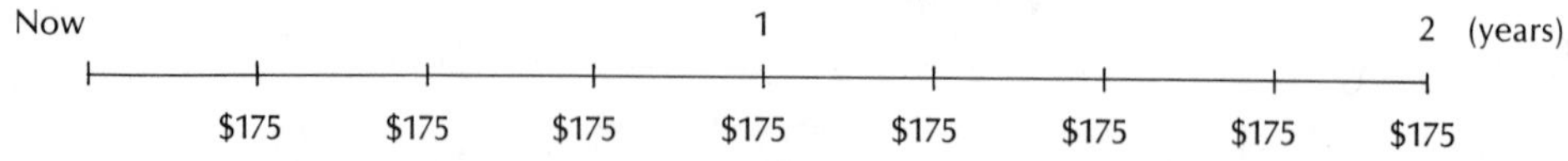

7. Two hundred dollars in invested semiannually in an account that bears $9\frac{1}{2}$%/a interest compounded semiannually. What will be the accumulated amount after three years? Use a time-line diagram to help you solve the problem.

8. What amount would need to be invested now at 9%/a compounded monthly to accumulate \$25 000 three years from now?

9. The Wagner's are selling their summer cottage and receive two offers. One buyer offers \$42 000 cash and the other offers \$25 000 cash plus an extra \$20 000 in five years. The money can be invested at 10.5%/a compounded semiannually. Which offer is better?

10. Calculate the accumulated amount of an annuity if deposits of $2000 are made at the end of each year for eight years and the interest rate is 10% per year.

11. Susan plans to save $50 per month at $8\frac{1}{2}$%/a compounded semiannually for four years. Will she be able to afford her European vacation if it costs $3000 at the end of the four years?

12. What amount will have to be invested at a rate of 10.5% annually to provide an income of $20 000 a year for 15 years?

13. A university has been endowed with $200 000 to fund a research program in mathematics education for five years at a cost of $50 000. The money is invested at $8\frac{1}{2}$%/a. Will the endowment be able to fund the program?

14. Great Western Wire Rope Company has just negotiated to buy new manufacturing equipment plus a maintenance agreement for $375 000. The terms of the sale are such that the company is to pay $200 000 now and then make annual payments of $35 000 over the next five years. How much should the company invest at 7.5%/a compounded monthly to be able to make the yearly payments on the equipment.

15. What is the quote price of a $5000 bond if its market value is $4880?

16. Jenna holds a $5000 bond which is selling at a premium of $103.50. What is the market value of the bond?

17. What is the market value and the redemption price of an $11\frac{3}{4}$%/a $20 000 bond that is quoted at $103.75 and the last paid interest was 30 days ago?

18. Kerry sells a $5000 Government of Canada Bond at $101.375 on September 30. The issue date was February 1 with interest of 9.75%/a payable semiannually. What purchase price should she expect?

19. What is the present value of the semiannual payments on a $10 000 bond that bears a $9\frac{1}{2}$%/a interest rate and has a five year term?

20. Find the quote price of a Suncor bond with 11 years left in its term at 13.5%/a for which a yield of $10\frac{3}{4}$%/a is needed.

21. Mark bought a $1000 ten year bond that bears 11% interest payable semiannually three years ago. If the going rate for bonds is $9\frac{1}{2}$%/a, what is a fair price for the bond?

22. Toby decides to invest money in a bond for tax purposes and would like a yield of $9\frac{3}{4}$%/a. Which is the better buy, a Nova bond at 11%/a with two years left in its term for $102.625, or a CIL bond for $111.75 at 12%/a with seven years left in its term?

Test

1. Determine the total amount due on a demand loan of $3500 after 90 days at an annual interest rate of 11.75%.

2. Downtown Stereo offers an instalment payment plan at 12.5%/a (compounded monthly) for the purchase of a $1000 stereo. Judith buys the stereo on September 15 with a $300 downpayment, and makes two payments of $300 each on October 15 and November 15. What final payment is due on December 15?

3. Find the effective rate of $8\frac{1}{2}$%/a compounded monthly.

4. Louis receives a $12 000 inheritance. He puts it in a three year term deposit that bears $9\frac{1}{2}$%/a interest compounded semiannually.
   a. What amount will he have at the end of the three year term?
   b. If Louis needed to accumulate $15 000 in the three year term, what amount would he have to invest?

5. Resort property on a lake will be worth $50 000 per acre in five years once the local highway is improved. If the current rate of interest is $8\frac{3}{4}$%/a compounded quarterly, what would be a fair price to offer the owners of the land?

6. What will be the accumulated amount of $250 deposited semiannually for five years in an account that bears $8\frac{1}{2}$%/a compounded semiannually?

7. Charlene invests $300 per month in an investment fund that guarantees a return of 11.6%/a compounded semiannually. At the end of the five years, will Charlene have enough money to make a $20 000 downpayment on a house?

8. What amount would have to be invested now at 10.5%/a compounded semiannually to provide an income of $15 000 per year for five years?

9. A $2500 bond is selling at a discount of $245.50. Find the market value and quote price for the bond.

10. On March 1, Jerry redeems a $1000 bond which was issued on January 1 and bears $12\frac{1}{4}$%/a interest compounded semiannually. The bond has a quote price of $101.301. What is the redemption price?

11. Find the quote price of a $10 000 Westcoast Transmission $9\frac{3}{4}$%/a bond with eight years left in its term if interest is paid semiannually and the desired rate of return is 9%/a.

Cumulative Review

1. Express each complex number in simplest form.
   a. $3 - \sqrt{-18}$ **b.** $10 + \sqrt{-32}$ **c.** $2i\sqrt{-63}$ **d.** $-5 - 2\sqrt{-125}$

2. Simplify.
   a. $\frac{3a^2 - 10a + 3}{2a^2 - 5a - 3} \times \frac{a^4 - b^4}{(a - b)^2}$ **b.** $\frac{4x^2 + 5x - 6}{2x^2 - 2a - 24} - \frac{4x^2 - x - 14}{-3x^2 + 3x + 6}$

3. Solve each system of equations.
   a. $2x - y + 3 = 0$, $y = 4x + 11$ **b.** $xy = -18$, $x + 3y = 0$ **c.** $5x - 2y + 18 = 0$, $x^2 + y^2 = 0$

4. Given that $f(x) = 2x - 1$, $g(x) = 4 - x^2$, and $h(x) = \frac{3}{x - 1}$, evaluate the following.
   a. $f(3) - g(5)$ **b.** $h(4) + g(-2)$ **c.** $2f(5) - 3g(4)$
   d. $\frac{g(3)}{f(6)}$ **e.** $\frac{2h(5) + g(1)}{f(2)}$ **f.** $\frac{h(-4)}{f(-1) - g(6)}$

5. Write an equation of the circle having centre at the origin and passing through the given point.
   a. $P(2, 5)$ **b.** $A(-1, 3)$ **c.** $X(5, -7)$ **d.** $B(-4, -9)$
   e. $M(3, \sqrt{5})$ **f.** $T(-3, 2)$ **g.** $R(\sqrt{2}, -3)$ **h.** $K(\sqrt{6}, -\sqrt{3})$

6. $QRST$ is a quadrilateral inscribed in a circle with centre C such that $\overline{TS}$ is a diameter. If the measure of $\angle QCT$ is 95°, find the measure of $\angle QRS$.

7. Given that x varies directly as y and inversely as z^2, and given also that the value of x is 36 when y is 8 and z is 3, find the value of x when y is 16 and also when z is 6.

8. Find the constant of variation, given that the ordered pair belongs to the variation.
   a. $y \alpha x^2$; (2, 10) **b.** $y \alpha x^2$; (3, 6) **c.** $y \alpha \frac{1}{x}$; (4, 8)
   d. $y \alpha \frac{1}{x^2}$; (2, 3) **e.** $y \alpha \frac{1}{x^2}$; (8, 6) **f.** $y \alpha \frac{1}{x^2}$; (3, 3)

9. The graph of each given function is transformed as indicated. Determine an equation of each transformed graph.
   a. $y = 2x$; translated two units down
   b. $y = 3x^2$; reflected in the x-axis
   c. $y = 6x - 5$; reflected in the y-axis
   d. $y = 2x^2 + 1$; translated up three units and then reflected in the y-axis

10. **a.** The first three terms of an arithmetic sequence are represented by $a + 5, 2a - 3, 4(a - 5)$. Find the value of the three terms.
    b. The first three terms of a geometric sequence are represented by $x + 10, 2x, 6(x - 6)$. Find the value of the three terms.

Mixed Problems

1. A soccer ball cover is made by sewing together 12 regular pentagons and 20 regular hexagons. A regular hexagon with side length s has an area of $A = \frac{3}{2}\sqrt{3}s^2$; a regular pentagon has an area of

$$A = s^2 \frac{5}{2}\left(\frac{\sqrt{10 + 2\sqrt{5}}}{10 - 2\sqrt{5}}\right)$$

What is the total surface area of the soccer ball when the side length of each polygon is 5 cm?

2. The transmission ratios for a small imported car are as follows:

   1st gear — 3.4 : 1   2nd gear — 1.9 : 1
   3rd gear — 1.4 : 1   4th gear — 0.95 : 1

   where the ratio indicates the number of motor revolutions : drive shaft revolutions. The rear end ratio of this car is 3.8 : 1 which is the number of drive shaft revolutions : wheel revolutions.

   The wheel and tire have a diameter of 55 cm. At what speed, in kilometres per hour, will the car travel in fourth gear if the engine speed is 4200 revolutions per minute?

3. Three hoses are used to fill a pool in $1\frac{1}{3}$ h. On its own, the first hose could fill the pool in double the time of the second hose and the third hose on its own would take one more hour that the second hose on its own. How long would it take the second hose to fill the pool?

4. Julia and Kim take the train from Port Livingston to Red Creek then cycle back. The train averages 80 km/h and the cyclists average 30 km/h. If the total round-trip time is 5.5 hours, how far is it between the two towns?

5. A pole sits on the edge of an 8 m cliff. A single guy wire 18 m long is fastened 3 m from the base of the pole at the top of the cliff, passes over the top of the pole, and is secured 5 m from the base of the cliff. What is the height of the pole?

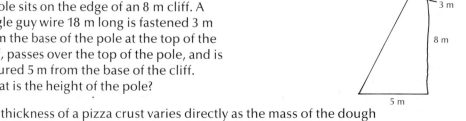

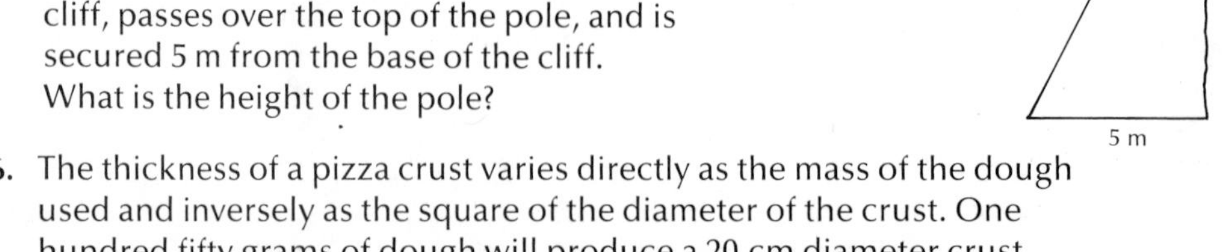

6. The thickness of a pizza crust varies directly as the mass of the dough used and inversely as the square of the diameter of the crust. One hundred fifty grams of dough will produce a 20 cm diameter crust 5 mm thick.

   a. How thick will a 30 cm pizza be if 200 g of dough are used?
   b. How much dough is needed to produce a 1 cm crust on a pizza 15 cm in diameter?

7. A population of fruit flies, under proper conditions, will double every 20 days.

   a. Construct an exponential equation to model this population growth.
   b. If you have 2 fruit flies on January 1, how many will you have on July 1 (no leap year)?
   c. On what date will the population first exceed 1 million fruit flies?

8. A federal tax law allows a business to depreciate office equipment at the rate of 30% per year. The office manager bought a copier for $6800.00 last year.

   a. What depreciation is allowed for that tax year?
   b. What is the depreciated value at the end of 3 years?
   c. When will the depreciated value be less than $1000.00?
   d. A typewriter's depreciated value at the end of 5 years is $150.00. What was the original cost of the typewriter?

9. When a pot of tea is left to cool, the difference between the temperature of the tea and the temperature of the surrounding air decreases exponentially with time. "Newton's Law of Cooling" gives the relationship between the temperature of the tea and time.

   $T = \text{(Temperature difference)} \left(\frac{1}{2}\right)^{\frac{t}{20}} + \text{(Room temperature)}$

   $T = \Delta T \left(\frac{1}{2}\right)^{\frac{t}{20}} + T_o$

   a. If the tea originally had a temperature of 100 degrees and room temperature is 20 degrees, what would be the temperature of the tea in 20 minutes?
   b. How long will it be before the tea is 50 degrees? (to the nearest minute)
   c. If the tea is put outside to cool where the temperature is 5 degrees, what will be the temperature in 20 minutes and how long will it take to cool to 50 degrees?
   d. The tea can be thought of as having a "temperature half-life" of 20 minutes. What would happen to that half-life if the teapot were insulated with a tea cozy?

10. A triangle has a height 2 cm greater than its base. A rectangle of equal area has a base 5 cm longer than the triangle and a height $\frac{1}{3}$ that of the triangle. Find the dimensions of each.

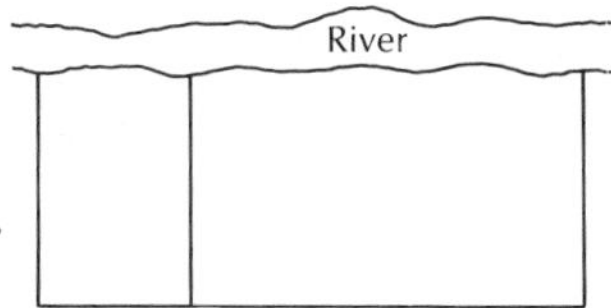

11. A rectangular field adjacent to a river is fenced with no fencing needed along the river. The total area is 28 800 m^2 and some of the fencing is used to make a partition fence perpendicular to the river. Find the dimensions of the field if 600 m of fence is used.

12. Keiji is twice as old as his sister. In twelve years the product of ages will be 630. Find their ages in 5 years.

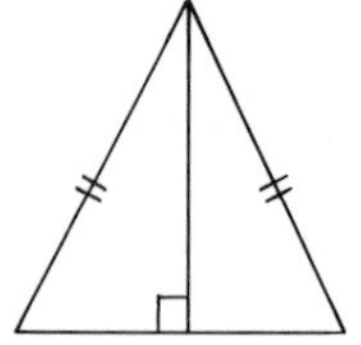

13. An isosceles triangle has its height 10 cm longer that its base. If the area of the triangle is 84 cm^2, then find the length of the congruent sides.

14. Four pencils and 2 pens together cost \$2.56. Two pencils and 3 pens together cost \$3.24. Find the cost of 3 pencils and 4 pens.

15. Two friends 100 km apart will meet in $\frac{1}{2}$ h if they drive towards each other. If they drive in the same direction, they will meet in $2\frac{1}{2}$ h. Find their rates of driving.

16. The cost of a wedding cake is partly constant to cover the cost of decorating and partly variable to cover the cost of the fruit. If a 6 kg cake costs \$110 and an 8 kg cake costs \$120, what amount is being charged for the decorating?

17. If 1 is subtracted from the numerator and denominator of a fraction, the result is $\frac{1}{3}$. If 1 is added to the numerator and denominator of the same fraction, the result is $\frac{1}{2}$. Find the fraction.

18. Two rectangular gardens are such that one is 4 times as long as it is wide while the other is twice as long as it is wide. If the total area is 34 m^2 and the total perimeter 38 m, find the dimensions of each.

19. In his pocket, Jamie found 3 dimes, 2 nickels and 2 pennies. Using at least 3 coins, how many amounts of money can be made from this collection of coins?

20. The houses on Beaumaris Drive are numbered consecutively from 1 to 200. How many house numbers

    a. contain at least one digit 2?
    b. contain exactly one digit 2?
    c. are divisible by 3?
    d. contain the digits 2 and 3?

21. Three coins look exactly alike, but one is counterfeit and weighs less than the others. In your science class, you have a balance scale which can compare two weights. Using this balance scale, how many weighings will it take to determine which is the counterfeit coin? How many weighings will it take to identify the counterfeit coin if there are 6 coins? 9 coins?

22. Lisa wants to cut a piece of material in the shape of a square. As she cuts each piece, she checks her work by bending each piece along its diagonal to see if the edges coincide. When Patti notices what Lisa is doing, she says that Lisa's test is invalid. Who is right? Explain. What test would you use to check that the piece of material is a square?

23. In a 3×3 magic square using the integers $1, 2, \ldots, 9$, show the following.

a. The sum of the numbers in any row, column, or diagonal must be 15.
b. The number in the centre must be 5.
c. The number 1 cannot go in a corner.

24. What is the last digit of 2^{100}, 3^{100}, and 5^{100}?

25. In February each year, the principal at Central High School hires two students to enter students' course selections from option sheets into the school's computer so that the timetable can be built for the following year. This year, Pat and Sandy applied for the job. It is estimated that Sandy alone can process the option sheets in 5 days and that Pat can complete the job in 6 days. How many days will it take both Sandy and Pat to process the option sheets if they are both hired?

26. The area of a parallelogram is represented by $4x^4 - 13x^2 + 9$ and its base is represented by $2x^2 - x - 3$. Find an expression to represent its height.

27. In a golden rectangle, like the large rectangle at the right, a smaller rectangle can be formed by cutting away a square. The length l and width w satisfy the proportion $\frac{l}{w} = \frac{l + w}{l}$.

In the western world, since the times of ancient Greece, this proportion has been considered an ideal of balance. Find the value of $\frac{l}{w}$, the golden ratio.

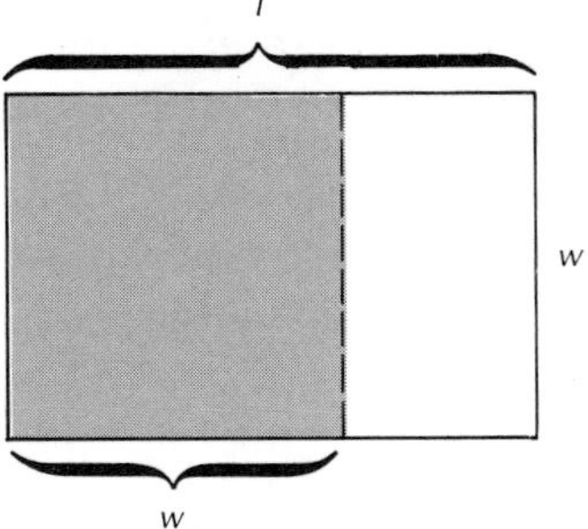

28. Carbonic acid is composed of Hydrogen, Carbon, and Oxygen in the ratio 1 : 6 : 24 by mass. A chemist decomposes a sample of the acid and collects 6 g of Oxygen. What mass of Carbonic acid was decomposed?

29. Rick has \$1200 to invest. A bond would give interest at 9% per annum but this interest would be taxed at 45%. A tax shelter investment returns 7.5% and has a tax rate of 37.5%. Which is the better option after tax return?

30. A football coach decided to use a "merit-pay" system for his team. He offered a bonus of \$5 for each tackle made and a penalty of \$10 for each tackle missed. "Moose" Taylor was in a position to make 24 tackles but received a bonus of only \$45. How many tackles did he make?

31. The cooling system of May's car holds 15 L. She needs a mixture that is 70% anti-freeze and 30% water to make it through the winter. Mary tests the coolant mixture and finds that it is only 20% anti-freeze. How much coolant should she drain off and replace with anti-freeze?

32. Ben wishes to complete a 10 km race in less than 35 min. At the 6 km point in the race his coach tells him that he has averaged 16.8 km/h so far. What speed must he run for the remainder of the race to meet his goal?

33.

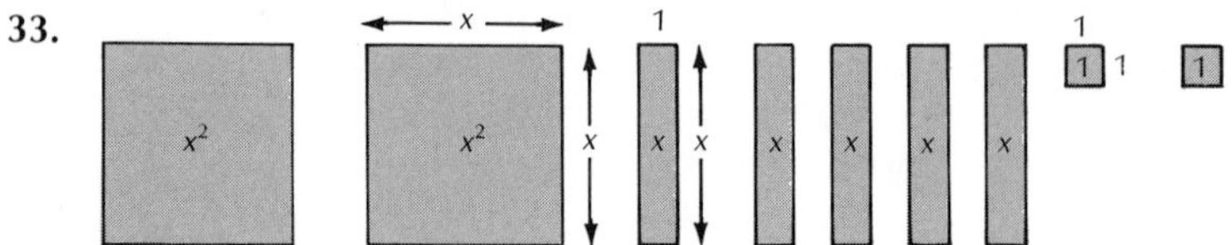

The nine rectangles above with areas x^2, x and 1 can be arranged to form one single rectangle. Algebra may be used to find the dimensions of this large rectangle and thus determine the arrangement.

a. Show how the rectangles should be arranged.
b. If there were one rectangle of area x^2, 11 of area x, and 28 with area 1, how would you arrange the rectangles to make one large rectangle?
c. How would you arrange three rectangles of area x^2, 11 with area x, and 6 of unit area?

34. All real numbers can be represented by points on the real number line. Thus there are points for irrationals such as $\sqrt{2}$ and $\sqrt{3}$. Copy the number line and use geometric construction to find lengths for $\sqrt{2}$ and $\sqrt{3}$.

−2 −1 0 1 2 3 4 5 6

35. For temperatures below 0°C, the coefficient of friction between the snow and a pair of skis varies partially with the square root of the absolute value of the temperature. At 0°, the coefficient is 0.02 and at −10°, the coefficient is 0.05. What would be the coefficient of friction at −20°?

36. The height of a model rocket above the earth is described by

$$h = v_0 t - 4.98t^2$$

where v_0 is the initial velocity (m/s) given the rocket and t (s) is the time since launch. Find the initial velocity required to make the rocket reach a maximum height of 250 m.

37. An airplane leaves an airport at 10:00 A.M. and flies due east at 300 km/h. A second plane leaves the same airport at 11:00 A.M. and flies due north at 360 km/h. At what time will the straight line distance between the two planes be 1000 km.

38. The intensity, B, in decibels, of sound is calculated by the formula

$$B = 10 \log \frac{I}{I_0}$$

where I is in watts/cm^2 and I_0 is the intensity of the threshold of hearing. If for the human ear a sound of 2.75×10^{-7} watts/cm^2 gives 94 decibels, what is the hearing threshold?

39. A curtain has n slots and m hooks. Give a condition on m and n which will ensure that the m hooks can be put in m of n evenly-spaced slots in such a way that the hooks are evenly-spaced.

40. The 1986 and 1987 Toronto Hydro Residential Rates are given in the following table (per two-month period).

Consumption	1986	1987
First 500 kilowatt hours	\$0.0727 per kWh	\$0.0792 per kWh
Remaining kilowatt hours	\$0.0541 per kWh	\$0.0570 per kWh
Minimum bill for two months	\$10.00	\$10.00

If the bill is paid promptly, there is a 10% prompt payment discount.

a. Let x be the consumption. For each of the 1986 and 1987 rates, determine a function which describes the amount of a bill which is paid promptly.
b. Sketch the graphs of the functions in **a.**
c. How much consumption is necessary in each of 1986 and 1987 in order to exceed the minimum bill.
d. How many kilowatt hours of electricity can be purchased by \$100 in 1986? in 1987? Assume prompt payment of the bill.
e. Did the rates increase by a fixed percentage for all consumption levels from 1986 to 1987? Justify your answer.

41. **a.** By factoring as a difference of squares, verify that

$$\left(\frac{x+y}{2}\right)^2 - \left(\frac{x-y}{2}\right)^2 = xy$$

b. Use **a.** to establish the arithmetic-geometric mean inequality

$$\sqrt{xy} \leq \frac{x+y}{2} \text{ whenever } x, y \geq 0$$

c. Two positive integers have a sum of 56. What is their largest possible product?
d. Two positive real numbers have product 2. What is their smallest possible sum?

42. Show how to express 312 588 as a difference of two squares.

43. When \$2.00 admission is charged for the school Variety Show, 550 people attend. A survey conducted by Students' Council has discovered that for every \$0.10 increase in ticket price, 50 people would not attend and that similarly decreasing the price \$0.10 would bring 50 more people.

a. Letting x represent the number of \$0.10 increases write an expression for the total admission receipts.
b. Find the ticket price that will bring in the maximum admission receipts.

44. Show that

$$144^2 - 143^2 + 142^2 - 141^2 + 140^2 - 139^2 + \ldots + 4^2 - 3^2 + 2^2 - 1^2$$
$$= 144 + 143 + 142 + 141 + 140 + 139 + \ldots + 4 + 3 + 2 + 1$$

45. Start with any two numbers a and b. Construct a sequence as follows. The sequence starts with a and b. If u and v are two adjacent numbers, then the next term is $\frac{v + 1}{u}$. For example,

$$5, 7, \frac{8}{5}, \frac{13}{35}, \ldots$$

are the first four terms of such a sequence.

a. Construct such a sequence with (a, b) : (1, 2); (1, 5); (3, 4).
b. Show that, regardless of the values of a & b, the sequence is periodic (i.e., its values repeat over and over).

46. Simplify **a.** $1 + \frac{2}{x} + \frac{2}{x(x - 1)}$

b. $1 + \frac{3}{x} + \frac{6}{x(x - 1)} + \frac{6}{x(x - 1)(x - 2)}$

c. $1 + \frac{4}{x} + \frac{12}{x(x - 1)} + \frac{24}{x(x - 1)(x - 2)} + \frac{24}{x(x - 1)(x - 2)(x - 3)}$

47. Find a solution in integers of
$x^2 + y^2 + z^2 + w^2 = xyzw$

48. Write any three one-digit numbers on the circumference of a circle. Write all three digit numbers that can be written if the numerals are selected in a clockwise rotation. Find their sum and divide by the sum of the original three digits.

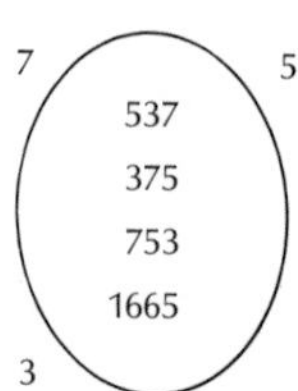

Repeat the process for another 3 digits, 4 digits, 5 digits, ...

A three-digit number can be represented by $100x + 10y + z$. Can you use this to show why the above number curiosity works?

Glossary

Absolute value The positive distance of a number from zero. The absolute value of n is written $|n|$.

Accumulated amount, A The principal, P, plus the interest, I.

Acute angle An angle measuring less than $90°$.

Additive inverse The number which, when added to a given number, gives a sum of zero.

Adjacent (ADJ) For a given angle in a right-angled triangle, the side which is adjacent to the angle and is not the hypotenuse.

Adjacent angles Two non-overlapping angles that share a common side and vertex.

Algebraic expression A mathematical expression containing sums, products, differences, or quotients involving variables.

Alternate angles Angles on opposite sides of a transversal that cuts two lines.

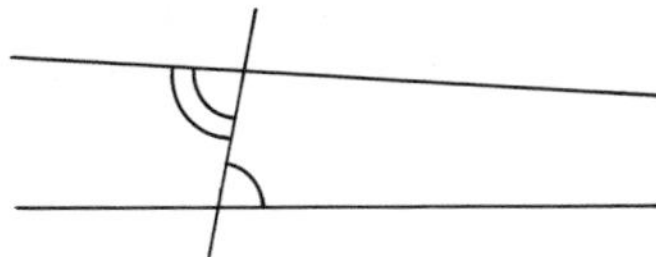

Altitude (of a triangle) A perpendicular line segment drawn from a vertex to the opposite side.

Amortization period The amount of time between the issue of a mortgage and the final payment.

Angle of depression The angle between the horizontal and the line of sight to a point below the horizontal.

Angle of elevation The angle between the horizontal and the line of sight to a point above the horizontal.

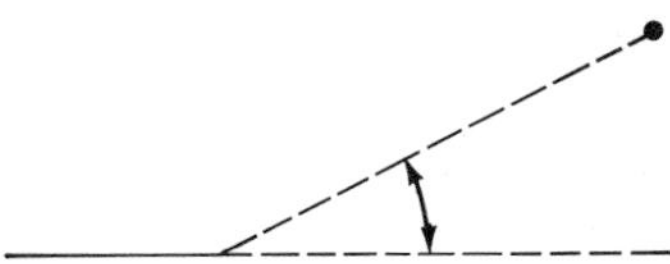

Annuity A series of equal deposits or payments made at regular intervals.

Arc A part of a circle's circumference.

Argand Plane The plane in which complex numbers are represented by rectangular coordinates. The horizontal axis is called the *real axis* and the vertical axis is called the *imaginary axis*.

Arithmetic sequence A sequence in which the difference between any two consecutive terms is a constant.

Arithmetic series The sum of the terms of an arithmetic sequence.

Arrow diagram A diagram used to represent a relation. The domain and range are separated and arrows pair each member of the domain with the member it corresponds to in the range.

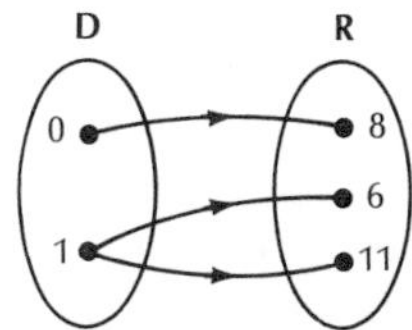

Associative property The property stating that, when three or more numbers are added or multiplied, the operations can be performed in any order.

$(a + b) + c = a + (b + c)$
$(a \times b) \times c = a \times (b \times c)$

Assumption A statement that is generally accepted and need not be proved. (also **axiom** or **postulate**)

Axiom A statement that is generally accepted and need not be proved. (also **assumption** or **postulate**)

Axis of Symmetry The line about which a figure is symmetrical.

Bar graph A graph displaying data in which the length of each bar is proportional to the number it represents.

Base (in a power) The factor repeated in a power.

Base (of a polygon) Any face of a polygon.

Biased sample A sample that results from a sampling method in which not all members of the population have an equal chance of being selected.

Biconditional statement A conditional statement and its converse combined.

Binomial A polynomial consisting of two terms.

Bisect To divide into two congruent parts.

Box-and-whisker graph An arrangement of data which facilitates a quick summary by highlighting the median, the extremes, and the hinge points.

Capacity The maximum amount a container can hold.

Cartesian Coordinate Plane A rectangular coordinate plane.

Census An official, usually periodic, enumeration of a population.

Centi- A prefix meaning hundredth.

Central angle An angle with its vertex at the centre of a circle and bounded by two radii. (also **sector angle**)

Centre of a circle The point that is the same distance from all points in a circle.

Centre of rotation The point about which a figure is rotated.

Centroid The point where the medians of a triangle intersect.

Chord (of a circle) A line segment with endpoints in the circumference of a circle.

Circle The set of all points in a plane that are equidistant from a fixed point, the centre. It can be represented by an equation of the form $(x + h)^2 + (y + k)^2 = r^2$, for $C(h,k)$ and radius r.

Circumcentre The centre of a circumcircle.

Circumcircle A circle that touches all the vertices of a polygon.

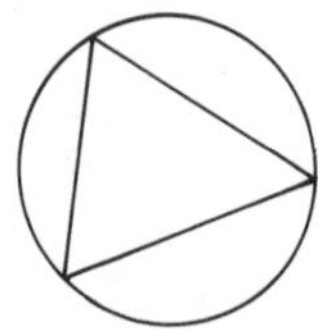

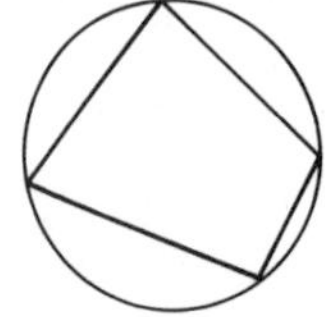

Circumference The perimeter of a circle.

Coefficient The numerical factor of an algebraic term.

Collinear points Points that lie in the same straight line.

Common difference, *d* The difference between successive terms in an arithmetic sequence.

Common ratio, *r* The constant ratio of successive terms in a geometric sequence.

Common shares Shares of a business which have the lowest priority of receiving dividends. (See **preferred shares.**)

Commutative property The property stating that two numbers can be added or multiplied in any order.

$a + b = b + a$

$a \times b = b \times a$

Complementary angles Two angles that have a sum of 90°.

Complex number A number of the form $a + bi$, where a and b are real numbers and $i^2 = -1$. **C** represents the set of complex or imaginary numbers.

Component (of a vector) A vector quantity which, with others, is equivalent to a given vector. The most useful pair is a pair at right angles lying along the x- and y-axes.

Composition of transformations The process of performing successive transformations one after another.

Compound interest loan The type of loan in which the interest is periodically added to the principal.

Concentric circles Circles that lie in the same plane and have the same centre.

Concurrent lines Two or more lines that intersect in one point.

Conditional statement A statement in the form "If...(*p*)..., then...(*q*)..." (also **implication**)

Cone A solid bounded by a circle and all line segments from a point outside the plane of the circle to all the points of the circle.

Congruent figures Figures with the same size and shape.

Conic Section The figure which results from the intersection of a plane and a cone.

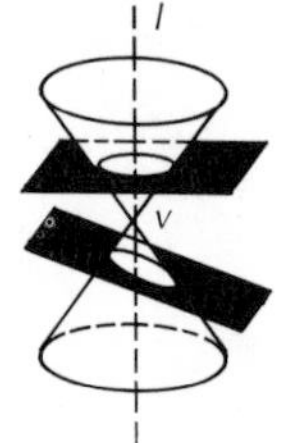

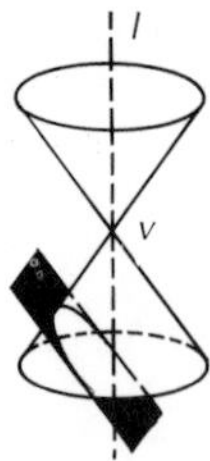

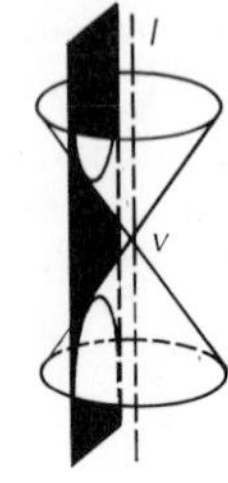

Conjugates The numbers $a\sqrt{b} + c\sqrt{d}$ and $a\sqrt{b} - c\sqrt{d}$, where a, b, c, d, are rational, are called conjugates. Their product has the form $a^2b - c^2d$, which is a rational number. The expressions $a + bi$ and $a - bi$ are *complex conjugates*, with real number product $a^2 + b^2$.

Consecutive numbers Numbers obtained by counting by ones from any given integer, such as 57, 58, 59, ...

Constant A quantity with a fixed value in a specified mathematical context.

Constant Function A function of the form $f(x) = k$, k is any number. It is represented graphically by a straight line parallel to the x-axis.

Constant of proportionality The constant k in a direct, inverse, or partial variation.

Constant of variation In an equation of the form $y = kx$ ($k = 0$), which specifies a linear direct variation, k is the constant of variation. It is also called the *constant of proportionality*.

Consumer price index The consumer price index, or CPI, is a measure of the change in retail prices of goods and services.

Continued radical A radical of the form

$$\sqrt{n + \sqrt{n + \sqrt{n + \sqrt{n + \ldots}}}}$$

Converse A statement in the form "If...(q)..., then...(p)...", given the original implication "If ...(p)..., then...(q)...".

Coordinate plane A number grid on a plane with an x-axis and a y-axis.

Coordinates The two numbers in an ordered pair that locate a point on a grid.

Coplanar lines Lines that lie in the same plane.

Corollary A theorem which follows easily as an extension of another theorem and is deducible from the first theorem.

Correlation A term used to indicate an obvious relation between two variables of statistical data, as displayed by some scatterplots.

Corresponding angles For a transversal that cuts two parallel lines, the angles on the same side of the transversal and on the same side of each line.

Cosine For a given angle in a right-angled triangle, the ratio of the length of the adjacent side to the length of the hypotenuse.

Cube (geometry) A regular polyhedron with six congruent square faces.

Cube (numeration) To raise a number to the third power.

Cube root The number which, when cubed, results in a given number.
$\sqrt[3]{8} = 2$; 2 is the cube root of 8.

Cyclic quadrilateral A quadrilateral with all vertices in the circumference of a circle. (also **inscribed quadrilateral**)

Cylinder A three-dimensional figure with two parallel, congruent, circular bases.

Deca- A prefix meaning ten.

Deci- A prefix meaning tenth.

Defined term A term that can be explained using other terms.

Degree of a polynomial The greatest degree of any term within the polynomial.

Degree of a term The sum of the exponents of the variables in the term.

Demand loan A type of bank loan. For such a loan, there is no specific accumulated amount due nor is there a specified date of payment.

Dependent events Two or more events in which the result of one event affects the result of the event after it.

Diagonal A line segment joining any two non-adjacent vertices of a polygon.

Diameter A chord of a circle that passes through its centre.

Difference of squares A binomial consisting of a squared term minus a different squared term.

Dilatation A transformation for which the shape of the image is the same as the shape of the object but the image may be enlarged or reduced in size.

Diophantine equation An equation for which all solutions must be whole numbers.

Direct congruence Having the same size, shape, and orientation.

Direct variation A function of two variables, say x and y, defined by an equation of the form $y = kx$, $k = 0$.

Discount The difference between the selling price and the face value of bonds, stocks, shares, or a currency, when the selling price is less than the par value.

Discriminant The expression $b^2 - 4ac$ is called the discriminant of the quadratic equation $ax^2 + bx + c = 0$. It determines the nature of the roots of the equation.

Disjoint sets Sets that have no elements in common.

Displacement The distance travelled in a given direction.

Distributive property The property that a product of a sum or difference can be written as a sum of or difference between two products.

$$a \times (b + c) = (a \times b) + (a \times c)$$
$$a \times (b - c) = (a \times b) - (a \times c)$$

Dividend The portion of a profit that is returned to a stock holder.

Domain The set of the first elements of the ordered pairs of a relation.

Double root (of an equation) Two equal solutions to a quadratic equation $ax^2 + bx + c = 0$.

Edge The intersection of two faces of a three-dimensional figure.

Effective interest rate The annual rate of interest which, when compounded annually, is *equivalent* to the nominal rate compounded more than once per year.

Elimination A process of solving a system of equations whereby two or more simultaneous equations are combined so that one variable is removed and the number of equations reduced by one.

Entire radical A radical that contains no coefficients outside the radical sign.

Equation A mathematical statement showing two or more numbers or quantities equal.

Equilateral triangle A triangle with three congruent sides and three congruent angles.

Equivalent equations Equations that are obtained by performing the same operation on each side of a given equation.

Equivalent fractions Fractions that reduce to the same lowest terms.

Equivalent ratios Ratios that can be expressed as equivalent fractions.

Equivalent vectors Vectors that have the same magnitude and direction.

Escribed circle A circle drawn externally to a polygon to touch three consecutive sides with the first and third sides extended.

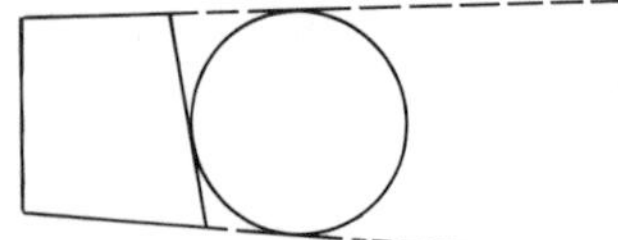

Event Any set of possible outcomes.

Experimental probability of an event The frequency of the occurrence of an event in a sample, divided by the total sample size.

Exponent (in a power) The number of times the base occurs as a factor.

Exponential equation An equation of the form $y = ab^x$, where the variable x appears in the exponent.

Expression A combination of mathematical symbols, variables, and numerals.

Exterior angles Angles on the outside of two lines cut by a transversal.

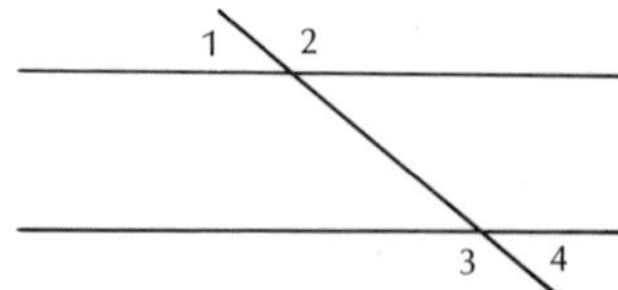

Extraneous root A solution to a radical expression which, when substituted into the expression, does not give the expected result. It usually arises when the two sides of a radical expression are squared to obtain the solution.

Extreme values The highest and lowest values in a set of numbers.

Face A flat surface of a three-dimensional figure.

Face value The price at which a bond was first offered.

Factor Any one of the numbers or expressions or variables used in multiplication to form a product.

Fibonacci sequence A sequence most commonly used to estimate animal populations. It is defined by the equation $f(n) = f(n - 1) + f(n - 2)$.

Fitted line In a scatterplot displaying either positive or negative correlation, the best-fitting line about which the points seem to fall. (also **median fit line**)

Formula An equation that states a rule about quantities represented by variables.

Frequency The number of times a particular value in a set of data occurs.

Frequency distribution table A table that shows the frequencies of values in a set of data, often including columns for cumulative frequency, midpoint of interval, and subtotal.

Function A relation in which each element of the domain corresponds to exactly one element of the range.

General Term, t_n, of a sequence The term by which a sequence may be defined.

Geometric sequence A sequence in which the quotient of any two consecutive terms is constant.

Geometric series The sum of the terms of a geometric sequence.

Glide reflection A transformation that is the combination of a reflection in a line and a translation parallel to the line.

Greatest common factor (GCF) The largest number that is a factor of each of a set of numbers or the expression that has the greatest degree and numerical coefficient common to each of a set of expressions. (also **greatest monomial factor** when dealing with polynomials)

Greatest monomial factor The largest number that is a factor of each of a set of numbers or the expression that has the greatest degree and numerical coefficient common to each of a set of expressions. (also **greatest common factor**)

Half Life The time it takes until only half of the original amount of a radioactive substance remains.

Half-turn symmetry A property exhibited in a figure for which there is a mapping that maps the figure onto itself under a rotation of 180°.

Hecto- A prefix meaning one hundred.

Height (of a polygon) The length of a perpendicular line segment from any vertex to the opposite side (or an extension of the opposite side).

Heptagon A polygon with seven sides.

Hexagon A polygon with six sides.

Hinges The values that are halfway between the median and an extreme value.

Histogram A graph used to display frequency distribution of data using touching bars and with the height of the bars representing frequencies and the width of the bars representing interval width.

Horizontal line test If a horizontal line cuts the graph of a function f in two or more places, then f^{-1} is not a function.

Hyperbola The name of the shape of a graph of inverse variation which can be represented by an equation in the form $xy = k, k \neq 0$.

Hypotenuse (HYP) The side opposite the right angle in a right-angled triangle.

Hypothesis The "p" statement in a conditional statement.

Identity elements 0 in addition and 1 in multiplication.

$a + 0 = a$ and $a \times 1 = a$

Identity function The function I which maps every member of its domain onto itself.

Image The figure resulting from a transformation.

Imaginary component In the complex number $a + bi$, b is the imaginary component.

Implication A statement in the form "If...(p)..., then...(q)..." (also **conditional statement**)

Inadmissible root A solution of an equation which has no meaning in the context of the application.

Incentre The centre of an incircle.

Incircle A circle that touches each side of a polygon.

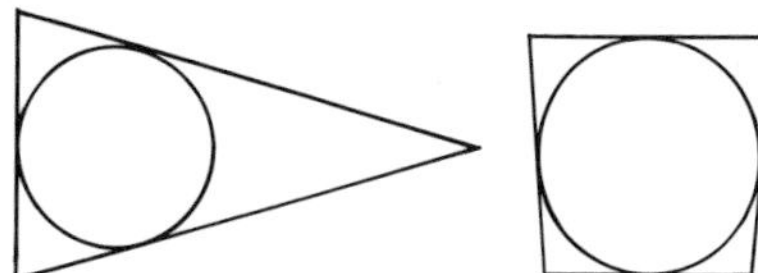

Inconsistent equations A system of equations which has no solution. The equations of parallel lines are inconsistent because they do not intersect.

Independent events Events that have no effect on one another.

Inequality A mathematical statement that one quantity is greater than (>) or less than (<) another.

Inscribed angle An angle formed by two chords of a circle with a common vertex in the circle.

Inscribed quadrilateral A quadrilateral with all vertices in the circumference of a circle. (also **cyclic quadrilateral**)

Integers The set of numbers consisting of $\{\ldots, -2, -1, 0, 1, 2, \ldots\}$

Integral exponent An exponent that is an integer.

Interest The sum of money paid for the use of the principal.

Interior angles Two angles on the inside of two lines cut by a transversal, and on the same side of the transversal.

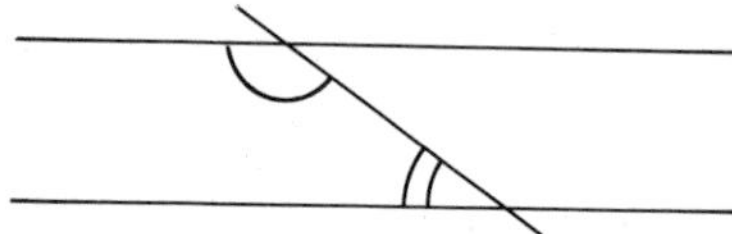

Interpolation Estimation of values between points of known values on a graph.

Intersecting lines Lines that have one point in common.

Interval (of statistical data) A set consisting of all the numbers between a pair of given numbers.

Inverse of a function A function g is the inverse of a function f if $g(f(x)) = x$, for all x in the domain of f. If f maps a domain element x onto a range element z, then the inverse of f, g, maps z onto x.

Inverse variation A function of two variables, say x and y, defined by an equation of the form $xy = k, k \neq 0$.

Irrational number A number that cannot be expressed as the quotient of two integers and whose decimal expansion neither terminates nor repeats.

Isolating a variable In a formula, solving for one variable in terms of the others.

Isometry A transformation that preserves distance between points.

Isosceles triangle A triangle with two congruent sides and two congruent angles.

Joint variation A function of more than two variables. A joint variation of x, y and z is defined by an equation of the form $z = kxy$, where k is a constant.

Kilo- A prefix meaning one thousand.

Kilogram The basic unit of mass in the metric system.

Lateral surface area The area of all lateral faces (all the faces of a three-dimensional figure excluding the bases).

Least common multiple (LCM) The smallest non-zero number that is a multiple of each of two or more given numbers.

Like radicals Radicals that have the same radicand when in simplest form.

Line A set of points in a straight path extending infinitely in both directions.

Line graph A graph made up of line segments used to show data representing changes over a period of time.

Line of sight A direct (imaginary) line from an observer to a sighted object.

Line of symmetry A line that divides a figure into two congruent parts that are reflection images of each other.

Linear direct variation An equation of the form $y = kx, k \neq 0$.

Linear equation An equation of degree one that can be put into the form $Ax + By = C$ (A and B not both $= 0$).

Linear function A function that is represented by a straight-line graph.

Linear programming The process of using inequalities to optimize business opportunities.

Linear relation A relation that is represented by a straight-line graph.

Litre The basic unit of capacity in the metric system.

Logarithm The exponent which changes a given number, called the *base,* into any required number.

Magnitude The absolute value of a number or a vector; size.

Magnitude of a complex number The real number value of the complex variable which is determined by
$|a + bi| = \sqrt{a^2 + b^2}$

Major and minor arcs of a circle A chord *YZ*, which is not a diameter, determines a major arc *YXZ* and a minor arc *YZ*. The measure of the minor arc is the measure of its central angle $\angle YOZ$. The measure of a major arc is found by subtracting the measure of the minor arc from 360°.

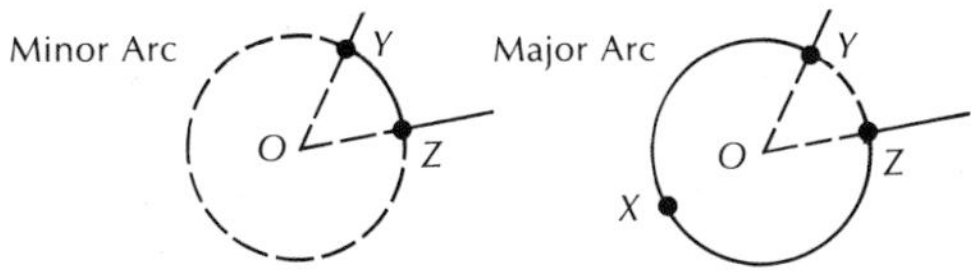

Many-to-one correspondence A relation in which more than one element in the domain corresponds to the same element in the range.

Mapping A correspondence of points or elements under some transformation or rule.

Market value The amount that someone would pay for a bond on a given day. It is determined by several varying factors.

Mass The amount of matter in a body.

Mean The sum of a given set of values divided by the number of values.

Measure of central tendency A single value representative of a set of data, such as mean, median, or mode.

Median (of a triangle) A segment joining a vertex to the midpoint of the opposite side.

Median (statistics) The middle value of a set of data when the data are listed in numerical order.

Median fit line In a scatterplot displaying either positive or negative correlation, a fitted line found by dividing the graph into three regions and using the medians of *x* and *y* values in the outer regions.

Metre The basic unit of length in the metric system.

Micro- A prefix meaning millionth.

Midpoint The point in a line segment which bisects the line.

Milli- A prefix meaning thousandth.

Mode The most frequently occurring value in a set of data.

Monomial A single-term expression which is either a numeral, one or more variables, or a product of a numeral and one or more variables.

Multiple (of a number) The product of a given number and an integer.

Multiplicative inverse The number which multiplies by a given number to yield a product of one.

Mutually exclusive events Events which do not have common outcomes.

Nano- A prefix meaning billionth.

Natural numbers The set of all positive integers {1, 2, 3,...}.

Negative correlation A relationship between two statistical variables in which one variable tends to increase as the other decreases.

Negative reciprocals Two numbers whose product is -1.

Net A pattern that can be folded into a three-dimensional shell.

Nominal annual interest rate (nominal rate) In an 8%/a interest compounded semiannually the 8% is the *nominal rate.*

Nonagon A polygon with nine sides.

Obtuse angle An angle between 90° and 180°.

Octagon A polygon with eight sides.

Octahedron A polyhedron with eight faces.

One-to-one correspondence A relation in which each element of the domain corresponds to exactly one element of the range and each element of the range corresponds to exactly one element of the domain.

Opposite angles Angles formed by two intersecting lines which have a common vertex and are opposite to each other.

Opposite (OPP) For a given angle in a right-angled triangle, the side which is opposite the angle.

Order of rotational symmetry The number of times that the tracing of a figure fits onto the figure in one full turn.

Ordered pair A pair of numbers in which order is important. (3, −2) and (−2, 3) are different ordered pairs.

Ordinary annuity An annuity whose deposits or payments are made at the end of each designated time period.

Orientation The determination of direction in terms of standard directions such as clockwise and counter-clockwise, or north, east, south, and west.

Origin The point where the x-axis and the y-axis intersect.

Orthocentre The point where the altitudes of a triangle intersect.

Orthographic projections The drawings of the front, side, and top views of a three-dimensional figure.

Outcome The result obtained from an action or an experiment.

Pantograph A tool used to copy a plane figure to a desired scale.

Parabola The name of the shape of a graph of quadratic direct variation which can be represented by an equation in the form $y = kx^2, k \neq 0$.

Paraboloid A three dimensional parabola.

Parallel lines Lines in a plane that do not intersect.

Parallel planes Planes in space that do not intersect.

Parallelogram A quadrilateral with opposite sides parallel.

Partial variation A function of two variables, say x and y, defined by an equation of the form $y = kx + b$.

Pascal's Triangle The triangular array of coefficients of the expansion of $(a + b)^n$, for $n = 0,1,2,\ldots$.

Row Number		Totals
$n = 0$	1	1
$n = 1$	1 1	2
$n = 2$	1 2 1	4
$n = 3$	1 3 3 1	8
$n = 4$	1 4 6 4 1	16
$n = 5$	1 5 10 10 5 1	32
$n = 6$	1 6 15 20 15 6 1	64

Pentagon A polygon with five sides.

Perfect square A number whose square root is an integer.

Period (of a repeating decimal) The set of digits which repeat, indicated by a solid line over the period. The period of $\frac{4}{11} = 0.363\,636\ldots = 0.\overline{36}$ is 36.

Periodic decimal A decimal fraction in which, after a certain decimal place, one digit, or a set of digits in the same order, is repeated indefinitely. (also **repeating decimal**)

Periodic interest rate, *i* The quotient of the actual interest rate of a loan, divided by the number of compounding periods.

Perpendicular bisector The line which bisects a segment and is perpendicular to it.

Perpendicular lines Lines that form 90° angles when they intersect.

Personal instalment loan A type of bank loan. The terms of this loan require the borrower to make fixed payments including principal and interest at regular intervals for a specified time.

Pi (π) The ratio of the circumference of a circle to its diameter. $\pi \doteq 3.1416$.

Piecewise linear Functions are said to be piecewise linear if their graphs consist of a line and line segments.

Plane A flat surface that has no thickness, extends infinitely in all directions, and contains the whole of a straight line drawn through any two points in it.

Plane figure A set of points in a plane.

Plane of symmetry A plane that divides a three-dimensional figure into two congruent parts that are reflection images of each other.

Plane symmetry A three-dimensional figure has plane symmetry if it has at least one plane of symmetry.

Point A point has an exact position. It has neither magnitude nor direction and is shown by a dot.

Point-slope form of a linear equation The equation of a straight line written in the form $y - y_1 = m(x - x_1)$, where (x_1, y_1) is a point in the line and m is the slope.

Point symmetry A figure has point symmetry if there is a point O such that the figure maps onto itself under a rotation about O.

Polygon A closed figure whose sides are three or more line segments.

Polyhedron A three-dimensional figure whose faces are polygons.

Polynomial A monomial or a sum of monomials.

Population The entire set of individuals, items, or scores from which a sample is drawn.

Positive correlation A relationship between two statistical variables in which both variables tend to increase or decrease together.

Postal function A function consisting of disjointed constant functions over finite domains. (also **step function**)

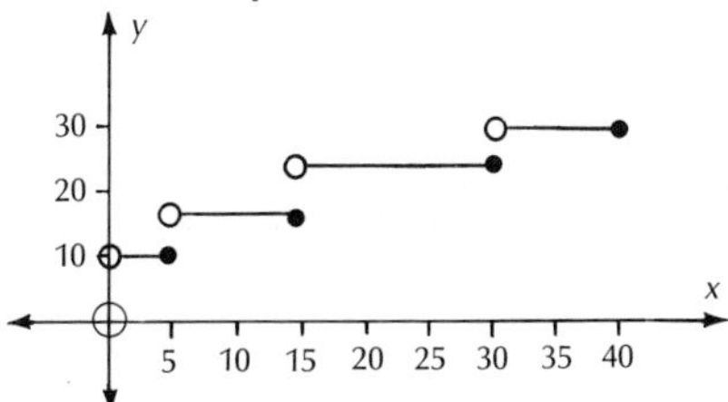

Postulate A statement that is generally accepted and need not be proved. (also **assumption** or **axiom**)

Power A product of equal factors; for $216 = 6^3$, 216 is the third power of 6.

Preferred shares Shares which are given priority in the distribution of dividends. If the profits are too small to be distributed to all share holders, the preferred share holders receive their dividends before the **common share** holders.

Premium The difference between the selling price and the face value of bonds, stocks, shares, or a currency, when the selling price is more than the par value.

Present value, $V_{present}$ The amount of money which needs to be paid or invested now to accumulate to a required amount after a specified amount of time.

Present value of an annuity The sum of the present value of each annual payment.

Principal The amount of money invested, or the amount of money borrowed from a lending institution.

Principal square root (of a positive number) The positive square root.

Prism A three-dimensional figure whose bases are congruent polygons in parallel planes and whose faces are parallelograms.

Probability The ratio of the number of times a certain outcome can occur to the total possible outcomes.

Promissory note A type of bank loan characterized by the borrower agreeing to pay the total amount of the loan plus the interest on a specified date.

Proportion An equality of ratios. The first and last terms are the *extremes*; the middle terms are the *means*.

Pure imaginary number A complex number $a + bi$, where $a = 0$.

Pyramid A three-dimensional figure whose base is a polygon and whose lateral faces are triangles.

Pythagorean triples Any three natural numbers a, b, and c satisfying the equation $a^2 + b^2 = c^2$.

Quadrant One of the four regions into which the coordinate axes separate the plane.

Quadratic direct variation A function of two variables, say x and y, defined by an equation of the form $y = kx^2$, $k \neq 0$.

Quadratic equation An equation of degree two that can be put into the form $Ax^2 + Bx + C = 0$, $(A \neq 0)$.

Quadratic function A quadratic equation which satisfies the properties of a function.

Quadratic inverse variation A function of two variables, say x and y, defined by an equation of the form $x^2y = k$, $k \neq 0$.

Quadratic-Quadratic system of equations A system of two quadratic equations.

Quadratic trinomial A three-term polynomial of degree two.

Quadrilateral A polygon having four sides.

Quote price The common name for the market value of a bond.

Radical expression An expression containing a square root.

Radical sign The symbol $\sqrt{\ }$.

Radicand The expression below the radical sign.

Radius A line segment that joins the centre of a circle to any point in its circumference.

Random number table A table of the digits 0 through 9 in which each digit is equally likely to occur in any place in the table.

Random sample A sample in which each member of the population is equally likely to appear.

Range (of a relation) The set of the second elements of the ordered pairs of a relation.

Range (of statistical data) The difference between the smallest and largest values of a set of data.

Rate of inflation The percentage change in the Consumer Price Index.

Ratio The relation existing between two quantities of the same kind.
The ratio of x to y is $\frac{x}{y}$.

Rational expression An expression that contains variables in the denominator.

Rational numbers The set of numbers that can be expressed as the quotient of two integers, the divisor not being zero.

Rationalizing the denominator The process of changing the denominator from an irrational number to a rational number.

Raw data Data that has not yet been organized.

Ray Part of a line extending without end in one direction only.

Real component of a complex number In the complex number $a + bi$, a is the real component.

Real number Any number that is either a rational number or an irrational number.

Reciprocal The number which multiplies by a given number to yield a product of 1.

Rectangle A parallelogram with four right angles.

Rectangular prism A prism with two parallel congruent rectangular bases.

Rectangular pyramid A pyramid with a rectangular base.

Recursive definition A sequence has a recursive definition if its terms are defined in relation to preceding terms.

Redemption The payment the issuer of a share, stock, or bond makes to the owner when he repurchases it.

Reflection A transformation that flips the points of a plane over a line.

Reflection line A line in which a figure is reflected (or mapped) onto its image.

Reflex angle An angle between 180° and 360°.

Regular polygon A polygon that is equilateral and equiangular.

Regular polyhedron A polyhedron whose faces are regular congruent polygons.

Relation A set of ordered pairs.

Relative frequency A ratio of the frequency of one element or interval of data to the total frequency.

Repeating decimal A decimal fraction in which, after a certain decimal place, one digit, or a set of digits in the same order, is repeated indefinitely. (also **periodic decimal**)

Replacement set (for a variable) The set of numbers which may be used to replace the variable.

Resultant vector The vector which is obtained by adding or subtracting two or more vectors.

Rhombus A quadrilateral with four congruent sides.

Right angle An angle measuring 90°.

Root (of an equation) A solution of an equation.

Rotation A transformation in which the points of the plane are turned about a fixed point.

Rotational symmetry A figure has rotational symmetry if a tracing of the figure rotates onto itself in less than one full turn.

Sample A set of elements drawn from a population.

Scalar multiplication The multiplication of a vector quantity by a scalar quantity in order to change its magnitude or reverse its direction.

Scalar quantity A quantity with magnitude only.

Scale drawing A drawing of an object with all dimensions in proportion to corresponding actual dimensions.

Scale factor A number representing the amount by which the dimensions of an object are multiplied to get the dimensions of its image.

Scale ratio The ratio of the size of the enlarged or reduced image to the object in a scale drawing.

Scalene triangle A triangle with no congruent sides or angles.

Scatterplot A statistical graph displaying a two-variable set of data as a set of points on a coordinate grid.

Scientific notation A method of writing a number as the product of a power of ten and a number between one and ten.

Secant A line that contains a chord, as $\overleftrightarrow{AB}$.

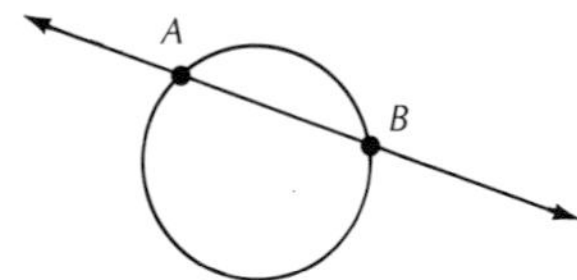

Sector (of a circle) A region bounded by an arc and two radii.

Sector angle An angle with its vertex at the centre of a circle and bounded by two radii. (also **central angle**)

Segment (of a circle) A region bounded by an arc and a chord.

Semicircle An arc which joins the endpoints of a diameter.

Sequence A function whose domain is consecutive natural numbers.

Series The sum of the terms of a sequence.

Set A group or collection of objects.

Shell A model of a solid whose interior is completely empty.

Sigma, Σ A symbol used to mean "the sum of", in abbreviating a series.

Similar figures Figures with the same shape but not necessarily the same size.

Simple interest The interest which is proportional to the length of time the loan is outstanding. The principal remains unchanged throughout the period.

Sine For a given angle in a right-angled triangle, the ratio of the length of the opposite side to the length of the hypotenuse.

Skew lines Lines that are not parallel and do not intersect. The distance between any pair is defined by the length of the unique line that is perpendicular to both.

Slant height The height of a lateral face of a pyramid.

Slope-intercept form of a linear equation The equation of a straight line in the form $y = mx + b$, where m is the slope of the line and b is the y-intercept.

Slope formula The slope of a line is the ratio $\frac{y_1 - y_2}{x_1 - x_2}$ where (x_1, y_1) and (x_2, y_2) are points on the line.

Slope of a line The steepness of a line; the ratio of the rise of a line to its run.

Smoothing (of data) A method for removing extreme highs and lows in statistical data collected over time, by substituting the median of three consecutive values for each original value, excluding the first and last values.

Solid A three-dimensional figure whose inside is completely filled.

Solution set The set of values in the replacement set for a variable that make the sentence true.

Sphere The set of all points in space which are a given distance from a fixed point.

Square (geometry) A rectangle with four congruent sides.

Square (numeration) To raise a number to the second power.

Square root A number which, when multiplied by itself, results in the given number.

Standard form of a linear equation The equation of a straight line written in the form $Ax + By + C = 0$, where $A, B, C \in \boldsymbol{R}$.

Statistics The study of methods of collecting and analysing data.

Stem-and-leaf graph An arrangement of data that facilitates the finding of the mean, median, and mode.

Step function See **postal function**.

Straight angle An angle measuring 180°.

Stratified sample A sample that randomly includes individuals from each of identified groups within the population in the same proportion as these groups appear in the population.

Subtend To be opposite to and to delimit, as chord *AB* or arc *AB* subtends $\angle APB$.

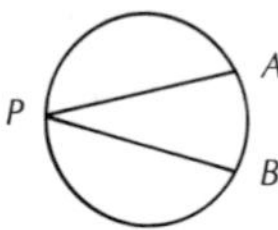

Supplementary angles Two angles that have a sum of 180°.

Surface area The total area of the polygonal regions (faces) of a polyhedron.

System of equations A set of equations in the same variables.

System of inequalities A set of inequalities in the same variables.

Tangent (of a circle) A line in the same plane as the circle that has one, and only one, point in common with the circle. The common point is called the point of contact.

Tangent (trigonometry) For a given angle in a right-angled triangle, the ratio of the length of the opposite side to the length of the adjacent side.

Term A mathematical expression using numerals or variables or both to indicate a sum, difference, product, or quotient.

Term (of a loan) The period of time that a financial agreement exists.

Tetrahedron A polygon with four triangular faces.

Theorem A statement that has been proved.

Theoretical probability The number of favourable outcomes divided by the number of possible outcomes.

Transformation A one-to-one mapping from the whole plane to the whole plane.

Transit An instrument equipped with a telescope, levels, and scales for measuring both vertical and horizontal angles.

Transversal A line crossing two or more lines.

Trapezoid A quadrilateral with one pair of opposite sides parallel.

Triangular prism A prism with two parallel, congruent, triangular bases.

Trigonometry An area of mathematical study involving the measurement of triangles.

Trinomial A polynomial consisting of three terms.

Trinomial square A three-term polynomial that is the product of squaring a binomial.

Unbiased sample A sample that gives a good representation the group being studied.

Variable A letter used to represent an unknown quantity.

Vector quantity A quantity with magnitude and direction.

Vector sum The vector which is obtained by adding two or more vectors.

Velocity Speed in a given direction.

Venn diagram A diagram used to show the relationship between two or more sets.

Vertex (of a parabola) The point where a parabola intersects its axis of symmetry.

Vertical line test A test to determine whether a relation is a function. If a vertical line cuts a graph of a relation in two or more distinct points then it is not a function.

Weight Force downwards due to gravity.

Whole numbers The set of all natural numbers and zero. {0, 1, 2, 3,...}

***x*-axis** The horizontal number line in a coordinate plane.

***x*-intercept** The *x*-coordinate of a point where a graph crosses the *x*-axis.

***y*-axis** The vertical number line in a coordinate plane.

***y*-intercept** The *y*-coordinate of a point where a graph crosses the *y*-axis.

Yield The return on an investment.

Answers to Exercises

UNIT 1

Exercise 1–1, pages 2–3

1. a. 54 **b.** 14 **c.** −3.05 **d.** $\frac{2}{5}$ **e.** $\frac{1}{12}$ **f.** 1.2 **g.** −1 **h.** 5 **i.** 7 **2. a.** $(4 - 6 \div 2) \times (3 + 8) = 11$ **b.** $3 \times (5 + 4 - 8) \times 3 = 9$ **c.** $(7 - 8 \div 2 + 3) \times 6 \div (4 - 1) = 12$ **d.** $(-3 \times 7 + 3 \times 5) \div 3 - 8 = -10$ **3. a.** 26 **b.** 9 **c.** 29 **d.** 41 **e.** 2 **f.** 0 **g.** 1 **h.** $-\frac{1}{2}$ **i.** −3 **j.** $\frac{1}{3}$ **4. a.** 7.5 m^2 **b.** 3.12 m^2 **c.** 2.83 cm^2 **d.** 25.91 m^2 **5. a.** 2.8 N **b.** 60.03 m **c.** 7.2 J **d.** 7.21 units **e.** 1050 Ω **6. a.** $T_t = 17.17$ N; $T_b = 66.17$ N **b.** 3.13 m/s **c.** The minimum speed required decreases. **d.** 9.5 m/s **e.** $v = 11.63$ m/s; $v = 6.72$ m/s **7. a.** 9600 N **b.** 6666.67 N

Exercise 1–2, pages 5–7

1. a. x^{10} **b.** x^6 **c.** x^{16} **d.** $64x^2$ **e.** x^8 **f.** 243 **g.** 9 **h.** a^3b^3 **i.** $9m^4$ **j.** $81m^4$ **k.** r^{15} **l.** a^4 **m.** $\frac{1}{5}$ **n.** $6m^5$ **o.** y^6 **p.** $-500m^5$ **2. a.** $\frac{5x}{y^2}$ **b.** $\frac{1}{r^3}$ **c.** $\frac{3r}{s^3}$ **d.** x^2 **e.** $\frac{n^3}{m^2}$ **f.** $\frac{1}{x^3}$ **3. a.** a^{-5} **b.** $17x^{-1}$ **c.** $3xy^{-1}$ **d.** $3^{-2}y^{-5}$ **e.** $4zx^{-3}y^{-2}$ **f.** $x^{-5}y^2$ **4. a.** $\frac{1}{8}$ **b.** $\frac{1}{25}$ **c.** 1 **d.** $\frac{9}{4}$ **e.** $\frac{10}{9}$ **f.** $\frac{7}{12}$ **g.** $\frac{27}{50}$ **h.** $-\frac{5}{3}$ **i.** $\frac{64}{27}$ **j.** $-\frac{3}{5}$ **k.** 9.803×10^{-3} **l.** 0.69 **5. a.** 2.7×10^3 **b.** 8.5×10^7 **c.** 3.95×10^{-3} **d.** 5.8×10^{-5} **e.** 3.8×10^5 **f.** 3×10^1 **g.** 5.2×10^{-5} **h.** 9.2×10^{-8} **6. a.** 2500 **b.** 0.000 000 016 **c.** 0.037 **d.** 46 **e.** 702 000 **f.** 850 **g.** 2900 **h.** 0.000 005 5 **7. a.** 1.65×10^{10} **b.** 1.5×10^8 **c.** 6.875×10^{-4} **d.** 1.2×10^{-3} **e.** 7.5×10^{-7} **f.** 4×10^{-11} **g.** 2.5×10^2 **h.** 2.4×10^{-8} **i.** 2.4×10^{-1} **8. a.** $64x^5y^8$ **b.** $108x^9y^{16}$ **c.** $\frac{a^{10}}{b^6}$ **d.** $108y^{14}$ **e.** $\frac{b^4}{25x^6}$ **f.** $\frac{5y^2}{2x^2}$ **g.** $4x^5y^2z^{12}$ **h.** a^7b **i.** $\frac{x^{12}z^3}{y}$ **j.** 3 **k.** $\frac{32m^4n^9}{5}$ **l.** $\frac{27x^3}{8y^6}$ **m.** $\frac{5}{6}$ **n.** $\frac{25}{9a^2b^2}$ **o.** $\frac{125y}{243x}$ **p.** $\frac{17}{4}$ **q.** $x^2 + y^3$ **r.** $\frac{-40b^7}{a^{11}}$ **9. a.** 2 **b.** 3 **c.** 2 **d.** 2 **e.** 3 **f.** 2 **g.** −2 **h.** −3 **i.** $\frac{1}{3}$ **j.** 0 **k.** $\frac{3}{4}$ **l.** −2 **10.** 53.57 h **11.** 1.1×10^5 km/h **12.** 463.8 m/s **13.** 9×10^{14} J **14. a.** $\sqrt{x}$ **b.** $\sqrt[3]{x}$ **15.** 4.48×10^4 **16.** 1 kilobyte = 1024 bytes, 1 megabyte = 1 048 576 bytes **17.** $12.94

Exercise 1–3, page 9

1. a. 3 **b.** 4 **c.** −5 **d.** 5 **e.** −8 **f.** −2 **g.** 6 **h.** 8 **i.** 4 **2. a.** $s = \frac{P}{4}$ **b.** $f = T - 3n$ **c.** $w = \frac{A}{l}$ **d.** $r = \frac{C}{2\pi}$ **e.** $h = \frac{A}{2\pi r}$ **f.** $t = \frac{d - x}{v}$ **g.** $m = \frac{L - d}{k}$ **h.** $r = \frac{P - 2l}{2\pi}$ **i.** $w = \frac{A - l^2}{4l}$ **j.** $h = \frac{A - 2\pi r^2}{\pi r}$ **k.** $m = \frac{E - kx^2}{gh}$ **l.** $h = \frac{E - \frac{1}{2}mv^2}{mg}$

3. a. 1 **b.** 2 **c.** −1 **d.** $1\frac{3}{8}$ **e.** 3 **f.** 2 **g.** 7 **h.** $1\frac{1}{2}$ **4. a.** 5 **b.** 6 **c.** 5 **d.** 15 **5.** 14 cm, 15 cm, 16 cm **6.** $163.50 **7.** 244 333 ha **8.** Douglas fir, 7 cords; alder, 5 cords **9.** Liberals, 80; Conservatives, 101

Exercise 1–4, page 11

1. a. 12 **b.** 50 **c.** 40 **d.** 20 **e.** 100 **f.** 72 **g.** 24 **h.** 2 **i.** 30 **2. a.** $-1\frac{3}{5}$ **b.** 3 **c.** $5\frac{2}{5}$ **d.** 6 **e.** 10 **f.** $\frac{1}{3}$ **g.** $5\frac{1}{2}$ **h.** 25 **i.** 3 **j.** $2\frac{2}{5}$ **k.** 7 **l.** 15 **3. a.** $\frac{3}{10}$ **b.** $14\frac{4}{15}$ **c.** $-1\frac{11}{15}$ **d.** $8\frac{3}{5}$ **e.** $\frac{63}{380}$ **f.** $-1\frac{1}{32}$ **g.** $-5\frac{4}{7}$ **h.** −3 **i.** $2\frac{1}{43}$ **4.** 1 min 12 s **5.** 60 km **6.** 6 h 40 min **7.** $3000 was deposited at 10%, $2000 was deposited at 15%. **8.** 24 h **9.** $1\frac{3}{7}$ L

Exercise 1–5, pages 14–15

1. a. Let x be age in years. $x \geq 18$ **b.** Let x be mass in tonnes. $x < 2.5$ **c.** Let x be the height of vehicles using the underpass in metres. $x < 2.2$ **d.** Let x be the age of any member of class 11B in years. $15 \leq x \leq 18$ **e.** Let x be the legal speed to travel on the freeway in kilometres per hour. $40 \leq x \leq 100$

2. a.

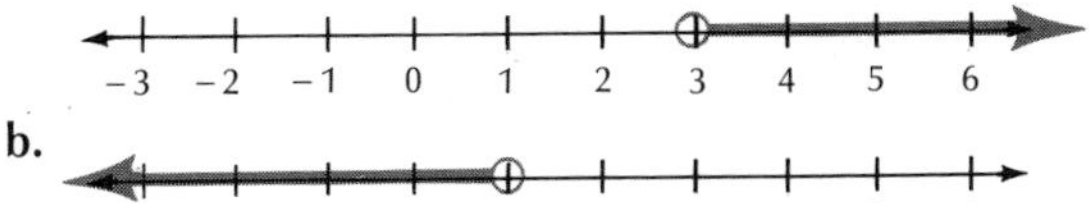

b.

c.

d.

3. a. $x \geq 1$ **b.** $x < 2$ **c.** $x \leq 3$ **d.** $x > -2$
4. a. $x < 10$ **b.** $x \geq -2$ **c.** $x \geq 2$ **d.** $x > -3$
e. $x \geq 6$ **f.** $x < 3$ **g.** $x \geq 4$ **h.** $x > -2$ **i.** $x \leq 1$
j. $x \geq 3$ **k.** $x \geq -\frac{1}{2}$ **l.** $x \geq 1$

5. a.

b.

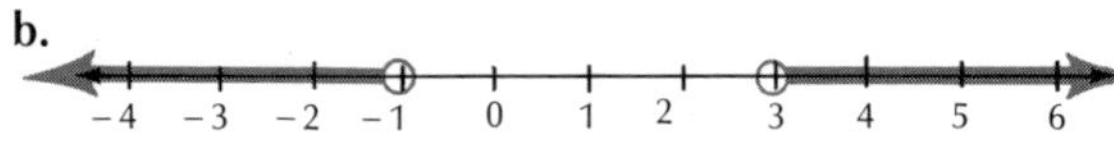

c.

d.

e.

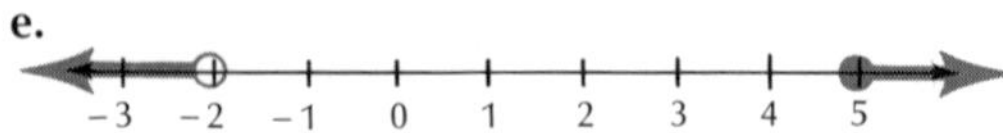

f.

6. a. $-2 \leq x < 2$ **b.** $-4 < x \leq 0$
c. $x < -3$ or $x > 1$ **d.** $1 \leq x \leq 5$
e. $x < -5$ or $x \geq 5$ **7. a.** $x < 2$ or $x > 6$
b. $1 \leq x \leq 2$ **c.** $x < 2$ or $x \geq 5$ **d.** $x > 3$ or $x < 1$
e. $-2 < x \leq 3$ **f.** $x < 1$ and $x > 3$, $x \in \emptyset$
g. $1 \leq x < 2$ **h.** $-1 < y < 2$ **i.** $0 < y < 4$
j. $-2 \leq x \leq 2$ **8. a.** $-4 < x < 8$ **b.** $x \in \boldsymbol{R}$
c. $x \leq -2$ or $x \geq 1$ **d.** $-2 \leq x \leq 3$
e. $x \leq -2$ or $x \geq 2$ **f.** $-4 < x < 0$
g. $y \leq -5$ or $y \geq -2$ **h.** $x \in \boldsymbol{R}$
i. $x \leq -5$ or $x \geq -1$
j. $\frac{2}{3} < x < 2$ **k.** $x < -1$ or $x > \frac{11}{5}$ **l.** $-4 \leq x \leq 12$
9. 56 h **10.** 24 min **11.** 138 votes or more
12. The set must be at least \$21.75.
13. 17 points. **14.** 266.67 mL
15. speed ≥ 20.83 km/h **16. a.** If any combination of lengths of two sides does not add to be greater than the length of the third side, then the three lengths cannot form a triangle.
b. $a + b + c > d$ The shortest distance between two points is a straight line, that is distance d. If the sum of a, b, and c are less than this, they will not reach from one end to the other end of line d.

Problem Solving, page 16
1. a. No **2.** 24 710.4 kg **3.** 14.44 m
4. Answers will vary. **5.** m/h: 0.22, 0.29, 0.38; m/h^2: 1.66×10^{-3}, 1.96×10^{-3}, 2.21×10^{-3}; m/h^3: 1.27×10^{-5}, 1.31×10^{-5}, 1.30×10^{-5}; m/h^3 is the most constant. **6.** Answers will vary.
7. Answers will vary.

Review, page 17
1. a. 8 **b.** 6 **c.** 1.25 **d.** $1\frac{17}{30}$ **e.** 0.1225 **f.** 56
2. a. 2187 **b.** $-\frac{1}{64}$ **c.** $195\frac{5}{16}$ **d.** 7.11 **e.** 64
f. $\frac{16}{25}$ **3. a.** $-27m^6$ **b.** $\frac{4n}{3p^2}$ **c.** $\frac{-y^6}{27x^9}$
d. $2a^2b^6$ **e.** $\frac{-27}{8x^3y^3}$ **f.** $\frac{1}{b^2}$

4. a.

b.

c.

d.

e.

f.

5. a. $x > 1$ **b.** $2 < x \leq 6$ **c.** $x > 2$ or $x \geq 4$
d. $x < -3$ or $x > 1$ **e.** $-1 \leq x < 5$
f. $x < 0$ or $x > 8$ **6.** 210 advance tickets were sold, and 220 tickets were sold at the door.
7. 44.44 d **8.** 14 min

Exercise 1–6, page 19
1. a. 1:3 **b.** 3:2 **c.** 4:5 **d.** 3:4:9 **e.** 5:8:18
f. 4:3 **g.** 3:2 **h.** 5:3 **2. a.** 14 **b.** 4 **c.** 22.5
d. 15 **e.** 5.4 **f.** 13.75 **g.** $k = 5$; $l = 3$
h. $a = 6\frac{2}{3}$; $b = 13\frac{1}{2}$ **i.** $r = 5\frac{1}{3}$; $t = 10$ **j.** $a = 2.625$; $b = 0.4$ **k.** $m = 0.53$; $n = 1.6$ **l.** $g = 12.8$; $h = 2\frac{2}{3}$
3. a. 3 **b.** 2 **c.** 12 **d.** 10 **e.** 10 **f.** 4
4. a. Hydrogen 1 g; Oxygen 8 g **b.** 800 000 kg Oxygen; 100 000 kg Hydrogen
5. length = 3.6 cm, width = 2.4 cm **6.** 42 and 20

Exercise 1-7, pages 20–21
1. a. 0.02 **b.** 0.0125 **c.** 30 **d.** 3 **e.** 0.08 **f.** 0.0001 **g.** 0.000 001 **h.** 0.46 **2. a.** 1:100 **b.** 1:200 **c.** 5:2 **d.** 18:1 **e.** 5:4 **f.** 1:100 000 **g.** 1:3 **h.** 1:30 **i.** 1:80 **j.** 15:2
3. a. 12.5 cm by 8 cm **b.** 4 cm by 5.5 cm **c.** 8.75 cm by 10 cm **d.** 4.25 cm by 2 cm **e.** 1.125 cm by 1.55 cm **4.** yes **5.** Answers may vary. **6.** scale ratio 1:50, scale factor 0.02
7. a. 1:2000, 0.0005 **b.** 1:2 000 000, 5×10^{-7} **c.** 3 cm, 0.006 **d.** 5000:1, 5000 **e.** 0.28 mm, 25:1 **f.** 54 cm, 18:5 **g.** 180 m, 1:5000 **h.** 23 cm, 0.000 01 **8.** 3.64 km

9. a. 1:50 **b.**

Length	Width	Height
2 m	1.4 m	3 m
0.9 m	1.2 m	4 m
1.2 m	1.8 m	4.6 m
1.6 m	1.6 m	4.8 m
1 m	1 m	1 m

Exercise 1–8, page 23
1. a. 40 km/h **b.** 400 m/s **c.** 0.08¢/mL **d.** 625 r/min **2. a.** 340 mL for \$1.00 **b.** \$1.53 for 300 g **c.** \$15.50 for 2.5 m **d.** 98¢ for 175 mL **e.** 12 kg for \$150.00 **f.** 27 cm for \$1.00 **3.** \$104.80 **4.** 9.53 km/h **5.** \$34.94 **6.** 800 km **7.** 2 h 40 min **8.** 20 km/h **9.** 9 km **10.** \$8.39/kg **11.** 22 kg of cheap coffee is blended with 28 kg of the expensive coffee. **12.** \$750.00 **13.** \$10 000 is invested at 12%, and \$6000 is invested at 15%.

Review, pages 24–25
1. 152 cm **2.** 34 cm^2 **3. a.** x^{-5} **b.** $3x^{-1}y^{-3}$ **c.** $a^{-3}b^2$ **4. a.** 4 **b.** 8 **c.** 2 **d.** 4 **e.** 9 **f.** 8 **g.** 2 **h.** 2
5. a.

b.

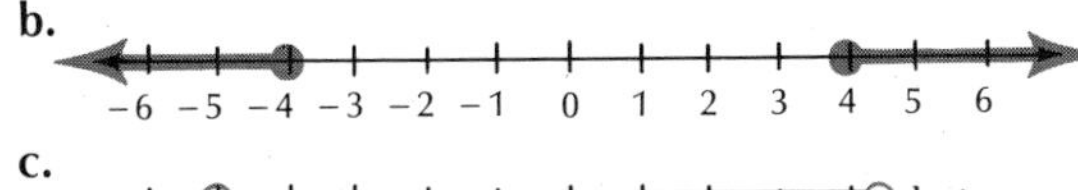

c.

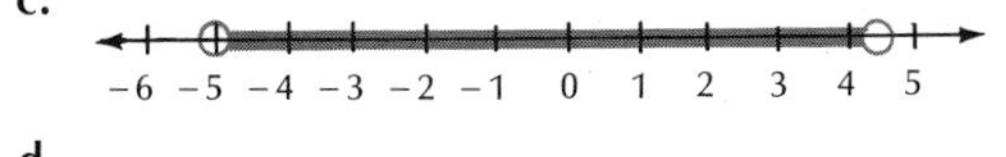

d.

6. 17 pages **7. a.** 3 **b.** 9 **c.** $11\frac{4}{7}$ **d.** $x = 8$; $y = 6\frac{2}{3}$ **e.** $a = \frac{5}{16}$; $b = 28$ **f.** 3 **g.** 7 **h.** 7
8. a. 0.005 **b.** 40 **c.** 0.000 01 **d.** $4\frac{1}{6}$

9. a. 62.5 km/h **b.** 300 r/min **c.** \$7.20/kg **d.** 18.75 m/s **10. a.** \$7.50 for 3.5 kg **b.** 1.5 m for 25¢ **c.** 3 items for the price of one **d.** the family size of 250 mL for \$5.20 **11.** no **12.** 500:1 **13.** 3.75 g **14.** 7:3; 875 mL flour, and 375 mL milk **15.** 80 km/h **16.** 2.25 m/s **17.** 7.5 cm, 10.5 cm, 12 cm **18. a.** 1:250 **b.** 0.004 **c.** 6 cm

Extra, page 25
$x = 25$ m/s $y = 15$ m/s

Test, page 26
1. a. -9 **b.** 35 **c.** -0.1875 **2.** 29.67 cm^2
3. a. $-27x^6$ **b.** 0.14 **c.** $30m^3n$ **4. a.** 6 **b.** 1 **c.** -1 **d.** $3\frac{2}{7}$ **e.** $-1\frac{3}{5}$ **f.** 3 **g.** $-4\frac{2}{3}$ **h.** $1\frac{2}{3}$ **i.** 8 **j.** $-\frac{1}{9}$ **5. a.** $x \leq 2$ **b.** $x < 1$ **c.** $-1 \leq x < 4$ **d.** $0 \leq x \leq 3$ **6.** \$562.50 **7. a.** \$937.40 **b.** \$1315.80

UNIT 2

Exercise 2–1, pages 28–29
1. self checking **2. a.** degree 1 **c.** degree 3 **d.** degree 2 **g.** degree 3 **h.** degree 5 **i.** degree 3 **3. a.** binomial **c.** trinomial **d.** binomial **g.** trinomial **h.** monomial
4. a. $2x^2 + x - 2$ **b.** y **c.** $5x^3 - 18x^2 - 4$ **d.** $-4z^3 + 2z^2 - 5z - 10$ **e.** $-2m$
5. a. $x^2 + 2xy + 2y^2$ **b.** $7a^3 + 4ab^2 - 2b^3$ **c.** $2c^4d - 4c^3d - 5c^2d^2 + 2cd + 3cd^3$
6. a. $x^2 - 5x + 2$; 16 **b.** $x^2 - 4x + 5$; 17 **c.** $x - 3y$; -11 **d.** $5x - 7y$; -31 **e.** $4x^2 + 3xy - 2y^2$; -20 **f.** $-x^2 + 2xy + 2y^2$; 2
7. a. $10x + 8$ **b.** $4x + 9$ **c.** $15x + 8$
8. a. $21x + 3$ **b.** 108 **9. a.** $a = 5$, $b = -3$ **b.** $a = -\frac{5}{2}$, $b = -6$

Extra, page 29
1. \$2110.57 **2.** \$419.77/h

Exercise 2–2, page 31
1. a. $3x^2 - 15x + 12$ **b.** $6x^3 - 10x$ **c.** $2x^2 + x - 15$ **d.** $9x^2 - 12x + 4$ **e.** $4x^2 + 20x + 25$ **f.** $x^3 - 7x^2 + 15x - 9$
2. a. degree 4; binomial **b.** degree 2; trinomial **c.** degree 2; binomial **d.** degree 4; trinomial **e.** degree 1; binomial **f.** degree 4; trinomial
3. a. $6t^2 + 13t - 28$ **b.** $6x^3 - 23x^2 + 33x - 18$ **c.** $16w^2 + 24w + 9$ **d.** $18x^3 - 12x^2 + 2x$ **e.** $16 - 9a^2$ **f.** $6x^4 + 15x^3 - 21x^2$

4. a. $x^2 + 2xy + y^2$ **b.** $x^3 + 3x^2y + 3xy^2 + y^3$
c. $x^4 + 4x^3y + 6x^2y^2 + 4xy^3 + y^4$
d. $x^5 + 5x^4y + 10x^3y^2 + 10x^2y^3 + 5xy^4 + y^5$
e. $x^6 + 6x^5y + 15x^4y^2 + 20x^3y^3 + 15x^2y^4 + 6xy^5 + y^6$
5. a. $5x^2 - 11x - 13$ **b.** $9x^2 + 34x + 9$
c. $-9x^2 - 7x - 16$ **d.** $11x^2 - 7x$
6. a. $5x^2y + 13xy - 6y$ **b.** $2x^2 - x - 3$ **c.** $5x + 13$
7. a. $6a^2 - 7ab - 3b^2$ **b.** $9p^2 - 12pq + 4q^2$
c. $45x^2 - 12xy - 12y^2$ **d.** $16x^2 - 49y^2$
e. $6m^3 + 4m^2n - 16mn^2$
f. $12x^4y^3 - 36x^3y^4 + 27x^2y^5$ **g.** $2a^2 - 25ab - 29b^2$
h. $24p^2 + 13pt + 7t^2$ **i.** $-60cd$
j. $6x^3 - 2x^2y + 7xy^2 - 3y^3$ **8. a.** -33 **b.** -39
c. -20 **d.** 0
9. a. $12x^5y^3 + 6x^4y^5 - 4x^3y^4 - 2x^2y^6$
b. $18c^4d - 18c^3d^2 - 20c^2d^3$
c. $6a^4 - 10a^3b + 4a^2b^2 - 9a^2b + 15ab^2 - 6b^3$
d. $4x^3 - 13x^2y + 4xy^2 + 12y^3$
e. $12x^3 - 3xy^2 - 8x^2y + 2y^3$
f. $2x^3 - 5x^2y - 6xy^2 + 9y^3$
g. $27p^3 - 27p^2q + 9pq^2 - q^3$ **h.** $11x^4 + 4y^6$

Exercise 2–3, page 33

1. a. 1, 7, x, $7x$ **b.** 1, 3, c, $3c$ **c.** 1, p
d. 1, 2, 4, y, yz, y^2, y^2z, $2y^2$, $4y^2$, z, $2y$, $4y$, $2z$, $4z$, $2yz$, $4yz$, $2y^2z$, $4y^2z$ **e.** 1 **f.** 1, 2, 4, k, k^2, $2k$, $2k^2$, $4k$, $4k^2$, $2l$, $2l^2$, kl, kl^2, k^2l, k^2l^2, $2kl$, $2kl^2$, $2k^2l$, $2k^2l^2$, $4kl$, $4k^2l$, $4k^2l^2$, l, l^2, $4l$, $4l^2$, $4kl^2$ **2. a.** $3x^2$ **b.** $10ts$
c. c **d.** 4 **e.** 1 **f.** $5x^2y^2$ **3. a.** $7x$ **b.** $3c$
c. p **d.** $4y^2z$ **e.** 1 **f.** $4k^2l^2$ **4. a.** $2m^2n^2$
b. $5x^4y^2z^2$ **c.** 1 **d.** $5b^2$ **e.** $3t^2s^2$ **f.** $3p^3q^2r$
5. a. $2x^2y\,(xz + 3y)$ **b.** $5m^3n^2(m - 2n)$
c. $bc(7a^2c - 5b)$ **d.** $3x^2z\,(5x^3y^2z + x^2yz - 7)$
e. $-2x^2y\,(xy^2 + 2y - 3)$ **f.** $11s^4t^5 + 30t^3 - 5s$
g. $-x^4y^4z\,(x^2z^2 + xz + 1)$
h. $7pqr\,(p^4q^2r + 4pq - 2q^2r + 3r)$
6. a. $3n\,(5m^4n - m^2 + 3n)$
b. $3a^3b\,(2b^2 + 7b - 6c)$ **c.** $-8(w^2z^4 + x^2y)$
d. $cd\,(3cd^2 - 5c^2 + 7cd - 9d)$ **e.** $abc\,(a + b - c)$
f. $\frac{1}{4}xy^2(2x - 3yz + 2y^2)$ **7. a.** $3xy\,(x + 2y)$
b. $2a^2\,(2ab - a^2 - 1)$ **c.** $4cd\,(7d + c)$
d. $yz\,(x^2y - xy^2z + z)$ **e.** $3mn\,(2mn - 3n^2 - 2m)$
f. $bc\,(5b + 3b^2c - 6)$ **8. a.** $2x\,(7xy + 3y + 3)$
b. $2xy\,(y - 3x)$ **c.** $2a\,(3b^2 + 2b - 4)$
d. $-6a^2 + 5ab + 2b + 6a$ **e.** $4xy\,(3x^2 + 6x + 4)$
f. $3m\,(m^3n - 2m^2n - 3m + 6 - n^3 + 7mn^2)$

Exercise 2–4, page 35

1. a. $2 \cdot 2 \cdot 3 \cdot b$ **b.** $2 \cdot 3 \cdot 3 \cdot a \cdot a$ **c.** $2 \cdot 2 \cdot 5 \cdot b \cdot b \cdot c$
d. $2 \cdot 2 \cdot 2 \cdot 2 \cdot x \cdot y \cdot y \cdot y$ **e.** $2 \cdot 2 \cdot 2 \cdot 3 \cdot x \cdot x \cdot x \cdot y \cdot y$
f. $2 \cdot 3 \cdot 5 \cdot f \cdot g \cdot g$ **2. a.** $3x^3 - x - 2$
b. $3x^3 - 2x^2 + 4$ **c.** $-5y^7 + 4y^3 - 3y$
d. $2xy^2 - y + 3x$ **3. a.** $x - 3$ **b.** $5x + 4$ **c.** $3x + 8$
4. a. $x^2 - 5x + 1$ **b.** $a^2 + 4a - 2$ **c.** $2y^2 + y - 1$
d. $3x^3 - 4x + 1$ **e.** $2c^2 + 3c - 1$ **f.** $4n^2 + 6n + 9$
5. a. $t^2 + 3t - 4$ **b.** $3x^2 - x + 1$ **c.** $x^4 - 2x^2 - 3$
d. $9p^4 + 12p^2 + 16$
e. $x^2 - 5x + 4 + \frac{20}{x - 4}$ **f.** $x^2 + 2x - 6 + \frac{10}{x + 3}$
g. $2k^2 + k - 3 - \frac{4}{2k - 1}$ **h.** $z^4 - z^2 + 5 - \frac{4}{2z^2 - 3}$
6. a. $x^2 - 2x - 3$ **b.** $m^2 + 2m + 1$
c. $s^2 + 2st - 3t^2$ **d.** $x^2 - 3xy + 2y^2$
e. $x^4 - 3x^2y + y^2$ **f.** $k^6 + 3k^3l^2 - l^4$
7. a. The constant term in the divisor goes evenly into the constant term of the original polynomial. **b.** Answers may vary. **8.** $6x^2 - 30x$

Exercise 2–5, pages 38–39

1. a. 1 **b.** 3 **c.** 4 **d.** 4 **e.** 4 **f.** 1
2. a. $(x - 1)(x - 2)$ **b.** $(b - 4)(b + 2)$
c. $(d - 1)(d - 8)$ **d.** $(w + 6)(w - 2)$
3. a. $(x + 9)(x + 2)$ **b.** $(y + 7)(y + 1)$
c. $(x + 6)(x - 3)$ **d.** $(z + 6)(z - 1)$
e. $(c + 6)(c - 2)$ **f.** $(a + 10)(a + 2)$
g. $(g - 8)(g - 3)$ **h.** $(b - 9)(b - 1)$
i. $(p - 14)(p + 2)$ **j.** $(a - 3)(a - 4)$
k. $(x + 8)(x - 1)$ **l.** $(d - 12)(d - 1)$
m. $(m - 4)(m - 5)$ **n.** $(w - 8)(w - 4)$
o. $(x - 3)(x - 2)$ **4. a.** $2(t - 9)(t - 1)$
b. $5x\,(x - 3)(x - 1)$ **c.** $3\,(x - 4)(x + 6)$
d. $3a\,(a - 4)(a + 2)$ **e.** $y\,(x - 16)(x + 3)$
f. $-5\,(x + 3)(x + 2)$ **g.** $2mn\,(m - 3)(m - 4)$
h. $ab\,(ab - 3)(ab + 2)$ **i.** $xy\,(xy + 2)(xy - 4)$
5. a. $-3x$ **b.** $10y$ **c.** $4xy$ **d.** $-9xy$ **e.** $5ab$
f. 0 **g.** $5k$ **h.** $-24fg$ **i.** $-7xy$
6. a. $(x - 13)(x + 3)$ **b.** $(x + 16)(x - 3)$
c. $(x - 4)(x - 9)$ **d.** $(z - 21)(z - 2)$
e. $(y + 15)(y + 2)$ **f.** $-(a - 5)(a + 2)$
g. $(b - 4a)(b - 3a)$ **h.** $(c + 10d)(c + 5d)$
i. $(6b - 1)(4b - 1)$ **7. a.** $2x\,(x + 15)(x - 4)$
b. $x^2\,(x - 9)(x - 3)$ **c.** $2xy\,(3xy + 1)(6xy + 1)$
d. $3y^2\,(x - 12)(x + 2)$ **e.** $2xy\,(x + 3)(x + 14)$
f. $-2a\,(4a + 1)(8a + 1)$ **g.** $y^2\,(x + 8y)(x - 5y)$
h. $5xy\,(x + 6y)(x - y)$ **i.** $2xy\,(xy - 5)(xy - 2)$
8. a. $(2x - 1)(x - 8)$ **b.** $(2c + 7)(3c - 5)$
c. $2xy\,(2xy + 3)(xy - 1)$ **d.** $(3x - 4)(5x - 12)$
e. $3\,(3z - 4)(3z + 8)$ **f.** $-a^2\,(a - 4b)(4a - b)$
g. $5xy\,(3x + 2)(7x - 12)$ **h.** $2x\,(5x - 6)(2x + 1)$
i. $2x\,(3xy + 1)(3xy + 4)$ **9. a.** $2x + 3$ **b.** $x - 4y$
c. $5xy - 4$ **d.** $4 - 3x$ **10. a.** $(x - y - 4)(x - y - 3)$
b. $(2x - 3y + 12)(2x - 3y - 4)$
c. $(y - 4)(y + 3)(y - 3)(y + 2)$ **d.** $(z + 3)(z - 3)$
e. $x\,(x - 7)$ **f.** $4(a + 2)(a - 4)$ **11. a.** $(x - 4)(x - 7)$
b. $(x + 24)(x - 2)$ **c.** $(2x - 1)(x + 6)$

Exercise 2–6, pages 41–43

1. a. $(5x)^2$ **b.** $(3a^3)^2$ **c.** not possible
d. $(7x^5y^6)^2$ **e.** $(8xy^2)^2$ **f.** $(6cd^2)^2$ **g.** $(5m^3n^4)^2$
h. $(4x^2y^5)^2$ **i.** not possible **j.** $(4x^3y^5)^2$
2. a. $(3x-7)(3x+7)$ **b.** $(8ab-1)(8ab+1)$
c. $(2c^4-5d^3)(2c^4+5d^3)$
d. $(9x^2+1)(3x+1)(3x-1)$
e. $(0.1x+0.5)(0.1x-0.5)$ **f.** $16(2x^2+1)(2x^2-1)$
g. $\left(\frac{5m}{4}-\frac{1}{2}\right)\left(\frac{5m}{4}+\frac{1}{2}\right)$ **h.** $\left(\frac{n}{2}-\frac{1}{3}\right)\left(\frac{n}{2}+\frac{1}{3}\right)$
i. $\left(\frac{2}{x}-1\right)\left(\frac{2}{x}+1\right)$ **j.** $\left(\frac{x^2}{y}-\frac{y}{x^2}\right)\left(\frac{x^2}{y}+\frac{y}{x^2}\right)$
3. a. $(7c-2)^2$ **b.** $(5x+3)^2$ **c.** $(3x-5y)^2$
d. $(2z-1)^2$ **e.** $(6xy+5)^2$ **f.** $(4-3xy)^2$
4. a. $2(5p-4)(5p+4)$ **b.** $4q^2(2q-3)(2q+3)$
c. $8x^2(2x-3)(2x+3)$ **d.** $5k(k-4l)(k+4l)$
e. $3xy(9x^2-25y)$ **f.** $4x^2(3xy-2)(3xy+2)$
5. a. $(x-y-7)(x-y+7)$
b. $(2x-3y-5)(2x-3y+5)$ **c.** $(x-8)(x+2)$
d. $(2h-6g-3)(2h-6g+3)$
e. $(7-10x-5y)(7+10x+5y)$ **f.** $5(6x+5)$
g. $(2r-11)(2r+1)$ **h.** $4(t-6)(t+1)$
i. $(2-x)(10+x)$ **j.** $(12-x^2+y)(12+x^2-y)$
k. $(w-2)(w+2)(w^2+2)$ **l.** $5(x-1)(9x+5)$
6. a. $(2x-3y-5)(2x+3y-1)$
b. $(3x-2y+6)(3x+2y+4)$ **c.** $16(x+1)(x-3)$
d. $3(x-y-1)(3x+3y-13)$ **e.** $(x-8)(7x-6)$
f. $24(x^2+1)(x+1)(x-1)$ **g.** $4(x+3)(4x-5)$
h. $15(x-3)(x+3)$ **i.** $(x+2)(x-2)(x^2-2x+4)$
7. a. $3(7a-5)^2$ **b.** $5x(9x-2)^2$ **c.** $2xy(4xy+7)^2$
d. $2f^2(5f+2g)^2$ **e.** $3xy^2(2x^2-3y)^2$
f. $4y^2(9y+1)(y+4)$ **g.** $3x(4x-3)^2$
h. $2(2m^3-9n)^2$ **i.** $4y^2(2x-3)^2(2x+3)^2$
8. a. $5x-4$ **b.** $2x-7$ **c.** $9x-2y$ **d.** $2x-5y$
9. a. 441 **b.** 1764 **c.** 961 **d.** 841 **e.** 324
10. a. $4x^2-12xy+9y^2-25$
b. $9x^2+30x+25-4y^2$ **c.** $64-x^2+2xy-y^2$
d. $4x^2-4xy+y^2-z^2+8z-16$
11. a. $(2x-1)(2x+1)(2x-3)(2x+3)$
b. $(3xy-1)^2(3xy+1)^2$
c. $(x-3)(x-4)(x+3)(x+4)$ **d.** $(2x+3)^2(2x-3)^2$
e. $4(x-1)(x-3)(x-4)$ **f.** $4(x-2)(x+1)(x+3)$
g. $(3x+1)^3(3x-1)$ **h.** $(x-3y)(x+3y)(x-7y)^2$
i. $(1-4x)(1+4x)^3$
j. $(3x+1)(3x+2)(-3x+2)(3x-1)$
12. a. $(4x^2-9)^2$ **b.** $3x(3x^2+1)^2(3x^2-1)^2$
c. $\left(\frac{1}{2}\right)(x-1)(25x-1)$ **d.** $(x-1+3y)^2$
e. $4(x-3)^2$ **f.** $(y^2-y-8)(y^2-y+8)$
g. $(y-4)^2(y-3)(y+3)$
h. $4(3y^2-4y+14)(3y-7)(y+2)$ **13.** $12x-20$
14. $10\pi x+8\pi$ **15.** $2x-3$

Extra, page 43

In going from line 4 to line 5 there is an error. Since $x = y$, then $(x-y) = 0$, and the right side of the equation in line 4 cannot be divided by it as shown.

Exercise 2–7, page 44

1. a. $a-3$ **b.** $x-4$ **c.** y^2-y+1
d. $4m^2+6m+9$ **e.** $16x^2-4x+1$
f. $4t^2-6st+9s^2$ **g.** $16-4a^2+a^4$
h. $16x^2+4xy^2+y^4$
2. a. $(5x-1)(25x^2+5x+1)$
b. $(y-2)(y^2+2y+4)$ **c.** $(1-3a)(1+3a+9a^2)$
d. $(2b^2+3)(4b^4-6b^2+9)$
e. $(xy-2)(xy+2)(x^2y^2+2xy+4)(x^2y^2-2xy+4)$
f. $(5-2d)(25+10d+4d^2)$
g. $(a^2+b^2)(a^4-a^2b^2+b^4)$
h. $(4mn-3)(16m^2n^2+12mn+9)$
i. $(2x^2y^2+5)(4x^4y^4-10x^2y^2+25)$
3. a. $3(2x^2+3)(4x^4-6x^2+9)$
b. $3y(3-y)(9+3y+y^2)$ **c.** $2(a-2)(4a^2+2a+7)$
d. $(5b-2c+6)(25b^2-20bc+4c^2-30b+12c+36)$
e. $3t^2(3-t)(9+3t+t^2)$ **f.** $9w(w^2-3w+9)$
g. $2(z-2)(13z^2-40z+31)$ **h.** $2y(27x^2+y^2)$
i. $(4a^2+3a-3b)(9a^2-12a^3-9ab+3b^2+16a^4)$

Exercise 2–8, page 47

1. a. $(2a-5)(3a-5)$ **b.** $(3y+4)^2$
c. $(2x-3)(2x+3)(3x-1)$ **d.** $4(m-2)(3n-7)$
e. $(2s-5)(2s-5-t)$ **f.** $3(3w-7)(w-3)$
2. a. $(2x-y-3)(2x-y+3)$ **b.** $4(a-6)(a+1)$
c. $(3c+5-5cd)(3c+5+5cd)$
d. $(2x-1)(2x+1)(10x^2-1)$ **e.** $-3(2ab-3)$
f. $(m-2)(m+2)(m-3)(m+3)$
3. a. $(2x-3)(x-5)$ **b.** $(5x+1)(3x-y)$
c. $(2t+1)(4s^2+9)$ **d.** $(b+4)(3a-c)$
e. $(2y-1)(5x-4)$ **f.** $(x^2-y)(y^2+x)$
4. a. $(2x-3-y)(2x-3+y)$
b. $(5x-y-7)(5x-y+7)$ **c.** $3(4+3y)(2-y)$
d. $(7y-2x+5)(7y+2x-5)$
e. $(5x+3z-8y)(5x+3z+8y)$
f. $(4z-2x+7)(4z+2x-7)$ **5. a.** $4(x-2)(3y+4)$
b. $(x-1)(x^2+4)$ **c.** $(y+3)(x-2)(x+2)$
d. $3x(x-5)(y+7)$ **e.** $(2x-5)^2(2x+5)$
f. $(x-3y)(x-3y-3)$ **g.** $(x^2-7)(x-3)(x+3)$
h. $(x-1)(x^3+x^2-x-9)$
6. a. $(2x^2+3-4y)(2x^2+3+4y)$
b. $(4x^2-1+5y)(4x^2-1-5y)$
c. $(4-y-y^2)(y^2+y+4)$
d. $2(2p-3-7q)(2p-3+7q)$
e. $3a(b-5a+1)(b+5a-1)$
f. $(4x^2y^2+5x-9)(4x^2y^2-5x-9)$

7. a. $(x - 6)(x - 2)(x^2 - 8x - 12)$
b. $f^2(f - 1 + 4f^2)(f - 1 - 4f^2)$
c. $(3y - x^2y^2 + x)(3y + x^2y^2 - x)$
d. $(4 - w)(z^2 - z - 5)$ **e.** $(y - 5)(x - 5)(x + 4)$
f. $(2x - 5)(x - 1)(x^2 + x + 1)$
g. $(3a - 5b - 2c - 1)(3a - 5b + 2c + 1)$
h. $(m - 3n - 2pq + 3)(m - 3n + 2pq - 3)$
8. a. $(x - \sqrt{5})(x + \sqrt{5})$ **b.** $(2x - \sqrt{3y})(2x + \sqrt{3y})$
c. $(\sqrt{6x} - 7)(\sqrt{6x} + 7)$ **d.** $(\sqrt{5x} - \sqrt{2})(\sqrt{5x} + \sqrt{2})$

Exercise 2–9, page 49

1. a. $\pm 18x$ **b.** $\pm 14y^2$ **c.** $\pm 84a^2b$
d. $\pm 88d^3c^4$ **e.** $\pm 72m^2n^3$ **f.** $\pm 16x^2yz$
2. a. $(x^2 + 2x + 3)(x^2 - 2x + 3)$
b. $(a^2 + 3ab + b^2)(a^2 - 3ab + b^2)$
c. $(m^2n^2 - 3 - 5mn)(m^2n^2 - 3 + 5mn)$
d. $(x^2 - 7xy - 3y^2)(x^2 + 7xy - 3y^2)$
e. $(3c^2 - 6cd - 2d^2)(3c^2 + 6cd - 2d^2)$
f. $4(2p^2 + 6pq + q^2)(2p^2 - 6pq + q^2)$
3. a. $(x^2 - 5x - 7)(x^2 + 5x - 7)$
b. $(y^2 - 2y + 8)(y^2 + 2y + 8)$
c. $(g^2 + 6g + 2)(g^2 - 6g + 2)$
d. $(z^2 - 2z - 9)(z^2 + 2z - 9)$
e. $(a^2b^2 + 5ab + 3)(a^2b^2 - 5ab + 3)$
f. $(j^2k^2 + 2jk + 7)(j^2k^2 - 2jk + 7)$
4. a. $(2x^2 + 4x - 3)(2x^2 - 4x - 3)$
b. $(3x^2 - x + 5)(3x^2 + x + 5)$
c. $(x^2 + 2x + 2)(x^2 - 2x + 2)$
d. $(8x^2 - 4x + 1)(8x^2 + 4x + 1)$
e. $(x - 2)(x + 2)(4x - 1)(4x + 1)$
f. $(5x^2 - 5xy - 3y^2)(5x^2 + 5xy - 3y^2)$
g. $(2x^2 - 7xy^2 + 7y^4)(2x^2 + 7xy^2 + 7y^4)$
h. $(8x^2 - 4xy - y^2)(8x^2 + 4xy - y^2)$
i. $(3c - d)(3c + d)(2c - 3d)(2c + 3d)$
j. $(2x + 3y)^2(2x - 3y)^2$
k. $(5x^2 - 3x + 3)(5x^2 + 3x + 3)$
l. $(x + 5)()x - 5)(x + 2)(x - 2)$
5. a. 64 **b.** 16 **c.** $4y^8$ **d.** $25y^6$ **e.** $36y^8$
f. $64y^2$ **6. a.** $(x^4 - 5x^2 - 1)(x^4 + 5x^2 - 1)$
b. $(3x^4 - 5x^2 + 5)(3x^4 + 5x^2 + 5)$
c. $(4x^4 - 2x^2y - y^2)(4x^4 + 2x^2y - y^2)$

Factoring Problems, page 50

1. The shaded region is $(a \times a) - (b \times b)$, therefore area is $a^2 - b^2$ which equals $(a + b) \times (a - b)$.
2. The set contains integers that are not prime numbers or are prime numbers but cannot be written in the form $4x + 1$ where $x \in \mathbf{Z}$.
3. $$\begin{aligned}(m^2 + n^2)^2 - (m^2 - n^2)^2 &= (m^2 + n^2 - m^2 + n^2)\\ &\quad(m^2 + n^2 + m^2 - n^2)\\ &= (2n^2)(2m^2)\\ &= (2mn)^2\end{aligned}$$
$$\therefore (2mn)^2 + (m^2 - n^2)^2 = (m^2 + n^2)^2$$
4. c. 784

6. $$\begin{aligned}&100^2 - 99^2 + 98^2 - 97^2 + 96^2 - 95^2 + \ldots + 2^2 - 1^2\\ &= (100 + 99)(100 - 99) + (98 + 97)(98 - 97) +\\ &\quad(96 + 95)(96 - 95) + \ldots + (2 + 1)(2 - 1)\\ &= (100 + 99)(1) + (98 + 97)(1) +\\ &\quad(96 + 95)(1) + \ldots + (2 + 1)(1)\\ &= 100 + 99 + 98 + 97 + 96 + 95 + \ldots + 2 + 1\end{aligned}$$
7. Let the integers be x, $x + 1$, $x + 2$, and $x + 3$.
$$\begin{aligned}&(x)(x + 1)(x + 2)(x + 3)\\ &= (x(x + 3))((x + 1)(x + 2))\\ &= (x^2 + 3x)(x^2 + 3x + 2)\\ &= (x^2 + 3x + 1 - 1)(x^2 + 3x + 1 + 1)\\ &= (x^2 + 3x + 1)^2 - 1\end{aligned}$$

Review, page 51

1. a. degree 5 **d.** degree 2 **2. a.** $10t - 27$
b. $4x^4 - 2x^3 - 30x^2$ **c.** $75m - 210m^2 + 147m^3$
d. $5v^2 - 11v - 7$ **e.** $15x^3 - 13x^2 + 5x - 2$
f. $-23y^2 + 16y + 1$ **3. a.** $7x^2(1 - 4x)$
b. $5xy^2(3x^2y - 5z)$ **c.** $-4y^2z(x^4 + 2yz + 3xz)$
d. $y^2z^3(x^5y^2 + 7x^3y - 28)$ **4. a.** $2x^3 - x^2 + 3x$
b. $4x^4y - 2y^2 + 3x$ **c.** $2x^3 - x^2 + x - 2$
d. $x^3 - 2x - 10 - \dfrac{15}{x-3}$ **e.** $3x^2 - 6x + 1$
f. $2x^3 - 5x^2 + 4x - 1$
5. a. All combinations of $2 \bullet 2 \bullet 3 \bullet 3 \bullet a$
b. All combinations of $2 \bullet 2 \bullet 2 \bullet 2 \bullet 3 \bullet x \bullet x$
c. All combinations of $2 \bullet 2 \bullet 3 \bullet 5 \bullet m \bullet n$
d. All combinations of $2 \bullet 5 \bullet 5 \bullet w \bullet w \bullet y$
e. All combinations of $2 \bullet 7 \bullet x \bullet x \bullet x \bullet y \bullet y$
6. a. $(x - 2)(x - 9)$ **b.** $(3b + 8)(2b - 3)$
c. $(x - 6)(x + 6)(x - 1)(x + 1)$ **d.** $3(5r - 4)(5r + 4)$
e. $(7t - 3)^2$ **f.** $(x - 2)(x + 2)(x - 3)(x + 3)$
g. $(w - 8)(w + 2)$ **h.** $5(n - 2)(2n - 3)$
i. $(x - y)(2x - 3)$ **j.** $(2x - 5)(2x - 9)$
k. $4(1 + x)(6 - x)$ **l.** $(3x - 5 - 7y)(3x - 5 + 7y)$
7. a. $(3 - x)(9 + 3x + x^2)$ **b.** $(2x + 1)(4x^2 - 2x + 1)$
c. $(3a + 2b)(9a^2 - 6ab + 4b^2)$
d. $(5x^2 - 4y)(25x^4 + 20x^2y + 16y^2)$
e. $(3x - 5)(3x^2 - 9x + 7)$
f. $3(3x - 4y^3)(9x^2 + 12xy^3 + 16y^6)$
8. a. $(2 - 5x)(2 + 5x)$ **b.** $(3x - 1)(17x + 1)$
c. $(4x - 1)(x - 25)$ **d.** $5(3x + 8)(x + 1)$
e. $3(x - 5)(x - 2)$ **f.** $12x(2x - 1)(2x + 1)$
g. $(5x - 3)(2y + 7)$ **h.** $(2x - 23)(2x - 13)$
i. $(5x - 3y - 4)(5x - 3y + 4)$ **j.** $-(2x + 1)(8x + 1)$
k. $3x(8x - 1)(3x - 4)$ **l.** $(6x + 5)(2x - 9)$
m. $3(3x - 5)(x - 3)$ **n.** $(x - 5)(x + 5)(x - 1)(x + 1)$
o. $(x - 4)(x + 4)(x - 2)(x + 2)$ **p.** $(y + 2)^2(y - 2)$
q. $(9x^2 - 2y)(9x^2 - 2y)$
r. $(x - 1)(x + 1)(y - 1)(y + 1)$

Exercise 2–10, page 53

1. a. $x \neq -\frac{7}{2}$ **b.** $x \neq 10$ and $x \neq 2$

c. $x \neq \frac{5}{3}$ and $x \neq 0$ **d.** $x \neq 0$ and $x \neq \pm 1\frac{2}{5}$

e. $x \neq \frac{5}{6}$ **f.** $x \neq 7y$ and $x \neq -3y$

2. a. $\frac{2}{t+5}$, $t \neq -5$ and $t \neq 3$

b. $\frac{x-5}{x-2}$, $x \neq 2$ and $x \neq -5$

c. $\frac{y-4}{2y-1}$, $y \neq -\frac{1}{2}$ and $y \neq 4$

d. $\frac{x-3}{3(x+3)}$, $x \neq -3$, $x \neq 0$, and $y \neq 0$

e. $-\frac{x+5}{x+3}$, $x \neq -3$ and $x \neq 5$

f. -5, $x \neq \frac{3}{2}$

3. a. $\frac{4b-1}{b+9}$ **b.** $\frac{6m-1}{2m-3}$ **c.** $\frac{3(v-3)}{2v+5}$

d. $\frac{x+5}{2(x+1)}$ **e.** $\frac{x-y}{2x-y}$ **f.** $\frac{7y-3x}{7y+3x}$

g. 1 **h.** $\frac{-(x-9)}{x+5}$ **i.** $\frac{11-x}{x+6}$

4. a. $\frac{y-1}{x-3}$, $x \neq 3$; $y \neq -\frac{4}{3}$ **b.** $y-1$, $y \neq -1$

c. $\frac{1}{x+1}$, $x \neq -1$, $x \neq 0$, and $x \neq 7$

d. $\frac{1}{x+3}$, $x \neq -3$, $x \neq 3$, and $y \neq -3$

e. $\frac{x-5}{2x+1}$, $x \neq -\frac{1}{2}$, and $x \neq 3y$

f. $\frac{x+2y}{x}$, $x \neq -y$, $x \neq 2y$, and $x \neq 0$

5. a. $\frac{2y-5x+1}{3xy}$ **b.** $\frac{3(2x^2-5)}{2(3x^2-1)}$ **c.** $\frac{x^2+3x+5}{x^2+5}$

d. $\frac{x-4}{x+4}$ **e.** $\frac{16x+9}{2(6x-7)}$ **f.** $\frac{(y+3)(x+2)}{2x}$

Using Your Calculator, page 53

1. $1 242 000 **2.** $3400.41 **3.** $2.36 **4.** $94.46

Exercise 2–11, pages 54–55

1. a. $x \neq -5$ and $x \neq -3$

b. $y \neq 4$, $y \neq -1$, and $y \neq -\frac{3}{2}$ **c.** $a \neq 0$ and $a \neq \pm 4$

d. $k \neq -\frac{3}{2}$, $k \neq 1$, $k \neq 0$, and $k \neq -5$

2. a. $\frac{x-3}{x+4}$ **b.** $\frac{m-3}{m+3}$ **c.** $\frac{a-5}{a+2}$

d. $\frac{2x-1}{2x+1}$ **e.** $\frac{r(r-5)}{2(r+5)}$ **f.** $\frac{(c-1)(c+6)}{(c-6)(c+1)}$

3. a. $\frac{4-5b}{2b-1}$ **b.** $\frac{x+4}{2x}$ **c.** $\frac{x-4}{12x-5}$

d. 1 **e.** $\frac{4xy+9}{3y}$ **f.** $\frac{4-x}{x+1}$

g. $6ab$ **h.** $\frac{-(3t-2)}{3t+2}$ **i.** 1

4. This is because the denominator factors into a pair of second degree polynomials with no x term, and no zero constants. The denominator cannot be zero for $x \in \mathbf{R}$.

5. a. $\frac{x+3}{x-3}$ **b.** $\frac{m+1}{m}$ **c.** $\frac{2x-3+7y}{2x-3}$

d. $\frac{-3(c-7)}{2(c+7)}$

6. a. $(x-a)(x+b)$, $x \neq \pm b$, and $x \neq -a$

b. $\frac{ax-2b}{ax+b}$, $x \neq \frac{-2b}{a}$, $x \neq \frac{-b}{a}$

Exercise 2–12, pages 58–59

1. a. $\frac{x+20}{24}$ **b.** $\frac{p+6}{20}$ **c.** $\frac{h+7}{12}$

d. $\frac{11x+7}{18}$ **e.** $\frac{17b+24}{60}$ **f.** $\frac{17a+37}{30}$

2. a. $5a^4b^3$ **b.** $24x^3y^4$ **c.** $6(c+5)(c-5)$

d. $(m-1)(m+1)(m+3)$

3. a. $\frac{10y-5x}{6xy}$ **b.** $\frac{3bc-4ac+5ab}{abc}$

c. $\frac{9xy^2y-14x^2y+25}{30x^3y^3}$ **d.** $\frac{12f^2+10ef-49}{28e^4f^3}$

e. $\frac{5t^2+7st-2s^2}{10st}$ **f.** $\frac{x-13}{8x}$

4. a. $\frac{x+23}{x^2+x-20}$ **b.** $\frac{-b^2-5b}{b^2+5b+6}$

c. $\frac{6}{x-5}$ **d.** $\frac{3}{y-3}$ **e.** $\frac{x-27}{x^2-9}$

f. $\frac{3d^2+17d-10}{d^2-25}$ **g.** 1 **h.** $\frac{-4x+3}{4x^2+2x}$

i. $\frac{15x^2+10x+2}{25x^2+5x}$ **j.** $\frac{2x+4}{21x^2-7x}$

k. $\frac{-2k-30}{k^2-25}$ **l.** $\frac{10z-10}{6z^2-15z}$

5. a. $\frac{x^2-26x+17}{x^2-2x-15}$ **b.** $\frac{26x^2-4x-7}{12x^2-x-1}$

c. $\frac{-35x}{6x^2-x-1}$ **d.** 1 **e.** 0 **f.** 1

6. a. $\frac{12x^2+7x+15}{16x^2-25}$ **b.** $\frac{-4p^2+16p+11}{4p^2-9}$

c. $\frac{y-1}{3y-5}$ **d.** $\frac{4x^2+4x-1}{6x^2+13x-5}$

e. $\frac{3x^2+5}{2x^2-3x-5}$ **f.** $\frac{a^2-a-15}{4a^2-11a-3}$

7. a. $\frac{b^2-27b+2}{b^3-b^2-4b+4}$, $b \neq 1$, $b \neq \pm 2$, and $b \neq -3$

b. $\frac{2x}{x^2-1}$, $x \neq 0$, $x \neq -3$, $x \neq 1$, $x \neq -5$, and $x \neq -1$

c. $\frac{7}{z^2-z-12}$, $z \neq 4$, $z \neq 2$, and $z \neq -3$

d. 1, $x \neq \frac{3}{2}$, $x \neq \frac{2}{3}$, and $x \neq -\frac{1}{5}$

e. $\frac{8x}{3x-1}$, $x \neq \frac{1}{3}$, $x \neq \frac{2}{5}$, and $x \neq -5$

f. $\frac{-5g^2-5}{2g^2+7g-15}$, $x \neq \pm 5$ and $x \neq \frac{3}{2}$

8. a. $\frac{-8xy}{x^2-4y^2}$, $x \neq \pm y$ and $x \neq \pm 2y$

b. $\frac{2x^2+3xy+3y^2}{x^2-xy-6y^2}$, $x \neq 3y$, $x \neq \frac{y}{3}$, and $x \neq -2y$

9. a. $\frac{4c-11}{c^3-6c^2+11c-6}$ **b.** $\frac{41}{d^3-4d^2-27d+90}$

c. $\frac{x^2+6x+12}{x^3+9x^2+26x+24}$ **d.** $\frac{1}{n+1}$

e. $\frac{1+3x-2y}{xy-3x+2y-6}$

10. a. $a = 1, b = 2$ **b.** $a = 2, b = -1$

Extra, page 59

The pattern is the sum of the first n odd integers.
2809,4489

Exercise 2–13, page 61

1. a. 5 **b.** -3 **c.** 0 **d.** $12\frac{1}{2}$ **e.** 6 **f.** $\frac{25}{28}$

2. a. 6 **b.** 6 **c.** 1 **d.** $-1\frac{1}{6}$ **e.** $\varnothing$ **f.** $\frac{6}{7}$ **g.** $-\frac{1}{5}$

h. 1 **i.** 3 **3. a.** 4 **b.** -3 **c.** $\varnothing$ **d.** $\frac{2}{3}$ **e.** 0

f. $\varnothing$ **g.** 5 **h.** $4\frac{1}{2}$ **4. a.** $1\frac{1}{4}$ **b.** $\varnothing$ **c.** $1\frac{3}{5}$ **d.** 0

e. $\varnothing$ **f.** 6 **g.** $\varnothing$ **h.** $1\frac{5}{6}$ **5. a.** $-\frac{5}{8}$ **b.** $-1\frac{1}{5}$

c. 5 **d.** 10

Exercise 2–14, page 63

1. a. $\frac{7}{48}$ **b.** $\frac{7}{12}$ **c.** $\frac{2}{15}$ **d.** $-\frac{37}{60}$ **2. a.** $\frac{27}{44}$ **b.** $\frac{1}{8}$

c. -2 **d.** $\frac{5}{18}$ **3. a.** $\frac{1}{7}$ **b.** $\frac{15}{16}$ **c.** $\frac{8x-16}{7x-9}$

d. $\frac{x-17}{8-x}$ **4. a.** $\frac{7}{6x+5}$ **b.** $\frac{55}{8}$

c. $\frac{3x+y}{x^2+y^2}$ **d.** $-\frac{7}{12}$ **e.** $\frac{1}{x+1}$

f. $\frac{x-1}{2x+4}$ **g.** $\frac{4x-1}{2x+1}$ **h.** $\frac{4}{3x}$

5. a. $\frac{3-x}{3x-2}$ **b.** $\frac{3x^2-2x-4}{2x^2+3x+6}$ **c.** $\frac{12-2x}{5x+6}$

d. $\frac{-3x-5}{27x+4}$ **e.** $\frac{11-12y}{15-12y}$ **f.** $\frac{2x^2-3x-1}{11x+3}$

g. $\frac{4x^2-2x+5}{6x^2+2x-5}$ **h.** $\frac{-7x-4}{14x+2}$

6. a. $\frac{6}{3x+11}$ **b.** $-\frac{2x+1}{2}$ **c.** $\frac{-4x^2-13x}{3x-7}$

Exercise 2–15, pages 65–66

1. a. 3, -5 **b.** $-\frac{3}{2}, \frac{1}{3}$ **c.** 3, -5 **d.** 0, -3

e. 0, 3 **f.** 0, 2 **g.** 3, -5 **h.** $\frac{5}{2}, -\frac{3}{5}$ **i.** $-\frac{3}{5}, \frac{5}{3}$

2. a. 2, 6 **b.** ± 7 **c.** $\pm\frac{3}{2}$ **d.** $-9, -9$ **e.** $-14, 3$

f. 8, -1 **g.** $\pm\frac{8}{5}$ **h.** 10, -3 **i.** 4, -6

3. a. $x = 5, y = -3$ **b.** $\frac{3}{2}, -1$ **c.** $a = 3, b = -6$

d. $-\frac{5}{3}, -3$ **e.** $x = 2, y = 3$ **f.** $-\frac{1}{4}, -9$

g. $x = \frac{3}{2}, y = -\frac{1}{3}$ **h.** $\frac{3}{5}, 1$ **i.** $0, \frac{1}{5}$ **4. a.** $\frac{1}{6}, 4$

b. $\frac{1}{2}, 8$ **c.** $\frac{3}{5}, -\frac{5}{2}$ **d.** $\pm\frac{5}{4}$ **e.** $-4, \frac{15}{4}$ **f.** $\frac{5}{3}, \frac{5}{3}$

g. $\frac{1}{6}, \frac{1}{2}$ **h.** $0, \frac{7}{5}$ **i.** $\frac{3}{2}, 4$ **5. a.** 11, 3 **b.** 1, 6

c. 0, 3 **d.** 9, -3 **e.** $\frac{1}{7}, 1$ **f.** $\pm 5, \pm 2$ **g.** $0, -5, 3$

h. $0, \pm\frac{5}{3}$ **i.** $x = \frac{5}{3}, y = -\frac{1}{5}$ **j.** $\pm 1, \frac{3}{2}$ **k.** 14, -2

l. $x = \frac{1}{5}, x = \frac{4}{3}, y = 0$ **6. a.** $-2, 1$ **b.** $-4, 2$

c. $-1, -1$ **d.** $-2, -2$ **e.** $\varnothing$ **f.** $0, \frac{1}{12}$ **g.** 6

h. $0, \frac{1}{4}$ **i.** $\varnothing$ **7.** 20 m × 30 m **8.** 15 cm, 8 cm

9. 5 cm × 6 cm × 7 cm **10.** 130 m

11. a. $x = \pm 1, y = \pm 2$ **b.** $x = \pm 3, \pm 2$

c. $x = \pm 5$ **d.** $x = \pm\frac{3}{2}, \pm 2$ **e.** $x = 0, \frac{5}{4}, 5$

f. $x = \pm 2, \pm 3$ **12. a.** 3, 5 **b.** 6, -12

c. $-1, -9$ **d.** 8, -4 **e.** 9, -11 **f.** 0, -12

g. $\frac{1}{2}, -\frac{3}{2}$ **h.** $\frac{5}{3}, -\frac{1}{3}$ **i.** 1, -3

Historical Note, page 66

$5 = 4 + 1$
$13 = 9 + 4$
$17 = 16 + 1$
$29 = 25 + 4$
$37 = 36 + 1$
$41 = 16 + 25$

Historical Note, page 67

1. $a^5 + 5a^4b + 10a^3b^2 + 10a^2b^3 + 5ab^4 + b^5$
2. $a^6 + 6a^5b + 15a^4b^2 + 20a^3b^3 + 15a^2b^4 + 6ab^5 + b$

Review, pages 68–69

1. a. $17x - 3$ **b.** $48x^2 - 120x + 75$
c. $6x^3y^4 + 12x^4y^4 - 9x^3y^6$ **d.** $10x^2 + 29x - 21$
e. $14x^2 - 8x - 67$ **f.** $2xy^3 - 3y^2 + 4xy$
g. $2x^3 + x^2 - 2x - 3$ **h.** $3x^2 + 6x - 1$
2. a. $A = 10x^2y^2 - 9xy - 9$, $P = 14xy$
b. $P = 5x^2y + x^2 - xy^2 - y^2$
c. $A = 15x^2 - 31x + 14$ **d.** $A = 2x^2 + 3x + 1$
3. a. $5(2a + 3)(2a - 3)$
b. $(5x - 7y + 2)(5x + 7y - 2)$ **c.** $(25x - 1)(x - 1)$
d. $(3b + 8)(10b - 3)$ **e.** $(3w^2 - 7)^2$
f. $3(x - 2)(3x - 1)$
g. $(y + 5)(\sqrt{3}x + 1)(\sqrt{3}x - 1)$ **h.** $(6m - 5)^2$
i. $4(k - 3)(3k + 2)$ **j.** $3(2x - 5y)(x + 2y)$
k. $(4xy - 1)(xy + 2)$ **l.** $2s^2(9t + 1)(1 - 2t)$

4. a. $4(x + 2y)(x^2 - 2xy + 4y^2)$
b. $8(2k^2 - 1)(4k^4 + 2k^2 + 1)$
c. $(m - 5)(7m^2 + 2m + 7)$
d. $(3d + 5cb^2)(9d^2 - 15cb^2d + 25c^2b^4)$

5. a. $\frac{2x}{x+6}$, $x \neq -3$ and $x \neq -6$

b. $\frac{8+x}{x+6}$, $x \neq 2$ and $x \neq -6$

c. $\frac{x-8}{x+4}$, $x \neq 6$, $x \neq -3$, $x \neq 4$, and $x \neq -4$

d. $\frac{x+14}{x+8}$, $x \neq 2$, $x \neq 10$, $x \neq -8$, and $x \neq -1$

e. $\frac{x}{2y}$, $x \neq 5$, $x \neq -3$, $y \neq 0$, and $y \neq 3$

f. $\frac{(2x+1)(2x-5)}{(2x+17)(x+1)}$, $x \neq \pm 3$, $x \neq -1$, $x \neq \frac{5}{2}$, and $x \neq -\frac{17}{2}$

6. a. $\frac{-x-17}{24}$ **b.** $\frac{-2y-22}{y^2+6y+5}$

c. $\frac{25w-6z+7}{10z^3w^3}$ **d.** $\frac{-x+23}{x^2+x-20}$

e. $\frac{-3x-7}{9x^2-1}$ **f.** $\frac{-20h}{h^2-25}$

g. $\frac{2r^2+12r+10}{r^2-2r-15}$ **h.** $\frac{12}{x-3}$

7. a. $x^2 - 3x + 5$ **b.** $y + 3$ **c.** $2x - 6 + 4y$
d. $3x^2 + 3$ **8. a.** 2 **b.** $\frac{1}{12}$ **c.** -2 **d.** $\varnothing$ **e.** 6
f. $-4\frac{1}{2}$ **9. a.** $\frac{17}{27}$ **b.** $\frac{x+10}{15x+3}$ **c.** $5x - 1$

10. a. 0, 3 **b.** $\frac{5}{3}$, -2 **c.** 0, $-\frac{4}{3}$ **d.** 8, 1
e. 0, $\pm\frac{6}{5}$ **f.** 13, 3 **g.** 3, 9 **h.** $\frac{4}{3}$, $-\frac{2}{5}$ **i.** ± 4, ± 1

11. 5 m × 12 m **12.** 7 cm, 24 cm
13. 11 m × 11 m, 12 m × 8 m

Test, page 70

1. a. $2t^2 - 12t - 3$ **b.** $-5x - 20$
c. $6a^3b^3 + 4a^3b^2 - 2a^2b$ **d.** $15m^2n^2 - 5mn$
e. $2x^2 - 7xy + 3y^2$ **f.** $2w^3 - w^2 + 3$
g. $4x^3 - 2x^2 - 5x + 2$ **h.** $10x^2 - 12xy - 33y^2$
2. a. $(x - 12)(x - 2)$ **b.** $(6q - 5)(q + 3)$
c. $4x^2(3y - 2)(3y + 2)$ **d.** $(5xy - 4)^2$
e. $4(7 - s)(s - 2)$ **f.** $(3v - 7)(3v + 7)(v - 1)(v + 1)$
g. $(5xy - 3)(4x + 3y)$ **h.** $(7x - 3y - 7)(7x - 3y + 7)$
3. a. $4x^2 + 2y^2 + 8$ **b.** $15x^2 + xy - 2y^2$
c. $6x^2 + 9x + 20$

4. a. $\frac{x+4}{x-5}$ **b.** $\frac{-2x}{3x+5}$ **c.** $\frac{x+7}{3}$

d. $\frac{4x-1}{4x+1}$ **e.** $\frac{x-10}{15}$ **f.** $\frac{2x-1}{3x-5}$

g. $\frac{-2x-1}{x^2+x-30}$ **h.** $\frac{2x-25}{x^2-9}$ **i.** $3x + y$

j. $\frac{x-3}{11x+1}$

5. a. 0, 3 **b.** $\frac{3}{2}$, $-\frac{5}{2}$ **c.** 1, $-\frac{1}{6}$ **d.** 2, $-\frac{4}{3}$
e. $\frac{5}{4}$ **f.** $\pm\frac{2}{3}$, $\pm\frac{1}{2}$ **g.** 0, $-\frac{1}{2}$, 5 **h.** $\frac{11}{4}$, $\frac{1}{4}$
6. 5, 12, 13 **7.** 12 m × 18 m

Cumulative Review, page 71

1. a. 6 **b.** 13 **c.** 4 **d.** 3 **2. a.** ab^{-3} **b.** xy^3
c. a^5 **d.** y^{-7} **3. a.** -3 **b.** 5 **c.** -5 **d.** 3
e. $2\frac{1}{3}$ **f.** -4

4. a. Let x be the size of a program. $x \leq 600$
b. Let x be any mark in the class. $42 \leq x \leq 97$
c. Let x be his reading speed. $x \leq 400$
d. Let x be the flowspeed of the river. $5 \leq x \leq 15$
e. Let x be the temperature of the fire. $200 < x < 500$ **f.** Let x be any length that cannot be accurately measured by the ruler. $x < 1$ or $x > 30$ **5. a.** 2:29
b. $x \geq 20.69$ cm, $y \geq 27.59$ cm **6.** 5 cakes/h

7. a. $-\frac{1}{3} \leq x \leq 3$ **b.** $x > \frac{3}{2}$ **c.** $x \geq \frac{3}{2}$ or $x < 1$
d. $x \geq \frac{1}{6}$ or $x \leq -\frac{5}{6}$ **8.** \$100 000 **9.** 24 days

UNIT 3

Exercise 3–1, pages 74–75

1. a. $6x^8$ **b.** a^6b^3 **c.** $-10x^3y^4$ **d.** z^{-6}
e. $c^{-4}d^6$ **f.** $12m^3n^3$ **g.** $4x^2y$ **h.** $g^{-9}h^{-2}$

2. a. 7 **b.** 16 **c.** $2\sqrt{2}$ **d.** $5\sqrt{2}$ **e.** $5\sqrt{5}$
f. $5\sqrt{7}$ **g.** 13 **h.** $11\sqrt{3}$ **3. a.** $\sqrt{9} = 3$
b. $\sqrt[3]{125} = 5$ **c.** $\sqrt{0.25} = \frac{1}{2}$ **d.** $\sqrt{\frac{4}{9}} = \frac{2}{3}$

e. $\sqrt[3]{0.125} = \frac{1}{2}$ **f.** $\frac{1}{\sqrt{25}} = 0.2$ **g.** $\frac{1}{\sqrt{\frac{1}{49}}} = 7$

h. $\frac{1}{\sqrt[3]{\frac{8}{27}}} = \frac{3}{2}$ **4. a.** 64 **b.** 25 **c.** 8 **d.** 8

e. 27 **f.** 4 **g.** 0.001 **h.** 0.0016 **5. a.** $x^{\frac{3}{2}}$ **b.** $y^{\frac{5}{3}}$
c. $z^{\frac{3}{4}}$ **d.** m^2 **e.** a^2 **f.** $x^{\frac{1}{2}}$ **g.** $y^{\frac{4}{3}}$ **h.** $m^{\frac{3}{5}}$

6. a. $\sqrt[3]{7^2}$ **b.** $\sqrt{5^5}$ **c.** $\sqrt[4]{8^3}$ **d.** $\sqrt[5]{a^4}$ **e.** $\sqrt[3]{x^4}$
f. $\sqrt{x}$ **g.** $\sqrt{3^3}$ **h.** $\sqrt[4]{6^3}$ **7. a.** 9 **b.** 9 **c.** $2^{\frac{7}{2}}$
d. $3^{\frac{5}{2}}$ **e.** $2^{\frac{1}{2}}$ **f.** $3^{\frac{1}{2}}$ **g.** $2^{\frac{3}{2}}$ **h.** $5^{\frac{1}{2}}$

9. a. 10 **b.** 2 **c.** 21 **d.** 12 **e.** 3 **f.** 11 **g.** 44 **h.** 5 **10. a.** $\frac{3}{4}$ **b.** $\frac{3\sqrt{5}}{2\sqrt{6}}$ **c.** $\frac{2}{5}$ **d.** $\frac{625}{256}$ **e.** $\frac{3}{5}$ **f.** 3125 **g.** 0.064 **h.** 0.25 **11. a.** 8 **b.** $7^{\frac{1}{2}}$ **c.** $2^{\frac{5}{6}}$ **d.** $2^{\frac{13}{12}}$ **e.** $2^{\frac{7}{3}}$ **f.** $31^{\frac{1}{2}}$ **g.** $5^{\frac{1}{3}} \times 2^{\frac{1}{2}} \times x^{\frac{5}{6}}$ **h.** $3\sqrt{5}x^{\frac{5}{2}}$ **i.** $a^{\frac{5}{6}}$

Exercise 3–2, page 77

1. a. true **b.** true **c.** true **d.** false **e.** true **f.** false **g.** true **h.** false **i.** false **j.** false **k.** false **2. a.** $0.8\overline{3}$ **b.** $0.\overline{2}$ **c.** $0.\overline{36}$ **d.** $0.15\overline{3}$ **e.** 2.125 **f.** $0.\overline{428\,571}$ **g.** $-0.\overline{380\,952}$ **h.** -1.64

3. a, b, e, g, h, j, l **4. a.** $\frac{3}{5}$ **b.** $\frac{7}{25}$ **c.** $\frac{1}{16}$ **d.** $\frac{7}{9}$ **e.** $\frac{2}{9}$ **f.** $\frac{16}{45}$ **g.** $\frac{7}{33}$ **h.** $\frac{122}{999}$ **i.** $-\frac{316}{999}$ **j.** $\frac{217}{990}$ **k.** $\frac{27}{11}$ **l.** $\frac{3491}{99}$ **m.** $\frac{47}{90}$ **n.** $\frac{43}{198}$ **o.** $-\frac{282\,773}{90\,000}$ **p.** $-\frac{5777}{999}$ **5.** Answers may vary.

Extra, page 77

$x = 0.\overline{9}$
$10x = 9.\overline{9}$
$10x - x = 9.\overline{9} - 0.\overline{9}$
$9x = 9$
$x = 1$

Exercise 3–3, pages 80–81

1. a. $2\sqrt{7}$ **b.** $2\sqrt{14}$ **c.** $4\sqrt{2}$ **d.** $8\sqrt{2}$ **e.** $5\sqrt{10}$ **f.** $7\sqrt{3}$ **g.** $5\sqrt{6}$ **h.** $9\sqrt{7}$ **2. a.** $3\sqrt[3]{2}$ **b.** $2\sqrt[3]{25}$ **c.** 4 **d.** $4\sqrt[3]{2}$ **e.** $2\sqrt[3]{3}$ **f.** $5\sqrt[3]{2}$ **g.** $\frac{1}{2}$ **h.** $0.1\sqrt[3]{2}$

3. a. $\sqrt{20}$ **b.** $\sqrt{147}$ **c.** $\sqrt{150}$ **d.** $\sqrt{28}$ **e.** $\sqrt{1.5}$ **f.** $\sqrt{500}$ **g.** $\sqrt{320}$ **h.** $\sqrt{200}$ **4. a.** $\sqrt[3]{135}$ **b.** $\sqrt[3]{48}$ **c.** $\sqrt[3]{-375}$ **d.** $\sqrt[3]{24}$ **e.** $\sqrt[3]{686}$ **f.** $\sqrt[3]{-500}$ **g.** $\sqrt[3]{384}$ **h.** $\sqrt[3]{-192}$ **5. a.** $\sqrt{41}$ **b.** $25\sqrt{15}$ **c.** $4\sqrt{5}$ **d.** $4\sqrt{13}$ **6. a.** $\frac{\sqrt{5}}{5}$ **b.** $\frac{\sqrt{7}}{7}$ **c.** $3\frac{\sqrt{2}}{2}$ **d.** $5\frac{\sqrt{6}}{6}$ **e.** $\frac{\sqrt{2}}{4}$ **f.** $\frac{\sqrt{6}}{3}$ **g.** $\frac{\sqrt{2}}{14}$ **h.** $\frac{\sqrt{10}}{10}$ **i.** $\frac{\sqrt{10}}{5}$ **j.** $\frac{\sqrt{21}}{7}$ **k.** $\frac{\sqrt{10}}{2}$ **l.** $\frac{\sqrt{2}}{2}$ **7. a.** $6\sqrt{3}$ **b.** $3\sqrt{7}$ **c.** $5\sqrt{2} + 4\sqrt{5}$ **d.** $5\sqrt{10} - 4\sqrt{6}$ **e.** $4\sqrt{2}$ **f.** $7\sqrt{3}$ **g.** $4\sqrt{3} + 6\sqrt{2}$ **h.** $2\sqrt{21} + 26\sqrt{3}$ **i.** $2\sqrt{6} - \sqrt{10}$ **j.** $8\sqrt{7} + 8\sqrt{5}$ **8. a.** $\sqrt{2x^2}$ **b.** $\sqrt{48m^3}$ **c.** $\sqrt{45a^5}$ **d.** $\sqrt{2x^3y^{-4}}$ **e.** $\sqrt{12m^5n^2}$ **f.** $\sqrt{49a^2bc^2}$ **g.** $\sqrt{75x^4y^{-1}z}$ **h.** $\sqrt{20a^3b^5c^{-1}}$ **9. a.** $\sqrt{3m^3}$ **b.** $\sqrt{12x^3y^2}$ **c.** $\sqrt[3]{40x^4}$ **d.** $\sqrt[3]{a^{-3}b^2c}$ **e.** $\sqrt[3]{-8a^3b^4}$ **f.** $\sqrt[3]{-54m^2n^5}$ **g.** $\sqrt[3]{-x^{-5}y^5z}$ **h.** $\sqrt[3]{250a^4b^2c^{-5}}$
10. a. $2xy\sqrt{7x}$ **b.** $2x^3y\sqrt{2y}$ **c.** $9x^5y\sqrt{y}$ **d.** $6m^3y\sqrt{2}$ **e.** $a^{-1}b^3y^2\sqrt{a^{-1}}$ **f.** $3m^2n^{-2}\sqrt{7mn^{-1}}$ **g.** $3x^{-1}y^{-2}\sqrt{3}$ **h.** $5m^3n^{-3}p^{-2}\sqrt{3mp^{-1}}$
11. a. $3xy\sqrt[3]{x^2}$ **b.** $2xy\sqrt[3]{2xy}$ **c.** $-2b^2\sqrt[3]{3ab}$ **d.** $mn^{-2}\sqrt[3]{n^{-2}}$ **e.** $-3x^{-1}y\sqrt[3]{2x^{-1}}$ **f.** $5abc^2\sqrt[3]{2a}$ **g.** $2m^{-1}n^{-1}\sqrt[3]{5m^{-1}n^{-2}p^2}$ **h.** $-y^{-1}z^{-1}\sqrt[3]{xy^{-2}z^{-1}}$
12. a. $2\sqrt{15}$ **b.** $5\sqrt{3}$ **c.** $3x\sqrt{2y}$ **d.** $7ab\sqrt{6}$ **e.** $2\sqrt{6}$ **f.** $2\frac{\sqrt{21}}{3}$ **g.** $\frac{\sqrt{2}}{2}$ **h.** $\frac{\sqrt{2x}}{4xy}$

13. a. $2\sqrt[3]{6}$ **b.** $2\sqrt[3]{25}$ **c.** $2a\sqrt[3]{3b^2}$ **d.** $2\sqrt[3]{5}$ **e.** $\frac{\sqrt[3]{100}}{15}$ **f.** $x\sqrt[3]{3}$ **14. a.** $3\frac{\sqrt{2}}{2}$ **b.** $7\frac{\sqrt{5}}{5}$ **c.** $6\frac{\sqrt{10}}{5}$ **d.** $\frac{\sqrt{2}}{2}$ **15.** $5\sqrt{106}$ m **16.** $30\sqrt{5}$ m

17. 0.24 mm **18.** Yes, but only when $a = a^2$ and $b = b^2$. So a and b must be either one of 1 or 0. **19. a.** $m\sqrt[6]{m}$ **b.** $\sqrt[15]{x^{14}}$ **c.** $a\sqrt[12]{a^5}$ **d.** $\sqrt[4]{b^3}$

Exercise 3–4, page 83

1. a. $3\sqrt{10}$ **b.** $21\sqrt{2}$ **c.** 9 **d.** $14\sqrt{2}$ **e.** $9 - \sqrt{3}$ **f.** $7 - 70\sqrt{2}$ **g.** $5\sqrt{6} - 5\sqrt{2}$ **h.** $18 + 6\sqrt{2}$
2. a. $-2 - 2\sqrt{5}$ **b.** $-1 - \sqrt{7}$ **c.** $14 - 7\sqrt{2}$ **d.** $-2 + 2\sqrt{5}$ **e.** -18 **f.** $15 + 12\sqrt{30}$ **g.** $3 - 14\sqrt{66}$ **h.** $15 - 4\sqrt{14}$ **i.** $32 + 6\sqrt{15}$
3. a. $1 + \sqrt{2}$ **b.** $3 - \sqrt{5}$ **c.** $2 + \sqrt{3}$ **d.** $4 - 2\sqrt{3}$ **e.** $\sqrt{5} - 2\sqrt{3}$ **f.** $3\sqrt{10} + 5$ **g.** $4\sqrt{7} + 3\sqrt{3}$ **h.** $2\sqrt{5} - \sqrt{13}$ **4. a.** -1 **b.** 4 **c.** 1 **d.** 4 **e.** -7 **f.** 65 **g.** 85 **h.** 7 **5. a.** $\frac{3\sqrt{5} - 3}{2}$ **b.** $\frac{5 + \sqrt{7}}{2}$ **c.** $8 - 4\sqrt{7}$ **d.** $4\sqrt{2} - 5$ **e.** $\frac{8\sqrt{3} + 6}{13}$ **f.** $5\sqrt{6} - 10$ **g.** $3\sqrt{3} + 4$ **h.** $4\sqrt{10} - 13$ **i.** $\frac{45 + 2\sqrt{6}}{23}$ **j.** $\frac{3 + 3\sqrt{3} - \sqrt{2} - \sqrt{6}}{7}$ **k.** $\frac{27 - \sqrt{15}}{42}$ **l.** $\frac{2\sqrt{15} - 9}{21}$
6. a. $\frac{\sqrt{x+1} - \sqrt{2}}{x - 1}$ **b.** $\frac{2\sqrt{x+3} + 2\sqrt{3}}{x}$ **c.** $\frac{x\sqrt{x+4} - x\sqrt{x}}{4}$ **d.** $-\sqrt{3} - \sqrt{y+3}$ **e.** $\frac{2\sqrt{x+y} + 2\sqrt{y}}{x}$ **f.** $\frac{5\sqrt{a} + 5\sqrt{a+b}}{-6}$ **g.** $\frac{m\sqrt{m+n} - m\sqrt{n}}{n}$ **h.** $\frac{3x\sqrt{x} + 3x\sqrt{y} - x}{2x - y}$ **i.** $\frac{(a-b)(\sqrt{a-b} - \sqrt{c})}{a - b - c}$ **7.** $\sqrt{2}$

8. a. $(x-\sqrt{2})(x+\sqrt{2})$ **b.** $(x-10\sqrt{10})(x+10\sqrt{10})$ **c.** $(x+\sqrt{5})^2$ **d.** $(y-\sqrt{3})^2$ **e.** $(a+2\sqrt{2})^2$ **f.** $(x+3\sqrt{7})(x+2\sqrt{7})$ **g.** $(x-2\sqrt{6})(x+\sqrt{6})$ **h.** $(m-\sqrt{5})(m-2\sqrt{5})$

Application, page 84
1. 0.25 m **2.** 0.04 m **3.** 8.52 m/s^2

Review, page 85
1. a. 16 **b.** 0.008 **c.** 243 **d.** 8 **2. a.** $\sqrt[3]{5^2}$ **b.** $\sqrt[4]{9^3}$ **c.** $\sqrt{7^3}$ **d.** $\sqrt[4]{8^3}$ **3. a.** $3^{3.2}$ **b.** $3^{2/3}$ **c.** $6^{2/3}$ **d.** $(5^{6/5}-5^2)^{1/4}$ **4. a.** 0.875 **b.** $1.\overline{4}$ **c.** $0.\overline{72}$ **d.** 1.416 **5. a.** $\frac{2}{25}$ **b.** $\frac{1}{16}$ **c.** $\frac{5}{33}$ **d.** $\frac{161}{495}$
6. Answers may vary.
7. a. $\sqrt{48}$ **b.** $\sqrt{150}$ **c.** $\sqrt{12}$ **d.** $\sqrt[3]{-135}$
8. a. $6\sqrt{2}$ **b.** 5 **c.** $5xy\sqrt{2x}$ **d.** $x^{-2}yz^2\sqrt{x^{-1}y}$ **e.** $x+1$ **f.** $3\sqrt[3]{10}$ **g.** $4xy^2\sqrt{3x}$ **h.** $2a^{-1}b\sqrt[3]{5a^{-2}b}$

9. a. $4\sqrt{6}$ **b.** $5\sqrt{3}$ **c.** $5\sqrt[3]{5}-3\sqrt[3]{2}$ **d.** $\frac{\sqrt{3}}{3}$

10. a. $18-2\sqrt{6}$ **b.** $70+15\sqrt{21}$ **c.** $10-\sqrt{2}$ **d.** $16\sqrt{3}+26$ **e.** $18-3\sqrt{15}$ **f.** 200 **g.** −33 **h.** −5 **11. a.** 2 **b.** −47 **c.** 1 **d.** 7

12. a. $\frac{\sqrt{6}}{2}$ **b.** $\frac{\sqrt{3}}{2}$ **c.** $-3\sqrt{2}-3$ **d.** $\frac{6-2\sqrt{2}}{7}$ **e.** $\sqrt{3}$ **f.** $\frac{17+7\sqrt{5}}{11}$ **g.** $6+\sqrt{14}$ **h.** $\frac{\sqrt{2}}{2}$

Exercise 3–5, page 87
1. a. 64 **b.** 9 **c.** 25 **d.** 16 **e.** no real solutions **f.** no real solutions **g.** 18 **h.** 3 **i.** 50 **j.** 25 **k.** no real solutions **l.** 25 **m.** no real solutions **n.** no real solutions **o.** 25 **p.** ±5 **2. a.** 8 **b.** 5 **c.** no real solutions **d.** 1 **e.** no real solutions **f.** 1 **3. a.** 4 **b.** 25 **c.** 10 **d.** $\pm 3\sqrt{2}$ **e.** 9, 5 **f.** 4, −2 **g.** 4 **h.** no real solutions **i.** 7 **4. a.** 8 **b.** 1 **c.** −15 **d.** −1 **e.** −2 **f.** 22 **g.** $\pm 2\sqrt{7}$ **h.** 48 **i.** −3 **5.** 3 m × 4 m × 5 m

Extra, page 87
1. 2 **2.** 3

Exercise 3–6, page 89
1. a. 9 **b.** 16 **c.** 25 **d.** 12, 3 **e.** 0 **f.** no real solutions **g.** 5 **h.** no real solutions **i.** 0, 8 **j.** 5

2. a. $\frac{10}{3}$ **b.** 6 **c.** 8 **d.** 5 **e.** 3 **f.** 2, 10

3. a. 5 **b.** $\frac{13}{4}$ **c.** 0, 10 **d.** 6 **e.** $\pm\frac{\sqrt{397}}{2}$

f. no real solutions **g.** 4 **h.** 16 **i.** 7 **j.** $2\pm\sqrt{10}$

k. $\frac{20}{3}$ **l.** no real solutions **m.** 5 **n.** 12 **o.** 9 **p.** 10 **4. a.** $R=\frac{GM}{V^2}$ **b.** $l=\frac{T^2g}{4\pi^2}$ **c.** $d=\frac{\sqrt{1-l^2f^2}}{f}$ **d.** $z=\left(\frac{rx}{x+r}\right)^2$ **5.** 4 m, 5 m

Exercise 3–7, page 91
1. a. 3^4 **b.** 5^3 **c.** 10^2 **d.** 2^{-4} **e.** $\left(\frac{1}{3}\right)^{-2}$ **f.** 10^{-3} **2. a.** 6 **b.** 5 **c.** 2 **d.** 5 **e.** 10 **f.** 7 **g.** 4 **h.** 3 **i.** 3 **3. a.** −3 **b.** −1 **c.** −4 **d.** −3 **e.** −4 **f.** −2 **g.** −3 **h.** −5 **i.** −4 **4. a.** 2 **b.** 8 **c.** 3 **d.** −1 **e.** −1 **f.** −1 **g.** −20 **h.** −6 **i.** −3 **5. a.** 2 **b.** 3 **c.** −2 **d.** 4 **e.** −3 **f.** −6 **g.** −21 **h.** −4 **i.** −4.5

6. a. $\frac{1}{2}$ **b.** $\frac{1}{2}$ **c.** $-\frac{1}{3}$ **d.** $\frac{2}{3}$ **e.** $-\frac{3}{2}$ **f.** $\frac{2}{3}$

7. b. 12.5 kPa **8. a.** 1.6×10^{16} J **b.** 7.1×10^{17} J, 1.5×10^{17} J

Application, page 93
1. a. 4 months **b.** 51 200 rabbits **c.** 4.43 years
d. no – carrying capacity of land
– development of predators
– disease
2. a. 6.25 mg **b.** less **c.** 35.2 years
3. a. 17 400 years **b.** 20% to 25%
4. a. 40 years, 46 years, 41 years, 39 years, 35 years, 32 years, 41 years, 32 years, 37 years, 35 years **b.** 28.9, 34.4, 41.0, 48.8

Review, pages 94–95
1. a. 27 **b.** 27 **c.** $\frac{1}{32}$ **d.** $\frac{125}{64}$ **2. a.** $\sqrt[4]{7^3}$ **b.** $\sqrt[3]{12^2}$ **c.** $\sqrt[5]{5^4}$ **d.** $\sqrt{11^3}$ **3. a.** $\sqrt[6]{3^7}$ **b.** 3 **c.** $\sqrt[6]{3^5}$ **d.** $\sqrt[4]{\frac{2}{5}}$ **4. a.** $4^{2.35}$ **b.** $2^{-2/3}$ **5. a.** $x^{2/3}$ **b.** $a^{3/4}$ **c.** $m^{6/5}$ **d.** z^2 **6. a.** $\frac{17}{25}$ **b.** $-\frac{1}{80}$ **c.** $\frac{4}{11}$ **d.** $\frac{119}{90}$ **7. a.** $\sqrt{45}$ **b.** $\sqrt[3]{-24}$ **c.** $\sqrt{3x^3y}$ **d.** $\sqrt[3]{-8a^4b^7}$ **8. a.** $3\sqrt{5}$ **b.** $2\sqrt[3]{2}$ **c.** $2xy^{-2}\sqrt{5x}$ **d.** $2x\sqrt[3]{9xy}$ **9. a.** $4\sqrt{6}$ **b.** $5\sqrt[3]{9}$ **c.** $\sqrt{\frac{x}{2}}$ **d.** $2\sqrt[3]{2}$ **e.** $2\sqrt{5}$ **f.** 5 **g.** $\frac{b}{3}$ **h.** $\sqrt[3]{9mn^2}$ **10. a.** $-4\sqrt{5}$ **b.** $3\sqrt{3}$ **c.** $\sqrt{5}+6\sqrt{2}$ **d.** $8\sqrt[3]{2}$ **11. a.** $2\sqrt{10}-5$ **b.** $6\sqrt{2}+36$ **c.** $3-\sqrt{3}$ **d.** $15-3\sqrt{10}+\sqrt{5}-\sqrt{2}$ **e.** $18+12\sqrt{2}$ **f.** $2\sqrt{3}+9\sqrt{2}-2\sqrt{6}-18$

12. **a.** −1 **b.** −11 **c.** 5 **d.** 19 **13. a.** $\frac{2\sqrt{5}}{5}$ **b.** $\frac{2\sqrt{5}-\sqrt{30}}{2}$ **c.** $\frac{5\sqrt{10}+32}{18}$ **d.** $\frac{2\sqrt{6}}{3}$

14. a. 25 **b.** 4 **c.** 19 **d.** −4, 1 **e.** 7 **f.** 514

15. a. 9 **b.** 9, 1 **c.** 4 **d.** $\frac{4}{7}$, 4 **e.** 5 **f.** 10

16. a. $E = \left(\frac{1}{2}\right)mv^2$ **b.** $I = \frac{m(a + b^2)^2}{12}$

17. a. 5 **b.** 6 **c.** −4 **d.** −2 **e.** 4 **f.** $\frac{4}{3}$ **g.** −1 **h.** 3 **i.** −6 **18. a.** $2\sqrt{3}$ **b.** $4\sqrt{5}$ **c.** $3\sqrt{11}$ **19. a. i.** 1×10^{-5} W/m² **ii.** 0.1 W/m² **iii.** 3.2×10^{-4} **b.** 180 dB

Test, page 96

1. a. 27 **b.** 0.0625 **c.** 125 **d.** $\frac{9}{4}$ **2. a.** $3\sqrt{2}$ **b.** 2 **c.** $\sqrt{7}$ **d.** $2\sqrt{2}$ **3. a.** $\frac{7}{20}$ **b.** $\frac{8}{11}$ **c.** $-\frac{34}{9}$ **d.** $\frac{107}{330}$ **4. a.** $\sqrt{44}$ **b.** $\sqrt[3]{-135}$ **c.** $\sqrt{x^5y^3}$ **d.** $\sqrt{12x^4y^5}$ **5. a.** $3\sqrt{10}$ **b.** $2\sqrt[3]{45}$ **c.** $2\sqrt{3}$ **d.** $3\sqrt[3]{2}$ **e.** $5\sqrt{2}$ **f.** $3\sqrt[3]{2}$ **g.** $x\sqrt{xy}$ **h.** $2b\sqrt[3]{2b^2}$

6. a. $13\sqrt{2}$ **b.** $\frac{25\sqrt{3}}{3}$ **c.** $3\sqrt[3]{2} - 2\sqrt{3} + 5\sqrt{2}$

7. a. $\frac{\sqrt{7}}{7}$ **b.** $\frac{\sqrt{3}}{6}$ **c.** $\frac{4\sqrt{10}}{5}$ **d.** $2 - \sqrt{3}$ **e.** $\frac{4 + \sqrt{6}}{2}$ **f.** $2\frac{\sqrt{5}}{5}$ **g.** $-2 - \sqrt{2}$ **h.** $\frac{17 + 4\sqrt{10}}{43}$

8. a. 8 **b.** 25 **c.** 5, −2 **d.** 4 **e.** 7 **f.** 8
9. a. 4 **b.** −2 **c.** 4 **d.** −3 **e.** 9 **f.** −4
10. a. \$8000 **b.** 33 years

Cumulative Review, page 97

1. a. $x^2 + 2xy - 4x + 4$ **b.** $6x + 5x^2 + 3y - 4$ **c.** $t^2 - 2t + 5$ **d.** $5x^4 + 6x^3 + 3x^2 + 3$
2. a. $5x^4 + 15x^3 + x^2 + 4x + 3$ **b.** $x^5 + 2x^4 + 2x^3 + 3x^2 + 2x + 2$ **c.** $x^3 + 13x^2 + 51x + 63$ **d.** $x^6 + x^4 + x^3 + x$ **e.** $5x^4 + 7x^3 - 15x - 21$ **f.** $x^6 + x^5 + 2x^4 + 5x^3 + 3x^2 + 6x + 6$

3. a. $x^2 + 4x - 2 + \frac{6}{x + 2}$ **b.** $x + \frac{1}{x}$ **c.** $x^2 - x + 2$ **d.** $x^4 + x^3 + x^2 + x + 1$ **4. a.** 3 **b.** 8 **c.** 2 **d.** 11, −12 **e.** $\frac{3}{8}, -\frac{5}{6}$ **f.** 4, −1

5. a. $(x + y)(x + 3)(x - 2)$ **b.** $(x - 3)(x^2 + x + 2)$ **c.** $4(3x^2 + 6x + 4)$ **d.** $(x + 1)(x^2 + 1)$

6. a. $\frac{(a + 2)(4a^2 + a + 1)}{(4a + 1)(a + 1)}$ **b.** $(a + 2)(a - 1)$

7. a. yes, 3 s **b.** 9 m **8.** 1684.2 km
9. a. 25 km/day **b.** 237.5 ha

UNIT 4

Exercise 4–1, pages 100–101

1. a. *C, G* **b.** *A* **c.** *B* **d.** *E* **2. a.** *x*-axis; *F* **b.** *y*-axis; *D* **3. a.** *C* **b.** *D* **c.** *F* **d.** *B*
4. a. *x*-intercept; 3 *y*-intercept; 2 **b.** *x*-intercept; −5 *y*-intercept; 4 **c.** *x*-intercept; 0 *y*-intercept; 0 **5. a.** −6 **b.** −2 **c.** $2\frac{1}{2}$ **d.** −3 **6. a.** 2; −6 **b.** 5; 4 **c.** 14; −2 **d.** −2; 4 **e.** −1; $-\frac{1}{3}$ **f.** 0; 0

9. a. (4, 2) **b.** (2, 1) **c.** (−2, 4) **d.** (2, −5)
10. a. \$250.00 **b.** 110 **11. a.** $y = 10x + 50$ **c.** $x \geq 0$ Animals cannot be kept for less than 0 days. **12. a.** $6x + 8y = 48$ **b.** $x = 8$ if Stephen bought only records, and $y = 6$ if he bought only tapes. **d.** 3
13. a. Let *x* be the number of courts booked in a year, and *y* be the total cost for the year. $y = 165 + 3.5x$ **c.** 32

Historical Note, page 101

$1^3 + 12^3 = 9^3 + 10^3 = 1729$

Exercise 4–2, page 103

1. a. 5 **b.** 4 **c.** $-\frac{9}{2}$ **d.** −1 **e.** $-\frac{5}{6}$ **f.** 0 **g.** $\frac{7}{3}$ **h.** undefined **i.** $\frac{6}{5}$ **2. a.** *c, e* **b.** *f* **c.** *b* **d.** *a, d*

3. $\overline{RS}$, $m = \frac{2 - 9}{5 - (-8)} = \frac{-7}{13}$

$\overline{SR}$, $m = \frac{9 - 2}{(-8) - 5} = \frac{7}{-13} = \frac{-7}{13}$

4. a. $\frac{4}{9}$ **b.** $\frac{13}{6}$ **7.** 0; 0 **8.** 1 **9.** (1, 5)
10. $(-6, -\frac{1}{5})$

12. An equation for the described line could be written, and then solved for the desired locations, or, let the unknown value be *n*, and develop an equation for slope using a known point and the unknown point, then solve for the unknown value, *n*. For exercise 9 let the point be (*n*, 5).

$\therefore m = \frac{-1 - 5}{8 - n} = \frac{-6}{8 - n}$ but $m = -\frac{6}{7}$

So $8 - n = 7$, and $n = 1$.

Exercise 4–3, pages 106–107

1. a. 8 **b.** $-\frac{2}{3}$ **c.** undefined **d.** 0 **2. a.** −3 **b.** undefined **c.** $-\frac{1}{5}$ **d.** $\frac{7}{2}$ **3. a.** parallel **b.** parallel **c.** perpendicular **d.** perpendicular
4. a. $\overline{AB}$: −1 $\overline{BC}$: 1 $\overline{AC}$: $-\frac{1}{13}$ **b.** $\angle ABC$
5. a., c. **6.** −2 **7.** −5 **8. a.** yes **b.** no **c.** yes **d.** yes **9.** $12\frac{1}{3}$ **10.** $\frac{1}{3}$ **11. a.** (4,0) **b.** (−1,0)
12. a. (0, 3) **b.** (0, 4)

13. slope of $\overline{AB} = \frac{1}{5}$; slope of $\overline{CB} = \frac{3}{2}$;
slope of $\overline{CD} = \frac{1}{5}$; slope of $\overline{AD} = \frac{3}{2}$
Opposite sides are parallel,
$\therefore$ $ABCD$ is a parallelogram

14. a. slope of $\overline{AB} = -\frac{3}{4}$; slope of $\overline{CD} = -\frac{3}{4}$
$\overline{AB}$ is parallel to $\overline{CD}$, $\therefore$ $ABCD$ is a trapezoid.
b. slope of $\overline{AB} = \frac{1}{3}$; slope of $\overline{CD} = \frac{1}{3}$
$\overline{AB}$ is parallel to $\overline{CD}$, $\therefore$ $ABCD$ is a trapezoid.

15. -40 16. $(10, -3)$, $(-2, -1)$ and $(-2, 5)$
17. $(-1, -8)$, and $(-5, -2)$ 18. 0, -6 19. $-\frac{4}{3}$
20. a. 7 b. $(4, -2)$
21. slope of $\overline{AC} = -1$; slope of $\overline{BD} = 1$
$\therefore$ The slopes of the diagonals are perpendicular.

Extra, page 107

Statement 4 is a direct result of 1 and 2.
Statement 6 is a direct result of statement 7.
Statement 1 is a direct result of statement 4.
Statement 2 is a direct result of statement 4.

Exercise 4–4, page 109

1. a. 13 b. 11 c. 4 d. 5 e. $\sqrt{41}$ f. $2\sqrt{26}$ g. 20 h. $\sqrt{221}$ i. $\sqrt{82}$ j. 5 k. $\sqrt{19}$ l. $2\sqrt{7}$
2. a. $\sqrt{61}$ b. $3\sqrt{5}$ c. $3\sqrt{13}$ 3. a. 5 b. 5 c. 13 d. 10 e. $3\sqrt{13}$ f. $2\sqrt{13}$ g. $\sqrt{65}$ h. $2\sqrt{13}$ i. $\sqrt{a^2 + b^2}$ j. $\sqrt{x_1^2 + y_1^2}$
4. $d = \sqrt{x_1^2 + y_1^2}$ 5. a. 30.7 b. 12.2 c. 35.8 d. 19.2 6. a. $AB = \sqrt{13}$ $BC = \sqrt{13}$ $AC = \sqrt{26}$
$AB^2 + BC^2 = 13 + 13 = 26 = AC^2$
$\therefore$ ABC is a right angled triangle.
b. $RS = \sqrt{41}$ $ST = 2\sqrt{41}$ $RT = \sqrt{205}$
$RS^2 + ST^2 = 41 + 164 = 205 = RT^2$
$\therefore$ $\angle RST$ is a right angled triangle.
7. a. $AB = 2\sqrt{10}$ b. $BC = \sqrt{10}$ $AC = 3\sqrt{10}$
b. Since $AB + BC = 2\sqrt{10} + \sqrt{10} = 3\sqrt{10}$, and $AC = 3\sqrt{10}$, then $AB + BC = AC$, and the points are collinear.
8. $PR = 10$ $RS = 5$ $PS = 15$ $PR + RS = PS$,
$\therefore$ R must be collinear with P and S.
9. a. $2q\sqrt{2}$ b. $\sqrt{16m^2 + 9n^2}$ c. x^2 d. $\sqrt{10a^2 + 32ab + 32b^2}$ 10. -2; 8 11. 1; 9
12. $GM = \sqrt{58}$ $MF = \sqrt{58}$
$\therefore$ Since $GM = MF$, M is the midpoint of $\overline{FG}$.

Exercise 4–5, page 111

1. a. $(5, 4)$ b. $(4, 4)$ c. $(6, 0)$ d. $(-1, -1)$ e. $(-\frac{1}{2}, \frac{1}{2})$ f. $(\frac{5}{2}, -1)$ g. $(9, \frac{3}{2})$ h. $(\frac{1}{2}, 3)$ i. $(\frac{5}{8}, \frac{1}{4})$
2. $a = -\frac{1}{2}$, $b = 23$ 3. $p = -7$, $q = \frac{1}{2}$
4. b. midpoint P of $\overline{AB}$, $(-2, 6)$
midpoint Q of $\overline{BC}$, $(-4, 0)$
c. slope of $\overline{PQ} = 3$; slope of $\overline{AC} = 3$
d. $PQ = 2\sqrt{10}$; $AC = 4\sqrt{10}$
e. $\overline{PQ} \parallel \overline{AC}$ and $AC = 2PQ$
f. Answers may vary. 5. $(-3, 3)$
6. a. $\left(\frac{a+c}{2}, \frac{b+d}{2}\right)$ b. $\left(\frac{-3a}{2}, \frac{11b}{2}\right)$ c. $(3x^2, 3x)$
7. a. slope of $\overline{AB} = -\frac{4}{3}$; slope of $\overline{BC} = \frac{2}{5}$
slope of $\overline{CD} = -\frac{4}{3}$; slope of $\overline{AD} = \frac{2}{5}$
$\therefore$ since opposite sides have equal slopes, the figure is a parallelogram.
b. midpoint of $\overline{AC}$, $\left(\frac{3}{2}, -2\right)$
midpoint of $\overline{BD}$, $\left(\frac{3}{2}, -2\right)$
$\therefore$ since the midpoints of the two diagonals are the same, the line segments bisect each other.
8. $(3x^2 - 3x, 2x^2 + 4x)$
9. a. $A\ (4, 3)$; $B\ (2, -2)$; $C\ (-4, -4)$; $D\ (-2, 1)$
b. slope of $\overline{AB} = \frac{5}{2}$; slope of $\overline{CD} = \frac{5}{2}$
slope of $\overline{AD} = \frac{1}{3}$; slope of $\overline{BC} = \frac{1}{3}$
$\therefore$ since opposite sides have equal slopes, the figure is a parallelogram.
10. a. slope of $\overline{AB} = -\frac{4}{3}$; slope of $\overline{CD} = -\frac{4}{3}$
slope of $\overline{AD} = \frac{3}{4}$; slope of $\overline{BC} = \frac{3}{4}$
$\therefore$ since opposite sides have equal slopes, the figure is a parallelogram.
But $\overline{AB}$ is perpendicular to $\overline{AD}$, so $ABCD$ is a rectangle.
b. $P\left(\frac{1}{2}, -1\right)$; $Q\ (6, 0)$; $R\left(\frac{17}{2}, 5\right)$; $S\ (3, 4)$
c. slope of $\overline{PQ} = \frac{2}{11}$ = slope of $\overline{RS}$
slope of $\overline{QR} = 2$ = slope of $\overline{SP}$
$PQ = \frac{5\sqrt{5}}{2} = QR = RS = SP$
since opposite sides have equal slopes and all four sides have the same length, $PQRS$ is a rhombus.

Exercise 4–6, pages 113–114

1. a. $\left(\frac{13}{2}, -\frac{5}{2}\right)$ b. $\left(-3, -\frac{9}{2}\right)$ c. $\left(\frac{11}{2}, -4\right)$ d. $(0, 0)$ 2. a. $(0, 9)$ b. $\left(5, -\frac{1}{5}\right)$ c. $(-5, 4)$ d. $(-4, 3)$ 3. a. 2:1 b. 1:3 c. 2:1
4. a. 1:2 b. 3:1 c. 1:2 5. a. $(-1, 2)$ b. $(-3, 2)$ c. $(1, 0)$ d. $(-3, 5)$ e. $(4, -1)$ f. $\left(-2, \frac{2}{3}\right)$ g. $\left(4, 3\frac{1}{2}\right)$ h. $(-2, -3)$

6. **a.** $\left(\frac{5}{8}, 2\right)$ **b.** $\left(\frac{25}{4}, -1\right)$ **c.** $\left(\frac{65}{8}, -2\right)$
d. $\left(\frac{5}{2}, 1\right)$ **e.** $\left(\frac{35}{8}, 0\right)$ **f.** $\left(\frac{-25}{8}, 4\right)$
g. $\left(1, \frac{9}{5}\right)$ **h.** $\left(4, \frac{1}{5}\right)$

7. $D(x, y) = \left(\frac{bx_1 + ax_2}{a+b}, \frac{by_1 + ay_2}{a+b}\right)$

8. **a.** $\left(0, 3\frac{2}{5}\right)$ **b.** $\left(1\frac{1}{7}, -1\right)$ **c.** $\left(-1\frac{11}{13}, 5\frac{3}{13}\right)$
d. $\left(-\frac{4}{9}, 4\frac{1}{3}\right)$ **9.** $L(0,0)$ $R(-3, -2)$

10. $q = -2; r = 0$ **11.** $s = -6; t = -5$

12. **b.** $L(-3, 2)$ **c.** $N(5,4)$ **d.** $\frac{1}{4}$ **e.** $\frac{1}{4}$
f. $\overline{YZ} \parallel \overline{LN}$

13. slope of $\overline{BC} = -\frac{1}{2}$; slope of $\overline{LN} = -\frac{1}{2}$
∴ since $\overline{BC}$ has the same slope as $\overline{LN}$, the two are parallel.

14. L divides $\overline{AB}$ and N divides $\overline{AC}$ in ratio $a:b$.
∴ $\overline{LN} \parallel \overline{BC}$ and $LN = \left(\frac{a}{a+b}\right)BC$

15. **a.** (10, 5) **b.** (7, 4)

Review, page 115

1. **a.** $x = 3; y = -4$ **b.** $x = 2; y = -4$
c. $x = -5; y = 1$ **d.** $x = 0; y = 0$
e. $x = -3$; no y – intercept
f. no x – intercept; $y = 4$

3. **a.** 13 **b.** $\frac{5}{12}$ **c.** $\left(3, \frac{7}{2}\right)$ **4.** $-\frac{17}{5}$

5. slope of $\overline{AB} = \frac{1}{4}$; slope of $\overline{BC} = \frac{3}{5}$
slope of $\overline{CD} = \frac{1}{4}$; slope of $\overline{AD} = \frac{3}{5}$
∴ since opposite sides have equal slopes, the figure is a parallelogram.

6. -23

7. $AB = 5$; $BC = 5\sqrt{5}$; $AC = 10$
$AB^2 + AC^2 = BC^2$, so $\triangle ABC$ is a right-angled triangle.
or slope of $\overline{AB} = \frac{3}{4}$; slope of $\overline{AC} = -\frac{4}{3}$
∴ since $\overline{AB}$ and $\overline{AC}$ are perpendicular, triangle ABC is right-angled.

8. $6\sqrt{2}$ **9.** $\left(1, -\frac{1}{2}\right)$

10. $AB = 5$; $BC = 5\sqrt{2}$; $AC = 5$
Two sides of the triangle are equal, so it is isosceles.

11. (0, 4) **12.** **a.** (6, 0) **b.** $\left(\frac{1}{2}, -1\right)$
c. $MB = \frac{5\sqrt{5}}{2}$; $MA = \frac{5\sqrt{5}}{2}$; $MC = \frac{5\sqrt{5}}{2}$

13. **a.** slope of $\overline{PQ} = -\frac{2}{7}$; slope of $\overline{QR} = \frac{3}{4}$
slope of $\overline{RS} = -\frac{2}{7}$; slope of $\overline{PS} = \frac{3}{4}$
∴ since opposite sides are parallel, the figure is a parallelogram.
b. the midpoint of $\overline{PR}$ $\left(\frac{5}{2}, \frac{3}{2}\right)$
the midpoint of $\overline{QS}$ $\left(\frac{5}{2}, \frac{3}{2}\right)$
The midpoints of the two diagonals are the same. So the segments bisect each other.

14. **a.** $C = 25 + 0.2d$ **c.** $40.00 **d.** 120 km

Exercise 4–7, pages 118–119

1. **a.** $x + 2y \geq 4$ **b.** $-3x + 4y \leq 12$ **c.** $y \geq 2x$
2. **a.** yes **b.** no **c.** no **d.** yes **e.** no **f.** yes
3. **a.** $x = 2; y = 8$ **b.** $x = 3; y = \frac{-15}{2}$
c. $x = 1; y = -7$ **d.** $x = -2; y = 1$
e. $x = -3; y = \frac{9}{2}$ **f.** $x = 0; y = 0$ **4.** **a.** $4x + y < 8$
b. $5x - 2y < 15$ **c.** $y > 7x - 7$ **d.** $y < \frac{1}{2}x + 1$
e. $3x + 9 > 2y$ **f.** $7x - 2y = 0$ **8.** **b.** 400 km
9. **a.** $0.08x + 0.09y > 260$ **10.** **a.** $10x + y < 20$
c. $\{10, 11, 12, \ldots, 19\}$ **11.** **a.** $6x + 5y \geq 3300$
b. $x \geq 0, y \geq 0, x, y \in \mathbf{Z}$ **12.** **a.** $7x + 3y = 63$
b. $x \geq 0, y \geq 0, x, y \in \mathbf{Z}$ **c.** 9 touchdowns, no field goals **d.** $7x + 3y > 63; x \geq 0, y \geq 0, x, y \in \mathbf{Z}$
13. **a.** $2l + 2w < 40$ **b.** $l > 0, w > 0$ **d.** 3 units by 16 units, and 4 units by 15 units, however, answers may vary.

Exercise 4–8, page 121

1. **a.** $-2, 4$ **b.** $-1, -6$ **c.** 5, 1 **d.** 0, 8
3. **a.** $y = -\frac{7}{5}x + 3$ **b.** $y = \frac{4}{5}x - 1$ **c.** $y = \frac{6}{5}x$
4. **a.** $y = 4x + 6$ **b.** $y = -3x + 5$ **c.** $y = -\frac{1}{3}x + \frac{1}{2}$
6. 8 **7.** **a.** 4 **b.** $-\frac{3}{5}$ **c.** $\frac{2}{7}$ **d.** $\frac{8}{3}$ **e.** undefined
f. 0 **8.** $y = 3x - 5$ **9.** **a.** $y = 4x$ **b.** $y = -5x$
c. $y = \frac{4}{5}x$ **d.** $y = -\frac{6}{7}x$ **e.** $y = 0$ **10.** **a.** 1
b. -3 **c.** $-\frac{1}{6}$ **d.** $-\frac{1}{5}$ **e.** $\frac{3}{4}$ **f.** $-\frac{4}{3}$
11. $y = -\frac{5}{6}x - 8$

Exercise 4–9, page 123

1. **a.** 3, 6, 6 **b.** 5, -2, -10 **c.** 1, -1, -6
d. 7, 1, -7 **e.** 0, 1, -3 **f.** 1, 0, 3 **g.** 4, -7, -28
h. 2, 1, -6 **i.** 6, -5, -30 **2.** **a.** (a) $-\frac{1}{2}$, -1
(b) $\frac{5}{2}$, -5 (c) 1, -6 (d) -7, 7 (e) 0, 3
(f) undefined, none (g) $\frac{4}{7}$, -4 (h) -2, 6

(i) $\frac{6}{5}$, -6 **4. a.** 7 **b.** -3 **c.** $\frac{1}{8}$ **d.** -2 **e.** $\frac{9}{4}$ **f.** $-\frac{5}{6}$ **5. a.** $-\frac{5}{4}$ **b.** $\frac{7}{2}$ **c.** -3 **d.** $\frac{1}{5}$ **e.** $-\frac{5}{9}$ **f.** $-\frac{1}{6}$ **6.** b, d **7.** c, d **8. a.** -2 **b.** -3 **c.** $a = 3$; $b = -2$ **9. b.** right-angled **10. a.** line parallel to x-axis **b.** line parallel to the y-axis **c.** line on the x-axis **d.** line on the y-axis

Exercise 4–10, pages 126–127

1. a. 3 (7, 8) **b.** -5 (-4, 3) **c.** $\frac{1}{4}$ (6, -2) **d.** $-\frac{7}{4}$ (-5, 5) **e.** $\frac{3}{2}$ (8, -1) **f.** $\frac{1}{6}$ (-1, 2)
2. a. $6x - y - 40 = 0$ **b.** $3x + y + 4 = 0$ **c.** $5x - y + 19 = 0$ **d.** $2x + y = 0$ **e.** $x - 2y - 4 = 0$ **f.** $3x + 4y - 7 = 0$ **g.** $7x - 6y - 29 = 0$ **h.** $2x + 5y + 3 = 0$ **i.** $2x - 3y - 21 = 0$ **3. a.** $y - 7 = 0$ **b.** $y - 9 = 0$ **c.** $y = 0$ **d.** $y + 2 = 0$ **e.** $5y + 6 = 0$
4. a. $x + 3 = 0$ **b.** $x - 6 = 0$ **c.** $x + 1 = 0$ **d.** $x + 3 = 0$ **e.** $x - 2 = 0$ **5. a.** $x - 4 = 0$ **b.** $y - 5 = 0$ **c.** $x - 7y + 61 = 0$ **d.** $6x + y + 19 = 0$ **e.** $x - 3y - 4 = 0$ **f.** $4x + 3y - 34 = 0$ **g.** $5x + 2y - 11 = 0$ **h.** $5x + 3y - 21 = 0$ **i.** $x - 5y = 0$ **j.** $x + 6y = 0$
6. $2x + 5y + 6 = 0$ **7.** $x - 5y + 53 = 0$
8. $6x + 7y - 43 = 0$ **9.** No. The slope of the line segment WT is 0, while the slope of the line is $\frac{3}{4}$.
10. $7x - 3y + 23 = 0$ **11.** $6x + 5y + 5 = 0$
12. a. $7x + 3y - 26 = 0$ **b.** $9x + 5y - 38 = 0$ **c.** $9x + 5y - 30 = 0$ **13.** $x + 2y - 13 = 0$
14. $x + y + 11 = 0$ **15.** $mx - y - ma = 0$
16. a. $4x + y - 32 = 0$ **b.** $3x - 4y + 21 = 0$ **c.** $3x + 6y - 2 = 0$ **d.** $14x + 2y + 35 = 0$
17. a. $(a, 0)$ $(0, b)$ **b.** $-\frac{b}{a}$ **c.** $bx + ay - ab = 0$
18. a. $4x + 3y - 12 = 0$ **b.** $5x + 6y + 30 = 0$ **c.** $3x - 4y - 2 = 0$ **d.** $20x + y + 4 = 0$

Exercise 4–11, pages 128–129

1. a. $2x - y + 4 = 0$ **b.** $2x + 5y - 30 = 0$ **c.** $13x - 5y - 111 = 0$ **d.** $6x - 5y - 15 = 0$ **e.** $11x - 10y + 4 = 0$ **f.** $4x - 5y = 0$ **g.** $4x - 3y - 1 = 0$ **h.** $32x - y - 18 = 0$ **i.** $bx - ay = 0$ **2.** $11x - 3y - 34 = 0$ $3x + 8y - 71 = 0$ $14x + 5y - 8 = 0$
3. a. (10, 2) **b.** $4x + 5y - 50 = 0$ **c.** $x - 2y - 6 = 0$ **4. a.** $8x - 5y + 26 = 0$ **b.** $\frac{74}{5}$
5. a. $3x - 5y - 15 = 0$ **b.** $3x + y + 3 = 0$ **c.** $2x + 3y - 1 = 0$ **d.** $4x - 12y - 3 = 0$
6. $11x - 3y - 82 = 0$ **7. a.** (7, -1) **b.** $x + 2y - 5 = 0$
8. a. slope of $\overline{AB} = -2$; slope of $\overline{CD} = -2$; slope of $\overline{BC} = \frac{2}{3}$ slope of $\overline{AD} = \frac{2}{3}$
∴ since opposite sides are parallel, the figure is a parallelogram.
b. $2x - 3y + 8 = 0$ **9. a.** $2x - y + 9 = 0$ $x - 11y - 27 = 0$ $3x + 2y - 11 = 0$ **b.** $5x + 8y - 9 = 0$ **c.** $x - y + 3 = 0$ **d.** $x - 4y + 15 = 0$ **10. b.** D (1, 3) **c.** E (3, 4) **d.** slope of $\overline{DE} = \frac{1}{2}$; slope of $\overline{BC} = \frac{1}{2}$

Exercise 4–12, pages 132–133

1. a. $\frac{1}{2}$ **b.** 2 **c.** $\frac{1}{3}$ **d.** $\frac{2}{3}$ **e.** 3 **f.** 5 **g.** $\frac{7}{3}$ **h.** $\frac{5}{3}$
2. a. $y = kx$ **b.** $r = kt$ **c.** $L = kx + b$ **d.** $Cost = k\,(mass) + b$ **e.** $I = kC^2$ **f.** $Distance = k\,(time) + b$
3 a. $y = \frac{5}{2}x$, direct variation **b.** $y = 3x + 2$, partial variation **c.** $y = \frac{5}{4}x + \frac{3}{2}$, partial variation **d.** $y = \frac{2}{3}x$, direct variation **e.** $y = \frac{3}{4}x$, direct variation **f.** $y = 5x + 1$, partial variation **g.** $y = \frac{1}{2}x + 3$, partial variation **h.** $y = \frac{6}{13}x + \frac{27}{130}$, partial variation
4. a. 20 **b.** 12.6 **c.** 24 **d.** 40 **e.** 400
5. 3.75 A **6. a.** 11.25 **b.** constant speed of car **c.** 112.5 m **7. a.** 41.67 L **b.** 8.33 L/100 km
8. \$6250
9. Fixed Cost = \$75.00 Meal Cost = \$6.00
10. 384 W **11.** 200.63 m **12. a.** $c = \frac{5}{2}n + 1200$ **b.** $h = \frac{6}{5}t + 18$ **13. a.** 33.3 m^2 **b.** 6 m
14. 125% **15.** a, b, c, f

Review, pages 134–135

1. a. 7, -14 **b.** 3, -6 **c.** $-\frac{4}{3}$, -4 **d.** $\frac{5}{2}$, -5
3. b. (4, -1) **5. a.** 6 **b.** 0 **c.** undefined **d.** -2 **e.** $\frac{5}{3}$ **f.** $\frac{5}{6}$
6. slope of $\overline{AB} = 2$; slope of $\overline{BC} = 2$
∴ B is collinear with $\overline{AC}$.
8. a. $y = 4x + 6$ **b.** $y = -9x - 5$ **c.** $y = \frac{2}{3}x + 3$ **d.** $x + 2y - 10 = 0$ **e.** $3x - y + 14 = 0$ **f.** $5x - 4y - 3 = 0$ **g.** $14x - 11y - 7 = 0$ **h.** $12x + 11y + 28 = 0$
9. a. $y = 8x + 19$ **b.** $y - 8 = 0$ **c.** $x - 7 = 0$ **d.** $4x + y - 2 = 0$ **e.** $8x - 5y - 46 = 0$ **f.** $4x - 3y = 0$ **g.** $2x - 3y - 12 = 0$ **10.** 3:2
11. $2x + y + 13 = 0$ **12. b.** $x + 3y - 23 = 0$ **c.** $x - 5y + 17 = 0$ **d.** $x - 3y + 7 = 0$

e. $3x - y + 1 = 0$
f. slope of $\overline{QR} = -3$; length of $\overline{QR} = 4\sqrt{10}$
slope of segment $= -3$
length of segment $= 2\sqrt{10}$
$\therefore$ the two segments are parallel, and the one joining the midpoints of the two sides is half that of $\overline{QR}$.
13. a. Let T be the total proceeds. $T = 5.5x + 4.5y$ **b.** $5.5x + 4.5y = 1640$
c. $x, y \geq 0, x, y \in \mathbf{Z}$ **d.** No, if no adults attended, then $\frac{1640}{4.5} = 364\frac{4}{9}$ students attended. A fraction of a student is clearly impossible.
14. a. $\frac{3}{8}$ **b.** $\frac{12}{7}$ **c.** $\frac{5}{2}$ **d.** $\frac{3}{2}$ **15. b.** $M(2, -5)$ $N(-1, 3)$ **c.** $AM = \sqrt{145}$, $CN = 2\sqrt{61}$ **d.** 2:1 **e.** 2:1 **16. b** $M(-1, 1)$ $N(1, 5)$ **c.** $AM = 15$ $CN = 3\sqrt{5}$ **d.** 2:1 **e.** 2:1 **b.** The intersection point of two medians of a triangle divides each median in the same ratio.

Test, page 136

2. a. $\frac{1}{3}, -5$ **b.** 3, 6 **c.** $-\frac{4}{7}, 4$ **3. a.** 0 **b.** undefined **c.** $\frac{4}{3}$ **d.** 1 **4.** $BE = 2$ $CD = 16$ $BC = 8\sqrt{2}$ **5. a.** $y + 3 = 0$ **b.** $x - 12 = 0$ **c.** $4x - 3y - 26 = 0$ **d.** $x - y = 0$
6. slope of $\overline{HJ} = -\frac{2}{3}$; slope of $\overline{JK} = -\frac{2}{3}$
Since the slopes are equal and there is a common point, J, then the three points are collinear.
7. a. 5 **b.** $4x + 3y - 8 = 0$
8. a. $8x - 9y - 12 = 0$ **b.** $5x - 3y + 16 = 0$ **c.** $9x + 8y - 86 = 0$ **9.** $(-4, 0)$ **10. b.** 4.5 The y-intercept represents the amount Cassie earns for delivering only the magazines. **c.** $10.50 **11.** 6.96 cm

Cumulative Review, page 137

1. a. $x^2 + 4x + 3$ **b.** $100x^2 - 81$ **c.** $2x^4 + x^3 - 4x^2 - 3x$ **d.** $2x + 1$ **e.** $x^3 + x + 5$ **f.** $x^3 + 2x^2 + 2x + 1 + \frac{x+1}{x^2+1}$
2. a. $3\sqrt{7}$ **b.** $12\sqrt{2}$ **c.** 32 **d.** $6\sqrt{114}$ **e.** $\sqrt{2341}$ **f.** $51\sqrt{3}$ **3. a.** -2; -1 **b.** $3\frac{4}{5}$ **c.** 21 **d.** $2\frac{1}{2}$ **e.** $\sqrt{3}$; $-\frac{1}{2}\sqrt{3}$ **f.** $\frac{3}{5}$ **4. a.** $x > 3$ **b.** $-2 \leq x \leq 1$ **c.** $w \leq 7$ **d.** $x \geq \frac{13}{5}$ or $x \leq 1$ **5. a.** 8 **b.** $\frac{1}{3}$ **c.** $\frac{1}{8}$ **d.** $\frac{1}{27}$ **e.** $\sqrt[3]{36}$ **f.** 9 **6. a.** 5 weeks **b.** 2 weeks **c.** 3 more weeks **7.** about 17.1 min
8. a. $74.08 **b.** $91.57 **c.** 1991 **9. a.** 0.15% **b.** 0.01%

UNIT 5

Exercise 5–1, pages 140–141

1. a., b., c., e.
2. a. down, $(-1, 2)$, $x = -1$ **b.** up, $(1, 0)$, $x = 1$ **c.** up, $(-1, -4)$, $x = -1$ **d.** down, $(-1, 3)$, $x = -1$ **e.** up, $(-2, 1)$, $x = -2$ **f.** up, $(-1, -2)$, $x = -1$
3. $(-2, 12)$, $y = 3x^2$
5. a. up, $x = 0$, $(0, 0)$, min $y = 0$
b. up, $x = 0$, $(0, 0)$, min $y = 0$
c. up, $x = 0$, $(0, 0)$, min $y = 0$
d. up, $x = 0$, $(0, 0)$, min $y = 0$
e. up, $x = 0$, $(0, 0)$, min $y = 0$
f. down, $x = 0$, $(0, 0)$, max $y = 0$
g. down, $x = 0$, $(0, 0)$, max $y = 0$
h. down, $x = 0$, $(0, 0)$, max $y = 0$
i. down, $x = 0$, $(0, 0)$, max $y = 0$
6. a. up, $(0, 1)$, $x = 0$, min $= 1$
b. up, $(0, -3)$, $x = 0$, min $= -3$
c. up, $(0, 4)$, $x = 0$, min $= 4$
d. down, $(0, 1)$, $x = 0$, max $= 1$
e. down, $(0, -2)$, $x = 0$, max $= -2$
f. up, $(0, 1)$, $x = 0$, min $= 1$
7. a. yes **b.** yes **c.** no **d.** yes **e.** no **f.** yes
8. a. $(-4, 5)$, $(-3, 0)$, $(-2, -3)$, $(-1, -4)$, $(0, -3)$, $(1, 0)$, $(2, 5)$ **9. a.** $(0, 1.75)$, $(1, 6.85)$, $(2, 2.15)$, $(3, -12.35)$, $(4, -36.65)$, $(5, -70.15)$ **b.** t is time and must be greater than 0. h is height relative to the point of release since height of release was zero, height < 0 means the ball is on the ground.
d. 1.75 m **e.** 6.85 m
10. a. $r > 0$ **b.** $r > 0$ **12. a.** $(0, 0)$, $y = 0$ **b.** $(1, 0)$, $y = 0$ **c.** $(0, 3)$, $y = 0$

Exercise 5–2, pages 144–145

1. a. up **b.** down **c.** down **d.** up **e.** down **f.** up **2. a.** $y = 3x^2$ **b.** $y = -4x^2$ **c.** $y = \frac{1}{2}x^2$ **d.** $y = -x^2$ **e.** $y = -2x^2$ **f.** $y = 9x^2$
3. a. 4 right, 3 up **b.** 1 right, 2 down **c.** 7 left, 5 down **d.** 1 left, 6 up **e.** 3 right **f.** 7 up **4.** no **5. a.** $(4, 3)$ **b.** $(1, -2)$ **c.** $(-7, -5)$ **d.** $(-1, 6)$ **e.** $(3, 0)$ **f.** $(0, 7)$
6. a. i $x = 4$ **ii** y min $= 3$ **b. i** $x = 1$ **ii** y min $= -2$ **c. i** $x = -7$ **ii** y min $= -5$ **d. i** $x = -1$ **ii** y min $= 6$ **e. i** $x = 3$ **ii** y min $= 0$ **f. i** $x = 0$ **ii** y min $= 7$
7. a. k up $k > 0$ **b.** h right $h > 0$ **c.** (h, k) **d.** $x = h$ **e.** y min $= k$ $a > 0$ **8. b.** $(3, 2)$ **c.** $x = 3$ **d.** min $= 2$
9. a. $(2, -1)$, $x = 2$, min $= -1$
b. $(-4, -2)$, $x = -4$, max $= -2$
c. $(1, 0)$, $x = 1$, min $= 0$ **d.** $(3, 0)$, $x = 3$, max $= 0$
e. $(-2, 0)$, $x = -2$, max $= 0$
f. $(-1, 3)$, $x = -1$, min $= 3$
g. $(-3, -1)$, $x = -3$, max $= -1$

h. $(-4, -3)$, $x = -4$, min $= -3$
i. $(2, -1)$, $x = 2$, max $= -1$ **11. a.** $y = 2(x-2)^2$
b. $y = 2(x+3)^2$ **c.** $y = 2x^2 - 5$
d. $y = 2(x+1)^2 + 4$ **e.** $y = 2(x-3)^2 - 1$
12. $y = 4x^2 - 2$ **13.** $a = 1$ **14.** $a = 3$ $b = 1$
15. $a = -3$ $b = 2$
16. a. $y = x^2 + 2$ **b.** $y = x^2 - 1$
c. $y = x^2 - 4x + 4$ **d.** $y - 2 = \frac{2}{9}(x-1)^2$ or
$y = \frac{2}{9}(x-1)^2 + 2$ **e.** $y = 2(x-1)^2 - 2$
f. $y = 2(x+2)^2 + 2$
17. a. $y = -2x^2$ **b.** $y = -x^2 - 1$ **c.** $y = -\frac{1}{2}x^2$
d. $y = -\frac{1}{25}(x-2)^2 - 1$ **e.** $y = -2x^2 + 2$
f. $y = -(x-3)^2 + 1$

Exercise 5–3, page 148
1. a. $x = 0$, $(0, -5)$, min $= -5$
b. $x = 0$, $(0, 1)$, min $= 1$ **c.** $x = 3$, $(3, 0)$, min $= 0$
d. $x = -1$, $(-1, 4)$, min $= 4$
e. $x = 2$, $(2, -1)$, min $= -1$
f. $x = -3$, $(-3, -2)$, max $= -2$ **2. a.** $x^2 - 6x + 9$
b. $x^2 + 10x + 25$ **c.** $x^2 - 14x + 49$
d. $x^2 + 8x + 16$ **e.** $3x^2 - 6x + 3$
f. $-2.5x^2 + 30x - 90$ **3. a.** 9 **b.** 25 **c.** $\frac{25}{4}$
d. $\frac{49}{4}$ **e.** 4 **f.** 1 **4. a.** $(4, 3)$ **b.** $(1, -2)$
c. $(-1, 6)$ **5. a.** $(x-3)^2 - 2$ **b.** $(x+5)^2 - 40$
c. $\left(x - \frac{5}{2}\right)^2 - \frac{13}{4}$ **d.** $2(x-3)^2 - 15$
e. $3\left(x - \frac{3}{2}\right)^2 - \frac{31}{4}$ **f.** $5\left(x - \frac{4}{5}\right)^2 - \frac{16}{5}$
6. a. $y = 2(x-1)^2 + 3$, parabola, opens upward
b. $y = -\left(x - \frac{5}{2}\right)^2 - \frac{3}{4}$, parabola, opens downward
c. $y = (x+3)^2 - 10$, parabola, opens upward
d. $y = -4(x+1)^2 + 7$, parabola, opens downward
e. $y = \frac{1}{2}(x-1)^2 - \frac{1}{2}$, parabola, opens upward
f. $y = -\frac{1}{2}(x-5)^2 + \frac{25}{2}$, parabola, opens downward
g. $y = -2\left(x + \frac{3}{2}\right)^2 + \frac{3}{2}$, parabola, opens downward
h. $y = \left(x + \frac{1}{2}\right)^2 + \frac{7}{4}$, parabola, opens upward
i. $y = 3\left(x + \frac{3}{2}\right)^2 - \frac{11}{4}$, parabola, opens upward
7. a. $(1, 3)$, $x = 1$, min $= 3$
b. $\left(\frac{5}{2}, -\frac{3}{4}\right)$, $x = \frac{5}{2}$, max $= -\frac{3}{4}$
c. $(-3, -10)$, $x = -3$, min $= -10$
d. $(-1, 7)$, $x = -1$, max $= 7$
e. $\left(1, -\frac{1}{2}\right)$, $x = 1$, min $= -\frac{1}{2}$
f. $\left(5, \frac{25}{2}\right)$, $x = 5$, max $= \frac{25}{2}$
g. $\left(-\frac{3}{2}, \frac{3}{2}\right)$, $x = -\frac{3}{2}$, max $= \frac{3}{2}$
h. $\left(-\frac{1}{2}, \frac{7}{4}\right)$, $x = -\frac{1}{2}$, min $= \frac{7}{4}$
i. $\left(-\frac{3}{2}, -\frac{11}{4}\right)$, $x = -\frac{3}{2}$, min $= -\frac{11}{4}$
8. $y = (x-3)^2 + 4$ **9.** $y = -3(x+1)^2 - 10$
10. b. 6.6 s **c.** 218 m

Review, page 149
2. a. $(4, 5)$, $x = 4$ **b.** $(-5, -6)$, $x = -5$
c. $(2, 0)$, $x = 2$ **d.** $(-2, 11)$, $x = -2$ **3. a.** $a > 0$
b. $a < 0$ **c.** $b = c = 0$ **d.** $c = -5$ **4. a.** $c = \frac{19}{4}$
b. $c = 5$ **5. a.** $y = -(x+1)^2 + 2$
b. $y = \frac{1}{2}(x+1)^2 - 2$ **c.** $y = 2(x+1)^2 - 4$
6. a. $y = (x+3)^3$, $(-3, 0)$, min $= 0$, $x = -3$
b. $y = -\left(x - \frac{1}{2}\right)^2 + \frac{47}{4}$, $\left(\frac{1}{2}, \frac{47}{4}\right)$, max $= \frac{47}{4}$, $x = \frac{1}{2}$
c. $y = 2\left(x + \frac{3}{2}\right)^2 - \frac{9}{2}$, $\left(-\frac{3}{2}, -\frac{9}{2}\right)$, min $= -\frac{9}{2}$,
$x = -\frac{3}{2}$ **d.** $y = (x+4)^2 - 4$, $(-4, -4)$, min $= -4$,
$x = -4$ **e.** $y = 3(x+1)^2 + 4$, $(-1, 4)$, min $= 4$,
$x = -1$ **f.** $y = 2\left(x - \frac{1}{4}\right)^2 - \frac{81}{8}$, $\left(\frac{1}{4}, -\frac{81}{8}\right)$,
min $= -\frac{81}{8}$, $x = \frac{1}{4}$ **g.** $y = \left(x + \frac{3}{2}\right)^2 + \frac{27}{4}$,
$\left(-\frac{3}{2}, \frac{27}{4}\right)$, min $= \frac{27}{4}$, $x = -\frac{3}{2}$
h. $y = -2(x-1)^2 - 1$, $(1, -1)$, max $= -1$, $x = 1$
7. $x = -4$ **8.** $x = 2$ **9.** $y = -\frac{1}{2}(x+3)^2 + 5$
10. a. 8.85 m **b.** 1.22 s **c.** 2.57 s

Exercise 5–4, pages 151–152
1. a. $x = -6$, $x = 4$ **b.** $x = 3$, $x = 8$
c. $x = -4$, $x = -8$ **d.** $x = 0$, $x = -\frac{2}{3}$
e. $x = 0$, $x = -\frac{8}{5}$, $x = \frac{3}{2}$ **f.** $x = 0$, $x = 6$, $x = -\frac{4}{5}$
2. a. $x = -1$, $x = 7$ **b.** $x = -8$, $x = 2$
c. $x = 3$, $x = 9$ **d.** $x = -8$, $x = -6$
e. $x = 1 + \sqrt{2}$, $x = 1 - \sqrt{2}$ **f.** no real number solution **g.** $x = -5$, $x = 3$ **h.** undefined in real number system **i.** $x = 3 + \frac{\sqrt{35}}{7}$, $x = 3 - \frac{\sqrt{35}}{7}$

3. a. $x = 7, x = -4$ **b.** $x = 4, x = 5$ **c.** $x = 1, x = 8$
d. $x = 0, x = -9$ **e.** $x = \frac{7}{3}, x = \frac{-4}{5}$ **f.** $x = -1, x = \frac{5}{3}$
g. $x = \frac{1}{4}, x = \frac{-2}{3}$ **h.** $x = \frac{5}{2}, x = \frac{3}{7}$ **i.** $x = -3, x = -1$
4. a. none **b.** two **c.** one **5. a.** $x = 4, x = -3$
b. $x = -2, x = -6$ **c.** $x = 7, x = -5$
d. $x = 4, x = 9$ **e.** $x = 0, x = 4$ **f.** $x = 0, x = 2$
g. $x = -4, x = 4$ **h.** $x = -7, x = 7$
i. $x = -\frac{5}{8}, x = \frac{7}{2}$ **6. a.** $x = -1 + \sqrt{2}, x = -1 - \sqrt{2}$
b. $x = -1 + \sqrt{5}, x = -1 - \sqrt{5}$
c. $x = \frac{-3 + \sqrt{29}}{2}, x = \frac{-3 - \sqrt{29}}{2}$
d. no real number solution
e. $x = \frac{3 + \sqrt{11}}{2}, x = \frac{3 - \sqrt{11}}{2}$
f. $x = -\frac{3}{2} + \frac{\sqrt{23}}{2\sqrt{3}}, x = -\frac{3}{2} - \frac{\sqrt{23}}{2\sqrt{3}}$
g. $x = \frac{1 + \sqrt{11}}{2}, x = \frac{1 - \sqrt{11}}{2}$
h. $x = -2 + \sqrt{\frac{22}{5}}, x = -2 - \sqrt{\frac{22}{5}}$
i. $x = -\frac{3}{14} + \sqrt{\frac{37}{196}}, x = -\frac{3}{14} - \sqrt{\frac{37}{196}}$
7. a. $x = 2, x = -4$ **b.** $x = -3, x = 4$
c. $x = -3 + \sqrt{6}, x = -3 - \sqrt{6}$
d. $x = 1 + \sqrt{6}, x = 1 - \sqrt{6}$
e. $x = -\frac{1}{2} + \sqrt{\frac{3}{4}}, x = -\frac{1}{2} - \sqrt{\frac{3}{4}}$
f. $x = -1 + \sqrt{\frac{8}{3}}, x = -1 - \sqrt{\frac{8}{3}}$
g. $x = \frac{3}{4} + \sqrt{\frac{33}{16}}, x = \frac{3}{4} - \sqrt{\frac{33}{16}}$
h. no real number solution **i.** no real number solution **8.** $\left(\frac{1}{6}, -\frac{25}{12}\right), x = \frac{1}{6}$
9. a. $\left(\frac{9}{4}, -\frac{121}{8}\right), x = \frac{9}{4}$ **b.** $(2, -2), x = 2$
c. $\left(\frac{1}{2}, \frac{5}{4}\right), x = \frac{1}{2}$ **10. a.** two different roots
b. two equal roots **c.** no roots
11. $x = -17, x + 1 = -16 \quad x = 16, x + 1 = 17$
12. a. -1 **b.** $y = \frac{1}{3}(x - 2)^2 - 3$ **13.** $2x^2 + 2x + 1$

Maximum/Minimum Problems, page 153

1. 36 **2.** 5, 5 **3.** −3, 3 **4.** 10 m × 10 m **5.** $\frac{1}{2}$
6. $y = \left(x - \frac{1}{2}\right)^2 + \left(k - \frac{1}{4}\right)$ $k - \frac{1}{4}$ is a minimum
7. 25 m × 50 m, 1250 m^2 **8.** 9 m × 13.5 m, 121.5 m^2

Exercise 5–5, pages 155–156
1. a. $a = 2, b = -6, c = 4$ **b.** $a = 1, b = \frac{5}{3}, c = -6$
c. $a = -\frac{1}{2}, b = -1, c = 0$ **2. a.** $x = 2, x = -2\frac{1}{3}$
b. $x = \frac{3 + \sqrt{3}}{2}, x = \frac{3 - \sqrt{3}}{2}$
c. $x = \frac{1 + \sqrt{41}}{10}, x = \frac{1 - \sqrt{41}}{10}$
d. $x = 4 + 2\sqrt{3}, x = 4 - 2\sqrt{3}$
e. No real roots since $\sqrt{-31}$ is not real.
f. $x = \frac{-1 + \sqrt{57}}{4}, x = \frac{-1 - \sqrt{57}}{4}$
g. $x = 4 + \sqrt{14}, x = 4 - \sqrt{14}$
h. $x = \frac{7 + \sqrt{409}}{30}, x = \frac{7 - \sqrt{409}}{30}$
i. $x = 7, x = -1$
j. No real roots since $\sqrt{-23}$ is not real.
k. $x = \frac{-2 + \sqrt{46}}{7}, x = \frac{-2 - \sqrt{46}}{7}$
l. $x = \frac{-3 + \sqrt{57}}{12}, x = \frac{-3 - \sqrt{57}}{12}$
3. a. $x = 4$ **b.** $x = \frac{15 + \sqrt{321}}{-12}, x = \frac{15 - \sqrt{321}}{-12}$
c. $x = 2, x = -3$ **d.** no real number solution
e. no real number solution **f.** $x = \frac{1}{2}, x = -\frac{2}{3}$
g. $x = \frac{1 + \sqrt{7}}{6}, x = \frac{1 - \sqrt{7}}{6}$
h. $x = \frac{1}{2}, x = -\frac{1}{2}$ **i.** $x = 4, x = \frac{4}{3}$
4. a. no solution **b.** $x = 0.83, x = -2.83$
c. $x = 8.80, x = -0.80$ **5. a.** $\frac{6}{7}, -\frac{9}{7}$ **b.** $-\frac{5}{3}, \frac{4}{3}$
c. $-\frac{8}{3}, \frac{1}{3}$ **d.** $-\frac{5}{7}, -\frac{9}{7}$ **e.** 0, 1 **f.** $\frac{5}{2}, 3$
6. $x = -\frac{5}{4}, b = 6$ **7.** $\frac{2}{7}, a = 7$ **8. a.** $c = 0$
b. $b = 0$ **c.** $a + b + c = 0$ **d.** $a = c$
9. $(-1, -10)$; $x = -1$; x-intercepts: $-2.8, 0.8$; y-intercept: -7 **10.** $(2, 6)$; $x = 2$; x-intercepts: 0.3, 3.7; y-intercept: -2 **11.** $x^2 - \left(\frac{-b}{a}\right)x + \frac{c}{a} = 0$
12. a. $x^2 + 2x - 35 = 0$ **b.** $x^2 - 17x + 72 = 0$
c. $x^2 + 10x + 24 = 0$ **d.** $6x^2 - 5x + 1 = 0$
e. $x^2 + \sqrt{3}x - 6 = 0$ **f.** $x^2 - 36 = 0$
g. $x^2 - 7x + 9 - \sqrt{3} = 0$ **h.** $x^2 + 10\sqrt{2}x + 14 = 0$
13. $V\left(-\frac{b}{2a}, c - \frac{b^2}{4a}\right)$ $x = -\frac{b}{2a}$

Using the calculator, page 157
1. a. 2.07, −0.87 **b.** 1.09, −1.84 **c.** 0.18, −1.61
d. 2.75, −2.42 **e.** −2.00, 1.50 **f.** −1.79, −0.79
g. −0.98, 1.68 **h.** 0.38, −0.23 **i.** −1.31, 1.96

Exercise 5–6, page 159

1. a. 0, 1 distinct real root **b.** 216, 2 distinct real roots **c.** −127, no real root **d.** 177, 2 distinct real roots **e.** 36, 2 distinct real roots **f.** 16, 2 distinct real roots **2. a.** 2 **b.** 1 **c.** 2 **d.** 2 **e.** 1 **f.** 2 **3. a.** not possible **b.** ±20 **c.** 2.25 **d.** 49 **e.** ±4 **f.** 3 **4. a.** $k < \frac{-4}{9}$ **b.** $-4 < k < 4$ **c.** $k > 5$ **d.** $k < \frac{-9}{2}$ **e.** $-4 < k < 4$ **f.** $k > \frac{2}{3}$

5. a. $p < 1$ **b.** $p \epsilon \boldsymbol{R}$ **c.** $p > \frac{-4}{5}$ **d.** $p \epsilon \boldsymbol{R}$ **e.** $p > \frac{\sqrt{5}}{3}, p < -\frac{\sqrt{5}}{3}$ **f.** $p > -\frac{1}{32}$

6. $n > 2\sqrt{14}, n < 2\sqrt{14}$ **7.** $D = k^2 + 80$

Since $k^2 > 0$, then $D > 0$. Hence y will always intersect the x-axis when $k \epsilon \boldsymbol{R}$. **8.** ±48

9. $5\frac{1}{4}$, 5, $4\frac{7}{12}$, 4, $3\frac{1}{4}$, $2\frac{1}{3}$, $1\frac{1}{4}$, 0 **10.** $(2a + 3)^2 \geq 0, a \epsilon \boldsymbol{R}$

11. $\left(\frac{1}{2}, 5\frac{3}{4}\right)$

Exercise 5–7, pages 162–163

1. a. $y \leq -x^2 + 4x + 1$ **b.** $y < 2x^2 + 4x + 4$ **c.** $y = -\frac{1}{2}x^2 + x + \frac{5}{2}$ **d.** $y > 3x^2 - 18x + 23$ **e.** $y \leq \frac{1}{4}x^2 - 2x + 5$ **f.** $y \leq -\frac{1}{3}x^2 + 2x + 3$

4. a. $y > (x - 2)^2$ **b.** $y < -(x - 5)^2$ **c.** $y > 2\,(x - 4)^2$ **d.** $y < -\frac{1}{2}x^2 - 4$ **e.** $y > 2\left(x + \frac{1}{4}\right)^2 + \frac{31}{8}$ **f.** $y < -(x - 2)^2 + 6$ **g.** $y < -\frac{1}{2}(x + 4)^2 + 8$ **h.** $y > 4\left(x + \frac{1}{2}\right)^2 - 2$ **i.** $y < 2\left(x - \frac{3}{4}\right)^2 - \frac{7}{8}$ **5. a.** $y < -2x^2 - 8x - 6$ and $y > -6$ **b.** $y \geq (x - 3)^2 - 2$ and $y > 5$ **c.** $y > \frac{1}{3}(x - 1)^2 - 4$ and $x \geq 0$ **d.** $x \geq 5$ **e.** $y > \frac{1}{4}(x - 1)^2$ and $x \geq 0$ and $y < 5$ **f.** $x \leq 0$ and $y \leq 0$ and $y < -\frac{1}{5}(x + 2)^2 + 4$

6. a.

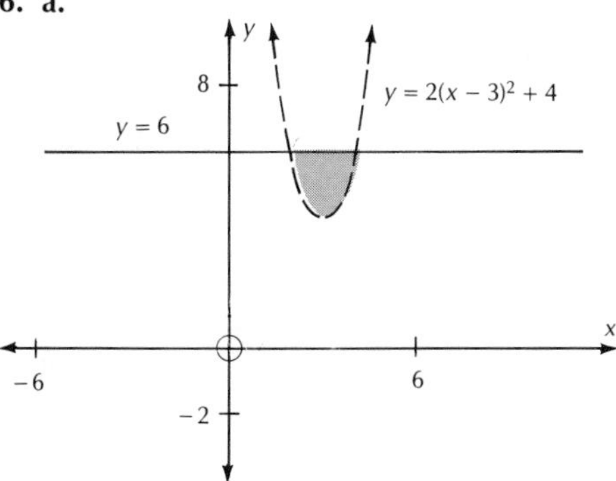

b.

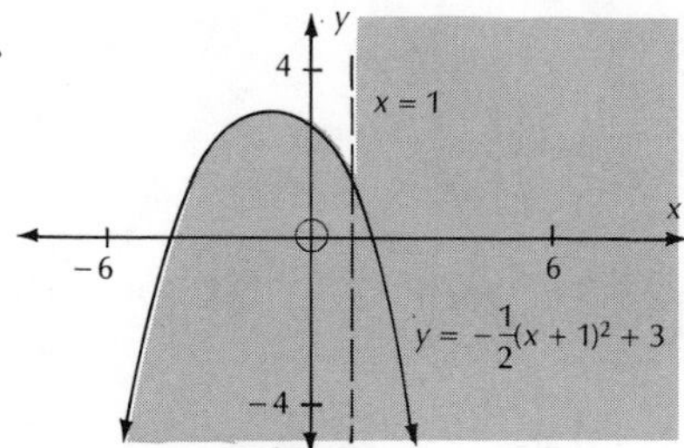

c.

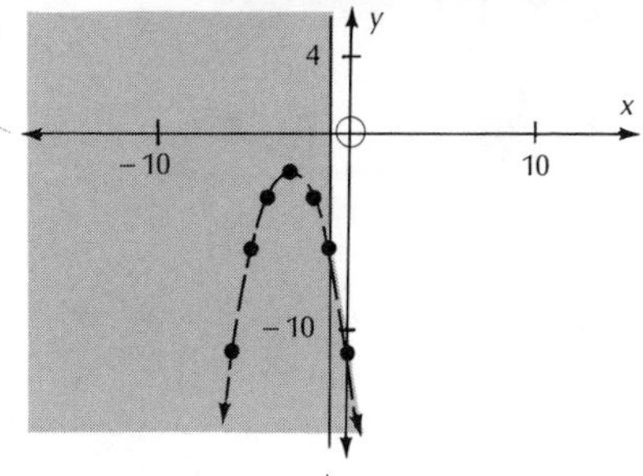

d.

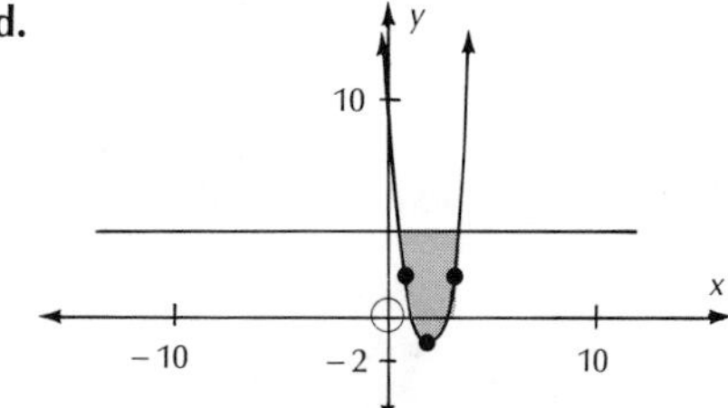

e.

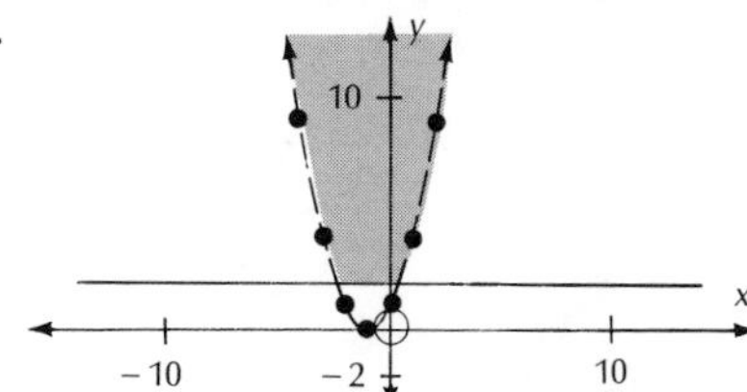

f.

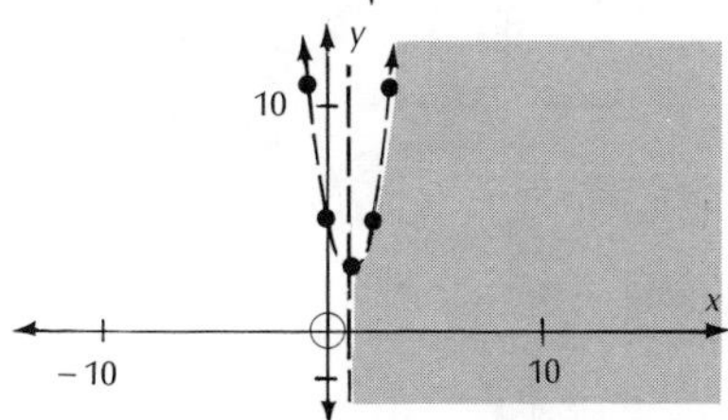

g.

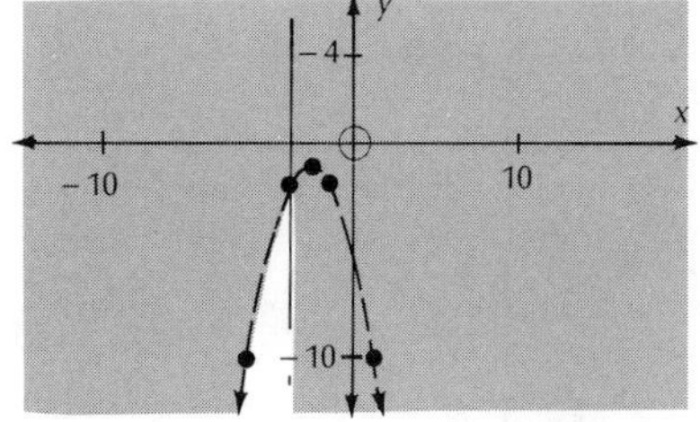

h. 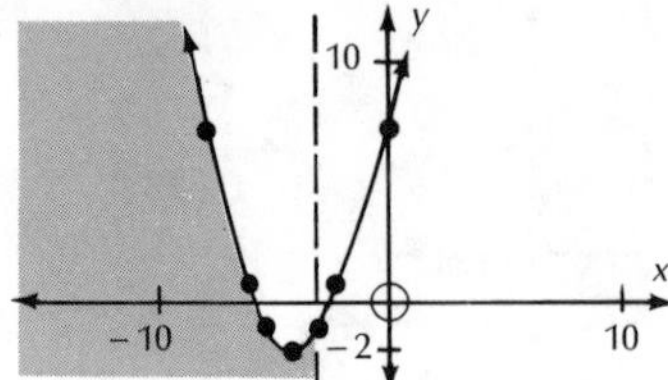

i. 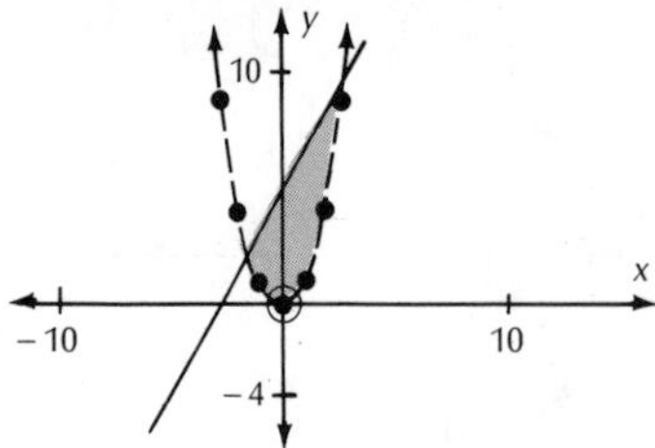

j. 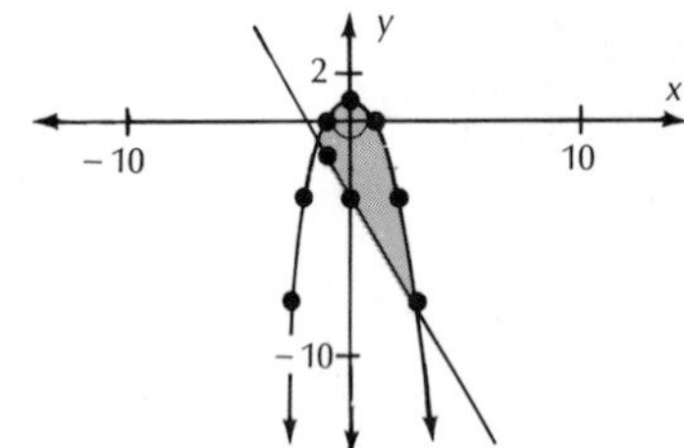

k. 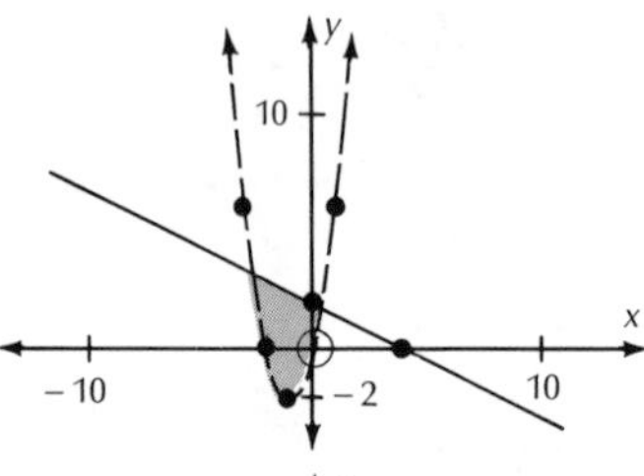

l. 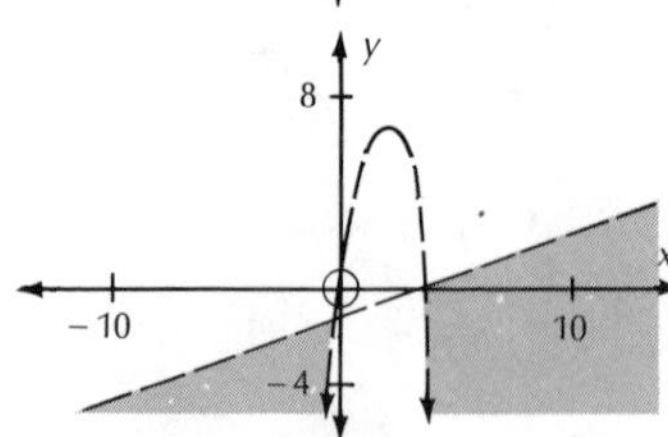

m. n. 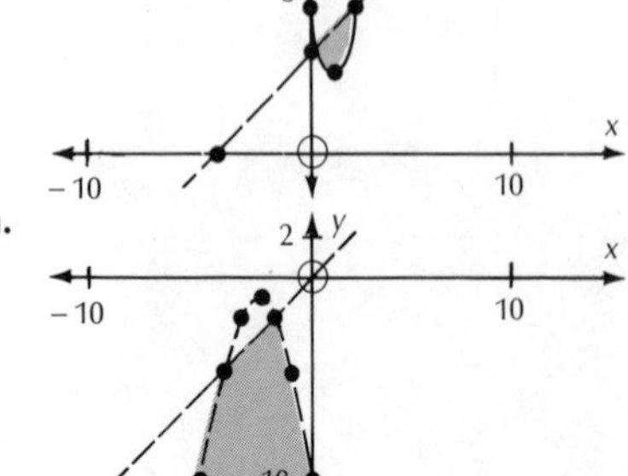

7. a. $y > x^2 + 1$ and $y > -\frac{5}{3}x + 5$
b. $y < -2(x-2)^2 + 4$ and $x \geq 0$
c. $y > 3(x-1)^2 - 3$ and $y \geq 0$

Exercise 5–8, pages 166–167
1. 37, 38 or −38, −37 **2.** 15, 17, 19 or −19, −17, −15 **3.** 9 cm × 12 cm
4. width = $-1 + \sqrt{365}$ m; length = $(-1 + \sqrt{365}) + 2$ m
5. 16 m × 12 m **6.** 3, 4, 5 **7.** 15, 18
8. 32 cm × 32 cm **9.** 25 **10.** 48 **11.** 8 cm, 16 cm
12. $4 + 2\sqrt{6}$ m × $4 + 2\sqrt{6}$ m **13.** ~33.2 m
14. a. 0.45 and 45 (first number is for flight up)
b. 24.2 m **c.** 4.4 s **15.** ~13.7 mm

Exercise 5–9, pages 170–171
1. a. $0 + 4i$ **b.** $0 + 7i$ **c.** $0 + 10i$ **d.** $0 + 6i$
e. $0 + 2\sqrt{3}i$ **f.** $0 + 2\sqrt{6}i$ **g.** $0 - 8\sqrt{3}i$
h. $6 - 25\sqrt{3}i$ **i.** $0 + \frac{7}{2}\sqrt{2}i$ **2. a.** 9 **b.** $3 + 3i$
c. $5 + 5i$ **d.** $-8 + \frac{3}{2}i$ **e.** $13 - 10i$ **f.** $2 - 7i$
g. $1 - 5i$ **h.** $-\frac{11}{2} + 3i$ **i.** $-8 + 14i$
5. a. $6 - 2\sqrt{3}i$ **b.** $4 + 5\sqrt{2}i$ **c.** $5\sqrt{5}i$ **d.** $2\sqrt{5}i$
e. $12 + 3\sqrt{3}i$ **f.** $-8 - 14\sqrt{2}i$ **g.** $50\sqrt{3} + 3i$
h. $\sqrt{11}i$ **6. a.** $15 + 6i$ **b.** $-21 + 14i$
c. $-6 - 18i$ **d.** 30 **e.** $37 - 50i$ **f.** −50
g. $21 + 20i$ **h.** $-5 - 12i$ **i.** $52 - 14i$
7. a. $i^3 = -i$ $i^4 = 1$ $i^5 = i$ $i^6 = -1$ $i^7 = -i$ $i^8 = 1$ $i^9 = i$ $i^{10} = -1$ **b.** If k is even and $\frac{k}{2}$ is even, then $i^k = 1$. If k is even and $\frac{k}{2}$ is odd, then $i^k = -1$. If k is odd and $\frac{k-1}{2}$ is odd, then $i^k = -i$. If k is odd and $\frac{k-1}{2}$ is even, then $i^k = i$.

8. a. $0 - \frac{1}{2}i$ **b.** $0 + \frac{1}{5}i$ **c.** $\frac{1}{5} - \frac{1}{10}i$ **d.** $\frac{2}{5} + \frac{1}{5}i$
e. $\frac{3}{34} - \frac{5}{34}i$ **f.** $-\frac{1}{5} - \frac{4}{5}i$ **g.** $-\frac{3}{20} + \frac{1}{20}i$
h. $\frac{7}{85} - \frac{6}{85}i$ **i.** $\frac{-3}{10} + \frac{1}{10}i$ **9. a.** $-2i$ **b.** $\frac{3}{5}i$
c. $\frac{1-5i}{3}$ **d.** $\frac{1+i}{2}$ **e.** $\frac{6-4i}{13}$ **f.** $\frac{8-20i}{29}$ **g.** i
h. $\frac{-5-12i}{13}$ **i.** $\frac{32-30i}{37}$ **j.** $\frac{-4-19i}{13}$ **k.** $\frac{39+25i}{37}$
l. $\frac{47+14i}{37}$ **10. a.** 0 **b.** 0 **c.** 1
11. a. $x = \frac{12+15i}{41}$ **b.** $x = \frac{7-22i}{13}$
c. $x = \frac{-13+82i}{61}$ **12. b.** $-2, 1 + \sqrt{3}i$
13. b. $-3, \frac{3}{2}(1 - \sqrt{3}i)$

Extra, page 171

1. a. $\sqrt{13}$ **b.** $\sqrt{34}$ **c.** $\sqrt{9.25}$ **d.** $2\sqrt{10}$
2. a. a circle **b.** a doughnut **c.** a disc

Exercise 5–10, page 173

1. a. 2, 3 **b.** $\frac{1+\sqrt{7}i}{2}, \frac{1-\sqrt{7}i}{2}$ **c.** $1, \frac{1}{2}$
d. $\frac{-2+\sqrt{14}i}{3}, \frac{-2-\sqrt{14}i}{3}$ **e.** $\frac{7}{4}, -1$
f. $\frac{5+\sqrt{73}}{4}, \frac{5-\sqrt{73}}{4}$ **g.** $\frac{2+\sqrt{2}i}{6}, \frac{2-\sqrt{2}i}{6}$
h. $\frac{-1+\sqrt{11}i}{2}, \frac{-1-\sqrt{11}i}{2}$ **i.** $\frac{3+\sqrt{3}}{2}, \frac{3-\sqrt{3}}{2}$
2. a. $x^2+9=0$ **b.** $x^2-4x+5=0$ **c.** $x^2+8=0$
d. $x^2-10x+29=0$
3. a. $\frac{3+\sqrt{103}i}{8}, \frac{3-\sqrt{103}i}{8}$
b. $\frac{(\sqrt{2}+\sqrt{10})i}{6}, \frac{(\sqrt{2}-\sqrt{10})i}{6}$
c. $\frac{-\sqrt{2}-i}{3}, \frac{\sqrt{2}-i}{3}$
d. $-(2+\sqrt{6})i, -(2-\sqrt{6})i$
e. $\frac{2i+\sqrt{11}}{3}, \frac{2i-\sqrt{11}}{3}$
f. $\frac{1+\sqrt{1+24\sqrt{3}}}{4\sqrt{3}}, \frac{1-\sqrt{1+24\sqrt{3}}}{4\sqrt{3}}$
g. $\frac{\sqrt{79}-i}{10}, \frac{-\sqrt{79}-i}{10}$ **h.** $\frac{1+\sqrt{31}i}{2\sqrt{2}}, \frac{1-\sqrt{31}i}{2\sqrt{2}}$
4. a. $(5-2i), x^2-10x+29=0$ **b.** $i+4$, $x^2-2ix-17=0$ **c.** $2\sqrt{3}-i, x^2-4\sqrt{3}x+13=0$
d. $4i+\sqrt{5}, x^2-8ix-21=0$ **5. a.** $x^2+1=0$
b. $x^2-5x+(7+i)=0$
c. $x^2-(12+i)x+(47-i)=0$
d. $x^2+4x+40=0$ **6. a.** $k \epsilon \mathbf{C}, k \neq \left\{\frac{25}{32}\right\}$
b. $k \epsilon \mathbf{C}, k \neq \{3\sqrt{3}i, -3\sqrt{3}i\}$ **c.** $k \epsilon \mathbf{C}, k \neq \left\{\frac{9}{16}\right\}$
d. $k \epsilon \mathbf{C}, k \neq \{-1+2\sqrt{15}, -1-2\sqrt{15}\}$
e. $k \epsilon \mathbf{C}, k \neq \left\{\frac{1}{8}\right\}$ **f.** $k \epsilon \mathbf{C}, k \neq \{-8, 4\}$
7. a. $x=2+i, x=1+i$ **b.** $x=i, x=i+3$
c. $x=7i, x=-i$ **d.** $x=i, x=-\frac{1}{3}i$

Review, pages 174–175

2. a. $v(0, -4), x=0, x=-2, x=2, y=-4$
b. $v(-3, -1), x=-3, x=-3+\frac{1}{\sqrt{2}}, x=-3-\frac{1}{\sqrt{2}}$, $y=17$ **c.** $v(0, 3), x=0, x=\sqrt{3}, x=-\sqrt{3}, y=3$
3. a. $y=3(x-2)^2$ **b.** $y=3(x+3)^2-1$
4. $y=\frac{5}{8}(x-7)^2-8$ **5. a.** $x=-\sqrt{5}, x=\sqrt{5}$
b. $x=4, x=3$ **c.** $x=-\frac{3}{2}, x=5$ **d.** $x=\frac{5}{3}, x=-3$
e. $x=0, x=-3$ **f.** $x=\frac{7}{3}, x=-\frac{1}{2}$
6. a. no real number solution **b.** $2\pm\sqrt{5}$ **c.** $\frac{1}{6}$
d. $-\frac{1}{2}, -1$ **e.** $\frac{-4\pm3\sqrt{2}}{2}$
f. no real number solution
7. a. $\left(-\frac{3}{2}, -12\frac{1}{4}\right)$; $x=-\frac{3}{2}$; x-intercepts: $2, -5$; y-intercept: -10, min $= -12\frac{1}{4}$ **b.** $(-1, 4)$; $x=-1$; x-intercepts: $-3, 1$; y-intercept: 3, max $= 4$
c. $\left(\frac{5}{2}, \frac{25}{2}\right)$; $x=\frac{5}{2}$; x-intercepts: 0, 5; y-intercept: 0; max $=\frac{25}{2}$ **d.** $(-1, -2)$; $x=-1$; x-intercepts: $-2, 0$; y-intercept: 0, min $= -2$ **e.** $(1, -5)$; $x=1$; x-intercepts: $1\pm\frac{1}{2}\sqrt{10}$; y-intercept: -3; min $= -5$
f. $\left(-\frac{3}{2}, -\frac{3}{4}\right)$; $x=-\frac{3}{2}$; no x-intercepts; y-intercept: -3; max $= -\frac{3}{4}$ **8.** $1, y=\frac{2}{3}(x-4)^2-6$
9. a. $3\pm\sqrt{13}$ **b.** $\frac{3\pm\sqrt{19}}{2}$ **c.** $\frac{1\pm\sqrt{13}}{6}$
d. $\frac{3\pm\sqrt{5}}{2}$ **e.** $\frac{-1\pm\sqrt{41}}{10}$ **f.** $\frac{7\pm\sqrt{17}}{8}$
10. a. $\frac{6}{5}, \frac{-3}{5}$ **b.** $0, -7$ **c.** $\frac{8}{3}, 0$ **d.** $\frac{3}{2}, 2$ **e.** $0, \frac{1}{3}$
f. $\frac{-1}{5}, \frac{-8}{5}$ **11.** $a=-\frac{1}{2}, -8$
12. $k=-12, x=\frac{9}{3}, x=\frac{3}{4}$ **13. a.** 2 real distinct roots **b.** 2 complex distinct roots **c.** 1 real distinct root **d.** 2 real distinct roots
e. 2 complex distinct roots **f.** 2 real distinct roots **g.** 2 complex distinct roots **h.** 2 real distinct roots **i.** 2 real distinct roots
14. $k > 4\sqrt{2}, k < -4\sqrt{2}$ **15.** $k=4$ **16.** $k > \frac{9}{8}$
17. a.

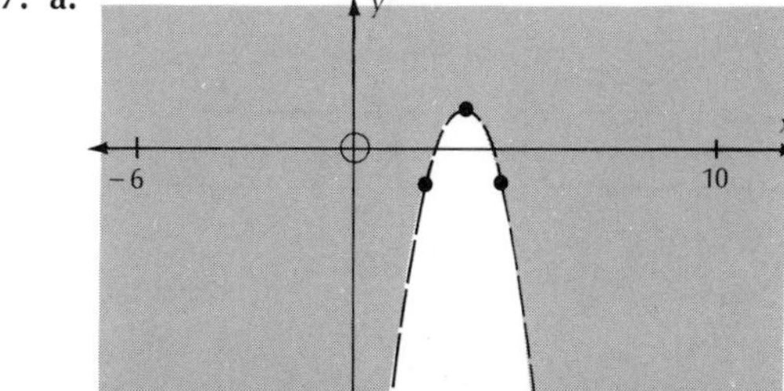

b.

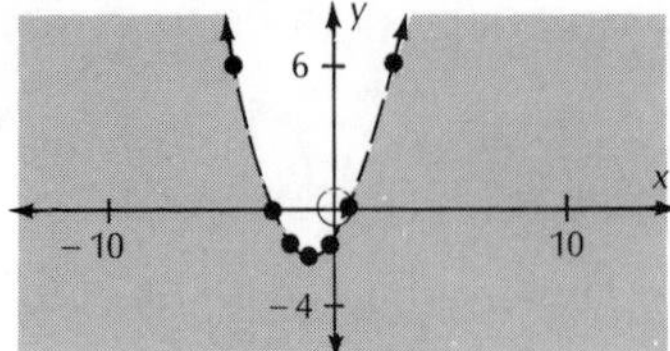

c.

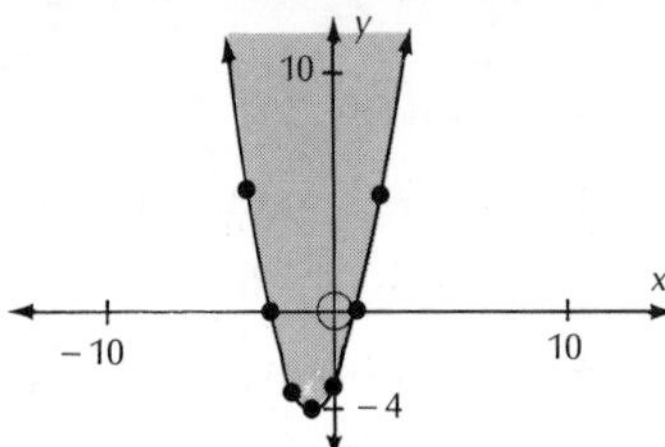

d.

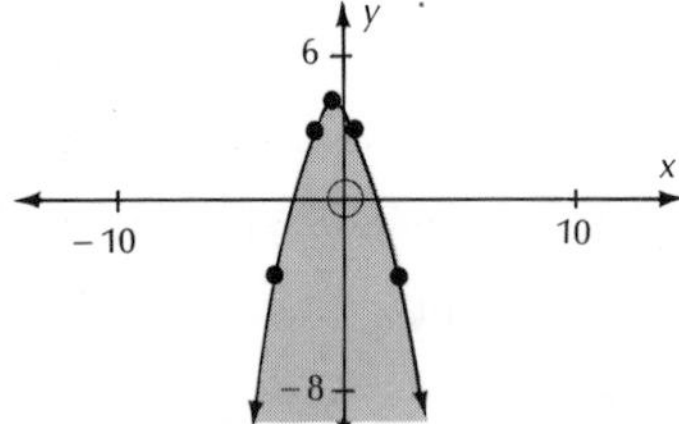

e.

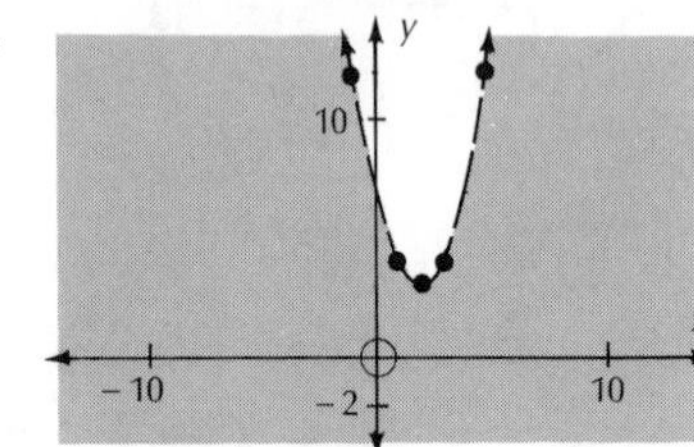

f.

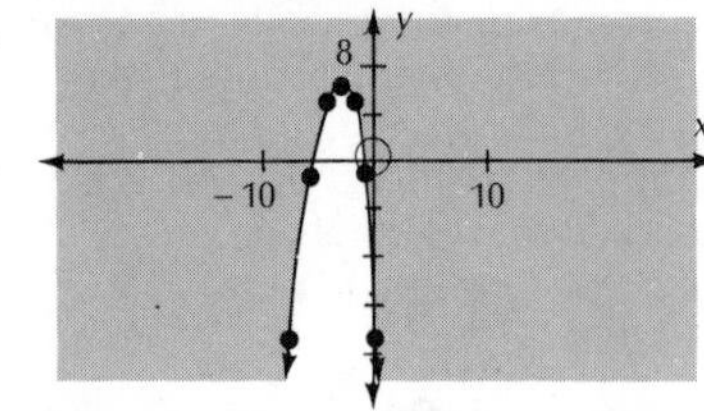

18.

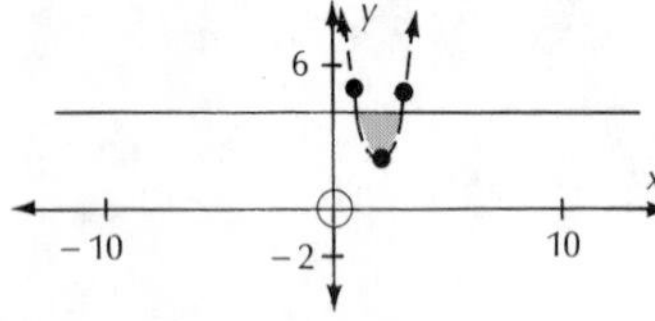

19.

20. a. $(-2, -8)$ **b.** $x = -2$ **c.** $-2 \pm \frac{2}{3}\sqrt{6}$; 4
21. a. $\left(\frac{1}{2}, \frac{25}{2}\right)$ **b.** $x = \frac{1}{2}$ **c.** 3, −2; 12
22. $(6 + 2\sqrt{5})$ cm × $(6 + 2\sqrt{5})$ cm
23. 10 cm walls, 20 cm floor

Test, page 176

1. a. $(0, -3)$; $x = 0$; $\pm\frac{1}{2}\sqrt{6}$; −3; min = −3
b. $\left(-\frac{1}{2}, -\frac{25}{2}\right)$; $x = -\frac{1}{2}$; 0, −5; 0; min = $-\frac{25}{2}$
c. $\left(\frac{1}{4}, -\frac{25}{8}\right)$; $x = \frac{1}{4}$; −1, 1.5; −3; min = −3
d. $\left(\frac{5}{2}, \frac{9}{4}\right)$; $x = \frac{5}{2}$; 1, 4; −4; max = $\frac{9}{4}$
3. $p > \sqrt{24} = 2\sqrt{6}$, $p < -\sqrt{24} = -2\sqrt{6}$
4. $-6 \pm 2\sqrt{5}$ **5. a.** 4, −5 **b.** $\frac{1}{7}$, 0 **c.** $\frac{2}{3}$, $\frac{4}{3}$
6. a. $x^2 - 2x - 15 = 0$ **b.** $x^2 + (\sqrt{3} - 6)x + 2 = 0$
c. $x^2 - 12x + 37 = 0$ **7.** $k = \frac{19}{8}$; $x = -10$
8. a. $-2 + i$ **b.** $10 - 6i$ **c.** $-40 - 42i$
9. $\frac{3 \pm \sqrt{7}i}{8}$ **10. a.** Parabola touches the x-axis, but doesn't cross it. **b.** Parabola does not cross the x-axis. **c.** Parabola crosses the x-axis. **11.** 86
12. b. 40.5 m **c.** 5.732 s

Cumulative Review, page 177

1. a. $-\frac{7}{6}$ **b.** vertical line **c.** 2 **d.** $-\frac{1}{4}$ **e.** 3
f. −2 **2. a.** yes **b.** no **c.** yes **d.** yes
3. a. $x - y - 3 = 0$ **b.** $6x - 7y - 5 = 0$
c. $y - 3 = 0$ **d.** $4x - 5y = 0$ **e.** $2x + 5y + 7 = 0$
f. $4x + y + 12 = 0$ **4. a.** $\left(\frac{9}{2}, \frac{3}{2}\right)$ **b.** $\left(\frac{11}{2}, 4\right)$
c. $(-2, 3)$ **d.** $\left(\frac{-5}{2}, -2\right)$ **e.** $(-1, -1)$
f. $\left(\frac{-5}{2}, -2\right)$ **5. a.** $N = 17(t - 2)$, $DI = 16t - 1$, $ND = 17t$, $SH = 19(t - 1) - 1$ **c.** N passes DI at 33 s, SH passes DI at $6\frac{1}{3}$ s, SH passes ND at 10 s
d. first is SH at 106.3 s, second is ND at 117.6 s, third is N at 119.6 s, fourth is DI at 125.1 s
6. $4\frac{2}{17}$ min **8. a.** $3x - 4y - 24 = 0$
b. $2x - y - 6 = 0$ **c.** $5x - y - 4 = 0$
d. $3x - 2y - 6 = 0$ **e.** $5x - y - 9 = 0$
9. a. 9.9994 kg **b.** 9.9988 kg **c.** 9.9880 kg
d. 8.0555 kg **e.** 0.9048 kg **f.** 0.0000 kg

UNIT 6

Exercise 6–1, pages 180–181
1. a. (2, −1) **b.** (0, 4) **c.** (−5, 3)
2. a. (−30, −100) **b.** (−40, 12) **c.** (3.4, 2.6)
3. a. independent **b.** dependent
c. ~~inconsistent~~ INDEPENDANT **d.** inconsistent **e.** independent
f. dependent **4. a.** $x = 8, y = 2$ **b.** $x = 7, y = -2$
c. $x = 0, y = -3$ **d.** no solution **e.** $x = -2, y = 6$
f. infinite solutions **g.** $x = 15, y = 25$
h. $x = 18, y = -7$ **i.** $x = -13, y = 12$
5. a. 45 dogs, 15 cats **b.** pen: 35¢, pencil: 15¢
c. 45 sedans, 25 sports cars **d.** 20 **e.** 8 m × 5 m
f. 9% : $200, 10% : $720 **6. a.** $x = -2, y = 3$
b. no solution **c.** $x = 4, y = 5$ **7.** $100, $20
8. $100, $12 **9.** $25, $30

Exercise 6–2, page 183
1. a. not equivalent **b.** equivalent
c. equivalent **d.** not equivalent
e. not equivalent **f.** not equivalent
2. a. $x = 4, y = -1$ **b.** $x = -2, y = 3$
c. $x = \frac{19}{6}, y = \frac{17}{6}$ **d.** $x = \frac{7}{3}, y = 3$ **e.** $x = 3, y = \frac{9}{4}$
f. $x = 4, y = \frac{-11}{3}$ **3. a.** (3, 2) **b.** no points of intersection **c.** (0, 0) **4. a.** $x = -2, y = 3$
b. $x = -2, y = 0$ **c.** $x = \frac{5}{2}, y = -3$
d. $x = \frac{-7}{3}, y = 7$ **e.** $x = 0, y = \frac{-11}{3}$ **f.** $x = \frac{10}{3}, y = \frac{-5}{2}$
5. a. $x = 6, y = -12$ **b.** $x = -8, y = 10$
c. $x = \frac{-1}{2}, y = \frac{-3}{2}$ **6. a.** $x = \frac{1}{2}, y = \frac{1}{3}$
b. $x = \frac{2}{3}, y = \frac{-3}{2}$ **c.** $x = \frac{3}{4}, y = \frac{-2}{5}$
7. a. $x = 5, y = 2, z = 3$ **b.** $x = 3, y = 4, z = -3$
c. $x = 3, y = -5, z = 2$

Exercise 6–3, page 185
1. a. $x = y - 8, y = x + 8$ **b.** $x = y + 4, y = x - 4$
c. $x = \frac{7}{2} - \frac{1}{2}y, y = 7 - 2x$ **d.** $x = 3y - 12, y = \frac{1}{3}x + 4$
e. $x = \frac{7}{4} - \frac{3}{4}y, y = \frac{7}{3} - \frac{4}{3}x$ **f.** $x = \frac{2}{5}y + \frac{6}{5}, y = \frac{5}{2}x - 3$
2. a. $y = 3$ **b.** $y = 1$ **c.** $y = -1$ **d.** $y = 2$
e. $y = \frac{-3}{2}$ **f.** $y = \frac{7}{6}$ **3. a.** $x = 7, y = 3$
b. $x = -2, y = 5$ **c.** $x = -4, y = -4$
d. $x = 3, y = -1$ **e.** $x = \frac{9}{5}, y = \frac{23}{5}$ **f.** $x = 1, y = 4$
4. a. $x = 6, y = -2$ **b.** $x = -5, y = -1$
c. $x = 13, y = -5$ **d.** $x = \frac{-1}{3}, y = \frac{7}{3}$
e. no solution exists **f.** $x = -2, y = \frac{7}{2}$

5. a. (7, −6) **b.** (−6, 5) **c.** (−8, −2)
d. $\left(\frac{-26}{25}, \frac{-4}{5}\right)$ **e.** $\left(\frac{15}{4}, \frac{29}{8}\right)$ **f.** $\left(\frac{27}{12}, \frac{-15}{4}\right)$
6. a. $x = 5, y = 15$ **b.** $x = 9, y = -4$
c. $x = 5, y = -7$ **7. a.** $x = 6, y = 8$
b. $x = 16, y = 12$ **c.** $x = -12, y = -4$
8. a. $x = 2, y = 7; x = -2, y = 7$ **b.** $x = 2, y = 6$
c. $x = 3, y = 7$

Exercise 6–4, pages 187–188
1. 13, 24 **2.** 7, 11 **3.** 6, 11 **4.** 41
5. 20 m × 10.5 m **6.** 6 cm, 9 cm, 9 cm
7. 3 cm, 5 cm **8.** 3.25 m, 5.25 m **9.** $12, $4.50
10. $54.25 **11.** 20 km/h, 10 km/h
12. 10 km/h, 25 km/h **13.** 8 km/h, 4 km/h
14. $4500, $8100 **15.** $7300, $8500 **16.** $15, 12¢
17. 29

Review, page 189
1. a. $x = -2, y = -3$ **b.** no solution
c. infinite solutions **2. a.** independent
b. inconsistent **c.** dependent
3. a. $x = 3, y = -6$ **b.** $x = 7, y = 2$ **c.** no solution **d.** $x = -6, y = 0$ **e.** infinite solutions
f. $x = \frac{3}{4}, y = \frac{-2}{3}$ **g.** $x = 10, y = -12$
h. $x = 8, y = -9$ **i.** $x = \frac{2}{3}, y = \frac{-1}{4}$
4. a. $x = -9, y = 2$ **b.** $x = 22, y = 26$
c. $x = -4, y = 7$ **d.** $x = -2, y = 5$
e. $x = 3, y = -5$ **f.** $x = \frac{-1}{2}, y = \frac{1}{3}$ **5.** $1680
6. $4800, $1200 **7.** $320, $580 **8.** $\frac{3}{13}$
9. 30 km/h **10.** 25 people

Exercise 6–5, pages 192–193
2. a. (4, 7), (−4, 7) **b.** (−1, −2) **c.** (3, 1)
d. (−1, 16), (4, 1) **e.** (−3, 3), (−2, 2) **f.** (0, 0), (4, 8)
3. a. independent **b.** independent
c. independent **d.** independent
e. independent **f.** independent
5. a. (−4, −3) and (−1, 0) **b.** (4, 3) and (3, −4)
c. (3, −4) and (−2, 6) **d.** (−2, 0), $\left(\frac{8}{5}, \frac{-9}{5}\right)$
e. (0, −13), (5, 12) **f.** no solution
g. (0, 0) and (−3, 9) **h.** (−3, 14) **i.** (−3, 18)
6. a. $x = 5, y = 12$ or $x = -5, y = -12$
b. $x = -6, y = -6$ or $x = \frac{9}{2}, y = 8$
c. $x = 3, y = 6$ or $x = \frac{3}{2}, y = \frac{-3}{4}$
d. $x = 4, y = -2$ or $x = -2, y = 7$
e. $x = \frac{3}{2}, y = \frac{21}{4}$ or $x = 1, y = 4$
f. $x = 13, y = 12$ or $x = -5, y = 0$ **7.** 514 m^2

8. 27 cm, 36 cm **9.** 10 cm, 8 cm
10. rectangle 12m × 10m, square 10m × 10m
11. 10 m × 7 m, 8 m or 9.5 m × 6.5 m, 8.5 m
12. a. (2, −1) and (−2, −1) **b.** (1, −2), (−2, −1)
c. no solution **d.** infinite solutions
e. (0, 3) and (4, 0) **f.** infinite solutions
13. a. independent **b.** independent
c. inconsistent **d.** dependent
e. independent **f.** dependent
14. a. $(x + y + 3)(x + y - 3) = 0$, $x - 2y = 0$
b. $(x + y + 3)(x - y - 3) = 0$, $x + 3y + 5 = 0$
c. $(2x + y + 4)(2x + y - 4) = 0$, $y = 8 - 2x$
d. $(x + 2y + 1)(x - 2y - 1) = 0$, $x = 2y + 1$
e. $(x - y + 3)(x - y - 4) = 0$, $3x + 4y = 12$
f. $(2x - y + 4)(2x - y - 5) = 0$, $2x - y = 5$

Exercise 6–6, pages 195–196
1. a. $x = 0, y = 3$ **b.** $x = -2, y = 0$ and $x = 2, y = 0$
c. no solution **d.** $x = 0, y = 1$ **e.** $x = 0, y = 4$ and $x = 2, y = 0$ **f.** no solution **g.** $x = 0, y = 0$ and $x = 2, y = 4$ **h.** $x = -2, y = 4$ **i.** $x = 1, y = 0$ and $x = -1, y = 0$ **4. a.** (7, 3), (−7, 3), (7, −3), (−7, −3) **b.** no solution **c.** (1, −4), (−1, −4)
d. (8, −6), (−8, 6), (6, −8), (−6, 8)
e. (2, 0), (−2, 0) **f.** $(2\sqrt{2}, 3)$, $(-2\sqrt{2}, 3)$
g. $(3, \sqrt{5})$, $(-3, \sqrt{5})$, $(3, -\sqrt{5})$, $(-3, -\sqrt{5})$
h. $(-\sqrt{6}, \sqrt{6})$, $(\sqrt{6}, -\sqrt{6})$, (−3, 2), (3, −2)
i. $(\sqrt{5}, \sqrt{2})$, $(\sqrt{5}, -\sqrt{2})$, $(-\sqrt{5}, \sqrt{2})$, $(-\sqrt{5}, -\sqrt{2})$
j. (0, −10), (6, 8), (−6, 8) **k.** (9, 3), (9, −3)
l. (0, 0), (2, 4) **5.** 9 cm and 12 cm
6. 6 m, 8 m × 4 m **7.** 11 m × 7 m, 7 m
8. 400 km/h, 5 h **9.** \$4.50 **10.** $4\sqrt{2}$ cm, 4 cm
11. \$9 **12.** 16 m × 10 m **13. a.** $x = 3, y = 0$ or $x = -3, y = 0$ or $x = 0, y = 3$ or $x = 0, y = -3$
b. $x = 3, y = 0$ or $x = -3, y = 0$ or $x = 0, y = -9$
c. $x = 3, y = 4$ or $x = -3, y = 4$ **d.** $x = 2, y = 4$ or $x = -3, y = 9$ **c.** $x = 4, y = 1$ or $x = -4, y = -1$ or $x = 1, y = 4$ or $x = -1, y = -4$ **f.** $x = 0, y = 4$ or $x = -4, y = 0$

Extra, page 197
1. a. 2 **b.** none **c.** 4 **d.** 4 **e.** 1
2. a. (−3, 9), (2, 4) **b.** (−3, −1), (−1, −3), (3, 1), (1, 3) **c.** (−4, −1), (1, 4), (−1, −4), (4, 1)
d. (0, −9), (−3, 0), (3, 0)

Exercise 6–7, pages 200–201
9. 8b, 8e, 8f, 8g and 8i
12. a. $x + y \leq 8$
$x \leq 6$
$x \geq 0$
$y \geq 0$
b. $x \geq 0$
$x - 2y \leq 0$
$2x + y \leq 10$

Exercise 6–8, pages 205–207
2. a. 9, 21, 36 **b.** 20, 42, 76 **c.** 30, 60, 120
3. a. (0, 9), (2, 3), (8, 0) **b.** (0, 12), (2, 6), (4, 4), (12, 0) **c.** (0, 20), (1, 15), (10, 6), (40, 0)
4. a. 9, 12, 19 **b.** 7, 10, 17 **c.** 8, 12, 40
5. yes, (10, 6) and (40, 0) **6. b.** (0, 4), (0, 15), (5, 15), (14, 6), (14, 4), (10, 0) **c.** max. = 76; min. = 4
d. max. = 15; min. = −24 **7. b.** (0, 40), (10, 20), (20, 15), (40, 10) **c.** min. = 65, when $x = 20$ and $y = 15$ **d.** min. = 40, when $x = 0$ and $y = 40$
8. a. $3x + 3y \geq 39$ **b.** $2x + 3y \geq 36$ **d.** Bill: 3 h, Mike: 10 h **9. a.** Molly: 8 h, Syd: 3 h **b.** \$55.00
10. a. $x + 2y \leq 16$ **b.** $2x + y \leq 16$ **c.** $x + y \leq 10$
e. A: 6, B: 4 **11. a.**\$40 000 in term deposit and \$20 000 in bonds **b.** \$5800 **12. a.** \$30 000 in Bank A and \$40 000 in Bank B **b.** \$6000
13. \$50 000 in Bank A and \$20 000 in Bank B; \$6100
14. a. 40, 60 **b.** \$52 **15. a.** 80, 20 **b.** \$58

Review, pages 208–209
1. a. $x = 3, y = 4$ **b.** $x = 21, y = -3$ **c.** $x = 2, y = 4$ or $x = -2, y = 4$ **d.** $x = 6, y = -8$
e. $x = 4, y = 11$ or $x = -1, y = -4$ **f.** no solution
2. a. (1, 5), (−1, 5) **b.** (−3, 3), (2, −2)
c. (3, −10), (−1, 6) **d.** (3, 0), $\left(\frac{-5}{2}, \frac{11}{4}\right)$ **e.** (1, −7)
f. no solution **3. a.** $x = -5, y = 0$; $x = 4, y = 3$; $x = 4, y = -3$ **b.** $x = \frac{2}{\sqrt{2}}, y = 2\sqrt{2}$; $x = \frac{-2}{\sqrt{2}}$, $y = -2\sqrt{2}$; $x = \frac{4}{\sqrt{2}}, y = \sqrt{2}$; $x = \frac{-4}{\sqrt{2}}, y = \sqrt{2}$;
c. $x = -4, y = -16$ **d.** $x = 0, y = -4$ or $x = 4, y = 0$ or $x = -4, y = 0$ **e.** $x = 3, y = 3$; $x = -3, y = -3$ **f.** $x = 5, y = 6$ **6.** 18 m × 15 m
7. 100 km/h, 4 h **8.** 7%, 9% **9. a.** (0, 0), (0, 400), (150, 250), (225, 125), (225, 0) **b.** (0, 120), (10, 90), (80, 20), (120, 0) **c.** (0, 4), (0, 8), (2, 8), (10, 0), (6, 0), (3, 1) **10. a.** 20, 130, 24; 595, 260, 40 **b.** −800, −240, −16; 225, 120, 10 **11.** Linear programming will yield more than one solution point when (1) one of the constraints and the equation to be maximized/minimized are coincidental, (2) the equation to be maximized/minimized is of degree 2 or more. **12.** 160 sofas, 50 loveseats **13.** 30, 20
14. A: 8, B: 12 **15.** A: 0, B: 16

Test, page 210
1. a. $x = -6, y = 1$ **b.** $x = -3, y = -4$ or $x = 2, y = 1$ **c.** $x = -1, y = 4$ or $x = -2, y = 1$
2. a. $x = \frac{-2}{3}, y = 1$ **b.** no solution **c.** $x = 3, y = -3$ or $x = -5, y = -1$ **d.** $x = -3, y = 3$
e. $x = 3, y = -4$; $x = -3, y = 4$; $x = 4, y = -3$; $x = -4, y = 3$ **f.** $x = -4, y = 3$ **g.** $x = 6, y = 0$ or

$x = -6, y = 0$ **h.** $x = -1, y = 6$ **i.** $x = 2, y = 3$ or $x = 2, y = -3$ or $x = -2, y = 3$ or $x = -2, y = -3$
4. \$27, \$12 **5.** 9 cm, 4 cm **6.** $\left(10, \frac{55}{3}\right)$, (10, 40), (20, 40), (40, 20), (40, 10), $\left(\frac{45}{2}, 10\right)$ **7. a.** 160, $\frac{200}{3}$
b. 30, −30 **8.** 100 cars, no vans **9.** 75, \$65 000

Cumulative Review, page 211

1. a. $(2x^2 + y^3)(x + y)$ **b.** $(5x + 3y)(2y + 7)$
c. $(12x + 35)(9x - 7)$ **d.** $y(3y + 2x)(4y - x)$
2. a. 2 **b.** 0 **c.** 1 **d.** 0 **e.** 2 **f.** 2
3. a. 54 s
4. a. $x^2 + 2x - 1 + \frac{3x + 3}{x^2 + 1}$ **b.** $x^2 + \frac{25}{x + 4}$
c. $6x^2 - 2x - 4 + \frac{9x + 6}{x^3 + x^2 + x + 1}$
d. $4x^3 + 5x^2 + 2x + 1$
e. $x^4 - \frac{1}{3}x^3 + \frac{1}{9}x^2 - \frac{1}{24}x + \frac{1}{81} - \frac{82}{243x + 81}$
f. $x + 5 + \frac{12}{x - 1}$
5. a. ~45 cells **b.** 134 217 728 cells **c.** 34 h
6. a. ~287 m **b.** ~7 65 s **7.** 2.1 min
8. 1.62 km/h

UNIT 7

Exercise 7–1, pages 214–215

1. a. $\overline{CA}, \overline{CD}, \overline{CB}$ **b.** $\overline{BD}, \overline{GH}$ **c.** $\overline{BD}$ **d.** $\overleftrightarrow{EF}$
e. $\overleftrightarrow{GH}$ **2. a.** $3\sqrt{2}$ **b.** 5 **c.** $4\sqrt{5}$ **d.** 5 **e.** $2\sqrt{5}$
f. $9\sqrt{2}$ **3. a.** $x^2 + y^2 = 64$ **b.** $x^2 + y^2 = 16$
c. $x^2 + y^2 = \frac{16}{9}$ **d.** $x^2 + y^2 = 0.25$ **e.** $x^2 + y^2 = q^2$
f. $x^2 + y^2 = 4a^2$ **g.** $x^2 + y^2 = 3$ **h.** $x^2 + y^2 = 20$
4. a. $C = (0, 0); r = 4$ **b.** $C = (0, 0); r = 10$
c. $C = (0, 0); r = \sqrt{5}$ **d.** $C = (0, 0); r = \sqrt{7}$
e. $C = (0, 0); r = \frac{\sqrt{5}}{\sqrt{2}}$ **f.** $C = (0, 0); r = \frac{4}{5}$
6. a, b, and **d** **7. a.** $x^2 + y^2 = 25$
b. $x^2 + y^2 = 169$ **c.** $x^2 + y^2 = 100$ **d.** $x^2 + y^2 = 7$
e. $x^2 + y^2 = 625$ **f.** $x^2 + y^2 = 25$ **g.** $x^2 + y^2 = 58$
h. $x^2 + y^2 = 14$ **8. a.** $x^2 + y^2 = 169$
b. $x^2 + y^2 = 100$ **c.** $x^2 + y^2 = 25$ **d.** $x^2 + y^2 = 52$
9. b. x-intercepts = ±2 y-intercepts = ±2
10. a. $x^2 + y^2 = 36$ **b.** $x^2 + y^2 = 16$
c. $x^2 + y^2 = 81$ **d.** $x^2 + y^2 = \frac{25}{4}$
11. a. x-intercepts = ±6; y-intercepts = ±6
b. x-intercepts = $\pm 4\sqrt{3}$; y-intercepts = $\pm 4\sqrt{3}$
c. x-intercepts = $\pm\frac{7}{2}$; y-intercepts = $\pm\frac{7}{2}$
d. x-intercepts = $\pm 3\sqrt{10}$; y-intercepts = $\pm 3\sqrt{10}$
12. a. $x^2 + y^2 = 64$ **b.** $x^2 + y^2 = 16$
c. $x^2 + y^2 = \frac{4}{9}$ **d.** $x^2 + y^2 = 0.04$

13. a. a point circle at (0,0)
b. a circle with centre at the origin and radius 3
c. a circle with centre at the origin and radius 4
d. a circle with centre at the origin and radius 4
14. a. interior **b.** exterior **c.** interior
d. exterior **e.** on the circle **f.** exterior
16. The graph is a half-circle with radius 10 and centre (0,0). The diameter lies on the x-axis with the half-circle located in the positive y-region only.
17. b. $x = \sqrt{64 - y^2}$ **18. a.** $y = \sqrt{25 - x^2}$
b. $x = -\sqrt{16 - y^2}$ **c.** $y = -\sqrt{4 - x^2}$
d. $x = \sqrt{12 - y^2}$
19. a. $x + 7y = 0$
b. The centre of the given circle is (0,0), and this point lies on $x + 7y = 0$.

Extra, page 215

$\frac{1}{4}\pi - \frac{1}{2} \doteq 0.285$

Exercise 7–2, page 217

1. a. ∠ACB, ∠BCD, ∠ACD, ∠DCR, ∠BCR
b. ∠GAR, ∠ARP **c.** arc AB, arc AG, arc PR
d. arc ADG, arc PAR, arc BAR
(Answers may vary.)
2. a. $\overline{AG}$ **b.** $\overline{CB}$ and $\overline{CD}$ **c.** ∠ARP
3. a. False, an inscribed angle of a circle is subtended by an arc and two chords of the circle.
b. true
c. False the area bounded by a semicricle and a diameter of a circle is given by $A = \frac{1}{2}\pi r^2$.
d. False, the intersection of a tangent to a circle and a diameter of the circle is called the point of contact.
e. False, every major sector of a circle as bounded by a major are and two radii.
4. a. $\frac{55}{18}\pi$ **b.** 10π **c.** $\frac{\sqrt{3}}{2}\pi$ **5. a.** $\frac{275}{36}\pi$
b. 45π **c.** $\frac{3}{2}\pi$ **6. a.** 6π units² **b.** 2π units
c. $(6\pi - 9\sqrt{3})$ units **7. a.** 16π **b.** $4\pi - 8$

Exercise 7–3, pages 220–221

1. a. $4\sqrt{13}$ **b.** $5\sqrt{5}$ **c.** 24 **d.** $3\sqrt{7}$ **e.** 20
f. $20\sqrt{2}$ **2. a.** 12 cm **b.** 16 cm
3. a. the longer chord **b.** closer by 17 cm
4. Construct the perpendicular bisectors of $\overline{RS}$, $\overline{ST}$, and $\overline{RT}$. The point of intersection of the three perpendicular bisectors is the centre of the circle that will pass through R, S, and T.
8. 40 cm **9.** 567 cm **10. b.** $y = \frac{1}{11}x$
c. $\left(\frac{11}{2}, \frac{1}{2}\right)$

d. The point $\left(\frac{11}{2}, \frac{1}{2}\right)$ satisfies the equation $y = \frac{1}{11}x$ **11. b.** $(\sqrt{74}, 0), (-\sqrt{74}, 0)$
12. a. 51.96 m^2

Exercise 7–4, pages 224–225

1. a. $x = 90°, y = 15°$
b. $x = 40°, y = 40°, z = 40°, w = 55°, t = 45°$
c. $x = 150°, y = 210°, w = 75°$
d. $x = 115°, y = 130°$
e. $x = 52°, y = 67°, z = 88°, w = 21°$
f. $x = 35°, y = 26°, z = 119°, w = 35°$
2. In $\triangle DEF$, $\angle DEF = 35°$, $\angle DFE = 35°$.
$\therefore \triangle DEF$ is isosceles.
In $\triangle ABD$, $\angle ABD = 35°$, $\angle BAD = 35°$.
$\therefore \triangle DEF$ is isosceles.
8. 135° **9.** 130°

Exercise 7–5, pages 228–229

1. a. 8 **b.** 12 **c.** $BA = 6$; $AD = 6\sqrt{2}$ **d.** 12
2. a. $x = 70°; y = 45°$ **b.** $x = 40°; y = 75°; z = 70°$
c. $x = 80°; y = 32°; z = 148°; a = 23°$ **5. a.** 38°
b. 55° **c.** 93° **d.** 38° **9.** $\angle X = 90°, \angle Y = 60°$
$\angle Z = 30°$

Extra, page 229

10 units from the centre of the sphere

Problem Solving, page 230

1. more, 150 m^2 **2.** yes, 1256.25 m^2

Review, page 231

1. a. $x^2 + y^2 = 36$ **b.** $x^2 + y^2 = 12$ **c.** $x^2 + y^2 = \frac{1}{4}$
2. a. $x^2 + y^2 = 58$ **b.** $x^2 + y^2 = 64$ **3.** $\frac{20}{9}\pi$
4. $\frac{50}{9}\pi$ **5.** 6 units **6. a.** $\overline{AB}$ **b.** 17 cm closer
8. a. $x = 42°; y = 38°$ **b.** $x = 122.5°$ **c.** $x = 84°$;
$y = 96°; z = 88°$ **d.** $x = 30°; y = 30°; z = 91°$
e. $x = 90°; y = 35°; z = 55°$ **f.** $x = 112°; y = 44°$;
$z = 20°$

Exercise 7–6, pages 233–235

1. a. $C(0, 3)$; $r = 10$ **b.** $C(-7, 0)$; $r = 4$
c. $C(7, 2)$; $r = 5$ **d.** $C(-1, 1)$; $r = 7$
e. $C(-6, -3)$; $r = 8$ **f.** $C(9, -4)$; $r = 6$
g. $C(-2, -3)$; $r = 2\sqrt{2}$ **h.** $C(5, -7)$; $r = 4\sqrt{3}$
3. a. $(x - 5)^2 + (y - 9)^2 = 25$
b. $(x + 3)^2 + (y - 4)^2 = 49$
c. $(x + 4)^2 + (y + 4)^2 = 9$
d. $x^2 + (y - 6)^2 = 100$
e. $(x + 2)^2 + y^2 = 4$
f. $(x - 6)^2 + (y + 1)^2 = 169$
g. $(x - 6)^2 + (y + 7)^2 = 7$
h. $(x - 2)^2 + (y + 9)^2 = 45$
i. $x^2 + (y + 4)^2 = 108$
4. a. $x^2 + y^2 - 12x + 8y + 48 = 0$
b. $x^2 + y^2 + 8x + 12y + 16 = 0$
c. $x^2 + y^2 + 2x - 4y - 11 = 0$
d. $x^2 + y^2 - 6x - 4y - 12 = 0$
e. $x^2 + y^2 + 10x - 10y + 25 = 0$
or $x^2 + y^2 - 10x - 10y + 25 = 0$
f. $x^2 + y^2 - 18x - 18y + 81 = 0$
or $x^2 + y^2 - 18x + 18y + 81 = 0$
5. a. $(7, -7), (7, -1)$ **b.** $(0, -8), (6, -8)$
6. a. $(x - 7)^2 + (y + 6)^2 = 2$
b. $(x + 7)^2 + (y - 6)^2 = 17$
c. $(x - 3)^2 + \left(y + \frac{9}{2}\right)^2 = \frac{117}{4}$
d. $(x - 2)^2 + \left(y - \frac{15}{2}\right)^2 = \frac{153}{4}$
e. $\left(x + \frac{11}{2}\right)^2 + \left(y - \frac{19}{2}\right)^2 = \frac{9}{2}$
f. $\left(x + \frac{3}{2}\right)^2 + \left(y - \frac{3}{2}\right)^2 = \frac{29}{2}$
7. $k = \frac{200}{3}$
8. a. x-intercepts = 2, 10; no y-intercept
b. x-intercepts = $6\sqrt{2} - 4$, $-6\sqrt{2} - 4$;
y-intercepts = $-3 + \sqrt{65}$, $-3 - \sqrt{65}$
c. x-intercept = 5;
y-intercepts = $6 + \sqrt{11}$, $6 - \sqrt{11}$
d. no x-intercept; no y-intercept
9. a. $(x - 8)^2 + (y + 9)^2 = 50$
b. $(x + 4)^2 + (y + 5)^2 = 208$
c. $(x + 2)^2 + (y - 6)^2 = 245$
10. $(x - 5)^2 + y^2 = 18$ or $(x + 5)^2 + y^2 = 58$
11. $(x - 3)^2 + (y - 3)^2 = 37$
12. $(x - 5)^2 + (y - 6)^2 = 260$ **13.** $x^2 + (y + 3)^2 = 9$
14. a. $C(1, -2)$; $r = 4$ **b.** $C(-4, -3)$; $r = 5$
c. $C(7, -3)$; $r = 3$ **d.** $C(7, 0)$; $r = 10$ **e.** $C(0, -12)$;
$r = 8$ **f.** $C\left(-\frac{1}{2}, 4\right)$; $r = 2$ **15.** $x^2 + (y - 3)^2 = 25$
16. $x^2 + y^2 = 40$ or $x^2 + (y - 4)^2 = 40$
18. $(x - 6)^2 + (y - 2)^2 = 26$
19. a. $4x - 7y - 25 = 0$ **b.** $x + 2y - 5 = 0$
c. $\left(\frac{17}{3}, -\frac{1}{3}\right)$ **d.** $\frac{5}{3}\sqrt{26}$
e. $\left(x - \frac{17}{3}\right)^2 + \left(y + \frac{1}{3}\right)^2 = \frac{650}{9}$
20. $\left(x - \frac{17}{14}\right)^2 + \left(y + \frac{13}{7}\right)^2 = \frac{19\,669}{196}$

Extra, page 235

1. $(x,y) \rightarrow (x - 3, y)$ **2.** $(x,y) \rightarrow (x + 5, y + 6)$
3. a. $(x + 5)^2 + y^2 = 16$ **b.** $x^2 + (y - 7)^2 = 16$
c. $(x + 8)^2 + (y - 6)^2 = 16$

Exercise 7–7, page 237
1. a. 1 **b.** 2 **c.** 1 **d.** 1 **e.** 2 **f.** 2
2. a. secant; $(-5, 0)$, $(3, -4)$ **4.** $A(-4, 2)$; $B(-2, -4)$; $|AB| = 2\sqrt{10}$ **7.** $B(8, 0)$ **8.** $(5, 6)$; $(8, -1)$

Exercise 7–8, page 239
1. a. $3x - 4y + 25 = 0$ **b.** $5x + 3y - 34 = 0$
c. $6x - y - 37 = 0$ **d.** $5x + 2y + 29 = 0$
e. $4x - 3y + 50 = 0$ **f.** $3x + 2y - 26 = 0$

2. a. $y = \frac{1}{\sqrt{7}}x + 4$; $y = -\frac{1}{\sqrt{7}}x + 4$

b. $y = \sqrt{\frac{5}{2}}\ x + 7$; $y = -\sqrt{\frac{5}{2}}x + 7$

c. $y = \sqrt{\frac{14}{11}}x + \frac{5\sqrt{14}}{\sqrt{11}}$; $y = -\sqrt{\frac{14}{11}}x - \frac{5\sqrt{14}}{\sqrt{11}}$

3. a. $2x + y - 12 = 0$ **4.** $3x - 4y - 60 = 0$
5. $5x - y + 26 = 0$ or $5x - y - 26 = 0$
6. a. $y = mx + 26$ **b.** $y = 5x + 26$ or $y = -5x + 26$
7. a. $y = x + 4$ or $y = -x + 4$ **b.** $y = 2x + 15$ or $y = -2x + 15$ **c.** $y = 4x + 17$ or $y = -4x + 17$
d. $y = 2x + 10$ or $y = -2x + 10$ **8. a.** $y = 5$ or $y = \frac{35}{12}x - \frac{185}{12}$ **b.** $y = \frac{11}{2}x + \frac{25}{2}$ or $y = -2x + 5$
c. $y = -\frac{1}{2}x - 5$ or $y = -\frac{11}{2}x - 25$ **d.** $y = \frac{1}{2}x + \frac{5}{2}$ or $y = -2x - 5$ **e.** $y = 41x - 116$ or $y = x + 4$
f. $y = -\frac{1}{3}x - \frac{10}{3}$ or $y = 3x - 10$
9. a. $y = -\frac{2}{11}x + \frac{34}{11}$ or $y = -2x - 6$
10. a. $y = 4x - 11$ or $y = 4x - 45$
11. $y = \frac{62}{19}x + 15$ or $y = -2x + 15$

Exercises 7–9, page 241
4. c. $PA \doteq 9.85$ **d.** $PC \doteq 10.63$; $CA = 4$
5. c. $QA \doteq 10.25$ **d.** $QC \doteq 11.40$; $CA = 5$

Application, page 242
1. a. $r = \frac{d^2 + 4h^2}{8h}$ **b.** ~ 11.15 **c.** ~ 16.04 m
2. 1.9 m **3.** ~ 0.384 m

Review, page 243
1. a. $C(0, 0)$; $r = 9$; x-intercepts $= \pm 9$; y-intercepts $= \pm 9$ **b.** $C(0, 0)$; $r = \frac{3}{2}$; x-intercepts $= \pm\frac{3}{2}$; y-intercepts $= \pm\frac{3}{2}$
c. $C(0, 2)$; $r = 2$; x-intercept $= 0$; y-intercepts $= 0, 4$ **d.** $C(4, -3)$; $r = 4$; x-intercepts $= 4 + \sqrt{7}, 4 - \sqrt{7}$; y-intercept $= 0$
2. $(x - 2)^2 + (y - 5)^2 = 4$
3. $(x + 2)^2 + (y - 3)^2 = 136$ **4.** $\frac{112}{9}\pi\,\text{cm}^2$; $\frac{28}{9}\pi$ cm

6. a. 8 **b.** 1 **c.** $\sqrt{589}$ **7. a.** $x = 110°$; $y = 70°$; $z = 110°$ **b.** $x = 54°$; $y = 32°$; $z = 32°$; $r = 86°$; $w = 62°$ **c.** $x = 85°$; $y = 85°$; $z = 95°$;
8. b. $(-4, -2)$ **9. b.** $(-6, -3)$, $(1, -2)$
10. $y = \frac{3}{2}x - \frac{13}{2}$ **11.** $y = \frac{1}{3}x + \frac{20}{3}$ or $y = 3x - 20$

Test, page 244
2. a. $x^2 + y^2 = 49$ **b.** $(x - 5)^2 + (y + 2)^2 = 64$
c. $(x - 1)^2 + (y - 10)^2 = 4$ **3.** $\frac{8}{3}\pi$ units **4.** 2
6. $(x - 2)^2 + (y + 1)^2) = 136$ **7. a.** $x = 110°$; $y = 50°$ **b.** $x = 24$; $y = 24$; $z = 7$ **8.** 18.75 m
9. $3x + y + 20 = 0$

Cumulative Review, page 245
1. a. $\frac{33}{200} = 0.165$ **b.** 0.609 **c.** -42.875 **d.** 3.0
e. 0.1 **f.** 0.0992 **g.** 2.667 **h.** 1
2. a. $3x(2y + 5z + 4)$ **b.** $xy(x^2z + yz + 1)$
c. $(x + 1)^2$ **d.** $(9x - 5)(16x + 7)$
e. $(6y^2 - x^3)(36y^4 + 6y^2x^3 + x^6)$
f. $3(4x + 3)(4x - 3)$ **g.** $(3 + y)(x - y)$
h. $(2 + y)(x^2 - 4)$ **i.** $(4 + 3x)(z + 4y)$

3. a. $\frac{6y - y^2 + 9}{9 - y^2}$ **b.** $\frac{5a + 12}{5a\,(6 - 5a)}$ **c.** $\frac{2x + 30}{x^2 + 3x - 18}$

d. $\frac{6x^2 - 10x + 1}{-2x^2 + 5x - 3}$ **e.** $\frac{3(m^2 - 5)}{m^2 - 5m + 4}$

f. $\frac{36t^2 + 22t + 1}{10t^2 + 11t + 3}$

4. a. $\sqrt{13}$ **b.** $2\sqrt{29}$ **c.** $\sqrt{145}$ **d.** $\sqrt{122}$
e. $5\sqrt{5}$ **f.** $\sqrt{41}$ **g.** $\sqrt{65}$ **h.** $2\sqrt{82}$
5. a. $x = 5$ **b.** $x = 1$ **c.** $x = 6$ or $x = -1$
d. $x = \frac{19}{3}$ **e.** $x = -\frac{2}{3}$ or $x = -1$
f. $x = 0.379$ or $x = -0.879$

6. a.

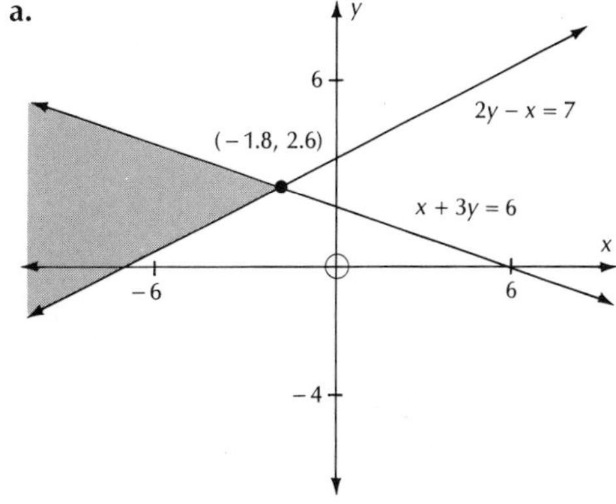

b.

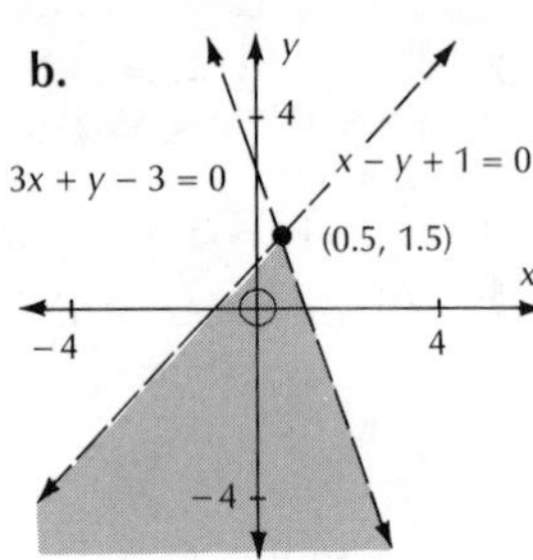

c.

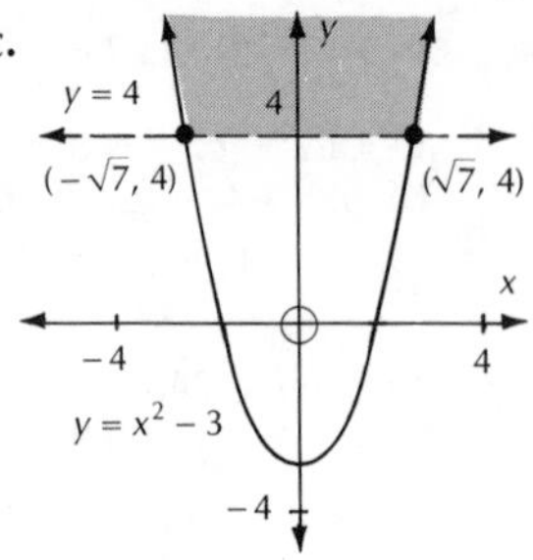

d.

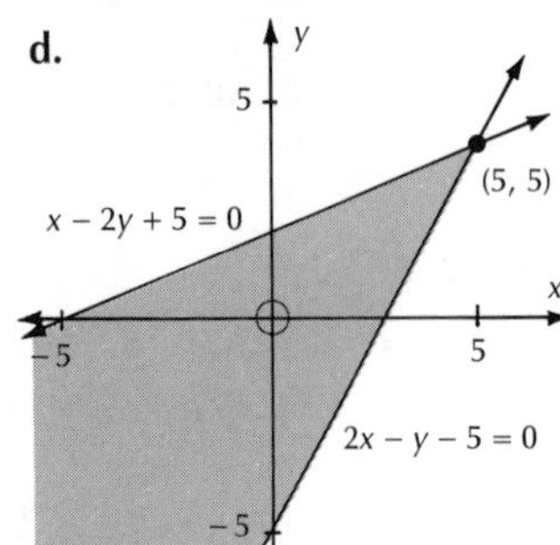

e.

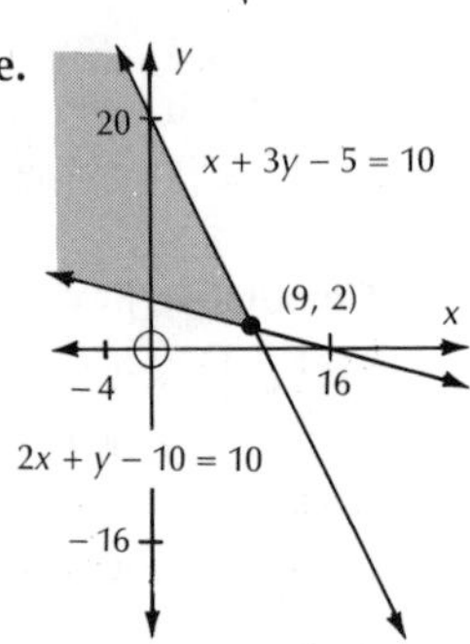

f.

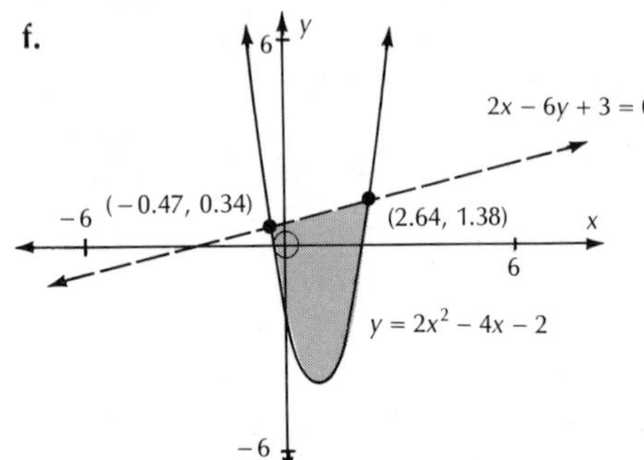

7. a. $3\sqrt{14} = 11.225$ **b.** $7\sqrt{3} = 12.124$
c. $\sqrt{119} = 10.909$ **d.** $3\sqrt{7} = 7.94$ **e.** $xy\sqrt{x}$
f. $3\sqrt[3]{19} = 8.005$ **g.** $xy\sqrt{yz}$ **h.** $6\sqrt{143} = 71.750$
8. a. $5\sqrt{2}$ cm = 7.071 cm **9.** 5 large, 5 small

UNIT 8

Exercise 8–1, pages 250–251

1. a. $f(4) = 7$, $f(-3) = -14$, $f(0) = -5$, $f(6) = 13$
b. $g(3) = 6$, $g(-1) = 2$, $g(4) = 12$, $g(-3) = 12$
c. $h(4) = 27$, $h(-4) = 27$, $h(0) = -5$, $h(7) = 93$
d. $m(3) =$ undefined, $m(-1) = -\frac{7}{8}$, $m(4) = 1$,
$m(6) = \frac{7}{27}$
2. a. function; domain $= \{x \mid x \in \boldsymbol{R}\}$,
range $= \{y \mid y \in \boldsymbol{R}\}$
b. function; domain $= \{x \mid x \in \boldsymbol{R}\}$,
range $= \{y \in \boldsymbol{R} \mid y \geqslant -3\}$
c. not a function; domain $= \{x \in \boldsymbol{R} \mid |x| \leq 3\}$,
range $= \{y \in \boldsymbol{R} \mid |y| \leqslant 3\}$
d. not a function; domain $= \{x \in \boldsymbol{R} \mid x \geq 1\}$,
range $= \{y \mid y \in \boldsymbol{R}\}$
e. function; domain $= \boldsymbol{Z}$, range $= \boldsymbol{R}$
f. function; domain $= \{x \mid x \in \boldsymbol{R}\}$,
range $= \{y \in \boldsymbol{R} \mid y = 5\}$
3. a. range = {10, 9, 8, 7, 6, 5, 4,}
b. range = {4, −1, −4, −5}
c. range = {0, 1, 2, 3}
d. range $= \left\{7, \frac{7}{2}, \frac{7}{3}, \frac{7}{4}, \frac{7}{5}, \frac{7}{6}, 1\right\}$
e. range = {−36, −12, −2, 0, 4, 18}
f. range $= \left\{-\frac{1}{8}, -\frac{1}{3}, 1\right\}$
4. a. range $= \{y: y \in \boldsymbol{R}, -2 \leq y \leq 2\}$
b. range $= \{y: y \in \boldsymbol{R}, 0 < y \leq 8\}$
5. a. 9 **b.** −2 **c.** −13 **d.** 17 **e.** undefined
f. $-\frac{5}{3}$ **g.** $-\frac{22}{3}$ **h.** undefined **i.** $-\frac{1}{18}$ **j.** $-\frac{20}{3}$
6. a. $3x^2 - 1$ **b.** $(3x - 1)^2$ **c.** $3\sqrt{x} - 1$
d. $\sqrt{3x - 1}$ **e.** x **f.** x **7. a.** $a = 5$
b. $b = -5, 5$ **c.** $c = -\sqrt{3}, \sqrt{3}$ **d.** $d = -2, 2$
e. $e = -1, 5$ **8. a.** $y = x - 1$ **b.** $y = \frac{1}{2}x - 2$
c. $y = \frac{1}{2}x^2 - 3$ **9. a.** $x^2 + 3x - 2$ **b.** $x^2 - 3x + 2$

Exercise 8–2, pages 254–255

1. a. linear **b.** not linear **c.** linear
d. not linear **e.** linear **f.** linear
2. a. range $= \{y \mid y \in \boldsymbol{R}\}$
b. range $= \{y \in \boldsymbol{R} \mid y \geq 0\}$
c. range $= \{y \in \boldsymbol{R} \mid y \geq 0\}$
e. range $= \{y \in \boldsymbol{R} \mid y \geq 0\}$
f. range $= \{y \in \boldsymbol{R} \mid y \geq 0\}$
4. a. $f(x) = x$, if $x \leq 2$; piecewise linear
$f(x) = 2$, if $x \geq 2$
b. $f(x) = -x$, $x \in \boldsymbol{R}$; linear
c. $f(x) = |x| + 1$, $x \in \boldsymbol{R}$; piecewise linear
d. $f(x) = \frac{6}{x}$, $x \neq 0$; none of above (discrete)
e. $f(x) = 5$, if $0 \leq x < 1$; piecewise linear
$f(x) = 2$, if $1 \leq x < 4$
$f(x) = 0$, if $4 \leq x < 5$
f. $f(x) = -x^2 + 3$, $x \in \boldsymbol{R}$; quadratic
5. b. $t = 2$ **c.** 50 m
6. a. minimum value = 5, when $x = 0$
b. maximum value = 5, when $x = 0$
c. minimum value = 3, when $x = 2$
d. maximum value = 7, when $x = -5$
e. minimum value = −2, when $x = -3$
f. maximum value = 13, when $x = 1$

Exercise 8–3, page 257

1. a. S^{-1}: {(6, 3), (4, 2), (2, 1), (0, 0)}
b. f^{-1}: {(5, −3), (7, 2), (−1, 6), (3, 4)}
c. T^{-1}: {(3, 9), (−2, 4), (2, 4), (−1, 1)}
d. G^{-1}: {(1, 1), (6, 2), (12, −3), (20, 4), (30, −5)}
2. a. domain of S^{-1} = {5, 1, 6}
b. range of Q^{-1} = {−3, −2, 5}
5. a. (7, 3) b. no c. range of S^{-1} = {0, 3, 4, −1}
d. domain of Q^{-1} = {0, 1, 4},
range of Q^{-1} = {−2, −1, 0, 1, 2}
Q^{-1} is not a function.
6. $x = k$; no, $x = k$ is not a function.
7. a. $2x + y = 5$ b. $x - 3y = -5$, $3y - x = 5$
c. $3x + 2y = 12$

Exercise 8–4, pages 261–262

1. a. $y = \frac{1}{3}x$ b. $y = x + 1$ c. $y = \frac{x-3}{2}$
d. $y = \frac{x-5}{3}$ e. $y = \frac{5x-2}{3}$ f. $y = \frac{3x-1}{2}$
g. $y = -x$ h. $y = \frac{x}{3} - 4$ i. $y = -\frac{x-5}{2}$ 2. b, c
3. a. $y = \frac{1}{x}$ b. $y = \pm\sqrt{x}$ c. $y = 3\sqrt[3]{x}$
d. $y = \frac{x+1}{x}$ e. $y = \pm\sqrt{\frac{1}{x}}$ f. $x = 3\sqrt[3]{\ }$
g. $y = \pm\sqrt{\frac{x+2}{3}}$ h. $y = \frac{1-3x}{2x}$
i. $y = \pm\sqrt{\frac{1+3x}{x}}$
4. a. $x \geq 0$ or $x \leq 0$ b. $x \geq 0$ or $x \leq 0$
c. $x \leq 2$ or $x \geq 2$ d. $0 \leq x \leq 3$ or $-3 \leq x \leq 0$
5. a. $f(g(x)) = x$; f and g are inverses
b. $f(g(x)) = x$; f and g are inverses
c. $f(g(x)) = \frac{3x-5}{2}$; f and g are not inverses
d. $f(g(x)) = \frac{1}{x^2}$; f and g are not inverses
e. $f(g(x)) = x$; f and g are inverses
f. $f(g(x)) = \sqrt{x^3 + 3x^2 + 3x + 2}$; f and g are not inverses
g. $f(g(x)) = x$; f and g are inverses
h. $f(g(x)) = \frac{1}{4x+3}$; f and g are not inverses
i. $f(g(x)) = x$; f and g are inverses
7. no
8. No restrictions except $a \neq 0$ needed.

Review, page 263

1. range = {−2, 1, 10}
2. a. domain = $\{x \mid x \in \mathbf{R}\}$, range = $\{y \mid y \in \mathbf{R}\}$
b. domain = $\{x \in \mathbf{R} \mid x \neq -2\}$, range = $\{y \in \mathbf{R} \mid y \neq 0\}$
c. domain = $\{x \in \mathbf{R} \mid x \neq 0\}$, range = $\{y \in \mathbf{R} \mid y > 0\}$
d. domain = $\{x \mid x \in \mathbf{R}\}$, range = $\{y \in \mathbf{R} \mid y \geq 3\}$
e. domain = $\{x \in \mathbf{R} \mid x \geq 4\}$, range = $\{y \in \mathbf{R} \mid y \geq 0\}$
f. domain = $\{x \in \mathbf{R} \mid |x| \geq 2\}$, range = $\{y \in \mathbf{R} \mid y \geq 0\}$
3. a. function b. not a function c. function
4. a. 11 b. 8 c. 3 d. 30 e. −9 f. 22
5. a. S^{-1} = {(7, 3), (5, 2), (3, 1), (1, 0), (2, −1), (3, −2)}
b. $f^{-1}(x) = 2x - 3$ c. $g^{-1}(x) = \frac{x-5}{2}$
d. h^{-1}: $y = \frac{1-3x}{x}$ e. k^{-1}: $y = x^2 + 2$
f. m^{-1}: $y = (x + 7)^3$ 6. a. not a function
b. function c. not a function
7. a. 6a: $x \leq 2$ or $x \geq 2$
6c: $x \geq 0$ or $x \leq 0$
b. 6a: piecewise linear function
6b: linear function
6c: quadratic function
8. a. $f(g(x)) = x$; inverses
b. $f(g(x)) = x$; inverses
c. $f(g(x)) = \pm x$; not necessarily inverses

Exercise 8–5, pages 266–267

1. a. translation 3 units to the right
b. reflection in the x-axis
c. translation 2 units up
d. translation 1 unit to the left
e. reflection in the y-axis
f. translation 5 units down
g. reflection in the x-axis, then reflection in the y-axis
h. reflection in the y-axis, then translation 2 units up
i. translation 2 units to the left, then reflection in the x-axis
j. translation 3 units to the left, then translation 1 unit up.
2. a. translated 5 units down
b. reflected in the x-axis
3. a. translated 2 units up
b. translated 2 units down
c. translated 1 unit to the left
d. translated 3 units to the right
e. reflected in the y-axis
f. reflected in the x-axis
g. translated 2 units up and 1 unit to the left
h. reflected in the x-axis and translated 1 unit to the left
i. translated 2 units down and reflected in the y-axis
j. translated 5 units down and 4 units to the right
4. a. $y = x + 2$ b. $y = -x^2$ c. $y = 2x + 7$
d. $y = (x - 7)^2 + 1$ e. $y = -3x + 5$ f. $y = 5x - 9$

g. $y = 2(x + 2)^2 + 1$ **h.** $y = 3x - 1$ **i.** $y = 2x^2$
j. $y = -3(x - 3)^2$

5. a.

b.

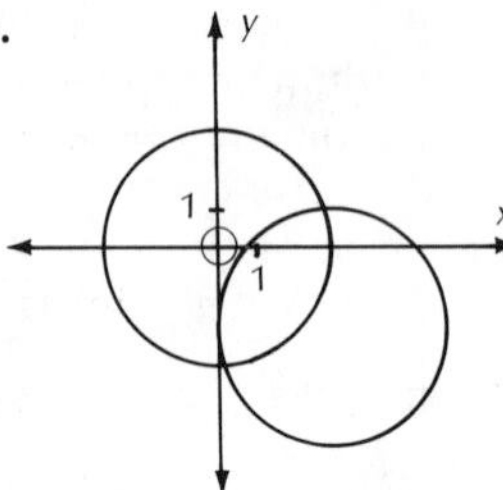

c.

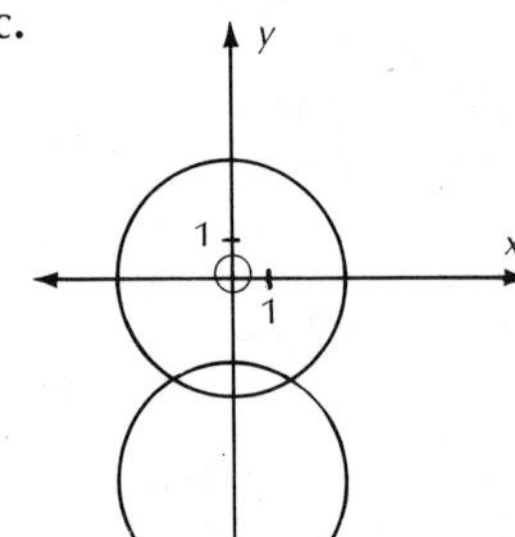

d.

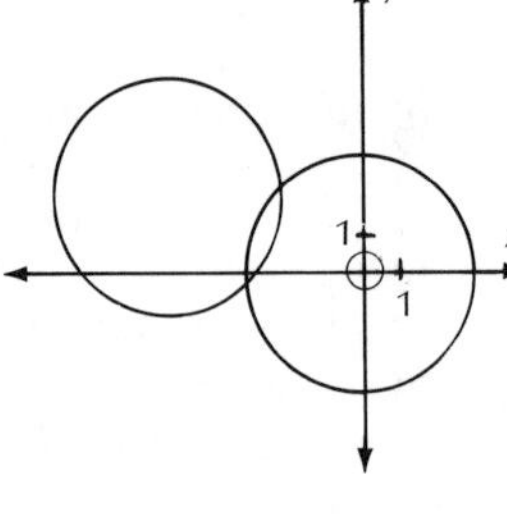

e.

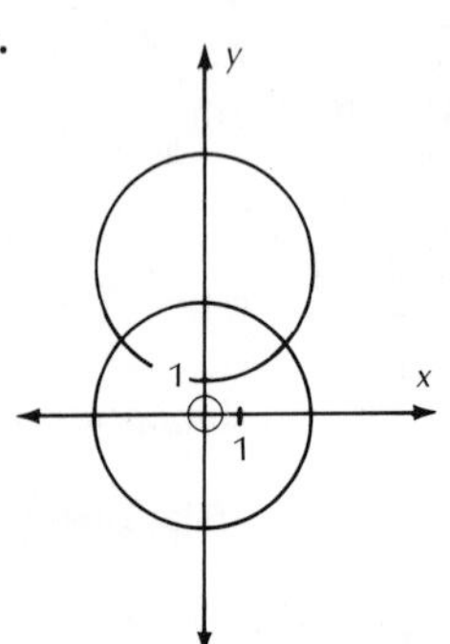

6. a. $y = -(x - 3)^2$
b. $(x + 3)^2 + (y - 4)^2 = 4$
7. a. Order of transformation does not affect image. Commutative.
b. Order of transformation does not affect image. Commutative.
c. Order of transformation does affect image. Not commutative.
d. Order of transformation does affect image. Not commutative.

Exercise 8–6, pages 270–271

1. a. horizontal stretch factor 2
b. vertical stretch factor 4
2. a. horizontal stretch factor $\frac{1}{5}$
b. vertical stretch factor 2
c. horizontal stretch factor 3
d. vertical stretch factor $\frac{1}{5}$
e. vertical stretch factor 3
f. vertical stretch factor $\frac{1}{2}$, translation downward 1 unit
3. a. $y = \frac{1}{2}|x| - 2$ **b.** $(2x)^2 + y^2 = 16$
c. $\frac{1}{3}x + y = 2$ **d.** $y = 2x^2 - 6$
5. a. vertical stretch factor 5, horizontal stretch factor 5
b. vertical stretch factor 3, horizontal stretch factor 2
c. vertical stretch factor 6, horizontal stretch factor 6
6. a. translation 2 units upward, horizontal stretch factor $\frac{1}{3}$
b. vertical stretch factor 2, translation 1 unit to the left
c. translation 3 units upward, horizontal stretch factor $\frac{1}{3}$
d. reflection in the x-axis, horizontal stretch factor 2
e. vertical stretch factor 3, reflection in the x-axis
f. vertical stretch factor 8, reflection in the line $y = x$

7. a.

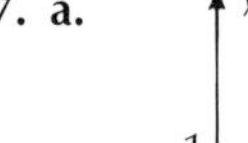

b.

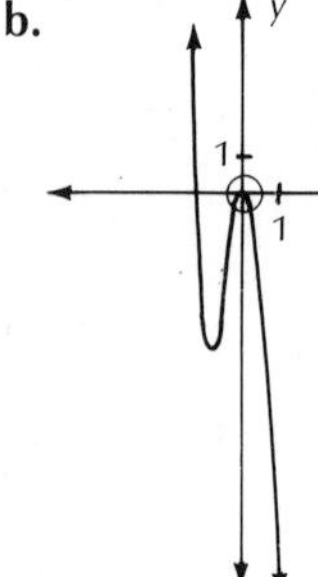

c.

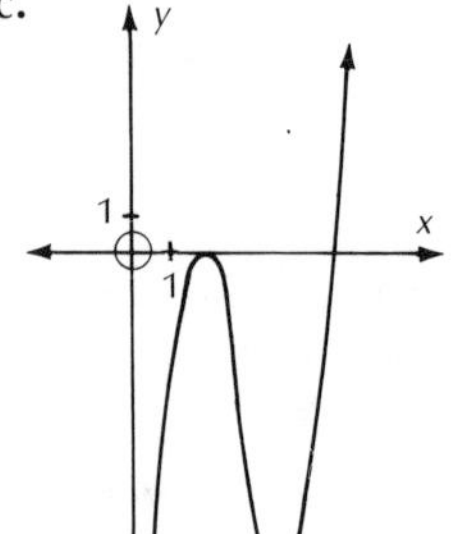

d.

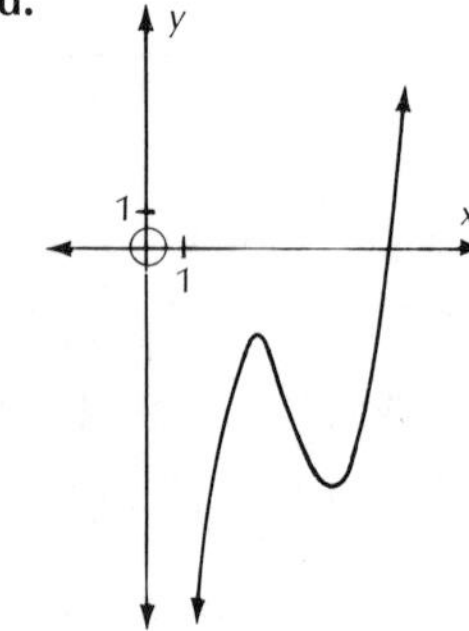

e.

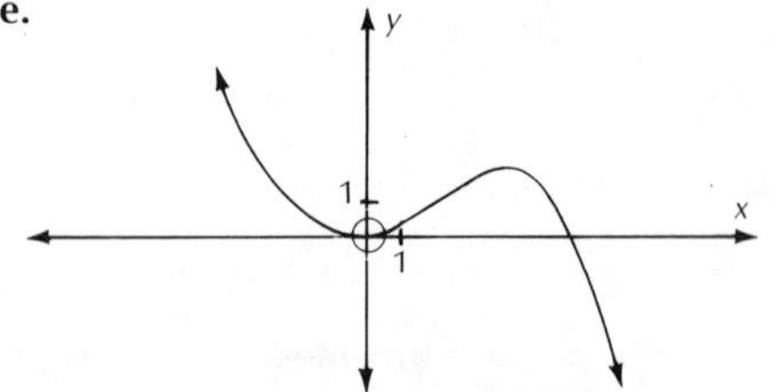

8. a. $y = 4x - 12$ **b.** $y = -\frac{1}{2x}$ **c.** $y = -3x^2$
d. $y = x$
9. a. horizontal stretch factor $\frac{1}{3}$, vertical translation down 1 unit

b. translation up 1 unit,
horizontal stretch factor $\frac{1}{2}$
c. horizontal stretch factor 2,
vertical translation down 2 units
d. horizontal stretch factor 2,
translation up 15 units, vertical stretch factor 3
e. reflection in y-axis, horizontal stretch factor $\frac{1}{3}$,
vertical translation up 6, vertical stretch factor $\frac{1}{2}$
f. a vertical stretch factor $\frac{1}{2}$

Exercise 8–7, page 273
1. a. 24 **b.** 10 **c.** 40 **d.** 0.9 **2. a.** 6 **b.** 7
c. 3.5 **3. a.** $Im = k$ **b.** $CR = k$ **c.** $at^2 = k$
d. $Id^2 = k$ **4. a.** 7.5 **b.** 0.018 **c.** 43.75
5. a. 1.25 **b.** 5 **c.** 0.4 **7.** yes **8.** 0.18 N
9. 370.37 kPa

Exercise 8–8, pages 276–277
1. a. 6 **b.** 1 **c.** 18 **d.** 10 **e.** 18 **f.** 12
2. a. $y = kvt$ **b.** $m = \frac{kg}{l}$ **c.** $d = kat^2$
d. $A = \frac{kr^2}{u}$ **e.** $f = \frac{kc}{n}$ **f.** $F = kma$ **g.** $F = \frac{kr}{d^2}$
h. $x = \frac{kl^2}{r^3}$ **3. a.** 2 **b.** 36 **c.** 100 **d.** $\frac{1}{25}$ **e.** 8
f. $\frac{1}{3}$ **g.** $\frac{3}{2}$ **h.** 18 **i.** $\frac{1}{5}$ **4. a.** $x = kyz$ **b.** $\frac{5}{12}$
c. 10 **5. a.** $A = klw$ **b.** $\frac{7}{32}$ **c.** 14
6. a. $r = \frac{kd}{t}$ **b.** $k = 9; r = \frac{kd}{t}$ **c.** 9 **7.** $k = 180;$
$a = 60$ **8.** 21 **9.** 25 L/h **10.** 23.08 r/min
11. 23 040 kg **12.** 3 Ω

Historical Note, page 277
1.2×10^{23} m

Applications Involving Variation, pages 278–279
1. 315 000 kL **2.** 0.72 **3.** 50.4 km/h **4.** 11.43 cm
5. 1250 kPa **6.** 18.97 m^3 **7.** 630 s **8.** 20.42 m
b. $d = 4.9t^2$
9. Venus: 1.78×10^5 lx, Mars: 1.22×10^4 lx
Jupiter: 4.47×10^5 lx
10. a. Venus: 0.61 years = 223 d
Mars: 1.87 years = 684 d
Jupiter: 11.86 years = 4328 d
b. 0.24 of Earth's year = 88 d
c. 9.55 (in terms of Earth's distance)
= 1.43×10^9 km

Review, pages 280–281
1. a, c **2. a.** 7 **b.** 4 **c.** $\frac{1}{2}$ **d.** −15 **e.** 9 **f.** 40
g. −5 **h.** 10 **i.** 0
3. a. domain = {3, 2, 5, −3}, range = {1, −4, 6, 2}
b. domain = {0, 2, 7, −3}, range = {4, 1, 0, 5},
not a function
c. domain = $\{x \in \mathbf{R} \mid x > 3\}$, range = $\{y \mid y > 2\}$
d. domain = $\{x \mid -4 < x \leq 5\}$,
range = $\{y \mid 2 \leq y \leq 5\}$
4. a. linear **b.** quadratic **c.** discrete
d. constant **e.** step **f.** piecewise linear
5. a. function **b.** not a function
6. a. $y = x + 5$ **b.** $y = \pm\sqrt{x - 2}$ **c.** $y = \frac{x + 1}{2x}$
8. a. reflection in the x-axis
b. vertical translation up 3, horizontal translation left 2
c. vertical translation down 1, horizontal stretch factor $\frac{1}{3}$
d. vertical transltion down 2, reflection in y-axis, horizontal stretch factor 3
9. a. $y = \frac{1}{2}x + 3$ **b.** $y = -\frac{1}{2}x + 2$
c. $y = |x - 3| + 2$ **d.** $y = -x^2$
10. a. **b.**

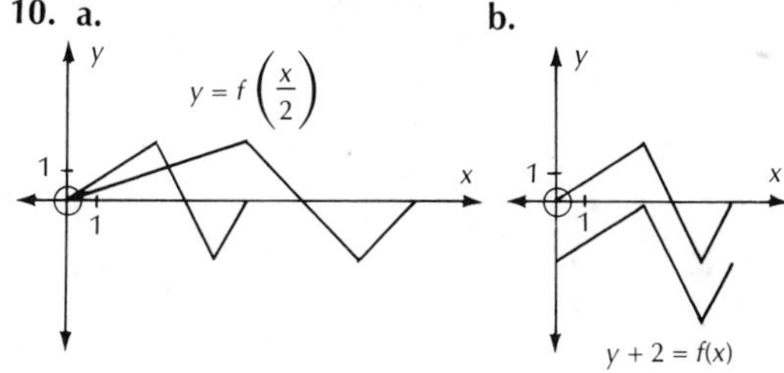

c.

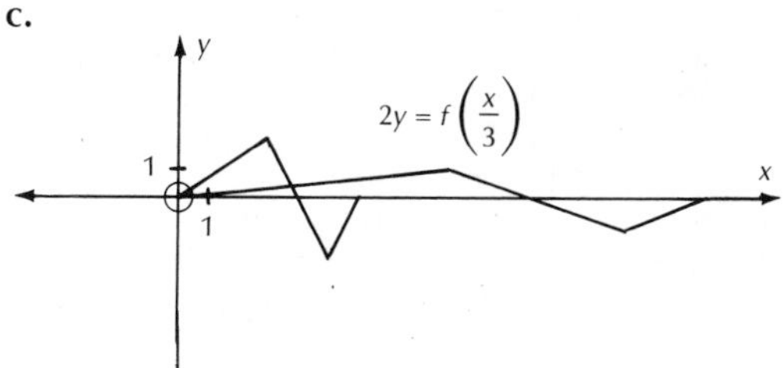

d. **e.**

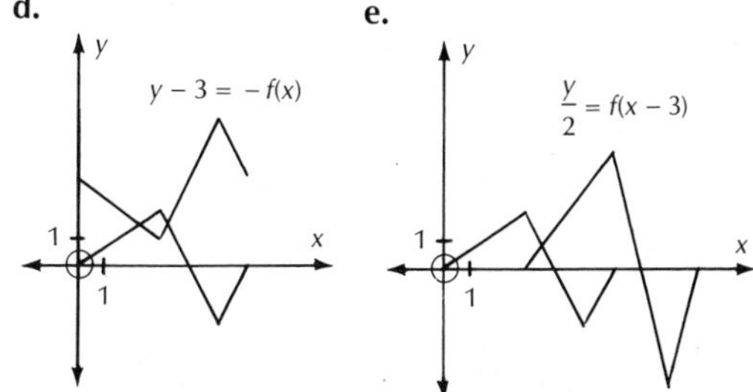

11. a. 13.5 **b.** 12.5 **c.** 8 **d.** 18
12. 3.36 min

Test, page 282

1. a. **b.**

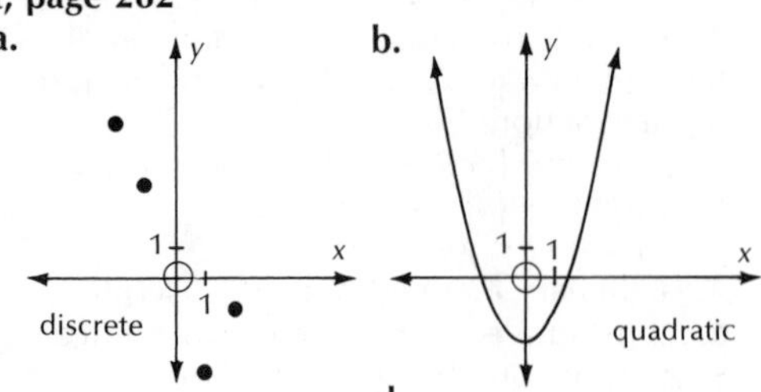

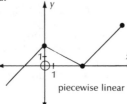

c. **d.**

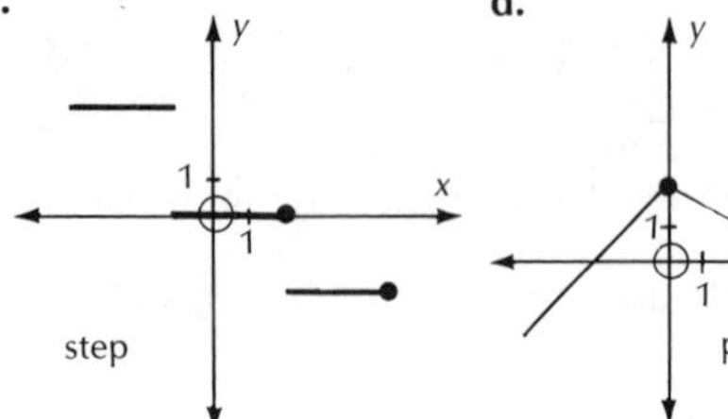

piecewise linear

e. **f.**

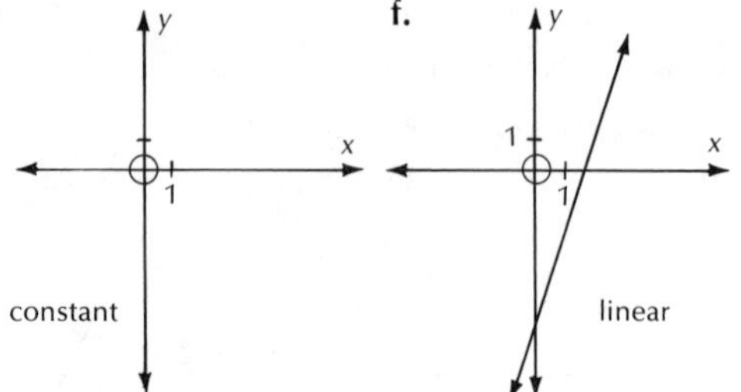

2. a. domain = $\{-2, -1, 0, 1, 2\}$
range = $\{-3, -1, 0, 3, 5\}$
b. domain = $\{x \mid x \in \mathbf{R}\}$,
range = $\{y \in \mathbf{R} \mid y \geq -2\}$
c. domain = $\{x \in \mathbf{R} \mid -4 \leq x \leq 5\}$,
range = $\{-2, 0, 3\}$
d. domain = $\{x \in \mathbf{R} \mid -4 \leq x < 8\}$,
range = $\{y \in \mathbf{R} \mid -2 \leq y < 4\}$
e. domain = $\{x \mid x \in \mathbf{R}\}$, range = $\{3\}$
f. domain = $\{x \mid x \in \mathbf{R}\}$, range = $\{y \mid y \in \mathbf{R}\}$
3. a. function **b.** not a function **c.** function

4. a. $y = \frac{1}{(x-3)^2}$ **b.** $y = -3x + 3$ **c.** $y = \frac{1}{3}x - \frac{1}{2}$

d. $(x + 4)^2 + (3y)^2 = 9$ **e.** $\frac{y}{4} = -x$ **5. a.** $S = \frac{kf}{L^2}$

b. 15 **c.** 1.2 **6.** 57.6 g

Cumulative Review, page 283

1. a. $\frac{5}{6}$ **b.** $\frac{7}{3}$ **2. a.** $x = \frac{49}{18}, y = -\frac{10}{9}$ **b.** $x = \frac{19}{5}$,

$y = \frac{16}{5}$ **c.** $x = \frac{11 - \sqrt{101}}{5}, y = \frac{9 + \sqrt{101}}{15}$

or $x = \frac{11 + \sqrt{101}}{5}, y = \frac{9 - \sqrt{101}}{15}$

d. $x = \frac{32 + 6\sqrt{209}}{25}, y = \frac{-24 + 8\sqrt{209}}{25}$

or $x = \frac{32 - 6\sqrt{209}}{25}, y = \frac{-24 - 8\sqrt{209}}{25}$

e. $x = \frac{9 - \sqrt{561}}{4}, y = \frac{-9 - \sqrt{561}}{10}$ or $x = \frac{9 + \sqrt{561}}{4}$,

$y = \frac{-9 + \sqrt{561}}{10}$ **f.** no real solution

3. a. parabola opening upwards with vertex $\left(\frac{1}{3}, \frac{14}{3}\right)$ and y-intercept (0, 5)

b. parabola opening downwards with vertex $\left(\frac{5}{4}, -\frac{39}{8}\right)$ and y-intercept (0, −8)

c. parabola opening downwards with vertex (6, 18) and y-intercept (0, 0)

4. a. −4, 1 **b.** $\frac{5 + \sqrt{145}}{6}, \frac{5 - \sqrt{145}}{6}$

c. no x-intercepts **5. a.** $x = 49°$, $y = 59°$
b. $x = 210°$, $y = 105°$ **6.** $C(-4, 6)$; radius = 10
7 a. $k = \pm 6\sqrt{5}$ **b.** $-6\sqrt{5} < k < 6\sqrt{5}$
c. $|k| > 6\sqrt{5}$
8. a.

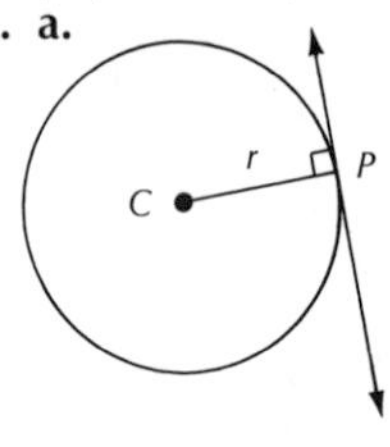

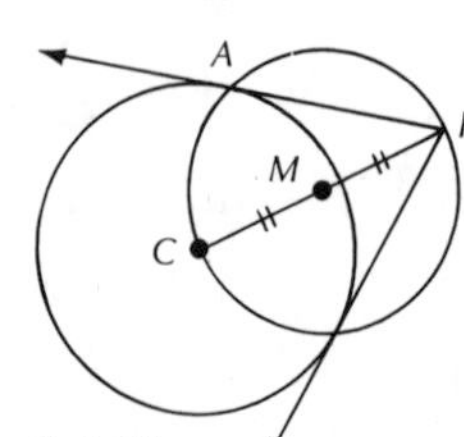

9. a. range = $\{15, 3, -1, 8\}$ **b.** range = $\{4, 3, 2, 1\}$
c. range = $\{7, 6, 5, 3\}$ **d.** range = $\{\pm 3\}$

UNIT 9

Exercise 9–1, pages 286–287

1. a. 10, 12, 14, 16 **b.** 36, 49, 64, 81 **c.** 11, 13, 15, 17 **d.** 125, 216, 343, 512 **e.** 1, 6, 1, 7
f. 2, 25, 2, 36 **g.** 5, 25, 6, 30 **h.** $75\sqrt{5}, 375, 375\sqrt{5}$, 1875 **2. a.** 2, 6, 10, 14, 18 **b.** 1, 4, 9, 16, 25
c. 5, 25, 125, 625, 3125 **d.** $\frac{1}{2}, 1, \frac{5}{4}, \frac{7}{5}, \frac{3}{2}$

e. 0, −2, −4, −6, −8 **f.** $\frac{1}{3}, 1, \frac{9}{5}, \frac{8}{3}, \frac{25}{7}$ **g.** 1, 2, 4, 8, 16
h. 6, 12, 03 24, 48, 96 **i.** 4, 13, 28, 49, 76
3. a. $t_n = 3n$ **b.** $t_n = 2_n - 3$ **c.** $t_n = n^2$
d. $t_n = 3(2^{n-1})$ **e.** $t_n = \frac{n+1}{n+2}$ **f.** $t_n = \frac{n+1}{n(n+2)}$

4. a. $t_7 = 32$, $t_{25} = 122$ **b.** $t_4 = 9$, $t_8 = 129$

5. a. 7, 11, 15, 19 **b.** −8, −32, −128, −512
b. 6, 8, 11, 15 **d.** −8, −25, −62, −139
e. 15, 82, 419, 2106 **f.** 0, 9, 25, 50
6. \$240, \$265, \$290, \$315, \$340, \$365, \$390
7. a. 1340, 1230, 1120, 1010, 900
b. $t_n = 1450 - 110n$ **c.** after 9 years
8. $t_n = t_{n-1} + t_{n-2}$, with $t_1 = 1$ and $t_2 = 1$
9. a. 5, 10, 20, 40, 80, 160 **b.** $t_n = 5\,(2^{n-1})$
c. $t_n = 2\,(t_{n-1})$, $t_1 = 5$
d. The general term is easier to use since the value of the previous term is not needed to solve for the value of the present term.
e. $t_{15} = 81.920$ **f.** 13 h **10. a.** \$9600
b. $t_n = 9600\,(0.95)^{n-1}$ **c.** \$7819.26
11. a. $t_n = 4\,842\,042\,000\,(1.015)^n$ **b.** 6 053 676 200

Extra, page 287
$t_5 = t_4 + 5 = 16$ regions. In general $t_n = t_{n-1} + n$

Exercise 9–2, pages 290–291
1. a., c.,d., e., g., h., i. **2. a.** 3 **c.** −2 **d.** −6
e. $\frac{1}{2}$ **g.** 10 **h.** $-q$ **i.** $3a$
3. a. $d = 5$; 22, 27, 32, ...
b. $d = -4$; −7, −11, −15, ... **c.** $d = -3$; 6, 3, 0, ...
d. $d = 4$; 8, 12, 16, ...
4. a. $t_{15} = 46$; $t_n = 3n + 1$
b. $t_{25} = -87$; $t_n = -7n + 88$ **c.** $t_9 = 7$; $t_n = \frac{2}{3}n + 1$
d. $t_{100} = -590$; $t_n - 6n + 10$
5. a. $t_n = 2n$ **b.** $t_n = 2n - 1$ **c.** $t_n = 5n$
d. $t_n = -7n$ **6. a.** 48 **b.** 37 **c.** 25 **d.** 99
7. a. $a = 5$, $d = 4$, $t_{100} = 401$
b. $a = -4$, $d = 6$, $t_{100} = 590$
c. $a = 5$, $d = -7$, $t_{100} = -688$
d. $a = 3$, $d = -4$, $t_{100} = -393$
e. $a = -1$, $d = -4$, $t_{100} = -397$
f. $a = -7$, $d = 5$, $t_{100} = 488$
8. a. 12 **b.** 18 **c.** −7.50 **9. a.** 3 **b.** −1 **c.** 4
d. 12 **10.** 12, 17, 22 **12.** no
13. a. $t_n = (2n - 1)(3n - 1)$ **b.** no
14. a. $t_n = \dfrac{2n - 1}{2n + 1}$ **b.** $t_n = \dfrac{2n}{4n + 1}$
c. $t_n = (2n)(4n - 1)$ **d.** $t_n = (2n + 5)(-3n + 15)$
15. 7, 10, 13 or 13, 10, 7 **16.** no

Extra, page 291
1. 20; 100 **2.** 1, 19; 1, 99
3. $t_n = t_{n-1} + (n - 1)$, $t_0 = 0$

Exercise 9–3, pages 294–295
1. a., b., c., f., g., h., j. **2. a.** 3 **b.** −1 **c.** 0.1
f. −2 **g.** 0.1 **h.** 1 **j.** $\frac{1}{4}$ **3. a.** $r = 2$; 192, 384, 768
b. $r = -1$; 8, −8, 8 **c.** $r = \frac{1}{3}$; 3^{-5}, 3^{-6}, 3^{-7}
d. $r = -\frac{1}{3}$; $\frac{2}{81}$, $-\frac{2}{243}$, $\frac{2}{729}$
e. $r = \sqrt{3}$; $9\sqrt{2}$, $9\sqrt{6}$, $27\sqrt{2}$
f. $r = \sqrt{5}$; $125\sqrt{5}$, 625, $625\sqrt{5}$
4. a. $t_7 = 128$, $t_{12} = 4096$
b. $t_7 = 6 \times 10^{-7}$, $t_{12} = 6 \times 10^{-12}$
c. $t_7 = \dfrac{5}{729}$, $t_{12} = \dfrac{-5}{177\,147}$ **d.** $t_7 = at^7$, $t_{12} = at^{12}$
5. a. $t_3 = 36$, $t_{10} = 78\,732$ **b.** $t_3 = 20$, $t_{10} = -2560$
c. $t_3 = \frac{9}{4}$, $t_{10} = \frac{9}{512}$ **d.** $t_3 = 0.06$, $t_{10} = -6 \times 10^{-9}$
e. $t_3 = 4$, $t_{10} = 32\sqrt{2}$ **f.** $t_3 = 72$, $t_{10} = 1944\sqrt{3}$
6. a. 4 **b.** 8 **c.** 8
7. a. $x = 6$, $y = 24$ or $x = -6$, $y = -24$
b. $x = 16$, $y = -128$
8. a. $n = 9$; $t_n = 25(5)^{n-1}$ **b.** $n = 9$; $t_n = 4(3)^{n-1}$
c. $n = 10$; $t_n = 32\left(-\frac{1}{4}\right)^{n-1}$
d. $n = 7$; $t_n = 0.1(1000)^{n-1}$
e. $n = 13$; $t_n = 36\left(\frac{1}{3}\right)^{n-1}$ **f.** $n = 4$; $t_n = 80(-5)^{n-1}$
9. $t_3 = x^3 - 2x^2 - 4x + 8$
10. $x = 8$; 45, 15, 5; $x = -2$; −5, −5, −5
11. 24, 72, 216 or −24, 72, −216
12. a $a = 12$, $r = 2$, $t_n = 12(2)^{n-1}$
b. $a = 15$, $r = \frac{1}{3}$, $t_n = 15\left(\frac{1}{3}\right)^{n-1}$
or $a = 15$, $r = -\frac{1}{3}$, $t_n = 15\left(-\frac{1}{3}\right)^{n-1}$
c. $a = -24$, $r = \frac{1}{2}$, $t_n = -24\left(\frac{1}{2}\right)^{n-1}$
or $a = -24$, $r = -\frac{1}{2}$, $t_n = -24\left(-\frac{1}{2}\right)^{n-1}$
d. $a = 0.1$, $r = 3$, $t_n = 0.1(3)^{n-1}$
13. $t_8 = 8748$ **14.** no **15. a.** 6 **b.** $x = \sqrt{ab}$
c. $q = 9$ **16. a.** 32 **b.** 35 **c.** $\frac{4}{9}$ **17. a.** 6, 12, 24
b. 48, 24, 12, 6 **18.** $x = 12$, $y = 18$ or $x = \frac{3}{4}$, $y = -\frac{9}{2}$
19. 3, 6, 12, 24, 48 or 7, −14, 28, −56, 112
20. 4, 12, 36, 108, 324, 972 **21.** 4, 8 or 8, 4
22. 32.7 Hz, 65.4 Hz, 130.8 Hz, 261.6 Hz, 523.2 Hz, 1046.4 Hz, 2092.8 Hz, 4185.6 Hz

Problem Solving, page 296
1. a. \$21 250 **b.** at the end of 9 years
2. 31 days **3.** 256 ancestors **4.** 16 steps
5. ~ 3939 **6.** \$5.75 **7.** after 8 weeks
8. 340.5 m/s **9. a.** 30 times **b.** yes

Review, page 297
1. a. 3, 7, 11, 15 **b.** −3, −5, −9, −17
c. $\frac{1}{4}$, $\frac{4}{5}$, $\frac{3}{2}$, $\frac{16}{7}$ **2. a.** geometric sequence
b. arithmetic sequence **c.** geometric sequence

d. neither
3. a. $t_n = 3(2)^{n-1}$; $n = 9$ **b.** $t_n = -4n + 22$; $n = 16$
c. $t_n = 0.5(0.1)^{n-1}$; $n = 7$ **d.** $t_n = n^2$; $n = 25$
4. $t_{10} = 56$ **5.** $t_6 = \frac{4}{27}$ **6.** 13 times
b. no; yes **c.** 1st, 5th, 11th. **d.** the 15th term
7. a. $\frac{1}{3}, \frac{2}{3}, 1$ **b.** 1, 3, 9 or $\frac{13}{7}, -\frac{39}{7}, \frac{117}{7}$ **8.** 5, 7, 9
9. 5, 15, 45 or $-\frac{5}{2}$, 0, 0 **10.** $x = 8$, $y = 24$
or $x = 2$, $y = 12$ **11.** 2500

Exercise 9–4, page 299
1. a. $1 + 3 + 5 + 7 + 9 + \ldots + 41$
b. $0.7 + 0.77 + 0.777 + 0.7777 + 0.77777$
c. $1 + 4 + 9 + 16 + 25 + 36 + \ldots + n^2$
d. $18 + 6 + 2 + \frac{2}{3} + \frac{2}{9} + \ldots + \frac{3}{243}$
2. $t_6 = 6$ **3. a.** $S_{10} = 55$ **b.** $S_{80} = 0$ **c.** $S_6 = 441$
d. $S_7 = 168$
4. a. $S_1 = 2, S_2 = 6, S_{10} = 110$
b. $S_1 = 4, S_2 = 11, S_{10} = 67$
c. $S_1 = 0, S_2 = 2, S_{10} = 90$
d. $S_1 = 10, S_2 = 4, S_{10} = -188$
e. $S_1 = 1, S_2 = 9, S_{10} = 3025$
f. $S_1 = 5, S_2 = 14, S_{10} = 230$
5. a. 2, 4, 6 **b.** 4, 7, 7 **c.** 0, 2, 4 **d.** 10, −6, −10
e. 1, 8, 27 **f.** 5, 9, 13 **6. a.** $t_n = 2n$
b. $t_1 = 4$; $t_n = 7, n > 1$ **c.** $t_n = 2n - 2$
d. $t_1 = 10$; $t_n = -4n + 2, n > 1$ **e.** $t_n = n^3$
f. $t_n = 4n + 1$
7. a. $S_1 = 1, S_5 = 25, S_{10} = 100$
b. $S_1 = 1, S_5 = 105, S_{10} = 760$
c. $S_1 = 0.5, S_5 = 1.63, S_{10} = 2.26$
8. a. $S_n = n^2$ **b.** $S_n = \frac{1}{2}(3^n - 1), n \geq 1$
c. $S_n = \frac{n}{n + 1}$ **d.** $S_n = \frac{n}{4n + 1}$

Exercise 9–5, pages 302–303
1. a. $2 + 4 + 6 + 8 + 10 + 12$
b. $2k + 2k + 2k + 2k + 2k + 2k + 2k + 2k + 2k$
c. $2 + 4 + 8 + 16 + 32$
d. $(-2) + (-1) + 0 + 1 + 2 + 3 + 4 + 5$
e. $2 + 5 + 10 + 17 + 26 + 37 + 50$
f. $\left(-\frac{1}{2}\right) + \frac{1}{3} + \left(-\frac{1}{4}\right) + \frac{1}{5} + \left(-\frac{1}{6}\right) + \frac{1}{7}$
2. a. $\sum_{n=1}^{15} n^3$ **b.** $\sum_{n=1}^{90} n$ **c.** $\sum_{k=1}^{n} k(k + 3)$
d. $\sum_{n=1}^{k} \frac{n}{n + 1}$ **e.** $\sum_{n=1}^{10} (19 + n)^2$
f. $\sum_{n=1}^{50} (-1)^{n+1} n$ **g.** $\sum_{n=1}^{19} \frac{1}{n(n + 1)}$ **h.** $\sum_{k=1}^{n} \frac{2k - 1}{2k(3k + 2)}$

3. a. $t_n = (n + 1)^2$; $S_n = \sum_{n=1}^{29} (n + 1)^2$
b. $t_n = 5n$; $S_n = \sum_{n=1}^{40} 5n$
c. $t_n = 85 - 5$; $S_n = \sum_{n=1}^{16} (85 - 5n)$ or $5\sum_{n=1}^{16} (17 - n)$
d. $t_n = 2^n$; $S_n = \sum_{n=1}^{10} 2^n$
e. $t_n = 4(3)^{n-1}$; $S_n = \sum_{n=1}^{9} 4(3)^{n-1}$ or $4\sum_{n=1}^{9} 3^{n-1}$
f. $t_n = 5(-2)^{n-1}$; $S_n = 5\sum_{n=1}^{12} (-2)^{n-1}$
g. $t_n = n(2 + 1)$; $S_n = \sum_{n=1}^{50} n(2n + 1)$
h. $t_n = n^2(4n + 1)$; $S_n = \sum_{n=1}^{12} n^2(4n + 1)$
i. $t_n = \frac{1}{n + 1}$; $S_n = \sum_{n=1}^{79} \frac{1}{n + 1}$
j. $t_n = \frac{1}{2n + 5}$; $S_n = \sum_{n=1}^{47} \frac{1}{2n + 5}$
4. a. 64 **b.** 196 **c.** 3272 **d.** −183 **e.** 0
f. 172 **8. a.** $2n + 4$ **b.** k **c.** $2(i + 3)^2 - 2$
d. $3(t - 2)^2 + 5$ **5.** 1728 **10.** $x = 3$ **11.** 146

Extra, page 303
3 × 5, 5 × 8, 8 × 13, 13 × 21

Exercise 9–6, pages 306–307
1. a. 49 **b.** 17 **c.** 30 **d.** 37 **e.** 101 **f.** 45
g. 25 **h.** 24 **2. a.** 36 **b.** 180 **c.** 28 **d.** 336
e. 176 **f.** 40 **g.** 18 **h.** 12 **3. a.** 38 **b.** 200
4. a. −30 **b.** 300 **5. a.** 90 300 **b.** 20 358
c. 19 404 **d.** 16 200 **e.** 165 **f.** 56 **g.** −110
h. 323 **i.** $400\sqrt{2}$ **j.** 147 **7. a.** 5050 **b.** 31 375
c. $\frac{(k + 1)(k + 2)}{2}$ **d.** 7809 **e.** 2438
f. $\frac{3k(k + 1)}{2}$ **8.** 4315 **9.** 816 **10.** 1633
11. $t_n = 6 - 2n$ **12.** 20 300 **13.** 4905
14. a. −1095 **b.** $t_n = 10 - 3n$ **15.** −42
16. a. 64; 100; $S_y = 10^2 = (1 + 2 + 3 + 4)^2$
125; 225; $S_s = 15^2 = (1 + 2 + 3 + 4)^2$
$\sum_{n=1}^{n} i^3 = \left(\sum_{n=1}^{n} i\right)^2 = \left(\frac{n(n + 1)}{2}\right)^2 = \frac{n^2(n + 1)^2}{4}$

Exercise 9–7, pages 310–311

1. a. 93 **b.** 366 **c.** $\frac{155}{16}$ **d.** $\frac{1845}{64}$ **e.** 0.444 44 **f.** $13\sqrt{3} - 12$ **2. a.** -512 **b.** -340 **3. a.** $\frac{1}{8}$ **b.** 127.875 **4. a.** $\frac{39\,364}{729}$ **b.** 22 960 **c.** 65 538 **d.** $\frac{1064}{81}$ **e.** $-30 + 15\sqrt{2}$ **f.** $0.333\,333\,333\,333 \doteq \frac{1}{3}$ **5. a.** -90 **b.** $\frac{116\,050}{2187}$ **6.** 2046 **7. a.** 1333.3332 **b.** 6554 **c.** $60\frac{61}{81}$ **d.** 0.333 333 333 333 3 **e.** $\frac{6305}{6561}$ **8. a.** 2046 **b.** $\frac{364}{729}$ **c.** $-12\,285$ **d.** $32\frac{1}{16\,384}$ **9. a.** 3 **b.** 3069 **10. a.** $\frac{p(p^n - 1)}{p - 1}$ **b.** $\frac{x^{k+1} - 1}{x - 1}$ **c.** $\frac{1 + y^{29}}{1 + y}$ **d.** $S_{\frac{12-n}{2}} = \frac{x^n - x^{12}}{1 - x^2}$ **11.** 67.04 m **12.** 99 461.36 **13. a.** 6 or -12 **b.** 6: 3, -12: -3

Review, pages 312–313

1. $t_n = 8n - 4$; $S_n = 4n^2$
2. $t_n = 4(3)^{n-1}$; $S_n = 2(3^n - 1)$
3. a. $t_{16} = 35$ **b.** $t_n = 2n + 3$ $S_{10} = 140$
4. a. $t_5 = -162$ **b.** $t_n - 2(-3)^{n-1}$ **c.** $S_{10} = 29\,524$
5. a. arithmetic **b.** neither **c.** geometric **d.** geometric **6. a.** $n = 25$; $t_n = 15 - 4n$ **b.** $n = 26$; $t_n = (n + 1)^2$ **c.** $n = 9$; $t_n = (3)^{n-1}$ **d.** $n = 10$; $t_n 12\left(-\frac{1}{2}\right)^{n-1}$
7. a. neither; 102 **b.** arithmetic; 129 **c.** geometric; $\frac{728}{27}$ **d.** geometric; 42 **e.** arithmetic; 54 **f.** neither; 225
8. a. $t_1 = 5$, $t_2 = 20$, $t_3 = 80$, $t_4 = 320$; geometric
b. $t_1 = 5$, $t_2 = 21$, $t_3 = 35$, $t_4 = 49$; neither
c. $t_1 = 4$, $t_2 = 1$, $t_3 = -2$, $t_4 = -5$; arithmetic
d. $t_1 = 2$, $t_2 = 6$, $t_3 = 18$, $t_4 = 54$; geometric
9. a. 15, 17, 19; $t_n = 2n + 3$
b. 127, 255, 511; $t_n = 2^{n-1} - 1$
c. 50, 65, 82; $t_n = n^2 + 1$
d. -160, 320, -640; $t_n = (5)(-2)^{n-1}$
e. 12×20, 14×23, 16×26; $t_n = 2n(3n + 2)$
f. $\frac{6}{27}, \frac{7}{31}, \frac{8}{35}$; $t_n = \frac{n}{4n + 3}$
10. a. arithmetic; $S_{39} = 3042$
b. arithmetic; $S_{36} = -1710$
c. geometric; $S_{12} = \frac{1365}{32}$ **d.** geometric; $S_8 = -9840$

11. a. 3 145 725 **b.** -670 **c.** $\frac{1\,048\,575}{32\,768}$ **d.** 0 **e.** 3492.7
12. $a = 10$, $d = -3$, $S_{10} = -35$ **13.** 3906
14. a. \$585.64 **b.** \$22 276.80 **15.** 156 **16.** 146
17. 1.17m
18. a. first job: arithmetic second job: geometric
b. \$20 000, \$19 679.63 **19.** 3905 **20.** 110

Test, page 314

1. $t_n = 3n + 3$, $t_{10} = 33$, $S_{10} = 195$
2. $t_5 = \frac{1}{2}$ **3.** 7, 14, 28, 56, 112; geometric
4. $t_1 = 16$, $t_n = t_{n-1} - 4$, $n > 1$ **5.** 9, 11, 13, 15
6. a. 5, 10, 20, 40 **b.** $t_{12} = 10\,240$
7. a. $S_n = n(n + 1)$
b. $S_n = \frac{3n(n + 1)}{2}$ **8.** 12 000 **9.** 64 **10.** 12
11. 10th day. **12.** \$2098.81

Cumulative Review, page 315

1. a. $x = 14$ **b.** $x = 0.257$ or $x = -2.59$ **c.** $t = -14$
d. $x = 7.37$ or $x = 1.63$ **e.** $a = \pm 25.495$
f. $m = -11$ **2. a.** 2 **b.** 2 **c.** 0 **d.** 2 **e.** 2 **f.** 0
3. a. 2 **b.** 2 **c.** 0
4. a. $(-8, 0)$, $(8, 0)$, $(0, -8)$, $(0, 8)$
b. $(-2\sqrt{6}\ 0)$, $(2\sqrt{6}, 0)$ $(0, -2\sqrt{6})$, $(0, 2\sqrt{6})$
c. $(\pm 3.5, 0)$ $(0, \pm 3.5)$ **d.** $(\pm 5\sqrt{3}, 0)$, $(0, \pm 5\sqrt{3})$
e. $(\pm\frac{5}{3}, 0)$, $(0, \pm\frac{5}{3})$
f. $(-1.12, 0)$, $(7.12, 0)$ $(0, -4.7)$, $(0, 1.7)$
5. a. yes **b.** no **c.** no **d.** yes **e.** yes **f.** no
6. a. $\left\{\frac{1}{2}, \frac{2}{5}, \frac{3}{5}, \frac{4}{5}, 1, \frac{6}{5}\right\}$ **b.** $\left\{2, -1, -4, -7\right\}$
c. $\left\{1, 3, 9, 19\right\}$ **d.** $\left\{\frac{13}{4}, \frac{7}{2}, 4, 5, 7, 11\right\}$
e. $\left\{0, 1, 2, 3\right\}$ **f.** $\left\{0, 1, 4, 9, 16\right\}$
7. a. $(x - 2)^2 + (y + 3)^2 = 1$
b. $(x - 2)^2 + y^2 = 4$, or $(x - 2)^2 + (y + 6)^2 = 4$
c. $(x - 3)^2 + (y - 7)^2 = 16$, or $(x - 3)^2 + (y + 1)^2 = 16$
8. \$177 500.00 **9. a.** 1.25 **b.** 0.013 **c.** 101.68

UNIT 10

Exercise 10–1, pages 318–319

1. a. Answers will vary.
2. a. It would be a better idea to save up to purchase small items than to face the high interest rates of loans.
b. There is a risk of falling behind on loan payments which results in the recall of the loan or the confiscation of property to cover the loan.

c. The institution may run into financial difficulty and fail to honour the loan promised.
3. a. \$20 **b.** \$431.25 **c.** \$3468.75 **d.** \$4500 **e.** \$2100 **f.** \$279.91 **g.** 5 months **h.** $1\frac{1}{2}$ years **i.** 1 year and 77 days **j.** 12.5% **k.** $13\frac{1}{4}$% **l.** $14\frac{3}{4}$% **4. a.** \$802 **b.** \$4945 **c.** \$2673.44 **d.** \$9131.25 **e.** \$15 500 **5.** \$625 **6.** 22.9 months **7.** \$3832.50 **8.** \$3375.96 **9.** \$10 954.25
10. Shira should take the money out of the term deposit.

Extra page 319
~6.265%

Exercise 10–2 pages 323–324
1. a. 4096 **b.** 38.44 **c.** 2.05×10^{14} **d.** 5.29×10^{-7} **e.** 63 700 992 **f.** 1.28 **g.** 1.23×10^{8} **h.** 8.64×10^{7} **2. a.** 6; 0.05 **b.** 6; 0.021 25 **c.** 14; 0.076 25 **d.** 30; 0.0067 **e.** 52; 0.0019 **f.** 20; 0.03 **g.** 11%; 4 years **h.** $10\frac{2}{3}$%; 6 weeks **i.** quarterly; 27 months
3. a. \$1608.11 **b.** \$10 712.58 **c.** \$2731.50 **d.** \$8453.70 **e.** \$1637.69 **f.** \$8255.85 **g.** \$3065.55 **h.** \$5245.95 **i.** \$5460.98 **j.** \$11 086.12 **4. a.** 12.55% **b.** 10.78% **c.** 8.84% **d.** 12.28% **e.** 13.86% **5.** \$25; \$38.13; \$47.13
6. A promissory note at 12%/a compounded semiannually.
7. \$3581.54 **8.** 13.5%/a compounded annually
9. $\$14.4 \times 10^{12}$ **10.** no **11.** \$586.66

Extra page 324
1. a. 10% **b.** 10.25% **c.** 10.38% **d.** 10.47% **e.** 10.51% **f.** 10.52% **g.** 10.52% **h.** 10.52%
2. It appears to approach a constant value of 10.52%

Extra, page 325
2. 1980–81
3. No. Because the total change is 1(1.0474)(1.0769)(1.1092)... (1.0401)(1.0409) − 1.
4. 17.7%
5. When the inflation rate is higher than the loan rate and wages are increasing with the inflation rate.
6. Their incomes are fixed, and so their purchasing power is steadily diminished.

Exercise 10–3, pages 326–328
1. $V_{present} = \frac{A}{(1+i)^n}$ **2. a.** $n = 5$; $i = 9\frac{1}{4}$%. **b.** $n = 16$; $i = 2\frac{1}{2}$% **c.** $n = 5$; $i = 4\frac{1}{2}$%
3. a. 20; 0.025 **b.** 5; 0.0425 **c.** 20; 0.0075 **d.** $9\frac{1}{2}$%; $3\frac{1}{2}$a **e.** 19.2%; quarterly **4. a.** \$676.84 **b.** \$1312.54 **c.** \$1477.64 **d.** \$1977.24 **e.** \$6058.45 **f.** \$8295.13 **g.** \$2147.09
5. \$9221.80 **6.** \$3039.23 **7.** \$2657.94
8. \$9319.05
9. \$290.77 at 8%/a compounded monthly; \$285.98 at $8\frac{3}{4}$%/a compounded annually; The second option is better.
10. \$1800 cash

Extra page 328
~7.10 a; ~7.02 a; ~6.96 a

Review, page 329
1. a. \$131.25 **b.** \$525 **c.** \$100.70 **d.** \$2800
2. \$106.52 **3.** \$1598.92 **4. a.** \$2339.72 **b.** \$1741.67 **c.** \$5269.26 **d.** \$7181.22
5. a. 9.2%/a compounded monthly.
b. 9.60%, 9.95%, 9.99%; The best rate for an investment is 9.75%/a compounded seminannually.
6. a. \$988.16 **b.** \$90.92 **7.** \$881.47

Exercise 10–4, pages 332–333
1. a. \$680.19 **b.** \$4216.42 **c.** \$1309.42
2. a. \$1061.62 **b.** \$1268.25 **c.** \$3022.31 **d.** \$1111.54 **e.** \$3483.91 **f.** \$390.41 **g.** \$955.92 **h.** \$1624.90 **i.** \$1308.06 **j.** \$514.44 **4.** \$1200.61
5. \$4115.27 **6.** \$16 722.01 **7.** \$3306.45
8. a. \$14 022.41 **b.** \$13 861.83 **9.** \$5977.34

Exercise 10–5, pages 335–336
1. a. \$3790.79 **b.** \$1088.97 **c.** \$580.95
2. a. \$3790.79 **b.** \$1310.53 **c.** \$1639.83 **d.** \$22 667.02 **e.** \$5246.86 **3.** \$45 331.91
4. \$6306.19 **5.** They should choose the \$42 000.00 cash. **6.** \$995 less 10% is a better deal.
7. \$127 693.66

Application, page 337
1. \$811.76 **2.** \$1234.90 **3.** \$570 590.48

Exercise 10–6, page 340
1. a. \$1013.75 **2.** \$83.60 **c.** \$468.125
2. a. Discount; \$312.50 **b.** Premium; \$487.50 **c.** Premium; \$22.50 **3. a.** \$53.75 **b.** \$293.75 **c.** \$1225.00 **4.** \$506.875 **5.** \$82.50 **6.** \$106.25
7. a. Market value = \$55 000
Redemption price = \$50 700
b. Market value = \$13 875
Redemption price = \$15 268.97

8. It would be more profitable to redeem the bond.

Exercise 10–7, page 344

1. a. \$13 797.42 **b.** \$488.53 **c.** \$10 028.71
2. a. \$1125 **b.** \$47.50 **c.** \$1312.50
3. a. \$7345.17 **b.** \$462.76 **c.** \$13 378.60
4. a. \$105.71 **b.** \$95.13 **c.** \$93.63
5. a. \$108.43 **b.** \$98.08 **c.** \$104.30 **6.** \$466.09
7. yes **8.** \$113.83 **9.** No, the asking price is high. **10.** \$106.73

Using the computer, page 345

12.03%

Review, pages 346–347

1. \$1561.41 **2.** \$2569.21 **3.** \$237.10
4. 12.13%, 12.40%; $11\frac{3}{4}$/a compounted quarterly is a better investment.
5. \$460.71 **6.** \$1254.77 **7.** \$1351.85
8. \$19 103.72 **9.** \$42 000 cash **10.** \$22 871.78
11. no **12.** \$147 876.49 **13.** yes
14. \$140 622.13 **15.** \$97.60 **16.** \$5175
17. Market value = \$20 750
Redemption Price = \$20 193.15
18. \$5148.89 **19.** \$3712.77 **20.** \$117.27
21. \$1075.44
22. The NOVA bond is the better buy.

Test, page 348

1. \$3601.40 **2.** \$112.70 **3.** 8.84%
4. a. \$15 852.78 **b.** \$11 354.48 **5.** \$32 435.05
6. \$3036.56 **7.** yes **8.** \$55 752.79
9. Market Value = \$2254.50; Quote Price \$90.18
10. \$1019.80 **11.** \$104.21

Cumulative Review, page 349

1. a. $3 - 3\sqrt{2}i$ **b.** $10 + 4\sqrt{2}i$ **c.** $6\sqrt{7}$
d. $-5 - 10\sqrt{5}i$
2. a. $\frac{(3a - 1)(a^2 + b^2)(a + b)}{(2a + 1)(a + b)}$ **b.** $\frac{5(4x^2 - 3x - 13)}{6(x - 4)(x + 1)}$
3. a. $(-4, -5)$ **b.** $(-3\sqrt{6}, \sqrt{6})$ and $(3\sqrt{6}, -\sqrt{6})$
c. No solution **4. a.** 26 **b.** 1 **c.** 54
d. −0.455 **e.** 1.5 **f.** −0.021
5. a. $x^2 + y^2 = 29$ **b.** $x^2 + y^2 = 10$
c. $x^2 + y^2 = 74$ **d.** $x^2 + y^2 = 97$
e. $x^2 + y^2 = 14$ **f.** $x^2 + y^2 = 13$
g. $x^2 + y^2 = 11$ **h.** $x^2 + y^2 = 9$
6. 137.5° **7.** $x = 72$ and $x = 9$
8. a. 2.5 **b.** $\frac{2}{3} = 0.67$ **c.** 32 **d.** 12 **e.** 384 **f.** 27
9. a. $y = 2x - 2$ **b.** $y = -3x^2$
c. $y = -6x - 5$ **d.** $y = 2x^2 + 4$
10. a. 14, 15, 16 **b.** 40, 60, 40 or −5, −30, −180

Appendix: Mixed Problems, pages 350–356

1. 1815 cm² **2.** 120.62 km/h **3.** 3 h **4.** 120 km
5. 4 m **6. a.** 2.96 mm **b.** 168.75 g
7. a. $P = P_0(2)^{\frac{t}{20}}$ where P = population of fruit flies at time t, P_0 = original population of fruit flies, t = time (in days)
b. 1060 **c.** January 14th of the following year
8. a. \$2040 **b.** \$2332.40 **c.** in six years
d. \$892.49 **9. a.** 60° **b.** 28 min.
c. 52.5°; ~ 22 min.
d. The half-life would increase.
10. triangle: base = 10 cm, height = 12 cm
rectangle: base = 15 cm, height = 4 cm
11. 120 m × 240 m; 80 m × 360 m
12. 23; 14 **13.** 25 cm **14.** \$4.37
15. 80 km/h; 120 km/h **16.** \$80 **17.** $\frac{3}{7}$
18. 2 m × 8 m; 3 m × 6 m **19.** 19
20. a. 38 **b.** 36 **c.** 67 **d.** 4 **21.** 1; 3; 4
22. Lisa's test is valid if she's folding each piece along both diagonals.
24. 6; 1; 5 **25.** 2.73 days **26.** $2x^2 + x - 3$
27. $l = 1 + \sqrt{5}$, $w = 2$ **28.** 0.25 g
29. The first option is better. **30.** 19 **31.** 9.375 L
32. 17.68 km/h **33. a.** $(2x + 1)(x + 2)$
b. $(x + 4)$ and $(x + 7)$ would be the dimensions of the rectangle.
c. $(3x + 2)$ and $(x + 3)$ would be the dimensions of the rectangle.
35. 0.062 **36.** 70 m/s **37.** 2.6 h
38. 1.095×10^{-16} W/cm²
39. $n = 3m + (m - 3)$, where $m \geq 3$
40. a. 1986: $y = 9$, if $x \leq 137.6$
$y = 0.065\,43x$, if $137.6 < x \leq 500$
$y = 32.715 + 0.048\,69\,(x - 500)$, if $x > 500$
1987: $y = 9$, if $x \leq 126.3$
$y = 0.071\,28x$, if $126.3 < x \leq 500$
$y = 35.64 + 0.0513\,(x - 500)$, if $x > 500$
c. 1986: 137.7 kWh; 1987; 126.4 kWh
d. 1986: 1881.91 kWh; 1987; 1754.58 kWh
e. No, the rates increased by a lesser extent for consumption levels of over 500 kWh.
41. c. 784 **d.** $2\sqrt{2}$
42. $628^2 - 286^2 = (628 - 286)(628 + 286)$
43. a. $(550 - 50x)(2 + 0.1x)$ = Total Admission Receipts **b.** \$2.00
45. a. 1, 2, 3, 2, 1, … .; 1, 5, 6, $\frac{7}{5}$, $\frac{6}{15}$, 1, … .;
3, 4, $\frac{5}{3}$, $\frac{2}{3}$, 1, 3, … .
46. a. 1 **b.** $\frac{x + 1}{x - 2}$ **c.** $\frac{x + 1}{x - 3}$
47. $x = y = z = w = 2$
48. Choose three one-digit numbers x, y, and z.
$$\frac{111x + 111y + 11z}{x + y + z} = 111$$

INDEX

Photograph Credits

Every effort has been made to ascertain proper ownership of copyrighted materials and obtain permission for their use. Any omission is unintentional and will be corrected in future printings upon proper notification.

Ryerson Polytechnical Institute: 8, 27
Abitibi-Price: 15
Marineland, Niagara Falls Canada: 16
Ontario Ministry of Transportation and Communications: 22
Gabriel V. Guillen: 72
Vancouver Sun (Dan Scott): 78
Canapress Photo Service: 90, 138, 186, 193, 246, 274, 278, 316, 327, 337
Warner-Lambert Canada, Inc.: 92
Just Music and Video Systems: 98
Ski Ontario: 102
Jim Chu/Central Technical Institute, Toronto: 122
General Motors Canada: 202
The Bettman Archive: 304
Bank of Canada: 338
Bank of Nova Scotia: 338, 339, 342
Toronto Star: 326
Globe and Mail: 341

Special thanks to the Metropolitan Toronto Central Library for pictures not listed above.

Photo Research: Jill Patrick